MOLECULAR TYPING METHODS FOR TRACKING FOODBORNE MICROORGANISMS

ADVANCES IN FOOD SAFETY AND FOOD MICROBIOLOGY

Anderson de Souza Sant'Ana and
Bernadette D.G.M. Franco - Series Editors

Advances in Food Safety and Food Microbiology
Anderson de Souza Sant'Ana and Bernadette D.G.M. Franco (Editors)
ISBN: 2152-2006

Probiotic and Prebiotic Foods: Technology, Stability and Benefits to Human Health
Nagendra P. Shah, Adriano Gomes da Cruz and
Jose de Assis Fonseca Faria (Editors)
2011. 978-1-61668-842-4

Stress Response of Foodborne Microorganisms
Hin-chung Wong (Editor)
2011. 978-1-61122-810-6

Advances in Post-Harvest Treatments and Fruit Quality and Safety
Manuel Vázquez and José A. Ramírez de Leon (Editors)
2011. 978-1-61122-973-8

Bacteriophages in Dairy Processing
Andrea del Luján Quiberoni and Jorge Alberto Reinheimer (Editors)
2012. 978-1-61324-517-0

New Trends in Marine and Freshwater Toxins: Food and Safety Concerns
Ana G. Cabado and Juan Manuel Vieites (Editors)
2012. 978-1-61470-324-2

Clostridium Botulinum: A Spore Forming Organism and a Challenge to Food Safety
Christine Rasetti-Escargueil and Susanne Surman-Lee (Editors)
2011. 978-1-61470-575-8

Enterococcus and Safety
Teresa Semedo-Lemsaddek, Maria Teresa Barreto-Crespo
and Rogério Tenreiro *(Editors)*
2011. 978-1-61470-569-7

ADVANCES IN FOOD SAFETY AND FOOD MICROBIOLOGY

MOLECULAR TYPING METHODS FOR TRACKING FOODBORNE MICROORGANISMS

STEVEN L. FOLEY
RAJESH NAYAK
TIMOTHY J. JOHNSON
AND
SANJAY K. SHUKLA
EDITORS

Nova Science Publishers, Inc.
New York

Library of Congress Cataloging-in-Publication Data

Molecular typing methods for tracking foodborne micoorganisms / editors, Steven L. Foley and Rajesh Nayak, Timothy J. Johnson.
      p. ; cm.
  Includes bibliographical references and index.
  ISBN 978-1-62100-643-5 (hardcover)
  I. Foley, Steven L. II. Nayak, Rajesh. III. Johnson, Timothy J. (Timothy James), 1977-
  [DNLM: 1. Food Microbiology. 2. Bacteria--pathogenicity. 3. Foodborne Diseases--microbiology.
4. Foodborne Diseases--prevention & control. 5. Molecular Typing--methods. QW 85]
  616.9'201--dc23
                              2011037420

Published by Nova Science Publishers, Inc. † New York

CONTENTS

PREFACE

Foodborne illness remains a major problem throughout the world. In the United States for example it is estimated that there are over 48 million illnesses each year associated with the consumption of contaminated foods. Of those with known etiologies, approximately 39% are associated with bacterial pathogens[1]. These bacterial infections often tend to be more severe than their viral counterparts resulting in approximately 64% of hospitalizations and deaths each year from foodborne pathogens. Thus being able to get to the source of the contamination of foods is an important endeavor to begin to develop strategies to lessen the burden of bacterial foodborne illness on the human population.

We thank Dr. Anderson de Souza Sant'Ana for the invitation to edit this book as part of the broader series on *Advances in Food Safety and Food Microbiology*. We hope that the book will be useful as a reference to students, practitioners and food safety scientists who need to gain a fundamental understanding of the different options available for molecular typing of foodborne pathogens. A goal of the book is to provide insights for scientists interested in using these molecular typing methods as part of source tracking protocols.

In the process of planning the book, we chose to break the book down into three major sections that will provide the reader with an integrated experience to understand the utility of molecular typing methods for tracking foodborne microorganisms. The first section focuses on bacterial foodborne pathogens and factors that play into their distribution and detection in the food production and processing environments. This section includes a brief introduction into the major foodborne pathogens and description of surveillance and outbreak investigation basics. The section then focuses on the genomics of the pathogens and the contribution of plasmids to microbial diversity and function. The final two chapters in the section explore the important topic of antimicrobial resistance and methods to rapidly detect the presence of bacterial pathogens in foods.

The second section will focus on the specific typing methods, providing insights into the methodology and utility of these methods for foodborne pathogens. The first chapter of the section provides an introduction both into the phenotypic methods for characterization of foodborne pathogens as well as a brief introduction the molecular methods covered in the rest of the section. We felt it important to cover the phenotypic methods because they still remain in use today and many laid the groundwork for current molecular methods. For the molecular

---

[1] Scallan E, Hoekstra RM, Angulo FJ, Tauxe RV, Widdowson MA, Roy SL, et al. Foodborne illness acquired in the United States-major pathogens. Emerg Infect Dis. 2011;17(1):7-15.

methods, pulsed field gel electrophoresis was given its own chapter due to its status as the "gold standard" method for many foodborne pathogens. Other chapters focus on some of the more commonly used techniques along with special focus on some of the more recent advances in typing methods (sequence-based methodologies, microarray, etc.).

The third section will focus on the analysis of the typing data and utility of molecular typing methods in a source tracking scheme. The first chapter examines the methods used to analyze the various types of molecular typing data, which is important for the interpretation of the results. The second chapter in the section focuses on the incorporation of molecular typing data into epidemiological investigations and the final chapter wraps up the book and hopefully provides some insights into the future of molecular typing of bacterial foodborne pathogens.

The views and information presented in the individual chapters are those of the authors and since they were invited to write the chapters based on their expertise in the subject areas. Likewise the views and editorial decisions in the book are those of the editors and do not necessarily represent those of our respective organizations, the U.S. Food and Drug Administration, Marshfield Clinic Research Foundation or the University of Minnesota. Additionally, the use of trade names in this book is for identification purposes only, and does not imply endorsement by the U.S. Food and Drug Administration or the U.S. Department of Health and Human Services.

We hope that you find this book useful and that you enjoy reading the information present herein.

Steven L. Foley
Rajesh Nayak
Timothy J. Johnson
Sanjay K. Shukla

FOREWORD

Diseases caused by foodborne pathogens are major causes of morbidity and mortality throughout the world. Estimates by the Centers for Disease Control indicate that there could be as many as 48 million cases of foodborne illnesses in the United States each year. While the incidence of disease caused by some foodborne pathogens has fallen in the past few years, the incidence of disease caused by pathogens such as *Salmonella enterica* seem to remain largely unchanged. The epidemiology of foodborne illnesses has been changing and the apparent proportion of cases associated with fresh fruits and vegetables has shown large increases. It has been estimated that viruses cause the largest number of foodborne illnesses. However, bacterial foodborne pathogens cause more severe diseases than their viral counterparts, account for the largest proportion of deaths, and many have developed resistance to the antimicrobial agents that are used to treat severe infections. Outbreak investigations have relied on the timely collection of accurate surveillance information including disease clusters, strain identification, and potential sources of contamination. Vital to any analysis of an outbreak is the use molecular technologies to characterize the cause of the infections and these technologies have been essential tools of source attribution. Molecular analyses of foodborne pathogens have been used to understand how these pathogens disseminate through the food production and processing environments and have been essential in the development of strategies to limit the exposure of consumers to foodborne pathogens. PulseNet, a pulsed field electrophoresis-based tool, has been an important tool implemented by the CDC and used in outbreak investigations. Thus, molecular subtyping methods are vital tools that are being used along with epidemiological investigations to implement successful microbial source tracking schemes that can help limit bacterial foodborne illnesses.

In the recent years there have been numerous reviews and research articles written about the use of various molecular subtyping for the characterization of bacterial foodborne pathogens. This book, *Molecular Typing Methods for Tracking Foodborne Microorganisms*, provides an integrated experience for the reader to gain a thorough understanding of the utility of the different molecular typing methods for identifying and tracking bacterial foodborne pathogens. The chapters in this book look at different subtyping methods in an integrated way and provide discussion of recent literature to bring the reader an up-to-date understanding of the current state of the field. The editors of the book have brought together an excellent group of authors with expertise in the areas of food safety and molecular subtyping that provide valuable insights for readers. This book should be a valuable reference for those who are interested in learning the fundamentals of the different types of molecular subtyping methods, as well as gaining insights on what the future of the molecular subtyping holds.

The editors have chosen to present the book in three major sections that include "Foodborne Pathogens", "Molecular Typing Methods" and "Analysis and Utility of Molecular Typing Methods", which will provide the reader with a logical flow from understanding the pathogens through to the interpretation and application of subtyping methods. The first section provides an overview of the pathogens, including chapters related to bacterial genetics, antimicrobial resistance, and methods to detect pathogens in the food production and processing environments. The second section focuses on the specific subtyping methods and the application of these methods to the characterization of foodborne pathogens. The third section focuses on the analyses of subtyping data, the utility of typing in epidemiological investigations and a look to the future of molecular subtyping for tracking foodborne pathogens. Because of the comprehensive nature of the book, I believe that it will be a valuable reference for students, practitioners and food safety scientists who need to gain a strong understanding of the molecular typing of foodborne pathogens.

Richard E. Isaacson, Ph.D.
Professor, Department of Veterinary and Biomedical Science
College of Veterinary Medicine
University of Minnesota
St. Paul, MN 55108

SECTION I. THE FOODBORNE PATHOGENS

In: Molecular Typing Methods for TFM
Editors: S. Foley, R. Nayak, T. Johnson et al.

ISBN: 978-1-62100-643-5
© 2012 Nova Science Publishers, Inc.

Chapter 1

INTRODUCTION TO FOODBORNE PATHOGENS AND INFECTIONS

Rajesh Nayak and Steven L. Foley
Division of Microbiology
National Center for Toxicological Research
US Food and Drug Administration
Jefferson, AR, US

ABSTRACT

Foodborne illnesses are a major public health concern worldwide. Foods of animal origin (meat, poultry and eggs), seafood, and raw and processed foods have been implicated in foodborne illnesses. In the US alone, there are over 48 million illnesses associated with foodborne pathogens, costing the US economy $10 to 83 billion annually. This chapter will highlight the characteristics of some leading agents that are involved in foodborne illnesses and the factors that are attributed to outbreaks caused by these pathogens. We address emerging foodborne pathogens and drug-resistant bacteria, and their contributions to food safety issues. Furthermore, we describe how foodborne investigations are carried out, the public health surveillance systems that monitor trends in infection rates of foodborne pathogens, and the agencies that are involved in investigating and monitoring operations. Lastly, we include some general strategies that can be used to reduce or eliminate the contamination of foods by these pathogens, thereby limiting the scope of accidental or deliberate outbreaks in human populations.

FOODBORNE ILLNESSES

Food is an important vehicle of transmitting diseases in humans. There are over 200 known microbial, physical and chemical agents that can cause food-related illnesses [1]. Foodborne pathogens are a major cause of morbidity and mortality throughout the world (http://www.who.int/foodsafety/foodborne_disease/ferg/en/index.html) [2-5]. There is limited epidemiological information available on the global burden caused by foodborne diseases [6]. In the United States, the Centers for Disease Control and Prevention (CDC) estimates that foodborne diseases cause approximately 48 million illnesses, 128,000 hospitalizations, and 3,000 deaths in the United States each year [7]. Of these, nearly 9.4 million illnesses, 56,000 hospitalizations, and 1,350 deaths are caused by known and identified pathogens [8]. These reported foodborne illnesses are only a small percentage of those that are actually occurring. According to the CDC, small outbreaks occurring in the US are unlikely to be reported to public health officials [9]. According to the US Department of Agriculture (USDA), foodborne illnesses cost the US economy 10 to 83 billion dollars each year [5]. The costs include loss of productivity, legal fees, medical expenses, loss of sales, loss of wages and loss of life [5, 10].

The leading bacterial species associated with illness include *Salmonella enterica, Campylobacter* spp., *Shigella* spp., *Clostridium* spp., *Escherichia coli* and *Yersinia enterocolitica* [4, 6]. In addition, viruses, such as hepatitis (A and E), Norwalk and Rotavirus [4, 11, 12], and parasites, such as *Cryptosporidium parvum, Entamoeba, Cyclospora* spp., *Giardia lambia, Toxoplasma gondii* and *Trichinella spiralis* [4, 13], have been implicated in food related illnesses. Foods of animal origin, particularly meat, poultry and eggs, have been associated with outbreaks [6, 14]. Other food vehicles associated with foodborne illnesses, include unpasteurized milk, other dairy products, raw fruits and vegetables, unpasteurized fruit juices and raw sprouts, fish and seafood and ready-to-eat foods (http://www.cdc.gov/ncidod/dbmd/diseaseinfo/foodborneinfections_g.htm#riskiestfoods) [15-19] . Outbreaks of foodborne illness have been attributed to rapid population growth, shifts in demographics and lifestyles, human behavior, changes in industry and technology, changes in travel and commerce, the shift towards a global economy, microbial adaptation, breakdowns in public health infrastructure, a higher proportion of immuno-compromised individuals, changes in farming practices, lack of knowledge on food safety and handling practices, and climate change [3, 4, 20-24].

Other valuable resources describing foodborne pathogens include the FDA Bad Bug Book (http://www.fda.gov/Food/FoodSafety/FoodborneIllness/FoodborneIllnessFoodborne PathogensNaturalToxins/BadBugBook/default.htm), the CDC website (http://www.cdc.gov/ foodsafety/diseases) and others, so this chapter will not include an in-depth look at each individual foodborne pathogen. Table 1, however, provides an overview of the microbial agents responsible for causing foodborne illnesses.

EMERGING PATHOGENS

The ability of bacterial pathogens to adapt to and survive unfavorable environmental and processing conditions has been attributed to the diverse genetic background [22]. The mechanisms by which these pathogens evolve vis-à-vis their pathogenicity, genome rearrangement and physiology has contributed to emergence of new pathogens [5]. These emerging pathogens may exhibit greater pathogenicity and antimicrobial resistance than their existing counterparts, resulting in serious public health implications [25-29].

Table 1. A selective list of agents involved in foodborne illnesses*

Agents	Basic Information	Incubation period	Duration of disease	Nature of disease/symptoms	Selective species/ serotypes involved in foodborne illnesses	Foods associated with outbreaks	Major outbreaks (Serotype)	Treatment
Salmonella	• Gram negative, rod shaped, motile bacterium. • >2,500 serotypes identified • Wide spread in animals, particularly poultry and swine. • Also found in the environment (water, soil, raw feces, and insects) and raw meat and poultry. • Infective dose 15-20 CFU.	1-3 days	4-7 days	Nausea, diarrhea, vomiting, cramps, fever, headaches, chronic arthritis. Complications may include reactive arthritis and Reiter's syndrome	Typhimurium, Enteritidis, Newport Heidelberg, Javiana	Contaminated eggs, poultry, unpasteurized milk, raw fruits and vegetables, sprouts	Shelled eggs (Enteritidis). Raw produce (St. Paul). Cantaloupe (Litchfield), Peanut (Tennessee), Tomatoes (Typhimurium) and ice cream (Enteritidis)	Supportive care. Severe cases treated with ampicillin, gentamicin, sulfa drugs or quinolones
Campylobacter	• Gram negative, slender, curved, and motile rod. • Microaerophilic • Relatively fragile and sensitive to environmental stresses (e.g., 21% oxygen, drying, heating, disinfectants, acidic conditions) • Animal pathogen • Leading cause of diarrheal disease in the US	2-5 days	2-10 days	Nausea, vomiting, cramps, fever, headaches, chronic arthritis. Complications may include reactive arthritis and Reiter's syndrome	*C. jejuni, C. coli*	Raw and undercooked poultry, contaminated milk and water	Clams, raw goat and cow milk, drinking water	Supportive care. Severe cases treated with erythromycin or quinolones

Table 1. (Continued)

Agents	Basic Information	Incubation period	Duration of disease	Nature of disease/symptoms	Selective species/ serotypes involved in foodborne illnesses	Foods associated with outbreaks	Major outbreaks (Serotype)	Treatment
Enterovirulent *E. coli* (ETEC, EPEC, EHEC and EIEC)	• Gram negative, rod shaped, motile bacterium. • Four major groups: enterotoxigenic, enteropathogenic, enterohemorrhagic, and enteroinvasive • *E. coli* O157:H7 is the major pathogen • Wide spread in humans, animals and environment (water, soil, feces, and insects)	1-8 days	5-10 days	Severe diarrhea, abdominal cramps, low-grade fever, nausea and malaise. Severe infections are associated with hemolytic uremic syndrome (HUS) and thrombocytopenic purpura (TTP)	*E. coli* O157:H7, Non-O157:H7 EHEC	Undercooked or ground beef, alfalfa sprouts, unpasteurized fruit juices, dry-cured salami, lettuce, game meat, raw milk and cheese curds	Raw and under cooked hamburgers, cookie dough, fresh spinach, apple cider, green onions (all by EC O157:H7)	Supportive care. Antibiotics used to treat severe infections
Clostridium	• Gram positive, spore forming rod • Produces enterotoxins • Spores are heat resistant and survive minimally processed foods • Found in wild fowls, poultry, cattle and horses	12-72 h (children and adults) 3-30 days (infants)	Variable (from days to months)	Vomiting, diarrhea, blurred vision, diplopia, dysphagia and muscle weakness	*C. botulinum*, *C. perfringens*	Low acid canned (home and commercial) foods, baked potatoes in foil, meat, poultry	Hot dog chilli sauce, Sautéed onions, potato salad, peppers, vichyssoise soup (all with CB), roast beef (CP)	Supportive care
Listeria	• Gram positive, motile • Found in mammals and birds • Isolated from soil, silage • Hardy bacteria; resists the deleterious effects of freezing, drying, and heat • Can grow at refrigerated temperature (4°C)	9-48 hours (gastrointestinal) 2-6 weeks for invasive disease	Variable	Fever, muscle aches, nausea, diarrhea, premature delivery or still birth in pregnant women	*L. monocytogenes*	Soft cheeses, RTE deli meats, hot dogs and inadequately pasteurized milk	Mexican-style soft cheese, Camembert cheese, celery, Whittier pasteurized milk (all with LM)	Supportive care. Intravenous drugs (penicillin, ampicillin, sulfa drugs) for invasive disease

Agents	Basic Information	Incubation period	Duration of disease	Nature of disease/symptoms	Selective species/serotypes involved in foodborne illnesses	Foods associated with outbreaks	Major outbreaks (Serotype)	Treatment
Vibrio	• Gram negative, comma-shaped bacterium with polar flagellum • Can grow in estuarine and marine environment • 2 major groups: cholera non 01 (humans) and non 01 (foods)	1-7 days	2-8 days	Vomiting, watery diarrhea, abdominal pain, and bacteremia	*V. vulnificus* *V. parahaemolyticus*	Undercooked or raw shellfish (oysters)	Raw oysters and clams (VP, VV),	Supportive care and antibiotics (tetracycline and doxycycline) in severe cases
Yersinia	• Gram negative rods • Isolated from human clinical specimens, pigs, birds, beavers, cats	24-48 hours	1-3 weeks	Diarrhea, fever, vomiting, and abdominal pain	*Y. enterocolitica*	Undercooked pork, unpasteurized tofu, contaminated water, fish, oysters	Chocolate milk, tofu,	Supportive care, treat with gentamicin or cefotaxime in case of septicemia
Hepatitis A and E	• Enterovirus group of the *Picornaviridae* family • Single RNA molecule • Excreted in feces of infected people	15-50 days	2 weeks to 3 months	fever, malaise, nausea, anorexia, and abdominal discomfort, followed in several days by jaundice	Hepatitis A and E	Contaminated shellfish, raw produce, contaminated drinking water, and infected workers in food processing plants and restaurants	Green onions, cold cuts and sandwiches, fruits and fruit juices, milk and milk products, vegetables, salads, shellfish, and iced drinks	Supportive care; immuniza-tion

Table 1. (Continued)

Agents	Basic Information	Incubation period	Duration of disease	Nature of disease/symptoms	Selective species/serotypes involved in foodborne illnesses	Foods associated with outbreaks	Major outbreaks (Serotype)	Treatment
Noroviruses	• Small round structured viruses (SRSVs) which may be related to the caliciviruses • Infects mostly through fecal-oral cycle	12-48 hours	12-60 hours	Nausea, vomiting, abdominal cramping, diarrhea, fever, myalgia	Norwalk, Norwalk-like virus	Fecally contaminated shellfish, water and foods (salads, sandwiches, ice, cookies, fruit)	Clams, oysters, salads, sandwiches, cakes, frosting, raspberries, drinking water, and ice	Self limiting, supportive care (rehydration)
Cryptosporidium	• Single-celled protozoa • Obligate intracellular parasite • Infects many herd animals (cows, goats, sheep, deer and elk) • Sporocysts are resistant to most chemical disinfectants, but are susceptible to drying and the ultraviolet portion of sunlight	2-10 days	Weeks to months (remitting and relapsing)	Watery diarrhea, cramps, fever	*C. parvum*	food touched by a contaminated food handler, contaminated salad vegetables, contaminated surface or ground water, exposure to contaminated recreational water, animal-to-person contact, and person-to-person contact	Freshly pressed apple cider, public water supply, Waterborne outbreaks, Child day care centers	Supportive care, usually self limiting

Agents	Basic Information	Incubation period	Duration of disease	Nature of disease/symptoms	Selective species/ serotypes involved in foodborne illnesses	Foods associated with outbreaks	Major outbreaks (Serotype)	Treatment
Giardia	• Single celled protozoa, that moves with the aid of five flagella • Isolated from domestic animals (dogs and cats) and wild animals (beavers and bears)	1-2 weeks	Days to weeks	Diarrhea, stomach cramps, flatulence	*G. lamblia*	Uncooked food or food contaminated by an ill food handler, contaminated water	Waterborne outbreaks	Metronida-zole
Toxoplasma	• Protozoan parasite • Transmitted to humans by accidental ingestion of sporulated oocysts shed in feces	5-23 days	Months	Generally asymptomatic, 20% of infected persons may develop cervical lymphadenopathy and/or flu-like illness	*T. gondii*	Ingestion of contaminated substances (soil contaminated with cat feces), fruits and vegetables, raw or undercooked meat (pork, lamb or venison) contaminated with cysts	Unwashed raw fruits and vegetables, undercooked pork	Asympto-matic, but severe infections may be treated with combinations of pyrimetha-mine, spiramycin and sulfadiazine
Trichinella	• Nematode parasite occurring in rats, pigs, and humans	1-2 days	Months	Nausea, diarrhea, vomiting, fatigue, fever cramps, and general weakness	*T. spiralis*	Raw or undercooked meats (food animals or wild game animals)	Undercooked or infected pork, boar, or horse meat	Supportive care, severe cases treated with mebendazole or albendazole

Table 1. (Continued)

Agents	Basic Information	Incubation period	Duration of disease	Nature of disease/symptoms	Selective species/ serotypes involved in foodborne illnesses	Foods associated with outbreaks	Major outbreaks (Serotype)	Treatment
Entamoeba	• Single cell parasite • Infects humans and other primates • The cysts survive outside the host in water and soils and on foods, especially under moist conditions on the latter.	2-3 days to 1-4 weeks	Weeks to months	Bloody diarrhea, frequent bowel movements	*E. histolytica*	Uncooked food or food contaminated by an ill food handler, contaminated water (fecal-oral cycle)	Drinking water, contaminated foods (ice cream, raw fruit on ice)	Metronida-zole

* *Adapted from:* FDA Bad Bug Book
(http://www.fda.gov/Food/FoodSafety/FoodborneIllness/FoodborneIllnessFoodbornePathogensNaturalToxins/BadBugBook/default.htm)
CDC

http://www.cdc.gov/mmwr/PDF/ss/ss4901.pdf

http://www.cdc.gov/ncidod/dbmd/diseaseinfo/foodborneinfections_g.htm

Also references [2, 4, 12, 13]

.

According to the World Health Organization, new foodborne disease threats occur due to globalization of the food supply, inadvertent introduction of pathogens into new hosts and geographic environments, international commerce and travel, dynamic changes in microorganisms and human populations and life style changes (http://www.who.int /mediacentre/factsheets/ fs124/en). Some examples of emerging pathogens include multidrug resistant strains of *Salmonella* [30-33], non-O157:H7 shiga toxin-producing *E. coli* [3, 34, 35], *Listeria monocytogenes*, bovine spongiform encephalopathy (BSE) [36], toxin producing bacteria [37], *Cyclospora cayetanensis*, *Cryptosporidum* spp., and *Toxoplasma gondii* [13, 38-40] and viruses [41].

Addressing emerging foodborne diseases will require sensitive and comprehensive surveillance, enhanced laboratory methods of identification and subtyping, and effective prevention and control of pathogens [42, 43]. It will also require a comprehensive risk assessment approach to identify microbial hazards, exposure assessment, and characterization of the risks and hazards [29]. To reduce the burden caused by foodborne illnesses, a comprehensive farm-to-fork approach to limit contamination should be adopted by all pre- and post-harvest sectors of food production, with emphasis on hygiene and Hazard Analysis and Critical Control Point (HACCP) principles [44-46].

To begin to evaluate pathogen-associated factors that contribute to their ability to cause foodborne illness, a number of studies have begun to examine the genetics of the microorganisms. Genome sequences are now available for several bacteria, including *Salmonella enterica, E. coli* O157 : H7, *Campylobacter* spp., *Clostridium* spp., *Vibrio* spp., *Listeria monocytogenes* and *Bacillus* spp. that cause foodborne diseases [47, 48]. Advances in high throughput whole genome sequencing, microarrays (detection and transcriptional), and proteomics are providing valuable tools for rapid detection of pathogens, understanding their disease pathogenesis, and other complex biological processes, such as food spoilage and biofilm formation [49]. Furthermore, the genome information can be useful in assessing the biological diversity of these pathogens, how they respond physiologically to stress and the metabolic pathways that may contribute to their growth and ability to survive in different ecological niches and interact with foods, humans (hosts) and processing environments [47]. Whole genome comparison between pathogenic and non pathogenic strains can be useful in identifying virulence gene biomarkers that contribute to bacterial pathogenicity [50]. These biomarkers can be used as potential diagnostic markers for detecting, monitoring and surveillance of pathogens in the food chain. The genome sequence data can also provide insight into the evolution of these pathogens and their virulence mechanisms in reference to the habitats that they occupy [51]. Such genomic tools can be used for strengthening surveillance and risk assessment programs that help ensure the safety of foods [50]. Future challenges will include developing tools and bioinformatics platforms to process the data generated by whole genome sequencing and understanding the biological significance of the high throughput data as it relates to complex host-pathogen interactions, biological evolution, emerging pathogens and responses to different niches. Chapter 2 and 3 will describe in greater depth the impact of microbial genomics as it relates to foodborne pathogens.

Antimicrobial resistance in enteric pathogens continues to be a serious worldwide public health issue for both the agricultural and medical fields [26, 52-56]. The use of antimicrobials in food producing animals, such as cattle, poultry and swine, for growth promotion, therapy and disease prevention has increased the potential of foodborne pathogens, such as *Salmonella, Campylobacter* and *E. coli*, to develop cross resistance to drugs used for treatment of human infections [55, 57]. Enteric pathogens often harbor mobile genetic elements, such as transposons, plasmids or integrons that carry antimicrobial resistance genes, which can be readily transferred to other bacteria. Additionally, natural (commensal) microflora of animals and humans may acquire resistance genes following exposure to antimicrobials and serve as a reservoir of these resistance genes, which in turn could be transferred to foodborne pathogens. The public health consequences of increased resistance could include increased frequency of infections and treatment failures, increased hospitalizations and deaths (www.who.int/foodsafety/publications/micro/en/report.pdf).

Prudent use of antimicrobials in animal husbandry and treating diseases in humans is critical in the prevention and control of antimicrobial resistance in bacterial pathogens. Additionally, accurate diagnosis and antimicrobial susceptibility profile testing will be critical in implementing targeted treatment strategies that use the most appropriate antimicrobial and the administration route for a particular pathogen. Public health agencies throughout the world have antimicrobial resistance monitoring systems, such as the National Antimicrobial Resistance Monitoring System (NARMS) in the US, the Danish Integrated Antimicrobial Resistance Monitoring and Research Programme (DANMAP), the Japanese Veterinary Antimicrobial Resistance Monitoring System (JVARM), Canadian Integrated Program for Antimicrobial Resistance Surveillance (CIPARS), Australian Group on Antimicrobial Resistance (AGAR) and Swedish Veterinary Antimicrobial Resistance Monitoring (SVARM) to monitor the development and persistence of drug resistance in bacterial pathogens [58, 59]. These monitoring systems provide valuable data to improve understanding of the emergence and dissemination of resistance in their respective countries. The public health risk of emergence, spread and transmission of drug-resistant foodborne pathogens in the farm-to-the-fork continuum warrants appropriate actions by both the scientific community and the regulatory agencies in restricting the approval and use of new and existing drugs, respectively. Issues and trends related to antimicrobial resistance in foodborne pathogens are described in greater detail in Chapter 4.

PUBLIC HEALTH SURVEILLANCE

The surveillance of foodborne illnesses is essential for public health officials to monitor trends in infection rates of foodborne pathogens, identify breakdowns in the safety of food production and processing systems, identify emerging pathogens and control outbreaks [42, 60, 61]. The collection of data in a foodborne disease surveillance program can be either passive or active [62]. Active disease surveillance refers to an approach where the epidemiologists collecting the surveillance data actively seek out data on the foodborne illnesses at a particular location at defined times. Passive surveillance refers to a system where physicians report the cases of foodborne illnesses to a surveillance program following diagnosis of the reportable disease [62]. Surveillance programs allow epidemiologists to monitor trends in infectious diseases, and aberrations in the numbers from historical trends likely indicate potential issues of concern [60]. With the PulseNet program (www.cdc.gov/pulsenet), DNA fingerprint data for *Salmonella, E. coli* O157:H7, *Shigella, Listeria*, and *Campylobacter* isolates are routinely sent to the CDC by the state health departments (and some local health departments as well) and the prevalence of particular serovar or fingerprint patterns is analyzed [63]. A spike in a particular serovar/fingerprint pattern over historical averages likely signals an outbreak is underway [63, 64]. This information on potential outbreaks is distributed to the states and can trigger an investigation (see below) to determine the source, scope and nature of the outbreak and what steps need to be taken to limit the extent of the outbreak [60].

Throughout the world, foodborne disease surveillance programs provide valuable data on the trends of disease. In the US, agencies such as the CDC, Food and Drug Administration (FDA) and USDA coordinate foodborne illnesses monitoring and surveillance programs, including active surveillance programs, such as the Foodborne Diseases Active Surveillance Network (FoodNet; www.cdc.gov/foodnet) [65] and NARMS (www.cdc.gov/narms); and passive programs, such as PulseNet, electronic Foodborne Outbreak Reporting System (eFORS) [66], National Outbreak Reporting System-NORS (http://www.cdc.gov/healthywater/statistics/wbdoss/nors/index.html) and Epi-X (www.cdc.gov/epix). Similarly, the World Health Organization's Global Foodborne Infections Network (GFN) (http://www.who.int/gfn/en) and Foodborne Disease Burden Epidemiology Reference Group (FERG) [3], the OzFoodNet system in Australia [67], the electronic Foodborne and non-Foodborne Gastrointestinal Outbreak Surveillance System (eFOSS) in the UK [68], SurvNet in Germany [69], and a new system being formed in Japan [3] are some additional examples of surveillance systems that monitor disease outbreaks and estimate the burden of foodborne illnesses.

OUTBREAK INVESTIGATIONS

The goal of a foodborne outbreak investigation is to rapidly identify the source of food(s) that is responsible for causing the disease and recall it from the market to prevent further consumption and spread of illness [70]. Furthermore, an outbreak investigation should identify the gap in manufacturing or handling that resulted in contamination of the food product(s) and take corrective measures in management practices. Lastly, an outbreak investigation can be used to gather data/facts on how transmission has occurred for established and emerging pathogens, identify reservoirs and routes of transmission, and study the host-pathogen-environment interactions that could have led to the outbreak.

According to the CDC, seven steps are typically involved in foodborne outbreak investigation (http://www.cdc.gov/outbreaknet/investigations). These include the detection of the outbreak, defining and detecting cases, generating (interviews) and testing hypotheses (analytical/laboratory studies) to delineate a link between illnesses and food sources, identifying the source of food, implementing measures for controlling the spread of the outbreak (recalls and revised production steps) and deciding if the outbreak is truly over. In general, a foodborne outbreak investigation is broken down into three major stages [70]. The first stage is to conduct an acute investigation which involves identifying the pathogen, demographics and food vehicle. The goal of this stage is to limit the number of further illnesses by determining the source of the contamination and removing the contaminated product from the food supply. The second stage is to conduct trace-back investigation, typically using molecular typing methods, to identify the practices and circumstances that led to contamination. This stage also often involves a trace-forward investigation, which following the identification of the source of bacterial contamination allows public health officials to identify where the contaminated product has been sent and remove these from the food supply chain as well. This approach is especially important when the contaminated product is an ingredient used in the production of further processed items, because a wide range of products can then potentially expose consumers to foodborne pathogens. The goal of the third stage of an investigation is long-term prevention. This stage involves identifying the major factors that contributed to the outbreak and identify ways to prevent future outbreaks. Some of the key factors include determining the frequency of contamination that led to the outbreak and identifying the pre- or post harvest food processing operations that contributed to the event and then identifying steps to prevent future contamination. These steps include implementing improved production and processing procedures, needed regulatory or educational changes and continued monitoring and assessment of the changes to ensure that they have made a positive impact on reducing infection and preventing food-related outbreaks [70].

The detection and response to any outbreak investigation should be rapid and efficient. Advances in basic and applied research, such as mass spectrometry, biosensors and flow cytometry have aided rapid detection of foodborne pathogens from various food and environmental matrices [41, 57]. These methods should be rapid, accurate, sensitive, simple to perform, and cost effective. More importantly, they should be able to detect pathogen counts in the sample, preferably with little enrichment, and deliver results in real time. A detailed description of the rapid detection of pathogens is highlighted in Chapter 5.

The investigation program should contain comprehensive written preparedness, response, recovery and "lessons learned" action plans. Protocols should be established for chain of command, communications, investigative analytical tools and laboratory resources, electronic data transfer (information technology) and interagency collaboration between public health laboratories, regulatory agencies and industry [3, 60, 70, 71]. The general public should be kept abreast of the investigation by social networking and governmental websites, so that they can take appropriate action to minimize the potential for exposure to an implicated source. The FDA's Voluntary National Retail Food Regulatory Program Standard 5 for Foodborne Illness and Food Defense Preparedness and Response highlights the various requirements for investigating foodborne outbreaks (http://www.fda.gov/Food/FoodSafety/RetailFood Protection/ProgramStandards/ucm125043.htm). In addition, the Council to Improve Foodborne Outbreak Response (CIFOR) recently published a comprehensive set of guidelines aimed at improving outbreak response, and thereby limiting the public health impact of foodborne disease outbreaks (http://www.cifor.us/documents/CIFORGuidelinesforFoodborne DiseaseOutbreakResponse-updated.pdf).

CONCLUDING REMARKS

Foodborne illnesses continue to be a major public health issue because of their direct impact on morbidity and mortality in humans and other animals and their lasting social and economic costs. The innate ability of microorganisms to evolve and adapt to host environments and avoid pathogen control measures makes it difficult to keep a step ahead in the battle against foodborne illnesses. The mechanisms by which foodborne pathogens are transmitted through food production and processing to the human consumer are complex. Several mitigating factors contribute to this complexity, including the differential ability of pathogens to survive and proliferate in various food matrices, environments and the human gastrointestinal tract. Host-related factors, such as food consumption practices and deficiencies in innate immunity or adaptive immune responses, can lead to greater risks for foodborne infections. The evolving nature of potential pathogens can impact the ability of microorganisms to colonize and survive in food animal hosts, on contaminated produce and animal feeds, in processing plants, and retail settings, which may allow pathogens to occupy unique niches in the farm-to-fork continuum, and ultimately lead to human diseases.

When trying to ascertain the factors most important to the development of foodborne illness, a risk assessment/management approach should be developed to measure the burden of foodborne illnesses. A risk-based approach relies on an understanding of the interplay between pathogen characteristics, food products, susceptible populations, global trade/commerce and consumer lifestyles to generate a comprehensive assessment of risk and identify strategies to minimize the risk to consumers [29]. Educating veterinarians, medical professionals, public health officials, farmer workers and the general public is also essential to improve awareness of risks caused by foodborne/zoonotic pathogens to humans and make them cognizant of how these pathogens spread from the pre-harvest environment to final products along the food chain.

A combination of pre- and post-harvest intervention strategies can help deliver pathogen-free, fresh foods to consumers, thereby significantly reducing the medical and productivity costs associated with foodborne illnesses. A holistic approach to pathogen reduction, which includes animal welfare, husbandry, farm practices and management and vaccinations, will likely improve the safety of food-products leaving the pre-harvest production environment. Strategies for controlling microbial food safety hazards during processing include the use of good manufacturing and agricultural practices, food safety management practices, such as HACCP [5, 72], standard operation procedures for hygiene and sanitation, emergency action plans for addressing foodborne outbreaks and efficient information systems to monitor food safety management practices [43, 71]. To control foodborne pathogens on the retail side, retailers should ensure that refrigeration and storage conditions are optimal in transporting and storing foods and foods are rotated in a first in-first out fashion to ensure that products are replaced in a timely fashion. Food service operators should follow effective sanitation procedures, avoid cross contamination of raw meats, poultry and seafood with ready to serve items, and maintain effective time and temperature parameters through proper refrigeration, cooking, and holding temperatures. At home, consumers should take steps to avoid foodborne illnesses by using the USDA's core principles of "Clean", "Separate", "Chill" and "Cook" (www.foodsafety.gov; www.fightbac.org), which focus on the importance of sanitation, avoiding cross contamination and proper management of temperature for food storage and preparation. Advances can also be made in improving food processing technologies, such as canning, pasteurization, drying, freezing, refrigeration, modified atmosphere/vacuum packaging and irradiation to extend the shelf life and eliminate foodborne pathogens and spoilage organisms.

Outbreak investigations are essential for prevention of illnesses and disease spread at local, national and international stages. A dedicated effort towards robust and harmonized surveillance systems (i.e. PulseNet in the US and EnterNet in Europe) among local, state and federal public health laboratories will be necessary to rapidly identify an outbreak and contain the disease spread [73]. This multi-jurisdictional team effort should be dedicated towards using a cohort communication system, improving information technologies and databases, and refining molecular typing methodologies. The subsequent sections on molecular typing and their analyses have detailed descriptions of the different methods that have been used for DNA fingerprinting of foodborne pathogens, and how to interpret the biological significance of the data for source tracking and/or delineating transmission pathogens in outbreak investigations.

DISCLAIMER

The use of trade names is for identification purposes only, and does not imply endorsement by the U.S. Food and Drug Administration or the U.S. Department of Health and Human Services. The views presented in this manuscript do not necessarily reflect those of the FDA.

REFERENCES

[1]   Acheson DW. Foodborne infections. *Curr Opin Gastroenterol.* 1999;15(6):538-45.
[2]   Pigott DC. Foodborne illness. *Emerg Med Clin North Am.* 2008;26(2):475-97, x.
[3]   Tauxe RV, Doyle MP, Kuchenmuller T, Schlundt J, Stein CE. Evolving public health approaches to the global challenge of foodborne infections. *Int J Food Microbiol.* 2010;139 Suppl 1:S16-28.
[4]   Newell DG, Koopmans M, Verhoef L, Duizer E, Aidara-Kane A, Sprong H, et al. Food-borne diseases - the challenges of 20 years ago still persist while new ones continue to emerge. *Int J Food Microbiol.* 2010;139 Suppl 1:S3-15.
[5]   Nyachuba DG. Foodborne illness: is it on the rise? *Nutr Rev.* 2010;68(5):257-69.
[6]   Todd EC. Epidemiology of foodborne diseases: a worldwide review. *World Health Stat Q.* 1997;50(1-2):30-50.
[7]   Scallan E, Griffin PM, Angulo FJ, Tauxe RV, Hoekstra RM. Foodborne illness acquired in the United States–unspecified agents. *Emerg Infect Dis.* 2011;17(1):16-22.
[8]   Scallan E, Hoekstra RM, Angulo FJ, Tauxe RV, Widdowson MA, Roy SL, et al. Foodborne illness acquired in the United States--major pathogens. *Emerg Infect Dis.* 2011;17(1):7-15.
[9]   Centers for Disease Control and Prevention. Surveillance for foodborne disease outbreaks - United States, 2006. *MMWR Morb Mortal Wkly Rep.* 2009;58(22):609-15.
[10]   Buzby JC, Roberts T. The economics of enteric infections: human foodborne disease costs. *Gastroenterology.* 2009;136(6):1851-62.
[11]   Atreya CD. Major foodborne illness causing viruses and current status of vaccines against the diseases. *Foodborne Pathog Dis.* 2004;1(2):89-96.
[12]   Koopmans M, Duizer E. Foodborne viruses: an emerging problem. *Int J Food Microbiol.* 2004;90(1):23-41.
[13]   Dorny P, Praet N, Deckers N, Gabriel S. Emerging food-borne parasites. *Vet Parasitol.* 2009;163(3):196-206.

[14] Tietjen M, Fung DY. Salmonellae and food safety. *Crit Rev Microbiol.* 1995;21(1):53-83.

[15] Lynch MF, Tauxe RV, Hedberg CW. The growing burden of foodborne outbreaks due to contaminated fresh produce: risks and opportunities. *Epidemiol Infect.* 2009;137(3):307-15.

[16] Warriner K, Huber A, Namvar A, Fan W, Dunfield K. Recent advances in the microbial safety of fresh fruits and vegetables. *Adv Food Nutr Res.* 2009;57:155-208.

[17] Sivapalasingam S, Friedman CR, Cohen L, Tauxe RV. Fresh produce: a growing cause of outbreaks of foodborne illness in the United States, 1973 through 1997. *J Food Prot.* 2004;67(10):2342-53.

[18] Tribst AA, Sant'Ana Ade S, de Massaguer PR. Review: Microbiological quality and safety of fruit juices--past, present and future perspectives. *Crit Rev Microbiol.* 2009;35(4):310-39.

[19] Oliver SP, Jayarao BM, Almeida RA. Foodborne pathogens in milk and the dairy farm environment: food safety and public health implications. *Foodborne Pathog Dis.* 2005;2(2):115-29.

[20] Knabel SJ. Foodborne illness: Role of home food handling practices. *Food Technol.* 1995;49:119-31.

[21] Altekruse SF, Cohen ML, Swerdlow DL. Emerging foodborne diseases. *Emerging Inf Dis.* 1997;3:285-93.

[22] Hall RL. Foodborne illness: Implications for the future. *Emerging Inf Dis.* 1997 1997;3:555-9.

[23] Thiermann A. Emerging diseases and implications for global trade. *Rev Sci Tech.* 2004;23(2):701-7.

[24] MacKenzie AA, Allard DG, Perez E, Hathaway S. Food systems and the changing patterns of foodborne zoonoses. *Rev Sci Tech.* 2004;23(2):677-84.

[25] Trevejo RT, Barr MC, Robinson RA. Important emerging bacterial zoonotic infections affecting the immunocompromised. *Vet Res.* 2005;36(3):493-506.

[26] Molbak K. Human health consequences of antimicrobial drug-resistant *Salmonella* and other foodborne pathogens. *Clin Infect Dis.* 2005;41(11):1613-20.

[27] Tauxe RV. Emerging foodborne pathogens. *Int J Food Microbiol.* 2002;78(1-2):31-41.

[28] Oldfield EC, 3rd. Emerging foodborne pathogens: keeping your patients and your families safe. *Rev Gastroenterol Disord.* 2001;1(4):177-86.

[29] Schlundt J, Toyofuku H, Jansen J, Herbst SA. Emerging food-borne zoonoses. *Rev Sci Tech.* 2004;23(2):513-33.

[30] Lan R, Reeves PR, Octavia S. Population structure, origins and evolution of major *Salmonella enterica* clones. *Infect Genet Evol.* 2009;9(5):996-1005.

[31] Parry CM, Threlfall EJ. Antimicrobial resistance in typhoidal and nontyphoidal salmonellae. *Curr Opin Infect Dis.* 2008;21(5):531-8.

[32] Fluit AC. Towards more virulent and antibiotic-resistant *Salmonella?* *FEMS Immunol Med Microbiol.* 2005;43(1):1-11.

[33] Alcaine SD, Warnick LD, Wiedmann M. Antimicrobial resistance in nontyphoidal *Salmonella*. *J Food Prot.* 2007;70(3):780-90.

[34] Mathusa EC, Chen Y, Enache E, Hontz L. Non-O157 Shiga toxin-producing *Escherichia coli* in foods. *J Food Prot.* 2010;73(9):1721-36.

[35] Brooks JT, Sowers EG, Wells JG, Greene KD, Griffin PM, Hoekstra RM, et al. Non-O157 Shiga toxin-producing *Escherichia coli* infections in the United States, 1983-2002. J Infect Dis. 2005;192(8):1422-9.

[36] Harman JL, Silva CJ. Bovine spongiform encephalopathy. *J Am Vet Med Assoc.* 2009;234(1):59-72.

[37] Bielecki J. Emerging food pathogens and bacterial toxins. *Acta Microbiol Pol.* 2003;52 Suppl:17-22.

[38] Slifko TR, Smith HV, Rose JB. Emerging parasite zoonoses associated with water and food. *Int J Parasitol.* 2000;30(12-13):1379-93.

[39] Harrus S, Baneth G. Drivers for the emergence and re-emergence of vector-borne protozoal and bacterial diseases. *Int J Parasitol.* 2005;35(11-12):1309-18.

[40] Dawson D. Foodborne protozoan parasites. Int J Food Microbiol. 2005;103(2):207-27.

[41] Skovgaard N. New trends in emerging pathogens. *Int J Food Microbiol.* 2007;120(3):217-24.

[42] Jebara KB. Surveillance, detection and response: managing emerging diseases at national and international levels. *Rev Sci Tech.* 2004;23(2):709-15.

[43] Velusamy V, Arshak K, Korostynska O, Oliwa K, Adley C. An overview of foodborne pathogen detection: in the perspective of biosensors. *Biotechnol Adv.* 2010;28(2):232-54.

[44] Nayak R. Foodborne pathogens in poultry production and post-harvest control. Morgantown: West Virginia University; 2000.

[45] Collins JD, Wall PG. Food safety and animal production systems: controlling zoonoses at farm level. *Rev Sci Tech.* 2004;23(2):685-700.

[46] Rostagno MH. Can stress in farm animals increase food safety risk? *Foodborne Pathog Dis.* 2009;6(7):767-76.

[47] Abee T, van Schaik W, Siezen RJ. Impact of genomics on microbial food safety. *Trends Biotechnol.* 2004;22(12):653-60.

[48] Wells JM, Bennik MH. Genomics of food-borne bacterial pathogens. *Nutr Res Rev.* 2003;16(1):21-35.

[49] Puttamreddy S, Carruthers MD, Madsen ML, Minion FC. Transcriptome analysis of organisms with food safety relevance. *Foodborne Pathog Dis.* 2008;5(4):517-29.

[50] Bhagwat AA, Bhagwat M. Methods and tools for comparative genomics of foodborne pathogens. *Foodborne Pathog Dis.* 2008;5(4):487-97.

[51] Chen SL, Hung CS, Xu J, Reigstad CS, Magrini V, Sabo A, et al. Identification of genes subject to positive selection in uropathogenic strains of *Escherichia coli*: a comparative genomics approach. *Proc Natl Acad Sci U S A.* 2006;103(15):5977-82.

[52] McDermott PF, Zhao S, Wagner DD, Simjee S, Walker RD, White DG. The food safety perspective of antibiotic resistance. *Anim Biotechnol.* 2002;13(1):71-84.

[53] Powers JH. Antimicrobial drug development - the past, the present, and the future. *Clinical Microbiology and Infection.* 2004;10(s4):23-31.

[54] Walsh C, Fanning S. Antimicrobial resistance in foodborne pathogens--a cause for concern? *Curr Drug Targets.* 2008;9(9):808-15.

[55] Mathew AG, Cissell R, Liamthong S. Antibiotic resistance in bacteria associated with food animals: a United States perspective of livestock production. *Foodborne Pathog Dis.* 2007;4(2):115-33.

[56] Schroeder CM, Zhao C, DebRoy C, Torcolini J, Zhao S, White DG, et al. Antimicrobial resistance of *Escherichia coli* O157 isolated from humans, cattle, swine, and food. *Appl Environ Microbiol.* 2002;68(2):576-81.

[57] Han J, Shaheen B, Foley S, Nayak R. Prevalence, Mechanisms and Dissemination of Antimicrobial Resistance in Enteric Foodborne Bacteria. In: Khan A, Zarrilli R, editors. *Multidrug Resistiance A Global Concern.* Sharjah, U.A.E.: Bentham Science Publishers; 2011.

[58] Masterton R. The importance and future of antimicrobial surveillance studies. *Clin Infect Dis.* 2008;47 Suppl 1:S21-31.

[59] Hammerum AM, Heuer OE, Emborg HD, Bagger-Skjot L, Jensen VF, Rogues AM, et al. Danish integrated antimicrobial resistance monitoring and research program. *Emerg Infect Dis.* 2007;13(11):1632-9.

[60] Council to Improve Foodborne Outbreak Response. CIFOR Guidelines for Foodborne Disease Outbreak Resopnse. Atlanta, GA: Council of State and Territorial Epidemiologists; 2009.

[61] McCabe-Sellers BJ, Beattie SE. Food safety: emerging trends in foodborne illness surveillance and prevention. *J Am Diet Assoc.* 2004;104(11):1708-17.

[62] Vogt RL, LaRue D, Klaucke DN, Jillson DA. Comparison of an active and passive surveillance system of primary care providers for hepatitis, measles, rubella, and salmonellosis in Vermont. *Am J Public Health.* 1983;73(7):795-7.

[63] Gerner-Smidt P, Hise K, Kincaid J, Hunter S, Rolando S, Hyytia-Trees E, et al. PulseNet USA: a five-year update. *Foodborne Pathog Dis.* 2006 Spring;3(1):9-19.

[64] Swaminathan B, Barrett TJ, Hunter SB, Tauxe RV. PulseNet: the molecular subtyping network for foodborne bacterial disease surveillance, United States. Emerg Infect Dis. 2001;7(3):382-9.

[65] CDC. Preliminary FoodNet data on the incidence of infection with pathogens transmitted commonly through food--10 states, 2007. *MMWR Morb Mortal Wkly Rep.* 2008;57(14):366-70.

[66] Middaugh JP, Hammond RM, Eisenstein L, Lazensky R. Using the Electronic Foodborne Outbreak Reporting System (eFORS) to improve foodborne outbreak surveillance, investigations, and program evaluation. *J Environ Health.* 2010;73(2):8-11.

[67] Ashbolt R, Bell R, Crerar S, Dalton C, Givney R, Gregory J, et al. OzFoodNet: enhancing foodborne disease surveillance across Australia: quarterly report, January to March 2002. *Commun Dis Intell.* 2002;26(3):430-5.

[68] Health Protection Agency. Increase in reported foodborne outbreaks in 2009. *Health Protection Report.* 2010, 2010;4(19).

[69] Krause G, Altmann D, Faensen D, Porten K, Benzler J, Pfoch T, et al. SurvNet electronic surveillance system for infectious disease outbreaks, Germany. *Emerg Infect Dis.* 2007;13(10):1548-55.

[70] Sobel J, Griffin PM, Slutsker L, Swerdlow DL, Tauxe RV. Investigation of multistate foodborne disease outbreaks. *Public Health Rep.* 2002;117(1):8-19.

[71] McMeekin TA, Baranyi J, Bowman J, Dalgaard P, Kirk M, Ross T, et al. Information systems in food safety management. *Int J Food Microbiol.* 2006;112(3):181-94.

[72] NACMCF. Hazard analysis and critical control point principles and application guidelines. National Advisory Committee on Microbiological Criteria for Foods. *J Food Prot.* 1998;61(6):762-75.

[73] King LJ, Marano N, Hughes JM. New partnerships between animal health services and public health agencies. *Rev Sci Tech.* 2004;23(2):717-25.

In: Molecular Typing Methods for TFM
Editors: S. Foley, R. Nayak, T. Johnson et al.

ISBN: 978-1-62100-643-5
© 2012 Nova Science Publishers, Inc.

Chapter 2

MICROBIAL GENOMICS IN FOODBORNE PATHOGEN RESEARCH

James Robert White and W. Florian Fricke
Institute for Genome Sciences
University of Maryland School of Medicine
Baltimore, MD, US

ABSTRACT

Over the last decade, the field of genomics has rapidly changed the landscape in biological sciences with far-reaching consequences including for the food safety sector. Through advancements in high-throughput DNA sequencing technology and the development of novel bioinformatic tools for analyzing large sequence datasets, researchers are gaining new insights into the physiology and phylogeny of microbial pathogens and translating their findings into new applications for foodborne pathogen detection, classification and epidemiology. Today, the genomes of many foodborne pathogens as well as their non-pathogenic relatives have been sequenced and made available through public sequence databases, allowing for comparative analysis to discover genetic loci associated with virulence and antimicrobial resistance. Findings from these analyses are being used to identify marker genes and to develop screening assays for rapid and reliable classification. Traditional molecular fingerprinting tools such as pulsed-field gel electrophoresis (PFGE) and multi-locus sequence typing (MLST) are now being augmented by whole-genome sequence data, resulting in more precise phylogenetic analyses of unprecedented resolution. In this chapter, we give an introduction to the technology and bioinformatics of microbial genomics and discuss the state-of-the-art approaches and future challenges in genomics-driven applications for researchers and field experts working with foodborne pathogens.

INTRODUCTION

All organisms on the Earth maintain a set of hereditary information encoded by the *genome*, i.e. one or more stably inherited DNA molecules such as chromosomes and extra-chromosomal plasmid elements. Information is encoded in DNA using a simple set of four nucleotides (Adenine, Guanine, Cytosine, and Thymine). Not only does this code contain all information that is characteristic to an organism (and can thus be used to study its phenotypic appearance and physiology), but it also represents the most unique fingerprint of an organism distinguishing it even from its closest relatives. Genomics is the scientific study of the genetic code at the molecular level with the aim of characterizing and understanding the fundamental properties of life. In addition, genomic sequence analysis is beginning to expand beyond the scientific research field and evolving into a general molecular tool used to detect, identify, classify, and characterize pathogenic organisms in the clinic and public health sector.

Sequence data have to be analyzed informatically to produce useable results. Thus the bioinformatics field, which developed the computational tools for sequence processing and analysis–e.g. programs to assemble individual sequences into complete genomes, predict protein-coding genes in the genome sequence or provide algorithms to compare two sequences–evolved together with the genomics sector. From the beginning, the genomics and bioinformatics communities have fostered an open research culture that encourages free sharing of data and methods. In 1996, major players in genome research defined the "Bermuda principles" regarding this open culture [1], which ultimately led to the exponential growth of GenBank at the National Center for Biotechnology Information (NCBI) (http://www.ncbi.nlm.nih.gov). GenBank now serves as an online resource for all publicly available sequence data.

Early microbial genome sequencing projects had a strong focus on pathogenic organisms, aimed at identifying the molecular functions responsible for virulence and developing new diagnostic tools and treatment protocols. The first bacterial species to be completely sequenced was *Haemophilus influenzae* in 1995 [2]. Other early microbial genome projects targeted the laboratory model organisms *Escherichia coli* K-12 [3] and *Bacillus subtilis* strain 168 [4], as well as a number of foodborne and other pathogens (e.g. *Neisseria gonorrhoeae* [5], *Campylobacter jejuni* [6], *Chlamydia trachomatis* and *Chlamydia pneumoniae* [7], *Helicobacter pylori* [8], and *Mycobacterium tuberculosis* [9]). Today, most of these pathogenic species are represented in the NCBI public database by more than one genome sequence allowing for the comparison of closely related strains, thereby providing the basis for the identification of genetic determinants for very specific phenotypes.

Genome sequencing has become affordable and widespread, extending beyond the large genomics research centers and into small laboratories. There are over 1,300 complete microbial genomes in GenBank (> 150 are foodborne pathogens, see Table 1) and thousands of other draft genomes and ongoing sequencing projects (Figure 1). As of 2010, GenBank houses over 100 billion base pairs (100 Gbp) of annotated sequence. Novel sequencing technologies (e.g. pyrosequencing) have contributed to this explosion of genomic data by providing much higher throughput at lower cost. Higher throughput means more sophisticated questions may be answered about a single microbial species as well as entire microbial communities comprised of many species (also known as "metagenomics"). State-of-the-art machines can generate hundreds of Gigabases of sequence data in a single run, and the throughput rate has grown approximately fivefold per year. This growth rate is dramatically faster than Moore's law, which states that the number of transistors that can be placed on a computer chip doubles approximately every 24 months, a trend that has held for over 35 years. The magnitude of genomic information generated each day is so large that it must be analyzed using statistical and mathematical algorithms often requiring large-scale computing resources. Because of these increases, a microbial genome can now be fully sequenced for under $1,000. This is an important milestone as the field of genomics continues to strive toward the goal of sequencing an entire human genome for less than $1,000.

Table 1. Examples of foodborne pathogens with complete genome sequences in GenBank

Species	Phylum	Sources of infection	Completed genomes	References
Arcobacter butzleri	Epsilon-proteobacteria	animal products/water	1	[42-44]
Campylobacter jejuni	Epsilon-proteobacteria	poultry/water	7	[6, 45-47]
Campylobacter lari	Epsilon-proteobacteria	animal products/water	1	[48]
Bacillus cereus	Firmicutes	vegetables/milk/herbs	10	[49-52]
Bacillus licheniformis	Firmicutes	animals/vegetables	2	[53, 54]
Bacillus subtilis	Firmicutes	canned or processed foods	3	[4, 55, 56]
Clostridium botulinum	Firmicutes	canned meat and vegetables	11	[57, 58]
Clostridium perfringens	Firmicutes	meat/poultry	3	[59]
Listeria monocytogenes	Firmicutes	raw meat/milk/fish	7	[27, 60-62]
Staphylococcus aureus	Firmicutes	cooked meat/dairy	22	[63-66]
Enterobacter spp.	Gamma-proteobacteria	raw meat products	6	[67, 68]
Escherichia coli	Gamma-proteobacteria	meat/vegetables/nuts	41	[3, 69-73]
Klebsiella spp.	Gamma-proteobacteria	raw meat products	4	[74]
Salmonella enterica	Gamma-proteobacteria	meat/eggs/fruits	19	[75-77]
Shigella spp.	Gamma-proteobacteria	vegetables/water	8	[78-80]
Vibrio cholerae	Gamma-proteobacteria	shellfish/water	9	[81-83]
Vibrio vulnificus	Gamma-proteobacteria	shellfish/water	2	[84, 85]

In this chapter we will give an overview of the history and theory behind microbial genomics, including a brief introduction of present and future DNA sequencing platforms, post-sequencing analysis methods, and bioinformatics. We will illustrate the utility of genomics in foodborne outbreak investigations with selected case studies of genomics applied to foodborne pathogen research.

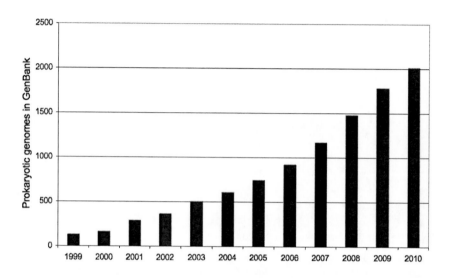

Figure 1. Cumulative prokaryotic finished and draft genomes available in GenBank through 2010. Publicly available sequence data continues to grow at an exponential rate.

TECHNOLOGY

The General Approach to Sequencing Technology

Most current sequencing technologies utilize a combination of target DNA enrichment and amplification to determine DNA sequences, where nucleotide-specific fluorescent markers are detected during or after their incorporation into the growing DNA strand. Continuous fluorescent signals are investigated along the DNA strand, and these signals are then converted into discrete base calls (A,C,G,T's). Each technology has its own challenges and biases, which will introduce some error in the sequence prediction. Depending on the sequencing platform one employs, there are specific error-correction and bias-reducing methods that should be used. Algorithms are available for all popular methods described below, so it is possible to obtain high-quality sequences from any approach.

Sanger – Sequencing by Chain-Termination

In the 1970s, Frederick Sanger was pivotal in developing the chain-termination method for sequencing, which is now referred to simply as "Sanger sequencing". This approach was used for the *H. influenzae* genome project in 1995 [2] and the majority of genomes during the following decade. Improved with automated robotics and computers, this technology not only allowed for the generation of the first high-quality microbial genome sequences, but also the first, much larger, eukaryotic genomes, including those of human [10, 11], mouse [12], and fruit fly [13]. Frederick Sanger was awarded the Nobel Prize for Chemistry in 1980 for his contributions to DNA sequencing methodologies.

The contemporary high-throughput Sanger method (known as capillary/microelectrophoretic sequencing) begins with a genomic library preparation consisting of genomic DNA shearing, followed by cloning of sheared fragments into vectors, transformation of *E. coli* cells and purification of recombinant vectors from *E. coli*. Each purified vector construct is then sequenced using a modified polymerase chain amplification (PCR) protocol in combination with individual fluorescently labeled dideoxynucleotide triphosphates or ddNTPs. During the PCR, a randomly incorporated ddNTP into the growing strand will terminate the extension, thus at the end of the PCR reaction, the resulting DNA fragments span all possible lengths. Using capillary gel electrophoresis, these fragments are size-separated with single nucleotide resolution, allowing for detection of the nucleotide-specific fluorescent label at the end of each sequence. Software monitors the fluorescence emission in order to call each base, thereby outputting the full DNA sequence or read.

Sequence error rates of contemporary Sanger sequencing reactions are often less than 0.01%. However, despite optimized protocols and automation, Sanger sequencing retains a relatively low throughput (384 sequences per run) and high cost per base pair (about $1 per 800 bp read in a 384 sample run). Additionally, the initial cloning step introduces biases, as the expression of foreign DNA can have toxic effects on the *E. coli* host cells. However, due to priming sites available at both ends of the recombinant vector construct from the Sanger library, each DNA fragment may be sequenced in both directions, providing paired-end reads separated by a known approximate size. Paired-end reads from different sequencing libraries with insert lengths between 3kbp and >50kbp can be highly useful for sequence assembly or other downstream applications and therefore still constitute a unique advantage of the Sanger sequencing technology over next-generation sequencing platforms.

Next-Generation Pyrosequencing

In 2003, a new method was introduced to determine the 30kbp genome sequence of an Adenovirus. This technology, created by the company 454 (now owned by Roche), introduced the concept of pyrosequencing, and was quickly dubbed the next-generation of DNA sequencing. Since then, a variety of new sequencing platforms have been introduced to the market, all under the umbrella of "Next-Gen" sequencing. These platforms have dramatically scaled up throughput (per bp) orders of magnitude over modern Sanger-based machines.

454, Illumina, & Helicos – Sequencing-by-Synthesis

The *sequencing-by-synthesis* approach uses photochemistry to detect nucleotide incorporations into a growing DNA strand as synthesis proceeds simultaneously in multiple reactions that are immobilized on a reaction plate. A camera monitors fluorescent signals during synthesis, which are translated into nucleotide sequences. Due to the high density with which the DNA synthesis reactions are placed on the reaction plate and detected with ultra-sensitive sensors, large numbers of sequence reads are produced during each sequencing run. Individual reads from all next-generation sequencing platforms that are available today, however, are still shorter than the average Sanger- read. To date, there exist three companies with production-ready systems that use the sequencing-by-synthesis method: 454/Roche, Illumina, and Helicos – each with its own characteristics.

For Illumina and 454 sequencing, sheared DNA fragments are ligated to short oligonucleotide adaptors to construct a library, which is then amplified using a water-oil emulsion PCR (454) or fold-back PCR on a glass substrate with anchored primers (Illumina). This localized amplification of each DNA fragment is designed to increase signal intensities during the later DNA synthesis detection process, but it can introduce a bias and represent a significant bottleneck for high-throughput sequencing. Helicos does not require an amplification step.

During the actual DNA synthesis step, DNA fragments immobilized on the sequencing plate are denatured and exposed to labeled nucleotides, which are then incorporated by a DNA polymerase and washed in repetitive cycles. One important distinction between the technologies is that on the 454 platform, "homopolymeric" stretches of identical nucleotides (e.g. 'AAAAAA') are incorporated into the growing DNA strand during a single cycle, whereas Illumina and Helicos only add one nucleotide at a time. As a consequence, a single sequencing run takes considerably longer for the latter two platforms (~8 days for the Illumina HiSeq 2000 system compared to ~10 hours for the 454 GS FLX system). The 454 sequencer measures the number of added nucleotides as an increase in the optical signal, which is not strictly proportional to the number of added nucleotides, thus typical 454 read errors involve incorrectly estimated homopolymeric stretches (e.g. 5 As vs. 6 As). This type of sequencing error is avoided through the stepwise addition of a single nucleotide per wash cycle during the Illumina and Helicos sequencing reaction. Illumina claims its approach represents the most accurate next-generation sequencing technology available today.

A single 4-hour run of the 454/Roche GS FLX Titanium pyrosequencer generates approximately 1 million reads with an average length of around 400 bp. This results in a total throughput of ~500Mbp at a cost of under $10,000 per run. A new chemistry, which is supposed to increase the average read length for the 454 GS FLX sequencer to >700 bp, has been announced for 2011. In contrast, a single 8-day Illumina HiSeq 2000 sequencing run has a total throughput of 200 Gbp with an average length of up to 150 bp. These relatively shorter reads, despite having a higher overall accuracy than 454 reads, present challenges for downstream bioinformatics analysis such as *de novo* genome assembly. Currently, these new technologies are typically used for re-sequencing experiments and single nucleotide polymorphism (SNP) analyses when there is a high-quality reference genome available or for *de novo* assembly of smaller (microbial) genomes. Additionally, next-generation sequencing-by-synthesis approaches are being applied to libraries of complimentary DNA (cDNA), generated from messenger RNA transcripts, in order to provide less-biased expression profiling (RNA-seq), as well as to DNA extracted during chromatin immunoprecipitation experiments (ChIP-seq).

Solid – Sequencing by Ligation

All current sequencing technologies described above rely on the accuracy of DNA polymerases in some way during the sequencing process. A different approach called *sequencing-by-ligation* has been developed in Applied Biosystem's (now Life Technologies) SOLiD platform. This technology uses a bead-based emulsion PCR step (similar to 454) followed by anchoring the beads to glass slides. Each anchored bead is then subjected to multiple ligation rounds with a set of four fluorescently labeled di-base octamer probes. Each ligation cycle with fluorescence detection is followed by a cleavage step and a primer reset with a single base pair offset. This allows for multiple measurements of each base in the fragment and overall better reliability of the sequencing results. One SOLiD run generates >100 Gbp with an accuracy of 99.94% and this is expected to increase in throughput in the coming years.

Technologies on the Horizon

There are several notable commercial DNA sequencing technologies on the horizon that will fundamentally alter the field of genomics. The company Pacific Biosciences has begun to deploy their new platform that uses single-molecule real-time (SMRT^{TM}) sequencing in 2011. This approach requires no amplification or washing steps; in contrast to the discussed protocols. In this method, a modified polymerase is immobilized on a sequencing plate instead of the sequence fragment to be amplified, and the incorporation of fluorescently-tagged nucleotides is detected by a camera sensor in a real-time fashion on the sequence fragments. This allows for much longer reads and faster runs and, in the future could also be applied to direct RNA sequencing (if RNA polymerases are immobilized on the sequencing plate rather than DNA polymerases). One run of the instrument is estimated to only take 15 minutes and produce 150 Mbp of sequence at a cost of $100.

Another platform in development by the company Ion Torrent (owned by Life Technologies) has created a novel way to identify nucleotides using semiconductor technology, which detects protons released during the DNA synthesis step. Because of this, no special labeling of nucleotides, or sequence fragments or modified enzymatic reactions are needed. Semiconductors were invented in the middle of the last century and have been heavily researched and refined. As a consequence, the fabrication of semiconductor chips has become very inexpensive, which is expected to support scalability and keep both the price of the Ion Torrent sequencing machine and the reagents used in the sequencing process low. Shipping of the Ion Torrent Personal Genome Machine (PGM) is expected to begin in early 2011, which will allow for the generation of at least 100,000 sequence reads with a read length of 100 to 200 bp in a single sequencing run at a cost of $250.

Nanopore sequencing, a revolutionary concept of DNA sequencing, is still in active development that may someday allow us to sequence a human genome for under $1,000 [14]. Like Ion Torrent, nanopore sequencing requires no fluorescent signal; the nanopore method would identify nucleotides by passing them single-file through a small channel with a persistent voltage. Different nucleotides would provide variable current interferences thereby allowing a machine to distinguish them in order. One company, Oxford Nanopore

Technologies, is frequently producing advancements in this area, though there are no formal announcements of a commercial device yet.

The Trend of Decentralization in the Sequencing Market

The current model for large-scale sequencing is *core-based*, in which an expensive infrastructure (e.g. electricity, spacious laboratories, IT services) and a team of specialists are typically required to run sequencing machines in a cost-effective manner. The *core* performs all necessary steps to take a sample from DNA prep to high-quality sequences. This trend has existed for years and about a dozen major sequencing facilities thrive across the United States. While this paradigm has succeeded in the early era of genomics, a new concept is now emerging in which researchers may be able to utilize alternative 'benchtop' sequencers. Life Science's Ion Torrent machine is one example of this new type of sequencer and a similar concept is pursued by Roche with the 454 GS Junior system. These low-cost machines provide relatively lower throughput, but are intended to bring massively parallel sequencing technology to virtually any laboratory. The ability to place a DNA sequencing machine next to other essential laboratory tools would enable even small research groups or service providers to rapidly genotype strains of interest or sequence and annotate isolated microorganisms. A similar trend of decentralization can be observed in the bioinformatics field, which will be described in the following paragraphs. Instead of installing complex local hardware infrastructures, bioinformatics applications are expected to increasingly take advantage of web-accessible on-demand cloud services [15].

Bioinformatics

The bioinformatics steps necessary for sequence processing and analysis are integral parts of any genomics project. Large amounts of sequences have to be processed computationally in order to identify useful information and to provide the basis for the following sequence analysis. Over the last decade the field of bioinformatics has grown significantly in order to tackle the numerous challenges associated with different sequencing technologies and applications.

Sequence Processing

Traditional genome sequencing projects involve three major post-processing steps: (1) individual sequence reads have to be assembled into large contiguous pieces (contigs) with the ultimate goal of completing an entire genome; (2) in the resulting genome, functional genetic units have to be identified including, e.g. protein-, tRNA- and mRNA-encoding genes or promoter regions with gene regulatory functions, etc.; and (3) the identified sequence features have to be functionally annotated, i.e. protein-coding genes are translated into protein sequences, which are assigned to, for example, functional or enzymatic role. Sequence assembly relies on the identification of similar sequence fragments between individual reads; protein-coding genes and other genome features are identified based on sequence composition analyses or comparison to known sequence elements, whereas functional annotations are mostly performed based on homology searches against curated protein or protein domain databases such as UniProt [16] or Pfam [17].

Newer sequencing projects often target organisms for which a closely related genome sequence exists in the public databases. In this case, the *de novo* sequence assembly, gene finding and annotation approach is often replaced with a reference-based approach. The annotated reference genome can be used to map genes and associated annotations onto the new sequence assembly, or the assembly component can be omitted entirely. Instead, individual sequence reads can be mapped directly onto a reference genome in order to provide information about the presence and absence of genome fragments in the newly sequenced genome, or to identify subtle sequence differences, such as SNPs. This method is especially attractive for the use of next-generation sequencing platforms that produce large amounts of short sequence reads, which pose challenges for traditional bioinformatics assembly programs [18].

Sequence Analysis

Most sequence analysis methods rely on a comparative approach of some sort. With the increasing availability of genome sequence data of closely related organisms, very specific questions about phylogenetic relationships among sequenced bacterial strains can now be asked. In addition, by carefully selecting the genomes to be compared, for example groups of closely related commensal and virulent *E. coli* strains, the genetic determinants responsible for a specific phenotype can be identified as well as marker genes that can help to distinguish and identify microbes of interest [19]. Comparative analyses involve challenges such as identifying orthologous genes in different genomes, defining a core set of genes, or reconstructing the phylogeny of available organisms. The task of identifying orthologs, i.e. genes in different genomes that diverged from a single common ancestral gene, involves searching for sequence similarity among the genomes using a program such as BLAST [20]. Once highly similar gene pairs are found, identifying the true orthologs is obfuscated by the existence of paralogs – divergent copies of genes within a single genome. Algorithms have been developed to identify and screen paralogs, which often have significantly different coding sequences relative to the true orthologous pairs.

Different sets of genes among a collection of genomes are often compared as well. For example, a *pan-genome* is the entire set of all genes in a group of genomes, while a *core genome* is the subset of genes that are ubiquitous across all organisms in a genus or species, which likely contains many genes essential for survival [21]. Using conserved genes from the core genome, researchers can perform a multiple sequence alignment to construct a more accurate phylogeny of the studied microbes. The resulting phylogenetic tree provides information about common ancestry and speciation events within the group [22].

Challenges

The analysis of data produced using different sequencing technologies will often require specific software. Many algorithms are designed for one particular platform e.g. Illumina or 454, but rarely multiple types. As a consequence, it can be difficult to combine hybrid sequence data that were generated from different platforms, e.g. when trying to assemble 454 and Illumina sequences from the same genome. As sequencing technologies continue to evolve and grow, so do the algorithms to process the data. Currently, state-of-the-art machines can produce so much sequence that post-processing and data management have become an analysis bottleneck. Computer scientists and statisticians are working to utilize innovative technologies to handle these massive datasets.

One area of significant interest to the scientific community is *cloud computing*, which allows researchers to access large computer clusters over the Internet, which are managed and leased out by a vendor. Essentially, a user can rent a subset of the computer cluster for any task from hosting websites, to performing comprehensive numerical simulations or run computationally intensive bioinformatics workflows. Compute clouds are either commercially driven (e.g. the Amazon Elastic Computer Cloud [http://aws.amazon.com /ec2/]) or freely available for the academic community such as the Magellan Cloud sponsored by the Department of Energy (http://magellan.alcf.anl.gov/). In the commercial case of the Amazon Elastic Compute Cloud, users pay per physical machine per cpu hour, thereby allowing for scaling up (or down) of a cluster size as needed. Additional fees are imposed for data transfer and long-term storage, but these are relatively low compared to cpu hour costs. The infrastructure developed by Amazon, which benefits from substantial economies of scale, keeps the price of using their services low. For many this represents a cost-effective alternative to building a private cluster and paying for ongoing costs including facility space, electricity, cooling, and information technology staff.

To run a parallelized software package in the cloud, the software and all dependencies should be present on all computers in the rented cluster. This presents a challenge as bioinformatics analyses employ many underlying programs, each of which must be adjusted for different operating systems and hardware platforms. To solve this problem, many developers are bundling their programs and all dependencies into *virtual machines*. A virtual machine is essentially a virtual computer within a computer – it maintains its own operating system, and can share the file system of a physical computer. Virtual machines house a suite of programs and can easily be migrated across a computer cluster, thereby facilitating parallel analysis.

The storage and manipulation of huge DNA sequence datasets (from many gigabytes to terabytes) is also a major concern in bioinformatics analysis. When datasets reach or exceed these levels, they are cumbersome to handle using standard scheduling programs and filesystems. One of the first groups to run into this problem was the Google Corporation, which needed to parse petabytes worth of webpages for its ingenious PageRank algorithm. Google's solution, called MapReduce, is a proprietary software framework for efficiently analyzing data in a distributed compute environment using a specialized filesystem. The concept of MapReduce involves three simple steps: a mapping step, followed by a shuffling/sorting step of mapping results, and finally a reduction step to aggregate the final results [23]. The advantage of MapReduce lies in its ability to rapidly perform the mapping and reduction steps in a parallelized fashion, and efficiently sorting the results. Apache has developed a free open source version of MapReduce called Hadoop, which is widely used among Internet companies (http://hadoop.apache.org). Recently, genomics researchers have begun to explore using Hadoop in the cloud for mapping short reads from pyrosequencers or *de novo* genome assembly [24, 25].

APPLICATIONS

Foodborne pathogen research has greatly benefited from three main applications of microbial genomics: (i) functional research into foodborne pathogenesis, including the identification of genetic determinants associated with virulence, antimicrobial resistance or other phenotypes; (ii) development of new diagnostics and surveillance protocols to detect and classify foodborne pathogens, and to assist clinical, public health and forensics experts in the field; and (iii) high-resolution epidemiological analyses of the emergence, spread and evolution of foodborne pathogens (Figure 2). As we will discuss below, researchers have been able to make progress in these directions by utilizing DNA sequencing with robust processing and post-processing of the data.

A Functional Approach to Foodborne Pathogen Research

The first microbial pathogens were sequenced with the goal to identify new virulence factors and improve our understanding of physiological functions or regulatory networks that play a role in pathogenesis [26]. This search for the molecular basis of pathogenicity has been be refined by comparing the genomes of closely related pathogenic and non-pathogenic organisms (see Table 1). For example, in 2001, the complete genome sequence of the Gram-positive pathogen *Listeria monocytogenes* EGDe (serotype 1/2a) was published along with its non-pathogenic phylogenetic neighbor *Listeria innocua* CLIP11262 (serotype 6a) [27]. By including the genome sequence of *L. innocua* in the study, researchers were able to examine which genomic regions were unique to *L. monocytogenes* or *L. innocua*, thereby proposing that the presence or absence of some unique regions in *L. monocytogenes* would be associated with virulence. Similar comparative studies have been carried out on the *Escherichia coli* species for which a wide spectrum of phenotypes exists ranging from host-associated to environmental, and non-pathogenic to uropathogenic, diarrheagenic and extraintestinal pathogenic strains [19].

Insights from the genome sequences can guide subsequent experimental characterizations of selected genes *in vitro* or in animal models. The term "reverse vaccinology" was used to describe a new approach for the identification of vaccine targets by *in silico* bioinformatics [28, 29]. This approach takes advantage of comparative genome analysis to identify those protein-coding genes that are uniquely found only in those organisms for which a vaccine is being developed. It was applied to develop a vaccine against meningococcal meningitis, caused by *Neisseria meningitidis*, which successfully passed the preclinical phase [30]. Reverse vaccinology is also being used for vaccine development against group A and B *Streptococcus*, *Staphylococcus aureus* and *Chlamydia pneumoniae* [29].

Another benefit of microbial genomics projects related to foodborne pathogens is the identification of mobile genetic elements that play an important role in rapid phenotype acquisition and transfer, especially for antimicrobial drug resistance [31]. In the U.S., where livestock is routinely raised with growth-promoting antimicrobial food additives, enteric populations of the foodborne pathogens *Salmonella enterica* and *E. coli* among others have been shown to serve as important reservoirs of antimicrobial resistance [32]. In order to predict the mobility of antimicrobial resistance determinants and to estimate the risk of resistance transfer to other bacterial populations, such as, for example, commensal *E. coli* strains in the human gut, it is important not only to characterize the resistance genes themselves but also their genetic context. In 1997, a broad-host range plasmid was identified as responsible for the first documented case of multidrug resistance (MDR) in the causative agent of plague, *Yersinia pestis* [33]. Later, highly similar MDR plasmids were identified in *S. enterica* and *E. coli* isolates from geographic locations in the U.S. where *Y. pestis* is endemic in rodent populations [34]. The observation that these plasmids were efficiently self-transferable from *S. enterica* to *E. coli* and *Yersinia ruckeri*, a fish pathogen and close relative of *Y. pestis*, has caused considerable alarm in the public health communities.

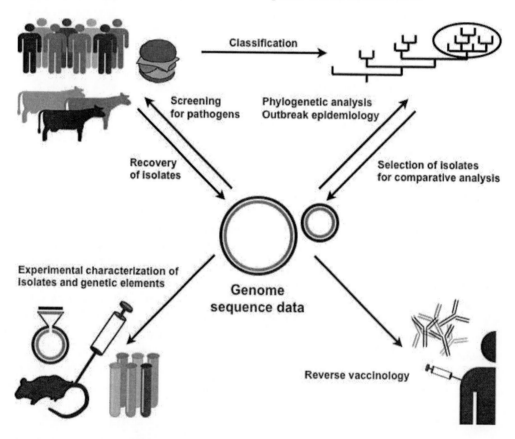

Figure 2. Microbial genomics applications in foodborne pathogen research.

A genomic study of an *S. enterica* Kentucky isolate, which is the predominant *S. enterica* serovar in chicken, identified resistance determinants to the antimicrobial compounds aminoglycosides, tetracyclines, and beta-lactams on two self-transferable plasmids [35]. The plasmid sequences were searched against the NCBI sequence database, resulting in a number of high-identity matches, including hits to virulence plasmids from avian pathogenic *E. coli* (APEC) isolates, which are involved in colibacillosis, a disease responsible for multimillion dollar losses in the poultry industry [36, 37]. Comparative analysis revealed that the plasmids shared a suite of virulence factors such as iron scavenging systems, which could play an important role for the colonization of the chicken habitat. The identification of genes for antimicrobial resistance and APEC virulence factors on the same plasmid provides insights into the potential propagation of virulence plasmids through antimicrobial selection in the agricultural environment. This highlights the need for more research into the spread of these mobile elements across pathogenic and non-pathogenic species in agricultural settings.

Diagnostics and Surveillance

The development of new molecular tools for the detection and classification of foodborne pathogens has proven essential for the early detection of outbreaks and assistance in outbreak mitigation efforts. Genome sequences represent unique signatures of pathogenic organisms and the wealth of genomes from foodborne pathogens available to scientists has led to a variety of novel approaches for the rapid detection and typing of unknown microbial samples. These approaches have helped in the identification of marker genes or SNPs specific for certain types of pathogens, i.e. virulent vs. non-virulence species or strains. Marker genes may be the virulence genes themselves or genes of unknown function whose presence or absence characterizes the genomes of all organisms from one group compared to a related control group. The screening of a large number of bacterial isolates for marker genes by PCR is a common method to classify bacterial isolates [38]. Today, the identification of unique signatures for diagnostic assays is facilitated by comparative sequence analysis tools.

Multilocus Sequence Typing (MLST) is commonly used for fast and inexpensive classification of microbes (see Chapter 9). A number of MLST typing schemes exist that use different sets of housekeeping genes to classify, for example, the Gram-negative enteric pathogens *E. coli*, *S. enterica*, and *C. jejuni* (http://www.mlst.net/) or the Gram-positive foodborne pathogens *Clostridium perfringens* and *Bacillus cereus* (http://pubmlst.org/). In addition, using genomic sequence information, high-density microarrays have been developed (see chapter 16) that interrogate the genomic diversity of microbial isolates by hybridizing DNA isolates to short oligomers that are immobilized on a microarray [39].

Based on an input dataset of several genome sequences, the bioinformatics tool *Insignia* can identify DNA regions that are uniquely shared among a set of target genomes, but not present in a background genome set [40]. For example, suppose if one wanted to find all 24bp-oligomers that are shared among all sequenced *Clostridium botulinum* strains, but absent from any other sequenced *Clostridium* species or any species at all for that matter. Insignia can identify these regions and sort them according to GC% content, melting temperature, or signature length. This tool has been extensively used to augment the TaqMan real-time PCR protocol for microbial diagnostics [40].

Epidemiology

Microbial epidemiology is a notoriously difficult practice for microbiologists particularly when appropriate phylogenetic information is limited. Traditional methods for differentiating pathogenic isolates such as MLST only measure sequence variability along a small subset of the total genome, and often lack resolution to distinguish closely related strains. Now high-throughput next-generation genome sequencing and short-read mapping algorithms are beginning to allow researchers to study isolate variation along the entire genome, thereby providing much more precise phylogenetic distances even between closely related strains.

Recently, a group studying the epidemiology of methicillin-resistant *Staphylococcus aureus* performed Illumina sequencing on 63 isolates (type ST239) recovered between 1982 and 2003 in global collections largely from Asia, Europe, and South America, and mapped the sequences from each isolate to the complete genome of a single strain [41]. By mapping these reads across the finished genome, SNPs could be identified between all isolates. A total of 6,714 high-quality SNP sites were detected using the complete genome, and this was winnowed down to 4,310 sites present in all isolates in the study. This information was then used to construct a maximum-likelihood phylogenetic tree describing the evolutionary distance between all members at a resolution unachievable by MLST-based approaches.

Using this tree, the researchers were able to describe the intercontinental transmission events of MRSA over the last decade. One example of this transmission was the clustering of two isolates from Europe with a phylogenetic clade largely composed of isolates from Thailand. In one case the subject from Europe was actually Thai, while the other European isolate, derived from a two-year outbreak in London, indicated that the source of the outbreak was a MRSA strain from Southeast Asia. Overall this study was able to use next-generation DNA sequencing technology to reconstruct very detailed relationships between isolates and follow the migration of the MRSA pathogen across multiple continents. As the cost of sequence generation is expected to further drop in the next few years, comparable studies of other organisms, including foodborne pathogens associated with specific outbreaks, are likely to become more common.

CONCLUSIONS

Merely 15 years after the release of the first microbial genome sequence, genomics has become an integral part of microbiological research. Early microbial genome projects were entirely research-driven, hoping to lay the basis for functional characterization of selected genetic elements in subsequent laboratory experiments. These genome sequences were soon complemented with sequence data from closely related organisms, in order to provide the basis for comparative analysis. Today, next-generation sequencing platforms have made large-scale genome projects involving hundreds or even thousands of bacterial isolates affordable. Consequently, new project designs are being developed that transform microbial genomics from a purely scientific context into a molecular tool for classifying strains and studying the epidemiology of globally emerging infectious diseases. This trend can be expected to continue, as less expensive sequencing platforms with greater throughput capabilities are appearing on the horizon. Based on this development genome sequencing can be expected to become a standard laboratory routine, similar to the application of PCR today. It is therefore likely that in the near future, microbial genomics will be omnipresent as a diagnostic tool in the public health sector. The benefits for foodborne pathogen and/or antibiotic resistance monitoring programs by directly sequencing multiple microbial isolates recovered from raw and processed food, patients and personnel in clinical settings, livestock animals, etc. are obvious. Similar surveillance programs could be highly useful in the early detection of foodborne disease outbreaks as well as emerging antibiotic resistance phenotypes. Outbreaks could be traced back to their origins, helping in the prevention of future outbreaks and hopefully reducing deaths from foodborne illness. It should be noted again that the increased affordability of sequence generation comes at the price of a bioinformatics bottleneck, which results from increasing demands in bioinformatics capacities to process and analyze the sequence data. Cloud computing provides a model that could help balance some of the effects of the bioinformatics bottleneck.

REFERENCES

[1] Bentley DR. Genomic sequence information should be released immediately and freely in the public domain. *Science.* 1996;274(5287):533-4.

[2] Fleischmann RD, Adams MD, White O, Clayton RA, Kirkness EF, Kerlavage AR, et al. Whole-genome random sequencing and assembly of *Haemophilus influenzae* Rd. *Science.* 1995;269(5223):496-512.

[3] Blattner FR, Plunkett G, 3rd, Bloch CA, Perna NT, Burland V, Riley M, et al. The complete genome sequence of *Escherichia coli* K-12. *Science.* 1997;277(5331):1453-62.

[4] Harwood CR, Wipat A. Sequencing and functional analysis of the genome of *Bacillus subtilis* strain 168. *FEBS letters.* 1996;389(1):84-7.

[5] Carrick CS, Fyfe JA, Davies JK. The genome of *Neisseria gonorrhoeae* retains the remnants of a two-component regulatory system that once controlled piliation. *FEMS microbiology letters.* 2000;186(2):197-201.

[6] Parkhill J, Wren BW, Mungall K, Ketley JM, Churcher C, Basham D, et al. The genome sequence of the food-borne pathogen *Campylobacter jejuni* reveals hypervariable sequences. *Nature.* 2000;403(6770):665-8.

[7] Stephens RS, Kalman S, Lammel C, Fan J, Marathe R, Aravind L, et al. Genome sequence of an obligate intracellular pathogen of humans: *Chlamydia trachomatis.* *Science.* 1998;282(5389):754-9.

[8] Tomb JF, White O, Kerlavage AR, Clayton RA, Sutton GG, Fleischmann RD, et al. The complete genome sequence of the gastric pathogen *Helicobacter pylori.* *Nature.* 1997;388(6642):539-47.

[9] Cole ST, Brosch R, Parkhill J, Garnier T, Churcher C, Harris D, et al. Deciphering the biology of *Mycobacterium tuberculosis* from the complete genome sequence. *Nature.* 1998;393(6685):537-44.

[10] Lander ES, Linton LM, Birren B, Nusbaum C, Zody MC, Baldwin J, et al. Initial sequencing and analysis of the human genome. *Nature.* 2001;409(6822):860-921.

[11] Venter JC, Adams MD, Myers EW, Li PW, Mural RJ, Sutton GG, et al. The sequence of the human genome. *Science.* 2001;291(5507):1304-51.

[12] Waterston RH, Lindblad-Toh K, Birney E, Rogers J, Abril JF, Agarwal P, et al. Initial sequencing and comparative analysis of the mouse genome. *Nature.* 2002;420(6915):520-62.

[13] Adams MD, Celniker SE, Holt RA, Evans CA, Gocayne JD, Amanatides PG, et al. The genome sequence of *Drosophila melanogaster.* *Science.* 2000;287(5461):2185-95.

[14] Branton D, Deamer DW, Marziali A, Bayley H, Benner SA, Butler T, et al. The potential and challenges of nanopore sequencing. *Nature Biotechnology.* 2008;26(10):1146-53.

[15] Stein LD. The case for cloud computing in genome informatics. *Genome Biol.* 2010;11(5):207.

[16] Wu CH, Apweiler R, Bairoch A, Natale DA, Barker WC, Boeckmann B, et al. The Universal Protein Resource (UniProt): an expanding universe of protein information. *Nucleic Acids Res.* 2006;34:D187-91.

[17] Finn RD, Mistry J, Tate J, Coggill P, Heger A, Pollington JE, et al. The Pfam protein families database. *Nucleic Acids Res.* 2010;38:D211-22.

[18] Trapnell C, Salzberg SL. How to map billions of short reads onto genomes. *Nature biotechnology.* 2009;27(5):455-7.

[19] Rasko DA, Rosovitz MJ, Myers GS, Mongodin EF, Fricke WF, Gajer P, et al. The pangenome structure of *Escherichia coli*: comparative genomic analysis of *E. coli* commensal and pathogenic isolates. *J Bacteriol.* 2008;190(20):6881-93.

[20] Altschul SF, Madden TL, Schaffer AA, Zhang J, Zhang Z, Miller W, et al. Gapped BLAST and PSI-BLAST: a new generation of protein database search programs. *Nucleic Acids Res.* 1997;25(17):3389-402.

[21] Medini D, Donati C, Tettelin H, Masignani V, Rappuoli R. The microbial pan-genome. *Current opinion in genetics & development.* 2005;15(6):589-94.

[22] Luo H, Shi J, Arndt W, Tang J, Friedman R. Gene order phylogeny of the genus *Prochlorococcus*. *PloS one.* 2008;3(12):e3837.

[23] Schatz MC. CloudBurst: highly sensitive read mapping with MapReduce. *Bioinformatics.* 2009 Jun 1;25(11):1363-9.

[24] Schatz MC, Langmead B, Salzberg SL. Cloud computing and the DNA data race. *Nature biotechnology.* 2010;28(7):691-3.

[25] Langmead B, Schatz MC, Lin J, Pop M, Salzberg SL. Searching for SNPs with cloud computing. *Genome Biol.* 2009;10(11):R134.

[26] Pallen MJ, Wren BW. Bacterial pathogenomics. *Nature.* 2007;449(7164):835-42.

[27] Glaser P, Frangeul L, Buchrieser C, Rusniok C, Amend A, Baquero F, et al. Comparative genomics of *Listeria* species. *Science.* 2001;294(5543):849-52.

[28] Rappuoli R. Reverse vaccinology. Current opinion in microbiology. 2000;3(5):445-50.

[29] Sette A, Rappuoli R. Reverse vaccinology: developing vaccines in the era of genomics. *Immunity.* 2010;33(4):530-41.

[30] Giuliani MM, Adu-Bobie J, Comanducci M, Arico B, Savino S, Santini L, et al. A universal vaccine for serogroup B meningococcus. *Proc Natl Acad Sci U S A.* 2006;103(29):10834-9.

[31] Wright GD. The antibiotic resistome: the nexus of chemical and genetic diversity. *Nat Rev Microbiol.* 2007;5(3):175-86.

[32] USDA. National Antimicrobial Resistance Monitoring System for Enteric Bacteria (NARMS): *Animal Arm Annual Report.* USDA, Washington DC; 2007.

[33] Galimand M, Guiyoule A, Gerbaud G, Rasoamanana B, Chanteau S, Carniel E, et al. Multidrug resistance in *Yersinia pestis* mediated by a transferable plasmid. *The New England journal of medicine.* 1997;337(10):677-80.

[34] Welch TJ, Fricke WF, McDermott PF, White DG, Rosso ML, Rasko DA, et al. Multiple antimicrobial resistance in plague: an emerging public health risk. *PloS One.* 2007;2(3):e309.

[35] Fricke WF, McDermott PF, Mammel MK, Zhao S, Johnson TJ, Rasko DA, et al. Antimicrobial resistance-conferring plasmids with similarity to virulence plasmids from

avian pathogenic *Escherichia coli* strains in *Salmonella enterica* serovar Kentucky isolates from poultry. *Appl Enviro Microbiol.* 2009;75(18):5963-71.

[36] Johnson TJ, Johnson SJ, Nolan LK. Complete DNA sequence of a ColBM plasmid from avian pathogenic *Escherichia coli* suggests that it evolved from closely related ColV virulence plasmids. *J Bacteriol.* 2006;188(16):5975-83.

[37] Skyberg JA, Johnson TJ, Johnson JR, Clabots C, Logue CM, Nolan LK. Acquisition of avian pathogenic *Escherichia coli* plasmids by a commensal E. coli isolate enhances its abilities to kill chicken embryos, grow in human urine, and colonize the murine kidney. *Infect Immun.* 2006;74(11):6287-92.

[38] Kuhnert P, Boerlin P, Frey J. Target genes for virulence assessment of *Escherichia coli* isolates from water, food and the environment. *FEMS Microbiol Rev.* 2000;24(1):107-17.

[39] Jackson SA, Mammel MK, Patel IR, Mays T, Albert TJ, LeClerc JE, et al. Interrogating genomic diversity of *E. coli* O157:H7 using DNA tiling arrays. *Forensic Sci International.* 2007;168(2-3):183-99.

[40] Phillippy AM, Ayanbule K, Edwards NJ, Salzberg SL. Insignia: a DNA signature search web server for diagnostic assay development. *Nucleic Acids Res.* 2009;37:W229-34.

[41] Harris SR, Feil EJ, Holden MT, Quail MA, Nickerson EK, Chantratita N, et al. Evolution of MRSA during hospital transmission and intercontinental spread. *Science.* 2010;327(5964):469-74.

[42] Miller WG, Parker CT, Rubenfield M, Mendz GL, Wosten MM, Ussery DW, et al. The complete genome sequence and analysis of the epsilonproteobacterium *Arcobacter butzleri. PloS One.* 2007;2(12):e1358.

[43] Miller WG, Wesley IV, On SL, Houf K, Megraud F, Wang G, et al. First multi-locus sequence typing scheme for *Arcobacter* spp. *BMC microbiology.* 2009;9:196.

[44] Stoeva K, Bruce Ward F. Genome mapping of *Arcobacter butzleri. FEMS Microbiol Letters.* 2006;256(2):290-7.

[45] Gundogdu O, Bentley SD, Holden MT, Parkhill J, Dorrell N, Wren BW. Re-annotation and re-analysis of the *Campylobacter jejuni* NCTC11168 genome sequence. *BMC Genomics.* 2007;8:162.

[46] Pearson BM, Gaskin DJ, Segers RP, Wells JM, Nuijten PJ, van Vliet AH. The complete genome sequence of *Campylobacter jejuni* strain 81116 (NCTC11828*). J Bacteriol.* 2007;189(22):8402-3.

[47] Wren BW, Linton D, Dorrell N, Karlyshev AV. Post genome analysis of *Campylobacter jejuni.* Symposium series (Society for Applied Microbiology). 2001(30):36S-44S.

[48] Miller WG, Wang G, Binnewies TT, Parker CT. The complete genome sequence and analysis of the human pathogen *Campylobacter lari. Foodborne Pathog Dis.* 2008;5(4):371-86.

[49] Ivanova N, Sorokin A, Anderson I, Galleron N, Candelon B, Kapatral V, et al. Genome sequence of *Bacillus cereus* and comparative analysis with *Bacillus anthracis. Nature.* 2003;423(6935):87-91.

[50] Qiu N, He J, Wang Y, Cheng G, Li M, Sun M, et al. Prevalence and diversity of insertion sequences in the genome of *Bacillus thuringiensis* YBT-1520 and comparison with other *Bacillus cereus* group members. *FEMS Microbiol Letters.* 2010;310(1):9-16.

[51] Rasko DA, Ravel J, Okstad OA, Helgason E, Cer RZ, Jiang L, et al. The genome sequence of Bacillus cereus ATCC 10987 reveals metabolic adaptations and a large plasmid related to *Bacillus anthracis* pXO1. *Nucleic Acids Res.* 2004;32(3):977-88.

[52] Xiong Z, Jiang Y, Qi D, Lu H, Yang F, Yang J, et al. Complete genome sequence of the extremophilic *Bacillus cereus* strain Q1 with industrial applications. *J Bacteriol.* 2009;191(3):1120-1.

[53] Rey MW, Ramaiya P, Nelson BA, Brody-Karpin SD, Zaretsky EJ, Tang M, et al. Complete genome sequence of the industrial bacterium *Bacillus licheniformis* and comparisons with closely related *Bacillus* species. *Genome Biol.* 2004;5(10):R77.

[54] Veith B, Herzberg C, Steckel S, Feesche J, Maurer KH, Ehrenreich P, et al. The complete genome sequence of *Bacillus licheniformis* DSM13, an organism with great industrial potential. *J Mol Microbiol Biotech.* 2004;7(4):204-11.

[55] Moszer I. The complete genome of *Bacillus subtilis*: from sequence annotation to data management and analysis. *FEBS letters.* 1998 Jun 23;430(1-2):28-36.

[56] Kunst F, Ogasawara N, Moszer I, Albertini AM, Alloni G, Azevedo V, et al. The complete genome sequence of the gram-positive bacterium *Bacillus subtilis*. *Nature.* 1997;390(6657):249-56.

[57] Sebaihia M, Peck MW, Minton NP, Thomson NR, Holden MT, Mitchell WJ, et al. Genome sequence of a proteolytic (Group I) *Clostridium botulinum* strain Hall A and comparative analysis of the clostridial genomes. *Genome Res.* 2007;17(7):1082-92.

[58] Sakaguchi Y, Hayashi T, Kurokawa K, Nakayama K, Oshima K, Fujinaga Y, et al. The genome sequence of *Clostridium botulinum* type C neurotoxin-converting phage and the molecular mechanisms of unstable lysogeny. *Proc Natl Acad Sci U S A.* 2005;102(48):17472-7.

[59] Shimizu T, Ohtani K, Hirakawa H, Ohshima K, Yamashita A, Shiba T, et al. Complete genome sequence of *Clostridium perfringens*, an anaerobic flesh-eater. *Proc Natl Acad Sci U S A.* 2002;99(2):996-1001.

[60] Gilmour MW, Graham M, Van Domselaar G, Tyler S, Kent H, Trout-Yakel KM, et al. High-throughput genome sequencing of two *Listeria monocytogenes* clinical isolates during a large foodborne outbreak. *BMC Genomics.* 2010;11:120.

[61] Nelson KE, Fouts DE, Mongodin EF, Ravel J, DeBoy RT, Kolonay JF, et al. Whole genome comparisons of serotype 4b and 1/2a strains of the food-borne pathogen *Listeria monocytogenes* reveal new insights into the core genome components of this species. *Nucleic Acids Res.* 2004;32(8):2386-95.

[62] Buchrieser C, Rusniok C, Kunst F, Cossart P, Glaser P. Comparison of the genome sequences of *Listeria monocytogenes* and *Listeria innocua*: clues for evolution and pathogenicity. *FEMS Immunol Med Microbiol.* 2003;35(3):207-13.

[63] Howden BP, Seemann T, Harrison PF, McEvoy CR, Stanton JA, Rand CJ, et al. Complete genome sequence of *Staphylococcus aureus* strain JKD6008, an ST239 clone of methicillin-resistant *Staphylococcus aureus* with intermediate-level vancomycin resistance. *J Bacteriol.* 2010;192(21):5848-9.

[64] Chua K, Seemann T, Harrison PF, Davies JK, Coutts SJ, Chen H, et al. Complete genome sequence of *Staphylococcus aureus* strain JKD6159, a unique Australian clone of ST93-IV community methicillin-resistant *Staphylococcus aureus*. *J Bacteriol.* 2010;192(20):5556-7.

[65] Baba T, Bae T, Schneewind O, Takeuchi F, Hiramatsu K. Genome sequence of *Staphylococcus aureus* strain Newman and comparative analysis of staphylococcal genomes: polymorphism and evolution of two major pathogenicity islands. *J Bacteriol.* 2008;190(1):300-10.

[66] Kuroda M, Ohta T, Uchiyama I, Baba T, Yuzawa H, Kobayashi I, et al. Whole genome sequencing of meticillin-resistant *Staphylococcus aureus*. *Lancet.* 2001 Apr 21;357(9264):1225-40.

[67] Ren Y, Ren Y, Zhou Z, Guo X, Li Y, Feng L, et al. Complete genome sequence of *Enterobacter cloacae* subsp. *cloacae* type strain ATCC 13047. *J Bacteriol.* 2010;192(9):2463-4.

[68] Taghavi S, van der Lelie D, Hoffman A, Zhang YB, Walla MD, Vangronsveld J, et al. Genome sequence of the plant growth promoting endophytic bacterium *Enterobacter* sp. 638. *PLoS Genetics.* 2010;6(5):e1000943.

[69] Chaudhuri RR, Sebaihia M, Hobman JL, Webber MA, Leyton DL, Goldberg MD, et al. Complete genome sequence and comparative metabolic profiling of the prototypical enteroaggregative *Escherichia coli* strain 042. *PLoS One.* 2010;5(1):e8801.

[70] Iguchi A, Thomson NR, Ogura Y, Saunders D, Ooka T, Henderson IR, et al. Complete genome sequence and comparative genome analysis of enteropathogenic *Escherichia coli* O127:H6 strain E2348/69. *J Bacteriol.* 2009;191(1):347-54.

[71] Durfee T, Nelson R, Baldwin S, Plunkett G, 3rd, Burland V, Mau B, et al. The complete genome sequence of *Escherichia coli* DH10B: insights into the biology of a laboratory workhorse. *J Bacteriol.* 2008;190(7):2597-606.

[72] Hayashi T, Makino K, Ohnishi M, Kurokawa K, Ishii K, Yokoyama K, et al. Complete genome sequence of enterohemorrhagic *Escherichia coli* O157:H7 and genomic comparison with a laboratory strain K-12. *DNA Res.* 2001;8(1):11-22.

[73] Perna NT, Plunkett G, 3rd, Burland V, Mau B, Glasner JD, Rose DJ, et al. Genome sequence of enterohaemorrhagic *Escherichia coli* O157:H7. *Nature.* 2001;409(6819):529-33.

[74] Fouts DE, Tyler HL, DeBoy RT, Daugherty S, Ren Q, Badger JH, et al. Complete genome sequence of the N2-fixing broad host range endophyte *Klebsiella pneumoniae* 342 and virulence predictions verified in mice. *PLoS Genetics.* 2008;4(7):e1000141.

[75] Chiu CH, Tang P, Chu C, Hu S, Bao Q, Yu J, et al. The genome sequence of *Salmonella enterica* serovar Choleraesuis, a highly invasive and resistant zoonotic pathogen. *Nucleic Acids Res.* 2005;33(5):1690-8.

[76] McClelland M, Sanderson KE, Spieth J, Clifton SW, Latreille P, Courtney L, et al. Complete genome sequence of *Salmonella enterica* serovar Typhimurium LT2. *Nature.* 2001;413(6858):852-6.

[77] Parkhill J, Dougan G, James KD, Thomson NR, Pickard D, Wain J, et al. Complete genome sequence of a multiple drug resistant *Salmonella enterica* serovar Typhi CT18. *Nature.* 2001;413(6858):848-52.

[78] Nie H, Yang F, Zhang X, Yang J, Chen L, Wang J, et al. Complete genome sequence of *Shigella flexneri* 5b and comparison with *Shigella flexneri* 2a. *BMC Genomics.* 2006;7:173.

[79] Wei J, Goldberg MB, Burland V, Venkatesan MM, Deng W, Fournier G, et al. Complete genome sequence and comparative genomics of *Shigella flexneri* serotype 2a strain 2457T. *Infect Immun.* 2003;71(5):2775-86.

[80] Jin Q, Yuan Z, Xu J, Wang Y, Shen Y, Lu W, et al. Genome sequence of *Shigella flexneri* 2a: insights into pathogenicity through comparison with genomes of *Escherichia coli* K12 and O157. *Nucleic Acids Res.* 2002;30(20):4432-41.

[81] Grim CJ, Hasan NA, Taviani E, Haley B, Chun J, Brettin TS, et al. Genome sequence of hybrid *Vibrio cholerae* O1 MJ-1236, B-33, and CIRS101 and comparative genomics with *V. cholerae. J Bacteriol.* 2010;192(13):3524-33.

[82] Chen Y, Johnson JA, Pusch GD, Morris JG, Jr., Stine OC. The genome of non-O1 *Vibrio cholerae* NRT36S demonstrates the presence of pathogenic mechanisms that are distinct from those of O1 *Vibrio cholerae. Infect Immun.* 2007;75(5):2645-7.

[83] Schoolnik GK, Yildiz FH. The complete genome sequence of *Vibrio cholerae*: a tale of two chromosomes and of two lifestyles. *Genome Biol.* 2000;1(3):1016.

[84] Quirke AM, Reen FJ, Claesson MJ, Boyd EF. Genomic island identification in *Vibrio vulnificus* reveals significant genome plasticity in this human pathogen. *Bioinformatics.* 2006;22(8):905-10.

[85] Chen CY, Wu KM, Chang YC, Chang CH, Tsai HC, Liao TL, et al. Comparative genome analysis of *Vibrio vulnificus*, a marine pathogen. *Genome Res.* 2003;13(12):2577-87.

In: Molecular Typing Methods for TFM
Editors: S. Foley, R. Nayak, T. Johnson et al.

ISBN: 978-1-62100-643-5
© 2012 Nova Science Publishers, Inc.

Chapter 3

PLASMIDS AND PLASMID ANALYSIS

Timothy J. Johnson

Department of Veterinary and Biomedical Sciences
College of Veterinary Medicine
University of Minnesota
St. Paul, MN, US

ABSTRACT

Bacterial plasmids are extrachromosomal genetic elements that play a powerful role in bacterial genome evolution. Plasmids are able to provide their host strains with of a variety of additional traits including antimicrobial resistance, virulence, and the metabolism of rare substances. A large number of plasmids are associated with the virulence and antimicrobial resistance capabilities in bacterial foodborne pathogens. This chapter will provide an overview of the key plasmids of *Campylobacter*, *E. coli*, and *Salmonella*, and their role in antimicrobial resistance and/or disease. In addition, an overview of the currently used typing schemes for plasmid populations will also be examined.

INTRODUCTION

Bacterial plasmids are extrachromosomal elements that are key agents of change in microbial populations [1, 2]. Naturally occurring plasmids play a powerful role in bacterial genome evolution. With a single transfer event, they are capable of introducing a variety of phenotypes to the recipient bacterial cell, including antimicrobial resistance, virulence and the degradation of rare compounds [3]. A great deal of research has focused on the mechanisms of plasmid transfer, stability and maintenance, and the regulation of plasmid-mediated bacterial virulence. However, due to the concerns presented by the emergence of multidrug resistant bacteria, recent work has focused on plasmid genomics and the use of these data to develop effective plasmid typing tools to study the evolution and dissemination of plasmids encoding virulence and/or multidrug resistance.

This chapter will provide an overview of the key plasmids of *Campylobacter*, *E. coli*, and *Salmonella*, and their role in antimicrobial resistance and/or disease. An overview of the currently used typing schemes for plasmid populations will also be examined.

PLASMIDS OF FOODBORNE PATHOGENS

Campylobacter Jejuni and C. Coli

Campylobacter jejuni and *C. coli* are causative agents of foodborne gastroenteritis [4, 5]. While infection in humans is usually self-limited, it occasionally requires antibiotic therapy for treatment. The virulence and antimicrobial resistance mechanisms of *Camplyobacter* spp. are incompletely understood, particularly with regards to plasmid-mediated functions. However, some key work has been done to define 'trademark' plasmids in *Campylobacter* populations. Taylor et al. [5] were among the first to identify transmissible plasmids among *C. jejuni* encoding for tetracycline resistance and confirm that these plasmids were likely transmissible to other *Campylobacter* strains via bacterial conjugation. Restriction mapping of these plasmids from *C. jejuni* and *C. coli* of human and animal sources revealed a highly conserved structure of about 44 kb in size [6].

Bacon et al. [7] identified plasmids pTet and pVir in *C. jejuni* strain 81-876. Mutational analysis of *comB3* and *virB11* revealed a reduction in adhesion and invasion of INT407 cells (*comB3* and *virB11*) and reduced virulence in the ferret diarrheal disease model (*virB11*). Bacon et al. [8] sequenced pVir and performed 19 additional gene knockouts, resulting in the identification of five additional genes involved in INT407 invasion. pVir was 37,468 bp in size, encoding an apparent type IV secretion system and a number of hypothetical proteins (Figure 1). Batchelor et al. [9] sequenced the pTet plasmids from strains 81-176 (*C. jejuni*) and pCC31 (*C. coli*). Both of these plasmids were ~45 kb in size, nearly identical in structure, and encoded for an additional type IV secretion system. A retrospective study was performed on patients with *C. jejuni*-caused gastroenteritis, and the presence of pVir was associated with the occurrence of bloody stool in the patient [10]. In contrast, Louwen et al. [11] were unable to identify a correlation between the presence of pVir and bloody diarrhea, and the prevalence of pVir was extremely low among these isolates. Therefore, the precise role of plasmids pTet and pVir in the pathogenesis of *Campylobacter* is unclear.

A number of studies have subsequently investigated the prevalence of the pTet plasmid, and corresponding high levels of tetracycline resistance among isolates of clinical, animal, and retail meat origin [12, 13]. Additionally, the prevalence of pVir has been sought in a number of studies, with variable results. Generally, the prevalence of pVir in *C. jejuni* and *C. coli* is low [10, 14], with comparatively higher levels of pTet carriage among these populations [15]. Furthermore, while whole plasmid comparative sequencing studies have identified a great deal of conservation among pVir and pTet plasmids in clinical isolates, some studies have identified additional resistance-encoding determinants on pTet-like plasmids, including genes encoding for aminoglycoside resistance [16]. Although pVir and pTet are the only *Campylobacter* plasmids studied in detail, *Campylobacter* also have a large and variable number of apparently cryptic plasmids that are not well described [17].

A typing scheme for *Campylobacter* plasmids is not well developed. However, approaches have been used to identify pTet and pVir among *Campylobacter* populations using microarrays, overlapping primer sets, or multiplex PCR for subsets of pVir and pTet genes [14, 15]. These approaches seem to work well due to the high degree of conservation among these plasmid types. Typing schemes for other *Campylobacter* plasmid types remain to be developed.

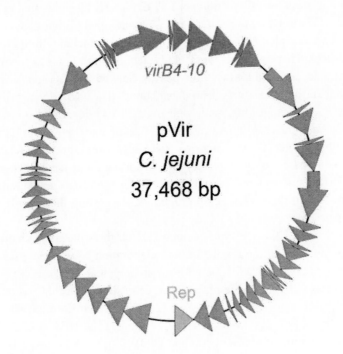

Figure 1. Circular map of pVir of *C. jejuni*. The type IV secretion system and replication gene commonly used for plasmid identification are noted in the figure.

E. coli and Shigella spp

Because *Escherichia coli* is one of the most-studied bacteria, we know more about its genomic repertoire than any other bacterial species [18]. *E. coli* is an extremely diverse species containing both commensal and pathogenic strains. Among the 'pathotypes' identified are enterotoxigenic *E. coli* (ETEC), enteroinvasive *E. coli* (EIEC), enteropathogenic *E. coli* (EPEC), enterohemorrhagic *E. coli* (EHEC), enteroaggregative *E. coli* (EAEC), and extraintestinal pathogenic *E. coli* (ExPEC). Each of these pathotypes has a predictable arsenal of virulence factors, many of which are plasmid-encoded. Below, each pathotype is described, with a focus on the virulence plasmids that they possess and the conserved targets that can be used for the typing of these plasmids.

ETEC-caused diseases have a great economic impact to humans in terms of lost productivity and health care costs. These strains generally cause a watery diarrhea referred to as 'traveler's diarrhea', but are also an important cause of disease in developing countries lacking modernized sanitation systems [19-21]. ETEC strains cause disease through a series of events starting with ingestion of the bacterium through the fecal-oral route. ETEC first colonize the host's intestinal epithelium using specific adhesins, most of which are plasmid-encoded [21]. Following attachment, they produce enterotoxins known as heat labile (LT) and/or heat stable (ST) that result in the rapid onset of watery diarrhea, which is mostly self-limiting but that without treatment can cause life-threatening dehydration.

While ETEC are known to have chromosome-encoded virulence factors, plasmids play a key role in the pathogenesis of this pathotype. ETEC possess plasmids that encode for their colonization factors (CFs or CSs), toxins (LT and ST), and other afimbrial adhesins [22]. The colonization factors are encoded on polycistronic operons that include fimbrial subunit genes, chaperones, and ushers. These systems were likely acquired via homologous recombination by prototype F plasmids, since all known CF types are flanked by insertions sequences and/or transposons residing on an IncF-like plasmid backbone. The evolutionary diversity of the ETEC colonization factors is striking, with well over 20 CFs identified that are genetically and antigenically distinct [22, 23]. In contrast, the LT and ST toxins within ETEC strains are more conserved although genetic variants do exist (23). Thus, the identification of ETEC based upon their toxin possession is relatively straightforward, but identification of their CFs is complicated. This is underscored by the fact that many LT/ST-containing ETEC lack known CF types but retain their pathogenic properties, suggesting that they harbor as-of-yet unidentified CF types [24].

Despite the diversity of the CF types among ETEC, their plasmids share a number of common homologs involved in the regulation and elaboration of virulence factors. The first ETEC CF type described was CFA/I, isolated from archetypical human ETEC strain H10407 [25]. In addition to this CF type, these plasmids or co-residing plasmids were also found to encode regulatory genes, such as *rns* and *cfaR* [26, 27]. Since the discovery of CFA/I, a number of additional CF types were discovered, including CFA/II, [28], (with three antigenically distinct components, CS1, CS2, and CS3) [29]; CFA/IV (expressing CS6 alone or in combination with CS5); and many others [22].

The first sequenced ETEC virulence plasmid was pCoo, from the CFA/I$^+$ ETEC strain C921b-1 [30]. This plasmid was identified as a cointegrate plasmid because it possessed two different plasmid replicons sharing homology with IncI1 plasmid R64 from *Salmonella enterica* serovar Typhimurium [31, 32] and IncFIIA plasmid R100 from *Shigella* spp. [33]. As expected, this plasmid possessed the *coo* operon containing four genes encoding the CS1 pilus. Additionally, pCoo was found to encode a serine protease autotransporter EatA, which has been implicated in ETEC virulence [34]. Overall, this plasmid seems to be conserved among CS1$^+$ ETEC isolates [30]. Following the sequencing of pCoo, strain H10407 (O78:K80:H11) was also sequenced [35]. It was found to possess multiple plasmids encoding a variety of virulence-associated genes, including CFA/I, EtpABC, and EatA, and LT. The plasmids of strain H10407 are all IncF-like plasmids, some containing intact conjugative transfer systems. The CFA/I$^+$ ETEC strain E24377A has also been sequenced to completion and was found to contain six plasmids, ranging in size from 5 to 80 kb [36]. The CF-encoding plasmid of E24377A is similar to that of pCoo in that both possess the CS1 operon within a RepI1 backbone region. From these analyses, it can be hypothesized that the CS1 operon was introduced into an ancestral IncI1 plasmid, and this occurred prior to the integration of IncFIIA backbone components and *eatA*. Strains possessing other ETEC CF types are currently in progress (http://www.genomesonline.org/), which will likely increase our understanding of the evolution of ETEC pathotype.

EAEC strains were first described by Nataro et al. for their distinct 'brick-like' aggregative adherence phenotype towards cultured HEp-2 cells [37]. Like ETEC, EAEC strains are implicated in traveler's diarrhea but also affect immunocompromised children in developing countries [38]. EAEC pathogenesis is dependent upon multiple bacterial factors and host immune status [39]. Still, some basic virulence mechanisms are employed by EAEC bacteria, including adherence to the intestinal mucosa using aggregative adherent fimbriae (AAF), production of a mucus-mediated biofilm on the enterocyte surface, and the release of toxins [38]. EAEC plasmids are key to some of these activities. The primary plasmid-encoded virulence factor of EAEC is the aggregative adherence phenotype [40], encoded by the AAF operon found on a 55- to 65-MDa pAA plasmid [37]. At least four different allelic variants of AAF have been identified, including AAF/I [41], AAF/II [39], AAF/III [42] and AAF/IV [43]. All of these allelic types are plasmid encoded [40], and they are regulated by an AraC-like transcriptional activator, AggR [44], which is a global regulator of EAEC virulence [45]. EAEC strains also possess *aap*, a dispersin that facilitates the movement of EAEC across the intestinal mucosa for subsequent aggregation and adherence [38]. This dispersin is exported out of the EAEC cell via the antiaggregation protein transporter system, encoded by the genes *aatPABCD* [46]. All of these genes/systems are plasmid-encoded (Figure 2). The EAEC plasmids can also encode toxins such as the plasmid-encoded toxins Pet and EAST1 [47], although relatively few EAEC strains actually possess these genes [48]. Plasmid sequencing has been performed on EAEC strains belonging to AAF types II and III. These plasmids are IncFIB plasmids with stability, maintenance, and transfer regions. Plasmid 55989p is considerably smaller than plasmids pO42 and pO86A1, which is due to truncations in the F transfer region.

The EHEC pathotype includes the infamous strains of O157:H7 responsible for severe cases of foodborne disease [18, 49]. EHEC is a subset of Shiga toxin-producing *E. coli* (STEC), which include strains capable of causing hemorrhagic colitis (HC) and hemolytic-uremic syndrome (HUS) in humans [50]. Strains within the EHEC pathotype are defined by their ability to produce Shiga toxin and to induce attaching and effacing lesions in intestinal epithelium. These strains are pathogenic for humans, but they can reside asymptomatically in many production animal types including poultry, swine, and cattle [50]. The recorded outbreaks of human disease have thus implicated food products, including undercooked or pre-cooked meats, fresh vegetables, unpasteurized milk and cider.

Chromosome-encoded traits are essential for the pathogenesis of O157:H7 strains. However, these strains also possess plasmids. Plasmid pO157 is found in 99 to 100% of clinical O157:H7 isolates from humans [51, 52]. While the role of pO157 in EHEC pathogenesis has not been clearly defined, correlations have been made between pO157 and adherence to intestinal epithelial cells [53]. The first O157:H7 plasmid sequenced was pO157 from outbreak-associated strain EDL933 [53]. This plasmid was found to be 92 kb in size, contain an IncFIB plasmid replicon, and carry virulence factors including a hemolysin operon (*ehx*), a type II secretion system (*etpC* to *etpO*), an extracellular protease (*espP*), and a *toxB* homolog (Figure 3). Subsequent sequencing efforts involving O157:H7 strains have revealed that this plasmid is highly conserved among this *E. coli* lineage.

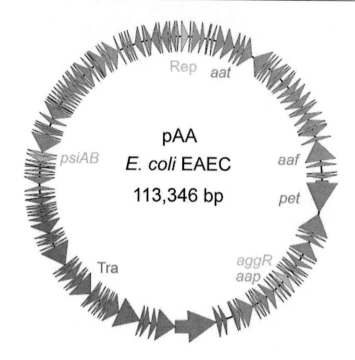

Figure 2. Circular map of pAA of EAEC strain O42. The *aat*, *aaf*, *pet*, *aggR*, and *aap* loci are depicted as genes commonly used for AAF plasmid identification.

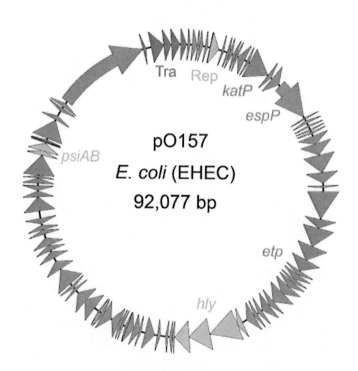

Figure 3. Circular map of pO157 from EHEC strain EDL933. The *katP*, *espP*, *etp*, and *hly* loci are depicted as genes commonly used for pO157 plasmid identification.

Non-O157:H7 EHEC strains also possess large plasmids [54]. Brunder et al. published the first plasmid sequence (pSFO157) from a sorbitol-fermenting O157:H⁻ isolate [55] and found that pSFO157 is an ancestor of pO157, which has evolved via reductive evolution involving a loss-of-transfer function [55]. Large hemolysin-encoding plasmids are found in the majority of STEC isolates, including those not belonging to the O157 serogroup [56]. For example, the completed sequence of plasmid pO113 from an isolate belonging to the O113 serogroup [56] demonstrated that it contained the *ehx* (*hly*) hemolysin operon, *espP*, and *iha* genes, where were also found in pO157. Thus, while EHEC strains are considerably diverse, they seem to share common lineages both from a chromosomal and plasmid evolutionary standpoint.

EPEC were first described in the 1940s for their association with infantile diarrhea during summer outbreaks, and can cause acute and persistent diarrhea in infants aged less than 5 years [57]. In developing countries, EPEC can be deadly, with mortality rates approaching 30% [57]. Defining traits of EPEC strains are their attaching and effacing histopathology [58] and localized adherence to human cell lines such as HEp-2 [59]. Attaching and effacing is associated with a chromosomal pathogenicity island, but the localized adherence phenotype is associated with the EPEC adherence factor (EAF) plasmid [60-62].

Three completed EAF plasmid sequences are publicly available. The first plasmid sequenced, pB171, was described by Tobe et al. [63]. This plasmid was isolated from EPEC strain B171-8, belonging to the O111 serogroup and implicated in human diarrhea. This plasmid was found to be 68,817 bp in size and to possess the IncFIB and IncFIIA replicons. Within this plasmid was a cluster of genes encoding bundle-forming pili (*bfp* genes), which are responsible for the localized adherence patterns exhibited by EPEC, and the *perABC* genes involved in the transcriptional activation of *bfp* and other chromosomally encoded virulence factors. The sequencing of a second plasmid, pMAR7, revealed a high degree of colinearity between pB171 and pMAR7 [64]. pMAR7 was derived from pMAR2 from EPEC strain E2348/69 belonging to the O127:H6 serotype. The primary differences between pMAR7/pMAR2 and pB171 is the presence of an intact F transfer region in pMAR7/pMAR2, which is completely absent from pB171, and 16 ORFs in pB171 not present in pMAR7/pMAR2, which are mostly mobile elements [64] (Figure 4). pMAR2 was sequenced as a part of a recent genome sequencing effort involving strain E2438/69, and pMAR7 and pMAR2 were reported to be identical outside of three SNPs and two single-base insertions/deletions within intergenic regions [65]. Although the sequenced EAF plasmids shared very strong similarities with one another, further plasmids from isolates representing different EPEC clonal types should be examined to better understand the overall evolution of the EAF plasmid.

EIEC and *Shigella* strains cause shigellosis or bacillary dysentery, respectively, in human hosts [66] and their conferred diseases result in nearly one million deaths per year from over 150 million cases [67]. These pathotypes are distinguished from other *E. coli* because of their invasive ability within the host's gastrointestinal tract. EIEC and *Shigella* strains possess a large plasmid, pINV, encoding the ability to invade host cells [66]. The Inv plasmid contains a great deal of plasticity; nearly one-third of the Inv plasmid encodes IS elements. Still, the pInv plasmids contain a subset of genes essential for their host strains' pathogenesis. One of these essential regions is a 30-kb region responsible for entry into epithelial cells [68], which includes transcriptional activators (*virB* and *mxiEab*), effectors (*ipaADCB*, *ipgB1D*, and *icsB*), chaperones (*ipgACE* and *spa15*), components of the needle complex (*mxiGHIJMD*), and inner membrane protein-encoding genes (*mxiA*, *spa24*, *spa9*, *spa29*, and *spa40*). Additionally, the expression of these and other pInv-encoded virulence factors is globally regulated by VirB and MxiE [68, 69].

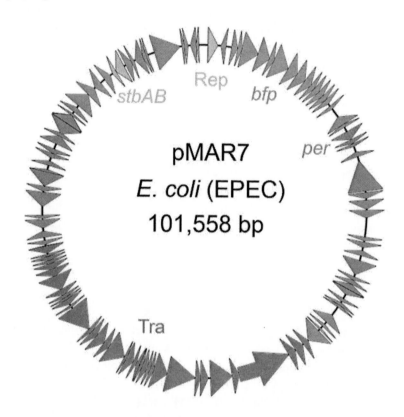

Figure 4. Circular map of pMAR7 from EPEC strain E2348/69. The *bfp* and *per* loci are depicted as genes commonly used for EPEC plasmid identification.

Phylogenetic studies involving the pInv plasmids has divided them into two distinct but related clusters [70]. The availability of several completed pInv plasmid sequences reveals that they have evolved via a series of deletion/acquisition events within a highly conserved backbone sequence, suggesting that the diversification of this plasmid lineage is relatively recent. Based upon the comparative analysis of the eight sequenced Inv plasmids [71], the core components of these plasmids include a IncFIIA-like plasmid replicon, *ospB*, *ospD2D1*, *sopAB*, *ospC1D3*, *ipaH*$_{9.8}$, and *traI*. It appears that the EIEC Inv ancestral plasmid contained a functional F-type transfer region, and that a deletion of this region occurred after its introduction into *Shigella* species. In addition to the loss of portions of the F transfer region, *Shigella* plasmids appear to have evolved from an EIEC plasmid ancestor through the acquisition of type III secretion system components. Overall, the pInv plasmids have undergone a stepwise evolution characterized by additions and deletions of large blocks of DNA within an apparently short evolutionary time frame. This rapid evolution has likely been shaped by an abundance of mobile elements within this plasmid type.

E. coli Virulence Plasmid Typing

Due to the diversity of human ETEC, typing of these plasmids is tedious and difficult, although PCR-based typing [72], antigenic typing [22, 73-75], and microarray approaches [76] have been used to identify human ETEC plasmid-encoded fimbriae, toxins, and other virulence determinants. PCR-based typing approaches can be applied to identify and differentiate between known colonization factor types and LT and ST toxins. Other virulence factors, such as *etpABC*, *eatA*, *tiaB*, *cexE*, are useful for further characterization of confirmed human ETEC [35, 36, 77]. However, the varying distributions of these genes among ETEC populations does not make them ideal candidates for the absolute identification of an ETEC, which currently can be achieved through the identification of LT and/or ST. Typical EAEC plasmids can be identified through the PCR-based identification of plasmid-encoded virulence factors specific to this pathotype's plasmid, pAA [78]. These include the AAF fimbrial types, the dispersin (*aap*) and its transport system (*aat*), and the toxin *pet*. Once again, caution should be taken when considering these typing approaches since there is considerable genetic diversity even within the EAEC pathotype. Furthermore, atypical EAEC lack these virulence factors and the AAF plasmid, and as such are more difficult to identify based upon genotype alone. The conserved nature of the core elements of pO157 and other non-O157 STEC plasmids makes their identification relatively straightforward. Genes conserved among pO157 and non-O157 STEC plasmids include those of the *ehx* (*hly*) operon, *espP*, and *iha* (Reference). Genes specific to pO157 or to the non-O157 STEC plasmids could also be used to further differentiate between these plasmid types. Typing for the EAF plasmid of EPEC can be performed through screening for genes of the *bfp* and *per* operons. For the *Shigella*/EIEC plasmids, PCR-based typing could be performed for the core genes of these plasmids, including *ospB*, *ospD2D1*, *sopAB*, *ospC1D3*, *ipaH*$_{9.8}$. The *Shigella* plasmids can be differentiated from the EIEC plasmids by the presence or absence of the Inv type III secretion system, respectively [71].

Salmonella enterica Virulence Plasmids

With greater than 2,500 serovars, *Salmonella enterica* is a diverse pathogen capable of causing numerous human and animal diseases [79]. These include gastrointestinal diseases of humans and systemic diseases of production animals. Like *E. coli*, many serovars of *Salmonella* carry plasmids encoding virulence determinants. These plasmids have been found among a number of different host-adapted *Salmonella* serovars, including Abortusovis, Paratyphi C, Enteritidis, Typhimurium, Dublin, Choleraesuis, Gallinarum, and Pullorum [80]. These plasmids do not appear to play a prominent role in *Salmonella* virulence, but certain components of these plasmids do contribute to their host strain's ability to cause systemic disease in specific animal hosts. A number of *Salmonella* virulence plasmids have been sequenced [81-84]. The *Salmonella* virulence plasmids were likely derived from multiple IncF plasmid backbones, containing an IncF-type replicon and portions of the F plasmid transfer (*tra*) region. Within the virulence-associated accessory regions of the *Salmonella* virulence plasmid is a five-gene *spv* region that is highly conserved among *Salmonella* serovars containing this plasmid (Figure 5). The exact function of this region in virulence is not completely understood. A fimbrial-encoding operon was also identified on the *Salmonella* virulence plasmid, encoded by the *pefABCDI* genes [80]. These plasmids can also carry the serum resistance-associated genes, *traT*, *rck*, and *rsk*. Finally, additional genes are contained on the *Salmonella* virulence plasmid whose roles have not yet been elucidated. Comparative analyses of *Salmonella* virulence plasmids suggests that certain virulence-related genes of these plasmids, such as the *spv* locus, are under negative selection, suggesting that they are important for host-adapted systemic virulence [82]. The conservation of such genes makes them good candidates for the typing of *Salmonella* virulence plasmids.

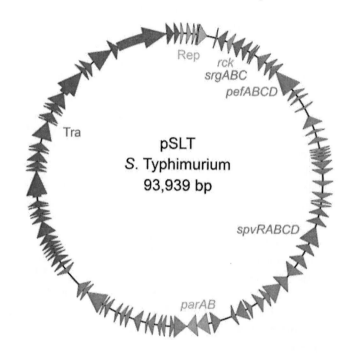

Figure 5. Circular map of pSLT from *S.* Typhimurium strain LT. The *rck*, *srg*, *pef*, and *spv* genes can be used for *Salmonella* virulence plasmid identification and differentiation.

E. coli and *Salmonella* Multidrug Resistance Plasmids

Recently, multidrug resistance-encoding plasmids have become widespread among certain bacterial populations, including foodborne pathogens such as *E. coli* and *Salmonella*. Many of these resistance determinants have been demonstrated to occur on transmissible plasmids belonging to the incompatibility groups A/C, I1, N, HI2, and FIIA [85]. Of these, the IncA/C plasmid group is particularly concerning. IncA/C plasmids are broad-host-range plasmids capable of carrying a large number of genes encoding for multidrug resistance [86]. These plasmids have been increasingly identified among *Salmonella* of animals raised for food production, including serovars Typhimurium [87], 4,[5],12:i:- [88], Choleraesuis [89], Newport [90, 91], and Senftenberg [92]. These plasmids have also been identified among clinical strains of extraintestinal *E. coli* [93-95]. IncA/C plasmids have gained recent attention for their ability to encode for the production of extended-spectrum beta-lactamases [94]. Recent genomics-based approaches have increased our understanding of the IncA/C core backbone components and accessory elements. Welch et al. [91] compared completed IncA/C plasmid sequences from multidrug-resistant strains of *Yersinia pestis*, *Y. ruckeri*, and *Salmonella enterica* serovar Newport. While these plasmids were isolated from bacteria from various sources, their plasmid backbone sequences possessed an extremely high degree of gene synteny and sequence identity, suggesting a recent ancestry. Furthermore, these plasmids possessed three integration hotspots that have apparently acquired a diverse array of mobile elements and genes encoding multidrug resistance. Call et al. [90] compared three IncA/C plasmids from cattle with the above-mentioned plasmids and also found high sequence similarity amongst the IncA/C plasmids examined. They concluded that recent horizontal gene transfer of similar IncA/C plasmids has occurred between *E. coli* and *S. enterica* hosts, and these sequences are divergent from IncA/C plasmids found among *Yersinia* hosts. Fricke et al. [86] compared these plasmids with an IncA/C plasmid isolated from the fish pathogen *Aeromonas hydrophila* in 1971 and a cryptic version of this plasmid obtained through conjugation containing apparently minimal machinery for IncA/C stability and maintenance. They found that these minimal backbone components served as the ancestor for the dissemination of the currently circulating broad host range IncA/C plasmids encoding multidrug resistance, and that the minimal IncA/C backbone encodes genes likely enabling persister cell subpopulations. The widespread distribution of IncA/C plasmids in enteric bacteria of production animals, coupled with their identification from environmental sources and wastewater effluent and receiving streams [96], presents an emerging threat to animal and human health.

IncI1 plasmids have long been associated with *S. enterica* [97]. Unlike IncA/C plasmids, the IncI1 plasmid has a narrow host range and is strictly limited to enterobacterial hosts. Multidrug resistance-encoding IncI1 plasmids are common among *E. coli* and *Salmonella* strains from production animal environments and cases of human disease [98-103]. These plasmids have been shown to carry a variety of resistance-associated genes, including bla_{CTX-M} [104, 105], bla_{TEM} [94, 106], bla_{CMY-2} [100, 107], bla_{SHV} [107], *aacC* [108], and *sul1* and *sul3* gene modules (109, 110). IncI1 plasmid replicons have also been found on some virulence plasmids of EAEC and ETEC [111].

While IncA/C and IncI1 plasmids are important agents of the dissemination of multidrug resistance, other plasmid type are also implicated in this ability. IncN plasmids are broad-host-range plasmids also capable of harboring genes encoding for antimicrobial resistance [96]. These plasmids have been shown to encode for resistance to carbapenems [112], other extended-spectrum beta lactamases [93, 105, 113-116], and quinolones [117, 118] in *E. coli*, *Salmonella*, and *Klebsiella*. IncH plasmids have also been identified for their associations with resistance to multiple antimicrobial agents, including tetracyclines, phenicols, aminoglycosides, and heavy metals [119]. Recent evidence suggests that these plasmids are also emerging as another plasmid type encoding for extended-spectrum beta-lactamases [120-122] and quinolone resistance [117, 123]. Finally, IncFII plasmids have been continually identified among *E. coli* isolates with the ability to encode extended-spectrum beta-lactamases [93, 95, 124-127]. Certainly, the wide array of plasmids among *E. coli* and *Salmonella* with the ability to confer multidrug resistance presents an alarming scenario with regards to our ability to treat bacterial infections.

PLASMID TYPING OF ENTEROBACTERIAL PLASMIDS

Beyond typing for specific virulence plasmid types among *E. coli* and *Salmonella*, other broader typing approaches exist that can be very informative regarding the plasmid complement of an isolate. In the absence of knowledge of the plasmid complement of an isolate, plasmid profiling can be performed using unrestricted or digested total plasmid DNA [128, 129]. However, since many wild type bacterial isolates possess multiple plasmids that vary in size and copy number, this approach often fails to identify and distinguish all of the plasmids within an isolate's genome. Initial efforts to classify plasmids in the 1960s were based upon their characterization as fi$^+$ (fertility inhibition) or fi$^-$, reflecting the property observed when fi$^+$ plasmids were able to inhibit the transfer of a plasmid with a similar conjugative system [130]. This basic concept was expanded in the 1970s to other plasmid types, using assessment of the ability of two plasmids to coexist in the same bacterial host cell [3]. The concept of incompatibility was derived when plasmids sharing similar replication mechanisms were unstable when placed in the same bacterial cell. A number of plasmid incompatibility groups were subsequently identified, prompting a need for a plasmid classification scheme.

Couturier et al. [131] developed an invaluable set of DNA probes specific for each known incompatibility group of the *Enterobacteriaceae* that allowed for the identification of replicon-associated regions that were unique to each known plasmid type using Southern hybridization. Based on these probes, others have developed PCR-based replicon typing schemes [132-137], which identify major Inc types occurring among the *Enterobacteriaceae*. Recently, a comprehensive approach was described by Carattoli et al. [132], and these PCR-based schemes are being continually refined to include additional plasmid types from multiple bacterial species in *Enterobactericeae* [135, 138]. PCR-based replicon typing is the most widely used approach to date for plasmid typing. The approach has been applied to a variety of bacterial populations, including commensal *E. coli* from animals [135, 139], *Klebsiella* from hospital- and community-acquired infection [140], *Salmonella* from animals [102, 141] and human disease [142-145], *E. coli* from animal [109, 135, 146] and human disease [89, 102, 124, 147], and environmental *E. coli* and *Salmonella* isolates [114].

Francia et al. [148] and Garcillan-Barcia et al. [149] proposed the use of conjugative relaxases as a plasmid-typing tool. There are several potential advantages to using this typing scheme over traditional replicon-based typing, including its ability to characterize a wider range of plasmids than plasmid replicon typing. Relaxase-based typing can theoretically be applied to any plasmid with either a mobilization region or a type IV secretion system. Since most plasmids contain only one relaxase, whereas plasmids often contain multiple plasmid replicons, it also may have greater specificity than plasmid replicon typing and might be a better marker for plasmid evolution [149]. Relaxase-based plasmid typing is still in its infancy but holds promise as a future classification schema.

A more sensitive approach has been applied within plasmid replicon types to examine phylogeny using multilocus sequence typing [107]. While this approach is complicated due to the mosaic nature of bacterial plasmids, the examination of multiple conserved genes within a plasmid group appears to be useful for determining their evolutionary relatedness. This approach was successfully initiated in the IncI1 plasmid group, using five conserved gene sequences, to study the dissemination of extended-spectrum beta-lactamase genes [107]. The approach has also been successfully applied to IncN [150], IncHI2 [151], and IncF [138] plasmids. Overall, the pMLST approach is a useful and rapid tool to study the epidemiological spread of plasmids of interest. A database has been developed for researchers to facilitate the community use of this approach (http://pubmlst.org/plasmid/). More information is available on MLST methods in chapter 9 of this book, which focuses on MLST and other sequence-based typing methods.

CONCLUSIONS

A large number of plasmids are associated with the virulence and antimicrobial resistance capabilities of bacterial foodborne pathogens. This chapter has provided a brief overview of some of these pathogens and their plasmids. However, because of the number of bacterial foodborne pathogens and the diversity of the plasmids that they harbor, it is surely not a comprehensive view of all plasmids important to strains implicated in foodborne disease. Nevertheless, the typing methods presented here represent approaches that could be theoretically applied to any plasmid type of interest.

REFERENCES

[1] Actis LA, Tolmasky ME, Crosa JH. Bacterial plasmids: replication of extrachromosomal genetic elements encoding resistance to antimicrobial compounds. *Frontiers in bioscience : a journal and virtual library.* 1999;4:D43-62.

[2] Frost LS, Leplae R, Summers AO, Toussaint A. Mobile genetic elements: the agents of open source evolution. *Nat Rev Microbiol.* 2005;3(9):722-32.

[3] Phillips G, Funnell BE. *Plasmid biology.* Washington, D.C.: ASM Press; 2004.

[4] Dasti JI, Tareen AM, Lugert R, Zautner AE, Gross U. *Campylobacter jejuni*: a brief overview on pathogenicity-associated factors and disease-mediating mechanisms. *Int J Med Microbiol.* 2010;300(4):205-11.

[5] Taylor DE, De Grandis SA, Karmali MA, Fleming PC. Transmissible plasmids from *Campylobacter jejuni. Antimicrob Agents Chemother.* 1981;19(5):831-5.

[6] Taylor DE, Garner RS, Allan BJ. Characterization of tetracycline resistance plasmids from *Campylobacter jejuni* and *Campylobacter coli. Antimicrob Agents Chemother.* 1983;24(6):930-5.

[7] Bacon DJ, Alm RA, Burr DH, Hu L, Kopecko DJ, Ewing CP, et al. Involvement of a plasmid in virulence of *Campylobacter jejuni* 81-176. *Infect Immun.* 2000;68(8):4384-90.

[8] Bacon DJ, Alm RA, Hu L, Hickey TE, Ewing CP, Batchelor RA, et al. DNA sequence and mutational analyses of the pVir plasmid of *Campylobacter jejuni* 81-176. Infect Immun. 2002;70(11):6242-50.

[9] Batchelor RA, Pearson BM, Friis LM, Guerry P, Wells JM. Nucleotide sequences and comparison of two large conjugative plasmids from different *Campylobacter* species. *Microbiology.* 2004;150(Pt 10):3507-17.

[10] Tracz DM, Keelan M, Ahmed-Bentley J, Gibreel A, Kowalewska-Grochowska K, Taylor DE. pVir and bloody diarrhea in *Campylobacter jejuni* enteritis. *Emerg Infect Dis.* 2005;11(6):838-43.

[11] Louwen RP, van Belkum A, Wagenaar JA, Doorduyn Y, Achterberg R, Endtz HP. Lack of association between the presence of the pVir plasmid and bloody diarrhea in *Campylobacter jejuni* enteritis. *J Clin Microbiol.* 2006;44(5):1867-8.

[12] Lee CY, Tai CL, Lin SC, Chen YT. Occurrence of plasmids and tetracycline resistance among *Campylobacter jejuni* and *Campylobacter coli* isolated from wholeket chickens and clinical samples. *Int J Food Microbiol.* 1994;24(1-2):161-70.

[13] Sagara H, Mochizuki A, Okamura N, Nakaya R. Antimicrobial resistance of *Campylobacter jejuni* and *Campylobacter coli* with special reference to plasmid profiles of Japanese clinical isolates. *Antimicrob Agents Chemother.* 1987;31(5):713-9.

[14] Schmidt-Ott R, Pohl S, Burghard S, Weig M, Gross U. Identification and characterization of a major subgroup of conjugative *Campylobacter jejuni* plasmids. *J Infect.* 2005;50(1):12-21.

[15] Friis LM, Pin C, Taylor DE, Pearson BM, Wells JM. A role for the tet(O) plasmid in maintaining *Campylobacter* plasticity. *Plasmid.* 2007;57(1):18-28.

[16] Nirdnoy W, Mason CJ, Guerry P. Mosaic structure of a multiple-drug-resistant, conjugative plasmid from *Campylobacter jejuni*. *Antimicrob Agents Chemother.* 2005;49(6):2454-9.

[17] Miller WG, Heath S, Mandrell RE. Cryptic plasmids isolated from *Campylobacter* strains represent multiple,el incompatibility groups. *Plasmid.* 2007;57(2):108-17.

[18] Kaper JB, Nataro JP, Mobley HL. Pathogenic *Escherichia coli*. *Nat Rev Microbiol.* 2004;2(1740-1526; 2):123-40.

[19] DebRoy C, Maddox CW. Identification of virulence attributes of gastrointestinal *Escherichia coli* isolates of veterinary significance. *Anim Health Res Rev.* 2001;2(1466-2523; 2):129-40.

[20] Nagy B, Fekete PZ. Enterotoxigenic *Escherichia coli* in veterinary medicine. *International Journal of Medical Microbiology.* 2005;295(6-7):443-54.

[21] Turner SM, Scott-Tucker A, Cooper LM, Henderson IR. Weapons of mass destruction: virulence factors of the global killer enterotoxigenic *Escherichia coli*. *FEMS Microbiology Letters.* 2006;263(1):10-20.

[22] Gaastra W, Svennerholm AM. Colonization factors of human enterotoxigenic *Escherichia coli* (ETEC). *Trends in Microbiology.* 1996;4(11):444-52.

[23] Lasaro MA, Rodrigues JF, Mathias-Santos C, Guth BE, Balan A, Sbrogio-Almeida ME, et al. Genetic diversity of heat-labile toxin expressed by enterotoxigenic *Escherichia coli* strains isolated from humans. *J Bacteriol.* 2008;190(7):2400-10.

[24] Wolf MK. Occurrence, distribution, and associations of O and H serogroups, colonization factor antigens, and toxins of enterotoxigenic *Escherichia coli*. *Clinical Microbiology Reviews.* 1997;10(4):569-84.

[25] Evans DG, Silver RP, Evans DJ, Jr., Chase DG, Gorbach SL. Plasmid-controlled colonization factor associated with virulence in Esherichia coli enterotoxigenic for humans. *Infection and Immunity.* 1975;12(3):656-67.

[26] Bodero MD, Harden EA, Munson GP. Transcriptional regulation of subclass 5b fimbriae. *BMC Microbiology.* 2008;8:180.

[27] Caron J, Coffield LM, Scott JR. A plasmid-encoded regulatory gene, rns, required for expression of the CS1 and CS2 adhesins of enterotoxigenic *Escherichia coli*. *Proceedings of the National Academy of Sciences USA*. 1989;86(3):963-7.

[28] Evans DG, Evans DJ, Jr. New surface-associated heat-labile colonization factor antigen (CFA/II) produced by enterotoxigenic *Escherichia coli* of serogroups O6 and O8. *Infection and immunity*. 1978;21(2):638-47.

[29] Smyth CJ. Two mannose-resistant haemagglutinins on enterotoxigenic *Escherichia coli* of serotype O6:K15:H16 or H-isolated from travellers' and infantile diarrhoea. *Journal of General Microbiology*. 1982;128(9):2081-96.

[30] Froehlich B, Parkhill J, Sanders M, Quail MA, Scott JR. The pCoo plasmid of enterotoxigenic *Escherichia coli* is a mosaic cointegrate. *Journal of Bacteriology*. 2005;187(18):6509-16.

[31] Kim SR, Komano T. The plasmid R64 thin pilus identified as a type IV pilus. *Journal of Bacteriology*. 1997;179(11):3594-603.

[32] Komano T, Yoshida T, Narahara K, Furuya N. The transfer region of IncI1 plasmid R64: similarities between R64 tra and *Legionella* icm/dot genes. *Molecular Microbiology*. 2000;35(6):1348-59.

[33] Nakaya R, Nakamura A, Murata Y. Resistance transfer agents in *Shigella*. *Biochemical and Biophysical Research Communications*. 1960;3:654-9.

[34] Patel SK, Dotson J, Allen KP, Fleckenstein JM. Identification and molecular characterization of EatA, an autotransporter protein of enterotoxigenic *Escherichia coli*. *Infection and Immunity*. 2004;72(3):1786-94.

[35] Crossman LC, Chaudhuri RR, Beatson SA, Wells TJ, Desvaux M, Cunningham AF, et al. A commensal gone bad: complete genome sequence of the prototypical enterotoxigenic *Escherichia coli* strain H10407. *J Bacteriol*. 2010;192(21):5822-31.

[36] Rasko DA, Rosovitz MJ, Myers GS, Mongodin EF, Fricke WF, Gajer P, et al. The pangenome structure of *Escherichia coli*: comparative genomic analysis of *E. coli* commensal and pathogenic isolates. *J Bacteriol*. 2008;190(20):6881-93.

[37] Nataro JP, Kaper JB, Robins-Browne R, Prado V, Vial P, Levine MM. Patterns of adherence of diarrheagenic *Escherichia coli* to HEp-2 cells. *Pediatric Infectious Disease Journal*. 1987;6(9):829-31.

[38] Huang DB, Mohanty A, DuPont HL, Okhuysen PC, Chiang T. A review of an emerging enteric pathogen: enteroaggregative *Escherichia coli*. *Journal of Medical Microbiology*. 2006;55(Pt 10):1303-11.

[39] Nataro JP, Deng Y, Cookson S, Cravioto A, Savarino SJ, Guers LD, et al. Heterogeneity of enteroaggregative *Escherichia coli* virulence demonstrated in volunteers. *Journal of Infectious Diseases*. 1995;171(2):465-8.

[40] Harrington SM, Dudley EG, Nataro JP. Pathogenesis of enteroaggregative *Escherichia coli* infection. *FEMS Microbiology Letters*. 2006;254(1):12-8.

[41] Nataro JP, Deng Y, Maneval DR, German AL,tin WC, Levine MM. Aggregative adherence fimbriae I of enteroaggregative *Escherichia coli* mediate adherence to HEp-2 cells and hemagglutination of human erythrocytes. *Infection and Immunity*. 1992;60(6):2297-304.

[42] Bernier C, Gounon P, Le Bouguenec C. Identification of an aggregative adhesion fimbria (AAF) type III-encoding operon in enteroaggregative *Escherichia coli* as a

sensitive probe for detecting the AAF-encoding operon family. *Infection and Immunity.* 2002;70(8):4302-11.

[43] Boisen N, Struve C, Scheutz F, Krogfelt KA, Nataro JP. New adhesin of enteroaggregative *Escherichia coli* related to the Afa/Dr/AAF family. *Infection and Immunity.* 2008;76(7):3281-92.

[44] Nataro JP, Yikang D, Yingkang D, Walker K. AggR, a transcriptional activator of aggregative adherence fimbria I expression in enteroaggregative *Escherichia coli.* *Journal of Bacteriology.* 1994;176(15):4691-9.

[45] Nataro JP. Enteroaggregative *Escherichia coli* pathogenesis. *Current Opinion in Gastroenterology.* 2005;21(1):4-8.

[46] Baudry B, Savarino SJ, Vial P, Kaper JB, Levine MM. A sensitive and specific DNA probe to identify enteroaggregative *Escherichia coli*, a recently discovered diarrheal pathogen. *Journal of Infectious Diseases.* 1990;161(6):1249-51.

[47] Eslava C, Navarro-Garcia F, Czeczulin JR, Henderson IR, Cravioto A, Nataro JP. Pet, an autotransporter enterotoxin from enteroaggregative *Escherichia coli. Infection and Immunity.* 1998;66(7):3155-63.

[48] Czeczulin JR, Whittam TS, Henderson IR, Navarro-Garcia F, Nataro JP. Phylogenetic analysis of enteroaggregative and diffusely adherent *Escherichia coli. Infection and Immunity.* 1999;67(6):2692-9.

[49] Nataro JP, Kaper JB. Diarrheagenic *Escherichia coli. Clinical Microbiology Reviews.* 1998;11(1):142-201.

[50] Yoon JW, Hovde CJ. All blood, no stool: enterohemorrhagic *Escherichia coli* O157:H7 infection. *Journal of Veterinary Science.* 2008;9(3):219-31.

[51] Ostroff SM, Tarr PI, Neill MA, Lewis JH, Hargrett-Bean N, Kobayashi JM. Toxin genotypes and plasmid profiles as determinants of systemic sequelae in *Escherichia coli* O157:H7 infections. *Journal of Infectious Diseases.* 1989;160(6):994-8.

[52] Ratnam S,ch SB, Ahmed R, Bezanson GS, Kasatiya S. Characterization of *Escherichia coli* serotype O157:H7. *Journal of Clinical Microbiology.* 1988;26(10):2006-12.

[53] Burland V, Shao Y, Perna NT, Plunkett G, Sofia HJ, Blattner FR. The complete DNA sequence and analysis of the large virulence plasmid of *Escherichia coli* O157:H7. *Nucleic Acids Research.* 1998;26(18):4196-204.

[54] Brunder W, Khan AS, Hacker J, Karch H.el type of fimbriae encoded by the large plasmid of sorbitol-fermenting enterohemorrhagic *Escherichia coli* O157:H(-). *Infection and Immunity.* 2001;69(7):4447-57.

[55] Brunder W, Karch H, Schmidt H. Complete sequence of the large virulence plasmid pSFO157 of the sorbitol-fermenting enterohemorrhagic *Escherichia coli* O157:H- strain 3072/96. *International Journal of Medical Microbiology.* 2006;296(7):467-74.

[56] Newton HJ, Sloan J, Bulach DM, Seemann T, Allison CC, Tauschek M, et al. Shiga toxin-producing *Escherichia coli* strains negative for locus of enterocyte effacement. *Emerging Infectious Diseases.* 2009;15(3):372-80.

[57] Chen HD, Frankel G. Enteropathogenic *Escherichia coli*: unravelling pathogenesis. *FEMS Microbiology Reviews.* 2005;29(1):83-98.

[58] Clarke SC, Haigh RD, Freestone PP, Williams PH. Virulence of enteropathogenic *Escherichia coli*, a global pathogen. *Clinical Microbiology Reviews.* 2003;16(0893-8512; 3):365-78.

[59] Nataro JP, Scaletsky IC, Kaper JB, Levine MM, Trabulsi LR. Plasmid-mediated factors conferring diffuse and localized adherence of enteropathogenic *Escherichia coli*. *Infection and Immunity.* 1985;48(2):378-83.

[60] Baldini MM, Kaper JB, Levine MM, Candy DC, Moon HW. Plasmid-mediated adhesion in enteropathogenic *Escherichia coli*. *Journal of Pediatric Gastroenterology and Nutrition.* 1983;2(3):534-8.

[61] Baldini MM, Kaper JB, Levine MM, Moon HW. Molecular nature of adhesion in enteropathogenic *Escherichia coli*. *Lancet.* 1983;2(8343):218.

[62] McConnell MM, Chart H, Scotland SM, Smith HR, Willshaw GA, Rowe B. Properties of adherence factor plasmids of enteropathogenic *Escherichia coli* and the effect of host strain on expression of adherence to HEp-2 cells. *Journal of General Microbiology.* 1989;135(5):1123-34.

[63] Tobe T, Hayashi T, Han CG, Schoolnik GK, Ohtsubo E, Sasakawa C. Complete DNA sequence and structural analysis of the enteropathogenic *Escherichia coli* adherence factor plasmid. *Infection and Immunity.* 1999;67(10):5455-62.

[64] Brinkley C, Burland V, Keller R, Rose DJ, Boutin AT, Klink SA, et al. Nucleotide sequence analysis of the enteropathogenic *Escherichia coli* adherence factor plasmid pMAR7. *Infection and Immunity.* 2006;74(9):5408-13.

[65] Iguchi A, Thomson NR, Ogura Y, Saunders D, Ooka T, Henderson IR, et al. Complete genome sequence and comparative genome analysis of enteropathogenic *Escherichia coli* O127:H6 strain E2348/69. *Journal of Bacteriology.* 2009;191(1):347-54.

[66] Parsot C. Shigella spp. and enteroinvasive *Escherichia coli* pathogenicity factors. *FEMS Microbiology Letters.* 2005;252(1):11-8.

[67] Kotloff KL, Winickoff JP, Ivanoff B, Clemens JD, Swerdlow DL, Sansonetti PJ, et al. Global burden of *Shigella* infections: implications for vaccine development and implementation of control strategies. *Bulletin of the World Health Organization.* 1999;77(8):651-66.

[68] Buchrieser C, Glaser P, Rusniok C, Nedjari H, D'Hauteville H, Kunst F, et al. The virulence plasmid pWR100 and the repertoire of proteins secreted by the type III secretion apparatus of *Shigella flexneri*. *Molecular Microbiology.* 2000;38(4):760-71.

[69] Le Gall T, Mavris M,tino MC, Bernardini ML, Denamur E, Parsot C. Analysis of virulence plasmid gene expression defines three classes of effectors in the type III secretion system of *Shigella flexneri*. *Microbiology.* 2005;151:951-62.

[70] Lan R, Lumb B, Ryan D, Reeves PR. Molecular evolution of large virulence plasmid in *Shigella* clones and enteroinvasive *Escherichia coli*. *Infection and Immunity.* 2001;69(10):6303-9.

[71] Johnson TJ, Nolan LK. Pathogenomics of the virulence plasmids of *Escherichia coli*. *Microbiol Mol Biol Rev.* 2009;73(4):750-74.

[72] Rodas C, Iniguez V, Qadri F, Wiklund G, Svennerholm AM, Sjoling A. Development of multiplex PCR assays for detection of enterotoxigenic *Escherichia coli* colonization factors and toxins. *J Clin Microbiol.* 2009;47(4):1218-20.

[73] Sjoling A, Wiklund G, Savarino SJ, Cohen DI, Svennerholm AM. Comparative analyses of phenotypic and genotypic methods for detection of enterotoxigenic *Escherichia coli* toxins and colonization factors. *J Clin Microbiol.* 2007;45(10):3295-301.

[74] Viboud GI, Binsztein N, Svennerholm AM. Characterization of monoclonal antibodies against putative colonization factors of enterotoxigenic *Escherichia coli* and their use in an epidemiological study. *J Clin Microbiol.* 1993;31(3):558-64.

[75] Ahren CM, Gothefors L, Stoll BJ, Salek MA, Svennerholm AM. Comparison of methods for detection of colonization factor antigens on enterotoxigenic *Escherichia coli. J Clin Microbiol.* 1986;23(3):586-91.

[76] Wang Q, Wang S, Beutin L, Cao B, Feng L, Wang L. Development of a DNA microarray for detection and serotyping of enterotoxigenic *Escherichia coli. J Clin Microbiol.* 2010;48(6):2066-74.

[77] Sahl JW, Steinsland H, Redman JC, Angiuoli SV, Nataro JP, Sommerfelt H, et al. A comparative genomic analysis of diverse clonal types of enterotoxigenic *Escherichia coli* reveals pathovar-specific conservation. *Infect Immun.* 2011;79(2):950-60.

[78] Savarino SJ, Fox P, Deng Y, Nataro JP. Identification and characterization of a gene cluster mediating enteroaggregative *Escherichia coli* aggregative adherence fimbria I biogenesis. *Journal of Bacteriology.* 1994;176(16):4949-57.

[79] Foley SL, Lynne AM. Food animal-associated *Salmonella* challenges: pathogenicity and antimicrobial resistance. *Journal of Animal Science.* 2008;86(14 Suppl):E173-87.

[80] Rotger R, Casadesus J. The virulence plasmids of *Salmonella. Int Microbiol.* 1999;2(3):177-84.

[81] Hong SF, Chiu CH, Chu C, Feng Y, Ou JT. Complete nucleotide sequence of a virulence plasmid of *Salmonella enterica* serovar Dublin and its phylogenetic relationship to the virulence plasmids of serovars Choleraesuis, Enteritidis and Typhimurium. *FEMS Microbiol Lett.* 2008;282(1):39-43.

[82] Yu H, Wang J, Ye J, Tang P, Chu C, Hu S, et al. Complete nucleotide sequence of pSCV50, the virulence plasmid of *Salmonella enterica* serovar Choleraesuis SC-B67. *Plasmid.* 2006;55(2):145-51.

[83] Haneda T, Okada N, Nakazawa N, Kawakami T, Danbara H. Complete DNA sequence and comparative analysis of the 50-kilobase virulence plasmid of *Salmonella enterica* serovar Choleraesuis. *Infect Immun.* 2001;69(4):2612-20.

[84] Chu C, Feng Y, Chien AC, Hu S, Chu CH, Chiu CH. Evolution of genes on the *Salmonella* virulence plasmid phylogeny revealed from sequencing of the virulence plasmids of *S. enterica* serotype Dublin and comparative analysis. *Genomics.* 2008;92(5):339-43.

[85] Suzuki H, Sota M, Brown CJ, Top EM. Using Mahalanobis distance to compare genomic signatures between bacterial plasmids and chromosomes. *Nucleic acids research.* 2008;36(22):e147.

[86] Fricke WF, Welch TJ, McDermott PF, Mammel MK, LeClerc JE, White DG, et al. Comparative genomics of the IncA/C multidrug resistance plasmid family. *J Bacteriol.* 2009;191(15):4750-7.

[87] Wiesner M, Calva E, Fernandez-Mora M, Cevallos MA, Campos F, Zaidi MB, et al. Salmonella Typhimurium ST213 is associated with two types of IncA/C plasmids carrying multiple resistance determinants. *BMC Microbiol.* 2011;11(1):9.

[88] Garcia P, Guerra B, Bances M, Mendoza MC, Rodicio MR. IncA/C plasmids mediate antimicrobial resistance linked to virulence genes in the Spanish clone of the emerging *Salmonella enterica* serotype 4,[5],12:i. *J Antimicrob Chemother.* 2010 21.

[89] Sirichote P, Hasman H, Pulsrikarn C, Schonheyder HC, Samulioniene J, Pornruangmong S, et al. Molecular characterization of extended-spectrum cephalosporinase-producing *Salmonella enterica* serovar Choleraesuis isolates from patients in Thailand and Denmark. *J Clin Microbiol.* 2010;48(3):883-8.

[90] Call DR, Singer RS, Meng D, Broschat SL, Orfe LH, Anderson JM, et al. blaCMY-2-positive IncA/C plasmids from *Escherichia coli* and *Salmonella enterica* are a distinct component of a larger lineage of plasmids. *Antimicrob Agents Chemother.* 2010;54(2):590-6.

[91] Welch TJ, Fricke WF, McDermott PF, White DG, Rosso ML, Rasko DA, et al. Multiple antimicrobial resistance in plague: an emerging public health risk. *PLoS ONE.* 2007;2(3):e309.

[92] Evershed NJ, Levings RS, Wilson NL, Djordjevic SP, Hall RM. Unusual class 1 integron-associated gene cassette configuration found in IncA/C plasmids from *Salmonella enterica. Antimicrob Agents Chemother.* 2009;53(6):2640-2.

[93] Diestra K, Juan C, Curiao T, Moya B, Miro E, Oteo J, et al. Characterization of plasmids encoding blaESBL and surrounding genes in Spanish clinical isolates of *Escherichia coli* and *Klebsiella pneumoniae. J Antimicrob Chemother.* 2009;63(1):60-6.

[94] Marcade G, Deschamps C, Boyd A, Gautier V, Picard B, Branger C, et al. Replicon typing of plasmids in *Escherichia coli* producing extended-spectrum beta-lactamases. *J Antimicrob Chemother.* 2009;63(1):67-71.

[95] Naseer U, Haldorsen B, Simonsen GS, Sundsfjord A. Sporadic occurrence of CMY-2-producing multidrug-resistant *Escherichia coli* of ST-complexes 38 and 448, and ST131 in Norway. *Clin Microbiol Infect.* 2010;16(2):171-8.

[96] Akiyama T, Asfahl KL, Savin MC. Broad-host-range plasmids in treated wastewater effluent and receiving streams. *J Environ Qual.* 2010-Dec;39(6):2211-5.

[97] Rangnekar VM, Banker DD, Jhala HI. Antimicrobial resistance and incompatibility groups of R plasmids in *Salmonella typhimurium* isolated from human sources in Bombay from 1978 to 1980. *Antimicrob Agents Chemother.* 1983;23(1):54-8.

[98] Rodriguez I, Barownick W, Helmuth R, Mendoza MC, Rodicio MR, Schroeter A, et al. Extended-spectrum {beta}-lactamases and AmpC {beta}-lactamases in ceftiofur-resistant *Salmonella enterica* isolates from food and livestock obtained in Germany during 2003-07. *J Antimicrob Chemother.* 2009;64(2):301-9.

[99] Woodford N, Carattoli A, Karisik E, Underwood A, Ellington MJ, Livermore DM. Complete nucleotide sequences of plasmids pEK204, pEK499, and pEK516, encoding CTX-M enzymes in three major *Escherichia coli* lineages from the United Kingdom, all belonging to the international O25:H4-ST131 clone. *Antimicrob Agents Chemother.* 2009;53(10):4472-82.

[100] Folster JP, Pecic G, Bolcen S, Theobald L, Hise K, Carattoli A, et al. Characterization of extended-spectrum cephalosporin-resistant *Salmonella enterica* serovar Heidelberg isolated from humans in the United States. *Foodborne Pathog Dis.* 2010;7(2):181-7.

[101] Bortolaia V, Guardabassi L, Trevisani M, Bisgaard M, Venturi L, Bojesen AM. High diversity of extended-spectrum beta-lactamases in *Escherichia coli* isolates from Italian broiler flocks. *Antimicrob Agents Chemother.* 2010;54(4):1623-6.

[102] Dierikx C, van Essen-Zandbergen A, Veldman K, Smith H, Mevius D. Increased detection of extended spectrum beta-lactamase producing *Salmonella enterica* and *Escherichia coli* isolates from poultry. *Vet Microbiol.* 2010 26;145(3-4):273-8.

[103] Moissenet D, Salauze B, Clermont O, Bingen E, Arlet G, Denamur E, et al. Meningitis caused by *Escherichia coli* producing TEM-52 extended-spectrum beta-lactamase within an extensive outbreak in a neonatal ward: epidemiological investigation and characterization of the strain. *J Clin Microbiol.* 2010;48(7):2459-63.

[104] Liu SY, Su LH, Yeh YL, Chu C, Lai JC, Chiu CH. Characterisation of plasmids encoding CTX-M-3 extended-spectrum beta-lactamase from Enterobacteriaceae isolated at a university hospital in Taiwan. *Int J Antimicrob Agents.* 2007;29(4):440-5.

[105] Suzuki S, Shibata N, Yamane K, Wachino J, Ito K, Arakawa Y. Change in the prevalence of extended-spectrum-beta-lactamase-producing *Escherichia coli* in Japan by clonal spread. *J Antimicrob Chemother.* 2009;63(1):72-9.

[106] Cloeckaert A, Praud K, Doublet B, Bertini A, Carattoli A, Butaye P, et al. Dissemination of an extended-spectrum-beta-lactamase *bla*TEM-52 gene-carrying IncI1 plasmid in various *Salmonella enterica* serovars isolated from poultry and humans in Belgium and France between 2001 and 2005. *Antimicrob Agents Chemother.* 2007;51(5):1872-5.

[107] Garcia-Fernandez A, Chiaretto G, Bertini A, Villa L, Fortini D, Ricci A, et al. Multilocus sequence typing of IncI1 plasmids carrying extended-spectrum beta-lactamases in *Escherichia coli* and *Salmonella* of human and animal origin. *J Antimicrob Chemother.* 2008;61(6):1229-33.

[108] Ho PL, Wong RC, Lo SW, Chow KH, Wong SS, Que TL. Genetic identity of aminoglycoside-resistance genes in *Escherichia coli* isolates from human and animal sources. *J Med Microbiol.* 2010;59(Pt 6):702-7.

[109] Wu S, Dalsgaard A, Hammerum AM, Porsbo LJ, Jensen LB. Prevalence and characterization of plasmids carrying sulfonamide resistance genes among *Escherichia coli* from pigs, pig carcasses and human. *Acta Vet Scand.* 2010;52:47.

[110] Curiao T, Canton R, Garcillan-Barcia MP, de la Cruz F, Baquero F, Coque TM. Association of composite IS26-sul3 elements with highly transmissible IncI1 plasmids of human *Escherichia coli* clones producing extended-spectrum Beta lactamases. *Antimicrob Agents Chemother.* 2011 22.

[111] Dudley EG, Abe C, Ghigo JM, Latour-Lambert P, Hormazabal JC, Nataro JP. An IncI1 plasmid contributes to the adherence of the atypical enteroaggregative *Escherichia coli* strain C1096 to cultured cells and abiotic surfaces. *Infection and immunity.* 2006;74(4):2102-14.

[112] Loli A, Tzouvelekis LS, Tzelepi E, Carattoli A, Vatopoulos AC, Tassios PT, et al. Sources of diversity of carbapenem resistance levels in Klebsiella pneumoniae carrying *bla*VIM-1. *J Antimicrob Chemother.* 2006;58(3):669-72.

[113] Psichogiou M, Tassios PT, Avlamis A, Stefanou I, Kosmidis C, Platsouka E, et al. Ongoing epidemic of *bla*VIM-1-positive Klebsiella pneumoniae in Athens, Greece: a prospective survey. *J Antimicrob Chemother.* 2008;61(1):59-63.

[114] Pignato S, Coniglio MA, Faro G, Lefevre M, Weill FX, Giammanco G. Molecular epidemiology of ampicillin resistance in *Salmonella* spp. and *Escherichia coli* from wastewater and clinical specimens. *Foodborne Pathog Dis.* 2010;7(8):945-51.

[115] Literak I, Dolejska M,oszowska D, Hrusakova J, Meissner W, Rzyska H, et al. Antibiotic-resistant *Escherichia coli* bacteria, including strains with genes encoding the extended-spectrum beta-lactamase and QnrS, in waterbirds on the Baltic Sea Coast of Poland. *Appl Environ Microbiol.* 2010;76(24):8126-34.

[116] Dolejska M, Jurcickova Z, Literak I, Pokludova L, Bures J, Hera A, et al. IncN plasmids carrying bla(CTX-M-1) in *Escherichia coli* isolates on a dairy farm. *Vet Microbiol.* 2010 8.

[117] Garcia-Fernandez A, Fortini D, Veldman K, Mevius D, Carattoli A. Characterization of plasmids harbouring *qnrS1, qnrB2* and *qnrB19* genes in *Salmonella. J Antimicrob Chemother.* 2009;63(2):274-81.

[118] Karah N, Poirel L, Bengtsson S, Sundqvist M, Kahlmeter G, Nordmann P, et al. Plasmid-mediated quinolone resistance determinants *qnr* and *aac*(6')-Ib-cr in *Escherichia coli* and *Klebsiella* spp. from Norway and Sweden. *Diagn Microbiol Infect Dis.* 2010;66(4):425-31.

[119] Gilmour MW, Thomson NR, Sanders M, Parkhill J, Taylor DE. The complete nucleotide sequence of the resistance plasmid R478: defining the backbone components of incompatibility group H conjugative plasmids through comparative genomics. *Plasmid.* 2004;52(3):182-202.

[120] Garcia A, Navarro F, Miro E, Villa L, Mirelis B, Coll P, et al. Acquisition and diffusion of *bla* CTX-M-9 gene by R478-IncHI2 derivative plasmids. *FEMS Microbiol Lett.* 2007;271(1):71-7.

[121] Chen YT, Lauderdale TL, Liao TL, Shiau YR, Shu HY, Wu KM, et al. Sequencing and comparative genomic analysis of pK29, a 269-kilobase conjugative plasmid encoding CMY-8 and CTX-M-3 beta-lactamases in *Klebsiella pneumoniae. Antimicrob Agents Chemother.* 2007;51(8):3004-7.

[122] Garcia Fernandez A, Cloeckaert A, Bertini A, Praud K, Doublet B, Weill FX, et al. Comparative analysis of IncHI2 plasmids carrying blaCTX-M-2 or blaCTX-M-9 from *Escherichia coli* and *Salmonella enterica* strains isolated from poultry and humans. *Antimicrob Agents Chemother.* 2007;51(11):4177-80.

[123] Tato M, Coque TM, Baquero F, Canton R. Dispersal of carbapenemase blaVIM-1 gene associated with different Tn402 variants, mercury transposons, and conjugative plasmids in Enterobacteriaceae and *Pseudomonas aeruginosa. Antimicrob Agents Chemother.* 2010;54(1):320-7.

[124] Naseer U, Haldorsen B, Tofteland S, Hegstad K, Scheutz F, Simonsen GS, et al. Molecular characterization of CTX-M-15-producing clinical isolates of *Escherichia coli* reveals the spread of multidrug-resistant ST131 (O25:H4) and ST964 (O102:H6) strains in Norway. *APMIS.* 2009;117(7):526-36.

[125] Zienkiewicz M, Kern-Zdanowicz I, Golebiewski M, Zylinska J, Mieczkowski P, Gniadkowski M, et al. Mosaic structure of p1658/97, a 125-kilobase plasmid harboring an active amplicon with the extended-spectrum beta-lactamase gene *bla*SHV-5. *Antimicrob Agents Chemother.* 2007;51(4):1164-71.

[126] Coque TM,ais A, Carattoli A, Poirel L, Pitout J, Peixe L, et al. Dissemination of clonally related *Escherichia coli* strains expressing extended-spectrum beta-lactamase CTX-M-15. *Emerg Infect Dis.* 2008;14(2):195-200.

[127] Smet A, Van Nieuwerburgh F, Vandekerckhove TT,tel A, Deforce D, Butaye P, et al. Complete nucleotide sequence of CTX-M-15-plasmids from clinical *Escherichia coli*

isolates: insertional events of transposons and insertion sequences. *PLoS ONE.* 2010;5(6):e11202.

[128] Kado CI, Liu ST. Rapid procedure for detection and isolation of large and small plasmids. *Journal of Bacteriology.* 1981;145(3):1365-73.

[129] Mayer LW. Use of plasmid profiles in epidemiologic surveillance of disease outbreaks and in tracing the transmission of antibiotic resistance. *Clin Microbiol Rev.* 1988;1(2):228-43.

[130] Watanabe T, Nishida H, Ogata C, Arai T, Sato S. Episome-Mediated Transfer of Drug Resistance in Enterobacteriaceae. Vii. Two Types of Naturally Occurring R Factors. *Journal of Bacteriology.* 1964;88:716-26.

[131] Couturier M, Bex F, Bergquist PL, Maas WK. Identification and classification of bacterial plasmids. *Microbiological Reviews.* 1988;52(3):375-95.

[132] Carattoli A, Bertini A, Villa L, Falbo V, Hopkins KL, Threlfall EJ. Identification of plasmids by PCR-based replicon typing. *Journal of Microbiological Methods.* 2005;63(3):219-28.

[133] Fekete PZ, Gerardin J, Jacquemin E, Mainil JG, Nagy B. Replicon typing of F18 fimbriae encoding plasmids of enterotoxigenic and verotoxigenic *Escherichia coli* strains from porcine postweaning diarrhoea and oedema disease. *Veterinary Microbiology.* 2002;85(3):275-84.

[134] Gotz A, Pukall R, Smit E, Tietze E, Prager R, Tschape H, et al. Detection and characterization of broad-host-range plasmids in environmental bacteria by PCR. *Applied and Environmental Microbiology.* 1996;62(7):2621-8.

[135] Johnson TJ, Wannemuehler YM, Johnson SJ, Logue CM, White DG, Doetkott C, et al. Plasmid replicon typing of commensal and pathogenic *Escherichia coli* isolates. *Applied and Environmental Microbiology.* 2007;73(6):1976-83.

[136] Mainil JG, Bex F, Dreze P, Kaeckenbeeck A, Couturier M. Replicon typing of virulence plasmids of enterotoxigenic *Escherichia coli* isolates from cattle. Infection and immunity. 1992;60(8):3376-80.

[137] Sobecky PA, Mincer TJ, Chang MC, Helinski DR. Plasmids isolated fromine sediment microbial communities contain replication and incompatibility regions unrelated to those of known plasmid groups. *Applied and Environmental Microbiology.* 1997;63(3):888-95.

[138] Villa L, Garcia-Fernandez A, Fortini D, Carattoli A. Replicon sequence typing of IncF plasmids carrying virulence and resistance determinants. *J Antimicrob Chemother.* 2010;65(12):2518-29.

[139] Lindsey RL, Frye JG, Thitaram SN, Meinersmann RJ, Fedorka-Cray PJ, Englen MD. Characterization of multidrug-resistant *Escherichia coli* by antimicrobial resistance profiles, plasmid replicon typing, and pulsed-field gel electrophoresis. *Microb Drug Resist.* 2011; doi:10.1089/mdr.2010.0148.

[140] Younes A, Hamouda A, Dave J, Amyes SG. Prevalence of transferable blaCTX-M-15 from hospital- and community-acquired *Klebsiella pneumoniae* isolates in Scotland. *J Antimicrob Chemother.* 2011;66(2):313-8.

[141] Lindsey RL, Fedorka-Cray PJ, Frye JG, Meinersmann RJ. Inc A/C plasmids are prevalent in multidrug-resistant *Salmonella enterica* isolates. *Appl Environ Microbiol.* 2009;75(7):1908-15.

[142] Herrera-Leon S, Gonzalez-Sanz R, Herrera-Leon L, Echeita MA. Characterization of multidrug-resistant Enterobacteriaceae carrying plasmid-mediated quinolone resistance mechanisms in Spain. *J Antimicrob Chemother.* 2011; 66(2):287-90.

[143] Antunes P, Coque TM, Peixe L. Emergence of an IncIgamma plasmid encoding CMY-2 ss-lactamase associated with the international ST19 OXA-30-producing ss-lactamase *Salmonella* Typhimurium multidrug-resistant clone. *J Antimicrob Chemother.* 2010;65(10):2097-100.

[144] Veldman K, Dierikx C, van Essen-Zandbergen A, van Pelt W, Mevius D. Characterization of multidrug-resistant, qnrB2-positive and extended-spectrum-beta-lactamase-producing *Salmonella* Concord and *Salmonella* Senftenberg isolates. *J Antimicrob Chemother.* 2010;65(5):872-5.

[145] Mataseje LF, Xiao J, Kost S, Ng LK, Dore K, Mulvey MR. Characterization of Canadian cefoxitin-resistant non-typhoidal *Salmonella* isolates, 2005-06. *J Antimicrob Chemother.* 2009;64(4):723-30.

[146] Poole TL, Edrington TS, Brichta-Harhay DM, Carattoli A, Anderson RC, Nisbet DJ. Conjugative transferability of the A/C plasmids from *Salmonella enterica* isolates that possess or lack *bla*(CMY) in the A/C plasmid backbone. *Foodborne Pathog Dis.* 2009;6(10):1185-94.

[147] Brolund A, Wisell KT, Edquist PJ, Elfstrom L, Walder M, Giske CG. Development of a real-time SYBRGreen PCR assay for rapid detection of acquired AmpC in Enterobacteriaceae. *J Microbiol Methods.* 2010;82(3):229-33.

[148] Francia MV, Varsaki A, Garcillan-Barcia MP, Latorre A, Drainas C, de la Cruz F. A classification scheme for mobilization regions of bacterial plasmids. *FEMS Microbiology Reviews.* 2004;28(1):79-100.

[149] Garcillan-Barcia MP, Francia MV, de la Cruz F. The diversity of conjugative relaxases and its application in plasmid classification. *FEMS Microbiology Reviews.* 2009;33(3):657-87.

[150] Zong Z, Yu R, Wang X, Lu X. *bla*CTX-M-65 was carried by a Tn1722-like element on an IncN conjugative plasmid of ST131 *Escherichia coli.* *J Med Microbiol.* 2011;60(Pt 4):435-41.

[151] Garcia-Fernandez A, Carattoli A. Plasmid double locus sequence typing for IncHI2 plasmids, a subtyping scheme for the characterization of IncHI2 plasmids carrying extended-spectrum beta-lactamase and quinolone resistance genes. *J Antimicrob Chemother.* 2010;65(6):1155-61.

In: Molecular Typing Methods for TFM
Editors: S. Foley, R. Nayak, T. Johnson et al.

ISBN: 978-1-62100-643-5
© 2012 Nova Science Publishers, Inc.

Chapter 4

ANTIMICROBIAL RESISTANCE IN FOODBORNE PATHOGENS

Warren E. Rose[1] *and Sanjay K. Shukla*[2]
[1] School of Pharmacy
University of Wisconsin-Madison
Madison, WI, US
[2] Center for Human Genetics
Marshfield Clinic Research Foundation
Marshfield, WI, US

ABSTRACT

Antimicrobial resistance continues to be a growing concern for the healthcare system. A significant contributor to this trend is the use of antimicrobials for the treatment of infections of veterinary animals and as well as in food animal production to promote growth. Geographic differences in antibiotic resistance in foodborne pathogens are often reflection of the relative regional antibiotic use in the agriculture and food industry. *Escherichia coli* and *Salmonella* spp. are two common organisms with increasing antibiotic resistance found in contaminated food. Isolated resistance to common antimicrobials including fluoroquinolones, sulfonamides, beta-lactams, tetracyclines, and aminoglycosides among others has been reported in these strains. There is concern for increasing incidence of listeriosis worldwide from *Listeria monocytogenes*, particularly in European countries, as well as the documented emergence of antibiotic resistant strains to tetracyclines, fluoroquinolones, and sulfonamides. *Campylobacter* spp, another common foodborne pathogen, has developed multi-drug efflux pumps that may render fluoroquinolones, macrolides, and tetracyclines inactive. Multi-drug resistance has been described in *Staphylococcus aureus* in humans, and has now been detected in contaminated food samples and agriculture settings. Transmission of antibiotic resistant *S. aureus* strains has been documented between these settings. Surveillance reports imply that antibiotic resistant *Enterococcus, Clostridium*, and *Yersinia* spp. are causes of contaminated food products and pose potential risks as foodborne pathogens. Some countries have adapted policies to combat excessive antimicrobial use in the food industry, however unregulated use by many countries is still an increasing threat to foodborne microorganism resistance. This problem is compounded by increasing antimicrobial use and overuse in the human population. Appropriate stewardship of antimicrobials in these environments is essential to controlling this problem in the future.

INTRODUCTION

Antimicrobial resistance development in foodborne pathogens has coincided with increased use of antimicrobials in the agricultural industry. Multidrug resistant strains now represent a significant percentage of strains isolated in humans, animals, and food products. Many of the infections from food contamination involve self-limiting gastrointestinal symptoms that do not require antimicrobial treatment. However in some cases, complications involving severe, systemic disease may require acute antimicrobial management. Patients with infections due to antibiotic resistant stains are at an increased risk of complications, which significantly increase health care costs and resources. Antibiotic resistant infections prolong the length of hospitalization, increase mortality and increase health care costs compared to infections with susceptible strains [1, 2]. The treatment of multidrug resistant infections, including those caused by foodborne pathogens, is limited to only a handful of antibiotics.

Bacteria are a diverse group of organisms capable of surviving a range of environmental exposures and conditions. Due to bacteria's relatively simplistic structure, antibacterial targets are limited to only a few cell processes, and resistance can develop rapidly. Antibacterial agents generally target one or more of four bacterial mechanisms: cell wall formation, protein synthesis, DNA synthesis, and folate metabolism. Cell wall inhibition is one of the more common and potent antimicrobial mechanisms employed by a number of antibiotics classes, including β-lactams, glycopeptides, lipopeptides, and polymyxins. Inhibition of protein synthesis through binding or interfering with ribosomal subunits occurs with macrolides and derivatives, tetracyclines, chloramphenical, linezolid, aminoglycosides, fusidic acid, and streptogramins. Inhibition of bacterial DNA synthesis often results in broad-spectrum activity found in fluoroquinolones and rifamycins. Finally, folate metabolism is a unique target for sulfonamides and trimethoprim. A single resistance mechanism can confer reduced susceptibility to one agent, within a class or mechanism, or multiple classes (multidrug resistance) regardless of the antibacterial target [3].

The lack of new antimicrobial development is a significant concern for future treatment of multidrug resistant infections. Since the early 1980s, the development of novel antimicrobial entities has steady declined to the point where only one new antibacterial agent was approved in the US in 2008-2009. This low rate of development is expected to continue into future years with the diminishing antimicrobial pipeline, and those that will be developed have limited activity against multidrug resistant strains [3]. A number of reasons for this occurrence have been identified, but two are of high importance: minimal economic return on investment and increased regulatory requirements for development. The Centers for Disease Control and Prevention (CDC) has recommended strategies to conserve antibiotics currently in use, while enhancing focus on increasing new antibiotic development by the year 2020.

This approach includes Strategies to Address Antimicrobial Resistance (STAAR) Act legislation to contain resistance through federal funding and coordination, antimicrobial stewardship in veterinary and human infections, and if not eliminating, then minimizing the use of antibiotics to promote growth in food producing animals (www.idsociety.org /10x20.htm).

Antibiotics are commonly used in the treatment of infections of veterinary animals and as well as in food animal production to promote growth. It is known that antibiotic use in this setting as well as treatment of human infections directly selects for resistant pathogens [4]. Clinically available antibiotics and derivatives are often used in agriculture and animal growth production as described in Table 1 [5]. Until recently there has been limited regulation of antibiotics in food production, but countries such as US, Canada, Japan and European Union have enforced campaigns to try to reign in the development of resistant pathogens. Multidrug resistant strains are described with increased frequency in many foodborne pathogens including *Escherichia coli, Salmonella, Campylobacter, Listeria* and *Staphylococcus* spp [6].

**Table 1. Antimicrobial agents approved for use
in human and veterinary medicine[a]**

Antimicrobial class/drug	Examples of antimicrobials used in human medicine	Examples of antimicrobials used in veterinary medicine or as growth promoters
Antimicrobial classes classified as 'critically important' for human health by the WHO		
Aminoglycosides	Amikacin, arbekacin, gentamicin, kanamycin, netilmicin, neomycin, tobramycin, streptomycin	Amikacin, apramycin, gentamicin, neomycin, streptomycin, dihydrostreptomycin, kanamycin, framycetin, paromomycin (aminosidine)
Ansamycins	Rifabutin, rifampin, rifaximin	Rifampicin
Carbapenems and other penems	Ertapenem, faropenem, imipenem, meropenem, doripenem	None approved or known to be used
Cephalosporins, third generation	Cefixime, cefotaxime, cefpodoxime, ceftazidime, ceftizoxime, cefoperazone, cefoperazone/sulbactam, ceftriaxone	Cefpodoxime, ceftiofur, cefoperazone, cefovecin
Cephalosporins, fourth generation	Cefepime, cefpirome, cefoselis	Cefquinome
Lipopeptides	Daptomycin, telavancin	None approved or known to be used
Glycopeptides	Teicoplanin, vancomycin	Avoparcin*
Macrolides, including 14-, 15-, 16-membered compounds, ketolides	Azithromycin, clarithromycin, erythromycin, midecamycin, roxithromycin, spiramycin, telithromycin	Erythromycin, pirlimycin, spiramycin, tylosin, tulathromycin, kitasamycin, oleandomycin, tilmicosin, jasamycin

Table 1. (Continued)

Antimicrobial class/drug	Examples of antimicrobials used in human medicine	Examples of antimicrobials used in veterinary medicine or as growth promoters
Oxazolidinones	Linezolid	None approved or known to be used
Penicillins, amino	Ampicillin/amoxicillin, ampicillin/sulbactam, amoxicillin/clavulanante, piperacillin, piperacillin/tazobactam	Ampicillin/amoxicillin, ampicillin/sulbactam, amoxicillin/clavulanate
Penicillins, natural	Penicillin G, penicillin V	Penicillin G, penicillin V
Quinolones	Cinoxacin, nalidixic acid, pipedemic acid, ciprofloxacin, enoxacin, gatifloxacin, gemifloxacin, levofloxacin, lomefloxacin, moxifloxacin, norfloxacin, ofloxacin, sparfloxacin	Nalidixic acid, oxolinic acid, flumequine, pipemidic acid, danofloxacin, difloxacin, enrofloxacin, lbafloxacin, marbofloxacin, sarafloxacin, orbifloxacin, moxifloxacin
Streptogramins	Quinupristin/dalfopristin, pristinamycin	Virginiamycin[‡]
Drugs used solely to treat tuberculosis or other mycobacterial disease	Cycloserine, ethambutol, ethionamide, isoniazid, para-aminosalicyclic acid, pyrazinamide	None approved or known to be used
Cephalosporins, first generation	Cefazolin, cephalexin, cephalothin, cephradine	Cephalothin, cephalonium, cephalexin, cefadroxil, cefazolin
Cephalosporins, second generation	Cefaclor, cefamandole, cefuroxime, loracarbef	Cefuroxime
Cephamycins	Cefotetan, cefoxitin	None approved or known to be used
Clofazimine	Clofazidime	None approved or known to be used
Monobactams	Aztreonam	None approved or known to be used
Penicillins, amino	Mecillinam	None approved or known to be used
Penicillins, antipseudomonal*	Azlocillin, carbenicillin, mezlocillin, ticarcillin, ticarcillin/clavulanate	None approved or known to be used
Polymyxins	Polymyxin B, colistin	Polymyxin B, colistin
Spectinomycin	Spectinomycin	Spectinomycin
Sulfonamides, dihydrofolate reductase inhibitors and combinations	Para-aminobenzoic acid, pyrimethamine, sulfadiazine, sulfamethoxazole, sulfapyridine, sulfisoxazole, trimethoprim	Sulfadiazine, sulfadimidime, sulfadimethoxine, trimethoprim, baquiloprim
Sulfones [antileprosy]	Dapsone	None approved or known to be used
Tetracyclines	Chlortetracycline, doxycycline, minocycline, oxytetracycline, tetracycline	Chlortetracycline, doxycycline, oxytetracycline, tetracycline
Amphenicols	Chloramphenicol, thiophenicol	Chloramphenicol, florfenicol, thiamphenicol

Antimicrobial class/drug	Examples of antimicrobials used in human medicine	Examples of antimicrobials used in veterinary medicine or as growth promoters
Cyclic polypeptides	Bacitracin	Bacitracin
Fosfomycin	Fosfomycin	Fosfomycin
Fusidic acid	Fusidic acid	Fusidic acid
Lincosamides	Clindamycin, lincomycin	Clindamycin, lincomycin
Mupirocin	Mupirocin	Mupirocin
Nitrofurans	Furazolidone, nitrofurantoin, nitrofurazone	Furazolidone, nitrofurantoin, nitrofurazone
Nitroimidazoles	Metronidazole, tinidazole	Metronidazole, dimetridazole
Penicillins, antistaphylococcal	Cloxacillin, dicloxacillin, flucloxacillin, methicillin, nafcillin, oxacillin	Cloxacillin, nafcillin, methicillin, oxacillin, dicloxacillin

[a] Modified with permission from [5]

* Up until 2000, avoparcin was used extensively as a growth promoter around the world [except in North America]

‡ Up until 2000, virginiamycin was used extensively as a growth promoter in Europe. It is still used extensively in North America, Australia and many other parts of the world.

An understanding of the regional variability of antibiotic resistance is important in diagnosis and initial treatment of foodborne illness. The resistance differences in these strains are often a reflection of the relative regional antibiotic use in the agriculture and food industry. Also, a number of countries, such as the US and those of the European Union, have developed systems to monitor antibiotic resistance in foodborne microorganisms, while developing countries lack extensive data on foodborne disease outbreaks. Surveillance reports of antibiotic resistance trends in all regions are of increasing importance as international travel, and food and patient mobility continues to increase, thus amplifying the difficulty of predicting local resistance patterns [7].

A number of risk factors have been identified that increase the propensity for acquisition of antimicrobial resistant foodborne pathogens. As previously mentioned, antibiotic use in animals is a primary driver of resistance. Patients with recent foreign travel are also at increased risk of infections with antimicrobial resistant strains and introducing them to their new environment. In countries where antibiotics are available without a prescription, misuse and overuse of antibiotics can lead to increased resistance rates. Antimicrobial exposure prior to pathogen acquisition increases the risk of resistant infections; this relationship has been reported with fluoroquinolone use in multiple infection types [8, 9]. Lastly, the risk of acquiring antibiotic resistant strains is greater during food consumption at commercial establishments rather than home preparation, likely due to overall environmental contamination [10]. This chapter reviews antibiotic resistance trends and mechanisms in key foodborne pathogens.

**Table 2. Antibiotic mechanism of action and related
resistance mechanisms in foodborne pathogens**

Antibiotic	Mechanism of action	Resistance mechanisms[s]
Aminoglycosides	Inhibit protein synthesis	Aminoglycoside modifying enzymes Ribosomal methylation
β-lactams	Inhibit cell wall synthesis	β-lactamase production Alteration in penicillin-binding protein
Chloramphenicol	Inhibit protein synthesis	Target ribosomal alterations Efflux pumps Chloramphenicol modifying enzymes
Fluoroquinolones	Inhibit DNA synthesis	Mutations in topoisomerase and/or DNA gyrase Efflux pumps
Lincosamide, Streptogramin	Inhibit protein synthesis	Target ribosomal alterations
Macrolides	Inhibit protein synthesis	Target ribosomal alterations Efflux pumps
Sulfonamides	Inhibit folate synthesis	Mutations in folate pathway targets and metabolism
Tetracyclines	Inhibit protein synthesis	Efflux pumps Target ribosomal alterations

ANTIBIOTIC RESISTANCE IN FOODBORNE PATHOGENS

Escherichia coli

Escherichia coli are one of the most prominent foodborne pathogens implicated both in overall prevalence and morbidity and mortality-associated gastrointestinal illness. Although *E. coli* is a nosocomial pathogen, the majority of cases of infection are attributed to foodborne transmission. Shiga-toxin producing *E. coli* (STEC) were first associated in outbreaks of hemorrhagic colitis following the consumption of undercooked beef, but recent reports have involved other commercial agriculture meats as well as vegetables [11, 12]. The diversity of this pathogen is represented by almost 60 individual STEC serotypes that have been associated with human diseases throughout the world. In North America, Europe and Japan, *E. coli* O157:H7 is the most common serotype associated with gastrointestinal infections [13]. The clinical manifestations of *E. coli* O157:H7 range from mild-nonbloody diarrhea to life-threatening hemorrhagic colitis. The high pathogenicity of this strain is due to Shiga toxin production, a potent cytotoxin, as well as other associated virulence factors [14]. Antibiotic treatment of STEC infections remains controversial since some studies suggest that antibiotics may increase the risk and severity of disease possibly through increased Shiga toxin production [14]. Nevertheless, surveillance studies often report antibiotic susceptibility in *E. coli* O157:H7 [13]; mechanisms and resistance rates in all infection types with *E. coli* are reviewed in this section.

The first reports of *E. coli* O157:H7 noted a highly antibiotic susceptible pathogen, but resistance to a number of antimicrobial classes has begun to emerge since the early 1990s. The CDC tracks enteric gram-negative antimicrobial resistance patterns, including O157:H7. The most recent annual reports compare these trends in the US (National Antimicrobial Resistance Monitoring System, NARMS) from 1999-2008 (http://www.cdc.gov/narms/). During the final year of this analysis [2008], *E. coli* O157:H7 was susceptible to most antimicrobial agents tested. The highest resistance rates were to ampicillin and sulfisoxazole (3.8% resistance), followed by tetracycline (2.8%), streptomycin and nalidixic acid (1.9%). Of these agents, ampicillin and nalidixic acid had an increased resistance trend over the 10-year study period, while the others remained stable or decreased. In food products from 1985-2000, only 61% of *E. coli* O157:H7 isolates were susceptible to all antimicrobial agents evaluated. Compared to isolates from NARMS data, isolates from this study had higher resistance rates to tetracycline, sulfamethoxazole, and ampicillin [15]. Selective pressure through antimicrobial exposure in the agriculture industry appears to be an important factor for increased resistance in *E. coli* O157:H7 from animals. Also, frequent fluoroquinolone exposure in the agricultural industry may induce the formation of resistant mutants *in vitro* with higher Shiga-toxin production capabilities [16].

Pathogenic and commensal *E. coli* can serve as reservoirs for the transfer of resistance mechanisms. This has been documented through spread of resistance genes in *E. coli* among humans and animals [11]. Also, resistance gene transfer may occur among bacteria as identified from *in vitro* experiments with *E. coli, Klebsiella* and *Salmonella* spp [17, 18]. In non-0157 STEC serotypes, antibiotic resistance profiles have displayed a similar antibiogram to O157. Data from healthy and infected patients with non-0157 STEC displayed 11% resistance to at least one antimicrobial class and 4% resistance to four or more classes [19]. More recent data reported a 53% resistance rate to at least one antimicrobial class in a non-0157 STEC serotype from North America and Europe [20].

E. coli, present as part of normal human flora, can cause significant extra-intestinal disease such as urinary tract infections, bacteremia, and meningitis. Although these strains are separate in many ways from Shiga-toxin producing strains found primarily in food animals and water, their resistance profiles present interesting insights. The primary resistance mechanism detected in community and nosocomial *E. coli* that reduces the effectiveness of a major antibiotic class is the production β-lactamase enzymes. β-lactamases can be chromosome, plasmid, or transposon encoded enzymes, and rapid spread of this mechanism is a major concern.

The emergence of extended spectrum β-lactamases (ESBLs) in systemic *E. coli* infections effectively further limits the available treatment options. The key resistance phenotype with ESBLs is their acquired resistance to broad-spectrum cephalosporins and monobactams. Along with *Klebsiella pneumoniae, E. coli* was one of the first identified nosocomial pathogens to produce ESBLs, mainly SHV or TEM type. However, the worldwide emergence of a new multidrug resistant strain has been attributed to a virulent nosocomial and community acquired ESBL clone, CTX-M-15 [21]. The highest rate of ESBL resistance in *E. coli* infections is in the Asia/Pacific region with rates between 35-42% [22]. ESBL resistance in European countries did not exceed 11% but displayed a steady increase from 2002-2008, while resistance in North America has been highly variable [23]. The rapid emergence of ESBL resistance in community acquired systemic *E. coli* infections may be due in part to acquisition of ESBLs from contaminated food and animal reservoirs. ESBL production in STEC has rarely been described, but recent reports indicate a potential for emergence of this resistance phenotype [24, 25].

A new ESBL with resistance to carbapenems conferred by New Delhi metallo-β-lactamase 1 (NDM-1) was detected among *E. coli* isolates in India and Pakistan from patients with variable infection sites. The bla_{NDM-1} gene is carried on various plasmids and confers additional resistance to carbapenems. This strain is rapidly transmitted and has been detected is select patients throughout the United States, Europe, and Australia [26-28]. The only two antimicrobial agents that maintain at least 50% susceptibility in NDM-1 have been colistin and tigecycline [26]. International travel to India where original strains were detected is directly linked to the rapid worldwide spread [26]. The community-acquired nature of the isolates with NDM-1 in India suggests that this strain is ubiquitous in the environment in this region [26]. These resistance mechanisms and ease of plasmid genetic transfer are concerning for potential transmission to STEC strains in foodborne illness, so careful surveillance of resistance patterns is important to direct necessary therapy.

Salmonella

Salmonella enterica are often located in multiple environmental settings and have been traditionally found to colonize all major livestock. Newer reports indicate that *Salmonella* spp. outbreaks are also linked to contaminated fruits and vegetables [29]. There are a number *Salmonella* serotypes, but 10-30% of human disease is attributed to *Salmonella enterica* serotype Typhimurium [*S.* Typhimurium]. Most of the infections caused by this pathogen present as gastroenteritis that are a result of ingestion of contaminated beef, dairy, and egg products. Other serotypes within *S. enterica* that have been identified in specific foodborne outbreaks include Enteritidis, Saintpaul, Newport, and Heidelberg. Many of the *Salmonella* strains found in contaminated food products have some degree of antibiotic resistance and now increasingly multidrug resistance.

Salmonella gastroenteritis is generally a self-limiting disease, however up to 5% of patients may develop bacteremia or other serious complications [30]. In these patients with serious disease, treatment with appropriate antibiotics is crucial and should be guided by susceptibility results. Surveillance studies of antimicrobial susceptibility in *Salmonella enterica* often describe results of localized geographic outbreaks or specific food types, so identifying global patterns may be difficult. An understanding of the regional antibiotic resistance characteristics in this pathogen is imperative to direct appropriate therapy.

Antimicrobial resistance in *Salmonella* is usually serotype and region dependent. In the recent report of *Salmonella* resistance by the European Centre for Disease Prevention and Control (ECDC) from 2008, antimicrobial susceptibility was tested on over 3,500 isolates from salmonellosis in patients, which represented approximately 37% of all cases. Eleven antibiotics were evaluated representing a variety of antimicrobial classes. In total, antimicrobial resistance was highest to tetracyclines (31%), ampicillin (21%) and sulfonamides (16%). An increase in tetracycline resistance occurred from the previous year 2007 (22%), while ampicillin and sulfonamide resistance remained similar. The lowest resistance occurred with cefotaxime 0.7% and the aminoglycosides kanamycin and gentamicin, 1.6% and 3.3%, respectively.

Longitudinal studies often provide the best evidence for changing antimicrobial susceptibility patterns. A 7-year study described 4,956 episodes of non typhoidal *Salmonella* (NTS) bacteremia among adults and children in Malawi [31]. During the study period from 1998 to 2004, resistance in *S*. Enteritidis to chloramphenicol, ampicillin, and trimethoprim-sulfamethoxazole rapidly increased up to 90% during the first 3 years, followed by a gradual decline over the next 4 years. *S*. Typhimurium maintained high-level resistance (>90%) throughout the study period and also acquired similar resistance to chloramphenicol by the end of the study. All isolates were susceptible to ciprofloxacin and third-generation cephalosporins. The emergence of these resistance types in *Salmonella* may have little impact on mortality if appropriate rapid therapy is instituted [31].

Fluoroquinolone or cephalosporin resistance in *Salmonella* presents significant problems to appropriate management since these agents are often given as first-line therapy. However, isolated epidemics with *Salmonella* pathogens containing these resistance types have been reported. A rising resistance mechanism in Enterobacteriaceae, including *Salmonella* is plasmid-mediated resistance to fluoroquinolones. The plasmid gene *qnr* encodes both a protein that protects DNA gyrase from the effects of quinolones and *aac[6']-Ib-cr*, an aminoglycoside modifying enzyme with activity against aminoglycosides [32]. Plasmid mediated resistance may also carry an ESBL gene to reduce the efficacy of cephalosporin antibiotics. A number of studies have found a variety of ESBL genes on these plasmids, such as CTX-M, AmpC, CMY, SHV, and OXA [33-35]. The spread of *Salmonella* strains with ESBL resistance has been well documented in disease outbreaks and most often involves low to middle income regions such as Central America, Africa and Asia [36, 37].

Reduced antimicrobial susceptibility in *Salmonella* spp can largely be attributed to the relatively recent emergence and dissemination of multidrug resistant strains, such as *S*. Typhimurium DT104 [38]. Since the 1990s, this strain has been implicated as an increasingly important cause of foodborne-related illness. DT104 with multidrug resistance was first identified in the United Kingdom and outbreaks have now been reported throughout the world [39]. The multidrug resistant phenotype in DT104 is resistant to ampicillin, chloramphenicol, streptomycin, sulfonamides, and tetracycline, and collectively termed phenotype ACSSuT or the genotypic designation *Salmonella* genomic island 1 [SGI-1] [40]. Another important feature of this pathogen is its ability to develop resistance to a number additional antimicrobial classes, including fluoroquinolones [40]. Acquisition of ciprofloxacin and aminoglycoside resistance *in vivo* has been documented following ciprofloxacin treatment for acute gastroenteritis [41]. The *in vivo* selection corresponded to appearance of the *aac*[6']-Ib-cr gene for aminoglycoside resistance and a Tyr change to Ser83 in gyrase producing high level fluoroquinolone resistance. The incidence of *Salmonella* infections due to DT104 has fluctuated, but overall it is increasing globally and is representing a larger percentage of *Salmonella* detected in human infections. In European countries where this strain has been prominent, evidence suggests that that its incidence has slowly waned, albeit still prominent [42]. In recent antibiotic susceptibility studies of *S*. Typhimurium in diseased livestock in European countries, 15-78% of isolates harbored the ACSSuT phenotype [43, 44]. A study of antimicrobial resistance in *Salmonella* from retail foods in China detected multidrug resistance in 30% of *Salmonella* isolates, and of those 17% displayed an ACSSuT resistance profile [45]. The wide variation in prevalence of DT104 and other multidrug related phenotypes, such as recently identified DT193 and DT120, of *Salmonella* spp indicate the importance of antimicrobial susceptibility testing and targeted therapy for this strain [46].

Another well described multidrug resistant strain is the *Salmonella* serotype Newport, which has been first detected in the northeastern US and has since been found throughout multiple regions of the country [47]. One clone of this strain has been identified as possessing resistance to at least nine antimicrobials, including broad-spectrum cephalosporins and beta-lactam/beta-lactamase inhibitors [47]. According to the CDC, this serotype was the most common ceftriaxone-resistant non-typhoidal *Salmonella* isolated in 2008 in the US. Worldwide spread of the multidrug resistant *S.* Newport strain has now been reported [48].

Campylobacter

Campylobacter spp. are curved gram-negative aerobic rods that are commonly present in a variety of animals such as poultry, sheep and swine. Although the genus contains over 17 species, gastroenteritis and related infections are most commonly caused by *C. jejuni* and *C. coli*, with the former recognized in the majority of cases in human infection [49]. Another reservoir for *Campylobacter* transmission is through unsanitized water supplies, which in developing countries such as Mexico and others in Latin American is the most common cause of traveler's diarrhea. The true incidence of *Campylobacter* gastroenteritis is likely underreported since many patients either may not seek treatment or have no cultures taken, but epidemiologic evidence suggest a bimodal age distribution occurring in both infants/children and middle adulthood [20-40 years] [49]. The gastrointestinal infection course of *Campylobacter* infections is usually self-limiting, but rare complications such as bacteremia, sepsis, urinary tract infections, and peritonitis among others contribute to morbidity and morbidity. These complications are more common in immunocompromised and elderly populations and are indications for antimicrobial therapy.

The antimicrobial treatments of choice for *C. jejuni* and *C. coli* gastroenteritis are fluoroquinolones or macrolides, however resistance to these drugs is now reported more frequently and subsequently contributes to increased adverse outcomes. For more serious invasive infections, treatment with aminoglycosides may be considered. The mechanism of *Campylobacter* fluoroquinolone resistance has been attributed to primarily point mutations in the DNA gyrase subunit A gene [*gyrA*]. Specifically single or double point mutations for *gyrA* have been described for high-level ciprofloxacin resistance in *C. jejuni* [50]. Point mutations in *parC* encoding for topoisomerase, a second bacterial target of fluoroquinolones has been reported in *Campylobacter*, however subsequent studies have failed to confirm this finding [51, 52]. An increasingly recognized secondary mechanism contributing to fluoroquinolone resistance is a multidrug efflux pump. One recently described is efflux pump in *C. jejuni* is CmeABC, which mediates reduced susceptibility to ciprofloxacin, ampicillin, tetracycline, and erythromycin [53].

Fluoroquinolone resistance in *Campylobacter* has been described since the 1980s and often is noted with ciprofloxacin. Fluoroquinolone resistance has reportedly varied according to region, but overall resistance appears to be increasing. Many studies indicate a 20-50% increase in fluoroquinolone resistance over 5-10 year study period [54, 55]. Some regions of Asia report fluoroquinolone resistance rates in *Campylobacter* of up to 80% [56].

Fluoroquinolone resistance may be more prevalent in food animals than the rates described previously from infected patients. The main contributor to this is the heavy use of agricultural fluoroquinolones that may select for resistance to those clinically available in this class [Table 1]. The use of enrofloxacin and sarafloxacin in the food industry began in the 1990s and has corresponded with increasing resistance in isolates from livestock animals. Comparative analysis of human and animal isolates from the same region and time period has revealed increased fluoroquinolone resistance in isolates of animal origin [57, 58]. Some government agencies have withdrawn the approval for use of fluoroquinolones in food producing animals due to the increased development of high-level resistance, but the long-term impact of this approach to fluoroquinolone resistance in *Campylobacter* has yet to be fully determined [59].

Macrolides are often considered the drug of choice when antibiotic therapy is required for *Campylobacter* infections due to its good safety profile and low resistance mutation rate. However, macrolide resistance has emerged and has shown a trend toward increased prevalence in both developed and developing countries. Macrolide resistance has been associated with both target ribosomal modification and active efflux pumps. Target site modification is a result of either enzyme-mediated methylation or by point mutation in the 23S rRNA and/or ribosomal proteins L4 and L22 [60]. The CmeABC multidrug efflux pump described previously in fluoroquinolone resistance also contributes to low-level macrolide resistance in *Campylobacter* [60]. Inactivation of the genes encoding CmeABC results in a significant reduction (up to 32 fold) in minimum inhibitory concentrations of telithromycin and azithromycin [61]. Macrolide resistance has been noted to exceed 50% of isolates in Taiwan, Singapore, and Nigeria, while European countries Spain, Germany, and Bulgaria have reported resistance rates between 25-35% (Reference). Low rates of macrolide resistance (<5%) have been reported in the US, Canada and Australia [60]. Recent evidence suggests that macrolide resistance is more common in *C. coli* than *C. jejuni* in patients with gastroenteritis, and a mutation in A2075G or A2074G in the 23S rRNA gene is associated with erythromycin resistance [62]. The use of macrolide and macrolide-like antibiotics in food animals has contributed to increasing resistance rates in this population. Due to this widespread use, macrolide resistance rates from animal sources are usually higher than that found in human isolates.

Aminoglycoside resistance has been described in many gram-negative pathogens including *Campylobacter* spp. The mechanism for this resistance is largely attributed to aminoglycoside-modifying enzymes. Resistance genes encoding these enzymes have been detected in many other gram-negative and gram-positive pathogens, suggesting that *Campylobacter* may acquire this resistance mechanism via plasmid transfer [63, 64]. Although aminoglycoside resistance mechanisms have been described, the overall rate of resistance in *Campylobacter* remains low [65].

Beyond the common treatment options for *Campylobacter* infections, resistance to other antibiotics is well documented. The majority of *C. jejuni* and *C. coli* strains are resistant to β-lactams, with the exceptions of broad-spectrum carbapenems [66]. The mechanism behind β-lactam resistance is not entirely clear but is most likely to involve novel β-lactamases against broad spectrum agents and intrinsic alterations in penicillin binding protein in narrow spectrum agents such as penicillin and first generation cephalosporins [67]. Tetracyclines can be given as an alternative for the treatment of *Campylobacter* infections, however multidrug resistance can preclude the use of this antimicrobial class. The mechanisms for tetracycline resistance include a variety of efflux pumps as well as protection of the ribosomal binding site. Resistance rates have varied widely but have been reported in the range of 30-80% [65, 68]. Tigecycline, a modified tetracycline with improved activity against multidrug resistant strains has no known resistance to date [65, 69].

Yersinia spp.

Yersinia enterocolitica and *Y. pseudotuberculosis* are identified as important foodborne pathogens. Gastroenteritis is more commonly caused by Y. *enterocolitica* as a result from consumption of contaminated water or raw foods, including beef, lamb, pork, and chicken. Occasional outbreaks of *Y. pseudotuberculosis* contamination of raw vegetables resulting in localized infectious processes and gastroenteritis have been reported [70]. *Y. pseudotuberculosis* is pan-susceptible to multiple antibiotics classes, while *Y. enterocolitica* can express relevant resistance determinants.

A number of serotypes of *Yersinia* have been identified and correspond to different antibiotic resistance profiles. The more common serotypes of *Y. enterocolitica* that have reported variable antibiograms include 0:8, O:3, and O:1,2,3. Most cases of *Yersinia* gastroenteritis are self-limiting and do not require antimicrobial treatment, however in cases of severe and systemic disease, treatment options include fluoroquinolones, trimethoprim /sulfamethoxazole and extended-spectrum cephalosporins. *Y. enterocolitica* often produces two types of β-lactamase enzymes A and B that result in resistance to ampicillin, penicillin and narrow spectrum cephalosporins [71, 72]. Studies suggest that the two β-lactamase enzymes A and B act synergistically to express resistance to this variety of β-lactams, but the presence of both enzymes varies according to strain subtype [7]). Extended spectrum activity in third-generation cephalosporins is still maintained in the presence of these enzymes [74]. *Y. enterocolitica* are susceptible *in vitro* to aminoglycosides, chloramphenicol, and tetracyclines.

Y. *enterocolitica* remain widely susceptible to fluoroquinolones even though some cases of resistance have been reported. Clinical resistance has occurred mostly with nalidixic acid and not the newer generation fluoroquinolones [75]. Laboratory derived resistance with ciprofloxacin has corresponded to four quinolone-resistance determinant regions in *gyrA* and *parC* as well as a multidrug efflux pump [76]. Trimethoprim/ sulfamethoxazole resistance overall is relatively uncommon (<10%), but some multidrug resistant clinical strains have resistance rates approaching 30% [77, 78]. *Yersinia spp.* have the ability to acquire multidrug antimicrobial resistance, and continued surveillance of regional susceptibility is warranted.

Listeria

Listeria monocytogenes is widely recognized as an important cause of foodborne illness. Humans as well as a variety of livestock animals are known carriers of this gram-positive rod that can be found widely throughout nature in soil, feces and other waste. The ubiquitous nature of this organism dictates that it easily contaminates a variety of foods including vegetables, dairy, and meat products among others during the manufacturing and distribution process. Listeriosis presents with a broad range of infection types ranging from asymptomatic carrier in mostly healthy individuals to encephalitis and meningitis more commonly found in immunocompromised hosts and the very young or old. Patients with neurologic involvement often have a high mortality rate or related sequelae upon survival [79]. The majority of listeriosis is transmitted from mother to child during birth, however this pathogen plays a significant role in foodborne disease because it can survive in food-processing environments and slowly replicate even under refrigerated conditions [80]. Biofilm formation in *L. monocytogenes* may be an essential mechanism for attachment to food or processing surfaces. Bacteria existing in a biofilm state are generally less susceptible to antibiotics [81], however the impact of this in *Listeria* spp. has not been established. There is concern with the increased incidence of listeriosis worldwide, particularly in European countries, as well as the documented emergence of antibiotic resistant strains.

Treatment of listeriosis involves high dose penicillin, usually ampicillin, in combination with an aminoglycoside. Second-line therapy may include vancomycin, trimethoprim /sulfamethoxaxole, or erythromycin depending on the patient and pathogen susceptibility. *Listeria* are susceptible to most antibiotics that have activity against gram-positive pathogens with overall populations remaining susceptible, however some outbreaks of reduced susceptibility and resistance have been reported [82, 83]. Numerous resistance mechanisms are described in *L. monocytogenes* with many of the encoding genes carried on plasmids, which are most likely transmitted from staphylococci and enterococci [84]. A number of outbreaks have reported the appearance of the tetracycline resistance genes *tet*(M) and (S) encoding for ribosomal protection in both food and clinical isolates, although efflux pumps and inactivating enzymes may also play a minor role [82, 83, 85]. Overall, tetracycline resistance remains low with most studies reporting rates between 1 to 10% [86, 87]. Resistance to other common antibiotics has also been reported in isolated cases. Erythromycin resistance confirmed by the presence of the *erm* gene has been detected in the food animal setting [88]. Fluoroquinolone resistance in *Listeria* is infrequent, but it has been attributed to the class active efflux pump Lde [87, 89]. Chloramphenicol resistance is also uncommon but is expressed through a *cat* gene encoding an acetyltransferase that catalyzes CoA-dependent acetylation of chloramphenicol at the 3-hydroxyl group [87, 90].

Specific cases of resistance to primary or secondary treatment options have been reported in *Listeria*. Ampicillin remains bactericidal against *L. monocytogenes* and has shown little resistance development. *In vitro* resistance to vancomycin has been created by conjugation of the vancomycin resistance gene *vanA*, however this has not been found in the clinical setting [84]. Trimethoprim resistance has been documented *in vivo* and is attributed to acquisition of the resistance gene *dfr*D commonly found in staphylococci. This high-level resistance results from a mutation in dihydrofolate reductase and has been found in both environmental and patient samples [87, 91, 92]. Multidrug resistance or resistance to at least 3 antimicrobial classes in *Listeria* remains relatively rare but isolated cases have been reported from Greece, Italy and more recently from France [87, 93]. Although *L. monocytogenes* remains largely susceptible to a variety of antimicrobial classes, the relatively poor bactericidal activity, especially against intracellular *Listeria* limits the availability of potent agents against this serious pathogen.

Staphylococcus aureus

Staphylococcus aureus is a widespread human pathogen in the community and hospital setting [94]. It is common commensal flora found on the skin, mucous membranes and upper respiratory tract of healthy humans and animals. Transmission of *S. aureus* has occurred between household members as well as from pets or livestock to humans. Infectious complications with *S. aureus* arise when there is a breakdown of barrier mechanisms such as skin integrity or respiratory function. In the case as a foodborne pathogen, *S. aureus* is one of the leading causes of food contamination and poisoning, although the exact incidence is unknown. Manifestations of ingestion of contaminated food usually involve gastroenteritis and vomiting with or without diarrhea. These symptoms are a result of pre-formed enterotoxins, which are known to cause emesis in as little as 2-8 hours after ingestion. Systemic symptoms such as fever and leukocytosis rarely occur in these cases, and local symptoms usually resolve within 24-48 hours. Multidrug resistant *S. aureus* is commonly encountered in invasive infections and has been increasingly described in animal and foodborne isolates [95].

The emergence of methicillin-resistant *S. aureus* (MRSA) was first reported in the 1960s after methicillin first became available. Alteration in penicillin-binding protein (PBP) 2a through expression of the *mecA* gene results in reduced affinity for β-lactams binding to PBPs in the cell membrane and limitating their activity. The *mecA* gene is carried on a mobile genetic element called staphylococcal cassette chromosome *mec* (SCC*mec*), which also contains regulatory genes and a cassette chromosome recombinase (*ccr*) gene complex. Eight SCC*mec* types have been clinically described (I-VIII) and correlate to community or health-care acquisition [96]. Over the past 3 decades, MRSA rates in the US have continued to rise and now account for as much as 60% of *S. aureus* infections from the community and hospital setting [94, 97]. Most other countries have similar MRSA rates with the exception of Denmark, Norway, Sweden, and The Netherlands where stricter infection controls has limited its spread in these settings.

MRSA has been detected in many animal species, including horses, dogs, cats, pigs, cattle, and poultry. In food production animals, a new MRSA strain (ST 398) has emerged and been transmitted among animals and humans [98]. The overall prevalence of MRSA in meat foods is unknown, but a survey from the Netherlands indicates 11.9% contamination in all types with the highest in poultry samples. Eighty-five percent of these strains belonged to ST 398 type [99]. Contamination of meat with MRSA often occurs upon contact with carcasses or other colonized parts during slaughtering of animals. However, the strain in contaminated samples may not be of animal origin. In the US, 5% of meat samples were contaminated with MRSA, which upon molecular typing revealed clones typically isolated in human infections and colonization [100]. Even though MRSA contamination is increasing in the food industry, the virulent potential of ST 398 strains in the food industry remains to be seen. ST 398 strains do not seem to harbor enterotoxins genes but have additional virulence genes such as hyaluronidase, SCIN (staphylococcal complement inhibitor) and vWbp (von Willebrand factor-binding protein) with a role in homeostasis [101, 102].

S. aureus possess additional resistance mechanisms to multiple antimicrobial classes. Fluoroquinolones are largely ineffective against this pathogen due to alterations in topoisomerase and DNA gyrase that modify target site interactions. Most strains either possess low- or high-level resistance to fluoroquinolones. In fact, excessive use of fluoroquinolones may actually increase the incidence of MRSA colonization in patients [103]. This may be a concern in the food industry where fluoroquinolone-like antibiotics are often used in agriculture. *S. aureus* has variable susceptibility to tetracycline antibiotics. Hospital associated strains are largely resistant to tetracyclines, while community isolates are highly susceptible. *S. aureus* from animals has displayed variable susceptibility to tetracyclines, but resistance rates above 50% have consistently been reported [104]. A significant percentage of clinical *S. aureus* possess macrolide-lincosamide-group B streptogramin [iMLSb]-inducible resistance that renders antibiotics in these classes ineffective, including erythromycin, clindamycin and quinupristin/dalfopristin. This resistance mechanism is expressed upon exposure to one of these antibiotics by modification of the ribosomal target [105]. The prevalence of this resistance determinant is not well studied in foodborne *S. aureus* isolates. As one of the primary treatment options, vancomycin has been used for decades to treat MRSA infections. Since the mid-1990s reduced susceptibility and full vancomycin resistance has been reported [106]. Full resistance is mediated through a plasmid acquisition of *van* genes found in *Enterococcus* spp. Reduced vancomycin susceptibility has not been reported in foodborne *S. aureus,* although this agent is not routinely tested.

Enterococcus spp.

Enterococci are multidrug resistant gram-positive cocci that are part of the gastrointestinal commensal flora in humans and animals. Infections with enterococci occur mostly within the hospital setting or those patients with comorbidities and healthcare contact. Enterococci are important microorganisms because they often are a reservoir for acquisition and transfer of resistance genes, mostly on plasmids, among various bacteria. Vancomycin resistant enterococci have been commonly isolated in animals and have been linked to overuse of the glycopeptide antibiotic avoparcin in animal production. Studies have indicated that the mechanism of vancomycin resistance (*van* gene) in VRE has been transferred between enterococci in animals and humans. Enterococci are commonly resistant to β-lactams, tetracyclines, fluoroquinolones, macrolides and many other antimicrobial classes. Contamination of meat products with enterococci has been identified, however, there has been no link of contamination with human disease, likely due to their limited virulence potential. Enterococci present a potential threat in foodborne illness due to their ability to transfer resistance to other more pathogenic microorganisms [107].

Clostridium difficile

C. difficile is increasingly described as major human pathogen responsible for severe to life-threatening diarrhea and colitis. This pathogen is overwhelmingly found in the hospital setting, and emerging cases in the community setting are a new development in its epidemiology. Antibiotic use and prior health care contact are associated risk factors for acquisition, but these have not correlated to patients with community transmission. Food has been identified as a potential reservoir in *C. difficile* community-related disease. Although this correlation has not been completely realized, *C. difficile* has been detected in meats and other retail food for human consumption [108, 109]. There is a potential role of foodborne infections with *C. difficile*, however documented infection from contaminated food products has yet to be reported [110].

C. difficile is a spore-forming gram-positive anaerobic organism that is part of human normal flora and is often highly antibiotic resistant with few treatment options.

Similar to many foodborne pathogens, *C. difficile* antibiotic susceptibility varies according to region. Inherent resistance and inactive antibiotics against *C. difficile* include macrolides, clindamycin, trimethoprim/sulfamethoxazole, penicillin, and ampicillin. Resistance to fluoroquinolones is variable, but some studies report rates exceeding 50%, and resistance has been linked to mutations in *gyrA* [111, 112]. Tetracycline resistance is often reported in < 10% of studies, but it does occur in select outbreaks due to mutations in *tetM* resulting in ribosomal protection [113]. The rifamycins, rifampin and rifaximin, have been used in the treatment of *C. difficile* infections, but evidence does not support their use in treatment or suppression [114]. Exposure of *C. difficile* to rifamycins directly correlates with the emergence of resistance through mutations in *rpoB* that reduces their binding to RNA polymerase [115].

The primary treatment options for *C. difficile* infections continue to be metronidazole for initial episodes of mild disease and vancomycin for initial episodes of severe disease or second or later recurrence [114]. Despite being the primary therapy for over two decades, metronidazole resistance has remained confined to rare outbreaks [116]. *C. difficile* has displayed a heterogeneous and inducible subpopulations as a potential mechanism of reduced susceptibility in outbreaks of the disease [117]. Metronidazole treatment failures are reported with susceptible *C. difficile*, which may be attributed to the low concentrations achieved in the stool that is unable to eradicate the organism. Oral vancomycin achieves high stool concentrations, but *C. difficile* clinical resistance may be increasing [118]. Mutations in *van* genes do not contribute to reduced vancomycin susceptibility in *C. difficile*, and no other specific mechanism has been identified.

CONCLUSION AND FUTURE DIRECTIONS

The recognition of unnecessary antibiotic use in the animal food industry leading to antimicrobial resistance is an important step in limiting the spread of these pathogens. Although some countries have adapted policies to combat excessive antimicrobial use in the food industry, unregulated use by many countries is still an increasing threat to foodborne microorganism resistance. In addition, inappropriate use in humans increases the exposure of these strains to potent antibiotics, and thereby increasing resistance risk. It has yet to be determined if policies in reducing antibiotic exposure will have a significant long-term impact on the overall resistance in foodborne pathogens.

Rapid diagnostic testing will likely play an increasing role in tracking foodborne disease outbreaks and antimicrobial resistance. The costs for performing molecular diagnostics continue to decrease and would improve understanding of resistance patterns in outbreaks from developing countries where current data is lacking. These tests are currently being performed in the clinical setting to rapidly identify MRSA and *C. difficile* carriage among others. Rapid identification of specific resistance types would help direct timely antibiotic therapy and improve patient care. The barriers to this approach in foodborne disease include sampling difficulties from farms, processing plants, or other sites as well as the large span of potential contaminants in the agricultural industry. Overall, the goal of any approach to reduce antibiotic resistance will improve animal and human health and retain viable treatment options when indicated.

REFERENCES

[1]   Mauldin PD, Salgado CD, Hansen IS, Durup DT, Bosso JA. Attributable hospital cost and length of stay associated with health care-associated infections caused by antibiotic-resistant gram-negative bacteria. *Antimicrob Agents Chemother.* 2010;54(1):109-15.

[2]   Roberts RR, Hota B, Ahmad I, Scott RD, 2nd, Foster SD, Abbasi F, et al. Hospital and societal costs of antimicrobial-resistant infections in a Chicago teaching hospital: implications for antibiotic stewardship. *Clin Infect Dis.* 2009 Oct 15;49(8):1175-84.

[3]   Boucher HW, Talbot GH, Bradley JS, Edwards JE, Gilbert D, Rice LB, et al. Bad bugs, no drugs: no ESKAPE! An update from the Infectious Diseases Society of America. *Clin Infect Dis.* 2009 Jan 1;48(1):1-12.

[4]   Hawkey PM. The growing burden of antimicrobial resistance. *J Antimicrob Chemother.* 2008;62 Suppl 1:i1-9.

[5]   Aarestrup FM, Wegener HC, Collignon P. Resistance in bacteria of the food chain: epidemiology and control strategies. *Expert Rev Anti Infect Ther.* 2008;6(5):733-50.

[6]   DuPont HL. The growing threat of foodborne bacterial enteropathogens of animal origin. *Clin Infect Dis.* 2007 Nov 15;45(10):1353-61.

[7]   Rolain JM, Parola P, Cornaglia G. New Delhi metallo-beta-lactamase (NDM-1): towards a new pandemia? *Clin Microbiol Infect.* Sep 27.

[8]   Smith KE, Besser JM, Hedberg CW, Leano FT, Bender JB, Wicklund JH, et al. Quinolone-resistant *Campylobacter jejuni* infections in Minnesota, 1992-1998. Investigation Team. *N Engl J Med.* 1999 May 20;340(20):1525-32.

[9]   Lodise TP, Miller CD, Graves J, Evans A, Graffunder E, Helmecke M, et al. Predictors of high vancomycin MIC values among patients with methicillin-resistant *Staphylococcus aureus* bacteraemia. *J Antimicrob Chemother.* 2008;62(5):1138-41.

[10] Kassenborg HD, Smith KE, Vugia DJ, Rabatsky-Ehr T, Bates MR, Carter MA, et al. Fluoroquinolone-resistant *Campylobacter* infections: eating poultry outside of the home and foreign travel are risk factors. *Clin Infect Dis.* 2004 Apr 15;38 Suppl 3:S279-84.

[11] Rangel JM, Sparling PH, Crowe C, Griffin PM, Swerdlow DL. Epidemiology of *Escherichia coli* O157:H7 outbreaks, United States, 1982-2002. *Emerg Infect Dis.* 2005;11(4):603-9.

[12] Maki DG. Don't eat the spinach--controlling foodborne infectious disease. *N Engl J Med.* 2006 Nov 9;355(19):1952-5.

[13] Surveillance for foodborne disease outbreaks - United States, 2006. *MMWR Morb Mortal Wkly Rep.* 2009 Jun 12;58(22):609-15.

[14] Wong CS, Jelacic S, Habeeb RL, Watkins SL, Tarr PI. The risk of the hemolytic-uremic syndrome after antibiotic treatment of *Escherichia coli* O157:H7 infections. *N Engl J Med*. 2000 Jun 29;342(26):1930-6.

[15] Schroeder CM, Zhao C, DebRoy C, Torcolini J, Zhao S, White DG, et al. Antimicrobial resistance of *Escherichia coli* O157 isolated from humans, cattle, swine, and food. *Appl Environ Microbiol*. 2002;68(2):576-81.

[16] Maurer C, Meunier D, Madec JY. Shiga toxin Stx2 production is promoted by enrofloxacin in experimental in vitro-selected mutants of *Escherichia coli* O157:H7 resistant to fluoroquinolones. *Foodborne Pathog Dis*. 2009;6(2):257-9.

[17] Poppe C, Martin LC, Gyles CL, Reid-Smith R, Boerlin P, McEwen SA, et al. Acquisition of resistance to extended-spectrum cephalosporins by *Salmonella enterica* subsp. enterica serovar Newport and *Escherichia coli* in the turkey poult intestinal tract. *Appl Environ Microbiol*. 2005;71(3):1184-92.

[18] Yan JJ, Chiou CS, Lauderdale TL, Tsai SH, Wu JJ. Cephalosporin and ciprofloxacin resistance in *Salmonella*, Taiwan. *Emerg Infect Dis*. 2005;11(6):947-50.

[19] Schmidt H, von Maldeghem J, Frosch M, Karch H. Antibiotic susceptibilities of verocytotoxin-producing *Escherichia coli* O157 and non-O157 strains isolated from patients and healthy subjects in Germany during 1996. *J Antimicrob Chemother*. 1998;42(4):548-50.

[20] Karama M, Johnson RP, Holtslander R, Gyles CL. Phenotypic and genotypic characterization of verotoxin-producing *Escherichia coli* O103:H2 isolates from cattle and humans. *J Clin Microbiol*. 2008;46(11):3569-75.

[21] Peirano G, Pitout JD. Molecular epidemiology of *Escherichia coli* producing CTX-M beta-lactamases: the worldwide emergence of clone ST131 O25:H4. *Int J Antimicrob Agents. 2010;35(4):316-21.*

[22] Hawser SP, Bouchillon SK, Hoban DJ, Badal RE, Hsueh PR, Paterson DL. Emergence of high levels of extended-spectrum-beta-lactamase-producing gram-negative bacilli in the Asia-Pacific region: data from the Study for Monitoring Antimicrobial Resistance Trends (SMART) program, 2007. *Antimicrob Agents Chemother*. 2009;53(8):3280-4.

[23] Oteo J, Perez-Vazquez M, Campos J. Extended-spectrum [beta]-lactamase producing *Escherichia coli*: changing epidemiology and clinical impact. *Curr Opin Infect Dis*. 2010;23(4):320-6.

[24] Ishii Y, Kimura S, Alba J, Shiroto K, Otsuka M, Hashizume N, et al. Extended-spectrum beta-lactamase-producing Shiga toxin gene (Stx1)-positive *Escherichia coli* O26:H11: a new concern. *J Clin Microbiol*. 2005;43(3):1072-5.

[25] Buvens G, Bogaerts P, Glupczynski Y, Lauwers S, Pierard D. Antimicrobial resistance testing of verocytotoxin-producing *Escherichia coli* and first description of TEM-52 extended-spectrum beta-lactamase in serogroup O26. *Antimicrob Agents Chemother*. 2010;54(11):4907-9.

[26] Kumarasamy KK, Toleman MA, Walsh TR, Bagaria J, Butt F, Balakrishnan R, et al. Emergence of a new antibiotic resistance mechanism in India, Pakistan, and the UK: a molecular, biological, and epidemiological study. *Lancet Infect Dis*. 2010;10(9):597-602.

[27] Detection of Enterobacteriaceae isolates carrying metallo-beta-lactamase - United States, 2010. *MMWR Morb Mortal Wkly Rep*. Jun 25;59(24):750.

[28] Poirel L, Lagrutta E, Taylor P, Pham J, Nordmann P. Emergence of metallo-beta-lactamase NDM-1-producing multidrug-resistant *Escherichia coli* in Australia. *Antimicrob Agents Chemother.* 2010;54(11):4914-6.

[29] Maki DG. Coming to grips with foodborne infection--peanut butter, peppers, and nationwide *Salmonella* outbreaks. *N Engl J Med.* 2009 Mar 5;360(10):949-53.

[30] White DG, Zhao S, Simjee S, Wagner DD, McDermott PF. Antimicrobial resistance of foodborne pathogens. *Microbes Infect.* 2002;4(4):405-12.

[31] Gordon MA, Graham SM, Walsh AL, Wilson L, Phiri A, Molyneux E, et al. Epidemics of invasive *Salmonella enterica* serovar enteritidis and S. enterica Serovar typhimurium infection associated with multidrug resistance among adults and children in Malawi. *Clin Infect Dis.* 2008 Apr 1;46(7):963-9.

[32] Strahilevitz J, Jacoby GA, Hooper DC, Robicsek A. Plasmid-mediated quinolone resistance: a multifaceted threat. *Clin Microbiol Rev.* 2009;22(4):664-89.

[33] Hopkins KL, Wootton L, Day MR, Threlfall EJ. Plasmid-mediated quinolone resistance determinant qnrS1 found in *Salmonella enterica* strains isolated in the UK. *J Antimicrob Chemother.* 2007;59(6):1071-5.

[34] Egorova S, Timinouni M, Demartin M, Granier SA, Whichard JM, Sangal V, et al. Ceftriaxone-resistant *Salmonella enterica* serotype Newport, France. *Emerg Infect Dis.* 2008;14(6):954-7.

[35] Whichard JM, Gay K, Stevenson JE, Joyce KJ, Cooper KL, Omondi M, et al. Human *Salmonella* and concurrent decreased susceptibility to quinolones and extended-spectrum cephalosporins. *Emerg Infect Dis.* 2007;13(11):1681-8.

[36] Zaidi MB, Leon V, Canche C, Perez C, Zhao S, Hubert SK, et al. Rapid and widespread dissemination of multidrug-resistant blaCMY-2 *Salmonella* Typhimurium in Mexico. *J Antimicrob Chemother.* 2007;60(2):398-401.

[37] Usha G, Chunderika M, Prashini M, Willem SA, Yusuf ES. Characterization of extended-spectrum beta-lactamases in *Salmonella* spp. at a tertiary hospital in Durban, South Africa. *Diagn Microbiol Infect Dis.* 2008;62(1):86-91.

[38] Threlfall EJ, Ward LR, Skinner JA, Graham A. Antimicrobial drug resistance in non-typhoidal *Salmonellas* from humans in England and Wales in 1999: decrease in multiple resistance in *Salmonella enterica* serotypes Typhimurium, Virchow, and Hadar. *Microb Drug Resist.* 2000 Winter;6(4):319-25.

[39] Glynn MK, Bopp C, Dewitt W, Dabney P, Mokhtar M, Angulo FJ. Emergence of multidrug-resistant *Salmonella enterica* serotype typhimurium DT104 infections in the United States. *N Engl J Med.* 1998 May 7;338(19):1333-8.

[40] Helms M, Ethelberg S, Molbak K. International *Salmonella* Typhimurium DT104 infections, 1992-2001. *Emerg Infect Dis.* 2005;11(6):859-67.

[41] Parry CM. Antimicrobial drug resistance in *Salmonella enterica. Curr Opin Infect Dis.* 2003;16(5):467-72.

[42] Butaye P, Michael GB, Schwarz S, Barrett TJ, Brisabois A, White DG. The clonal spread of multidrug-resistant non-typhi *Salmonella* serotypes. *Microbes Infect.* 2006;8(7):1891-7.

[43] Emborg HD, Baggesen DL, Aarestrup FM. Ten years of antimicrobial susceptibility testing of *Salmonella* from Danish pig farms. *J Antimicrob Chemother.* 2008;62(2):360-3.

[44] Targant H, Ponsin C, Brunet C, Doublet B, Cloeckaert A, Madec JY, et al. Characterization of resistance genes in multidrug-resistant *Salmonella enterica* serotype Typhimurium isolated from diseased cattle in France (2002 to 2007). *Foodborne Pathog* Dis. ;7(4):419-25.

[45] Yan H, Li L, Alam MJ, Shinoda S, Miyoshi S, Shi L. Prevalence and antimicrobial resistance of *Salmonella* in retail foods in northern China. *Int J Food Microbiol.* 2010 Oct 15;143(3):230-4.

[46] Hopkins KL, Kirchner M, Guerra B, Granier SA, Lucarelli C, Porrero MC, et al. Multiresistant *Salmonella enterica* serovar 4,[5],12:i:- in Europe: a new pandemic strain? *Euro Surveill.* 15(22):19580.

[47] Sangal V, Harbottle H, Mazzoni CJ, Helmuth R, Guerra B, Didelot X, et al. Evolution and population structure of *Salmonella enterica* serovar Newport. *J Bacteriol.* 2010;192(24):6465-76.

[48] Gonzalez-Sanz R, Herrera-Leon S, de la Fuente M, Arroyo M, Echeita MA. Emergence of extended-spectrum beta-lactamases and AmpC-type beta-lactamases in human *Salmonella* isolated in Spain from 2001 to 2005. *J Antimicrob Chemother.* 2009;64(6):1181-6.

[49] Allos BM, Moore MR, Griffin PM, Tauxe RV. Surveillance for sporadic foodborne disease in the 21st century: the FoodNet perspective. *Clin Infect Dis.* 2004 Apr 15;38 Suppl 3:S115-20.

[50] Ge B, McDermott PF, White DG, Meng J. Role of efflux pumps and topoisomerase mutations in fluoroquinolone resistance in *Campylobacter jejuni* and *Campylobacter coli. Antimicrob Agents Chemother.* 2005;49(8):3347-54.

[51] Gibreel A, Sjogren E, Kaijser B, Wretlind B, Skold O. Rapid emergence of high-level resistance to quinolones in *Campylobacter jejuni* associated with mutational changes in *gyrA* and *parC. Antimicrob Agents Chemother.* 1998;42(12):3276-8.

[52] Piddock LJ, Ricci V, Pumbwe L, Everett MJ, Griggs DJ. Fluoroquinolone resistance in *Campylobacter* species from man and animals: detection of mutations in topoisomerase genes. *J Antimicrob Chemother.* 2003;51(1):19-26.

[53] Pumbwe L, Piddock LJ. Identification and molecular characterisation of CmeB, a *Campylobacter jejuni* multidrug efflux pump. *FEMS Microbiol Lett.* 2002 Jan 10;206(2):185-9.

[54] Engberg J, Aarestrup FM, Taylor DE, Gerner-Smidt P, Nachamkin I. Quinolone and macrolide resistance in *Campylobacter jejuni* and *C. coli*: resistance mechanisms and trends in human isolates. *Emerg Infect Dis.* 2001 Jan-Feb;7(1):24-34.

[55] Hakanen A, Jousimies-Somer H, Siitonen A, Huovinen P, Kotilainen P. Fluoroquinolone resistance in *Campylobacter jejuni* isolates in travelers returning to Finland: association of ciprofloxacin resistance to travel destination. *Emerg Infect Dis.* 2003;9(2):267-70.

[56] Hoge CW, Gambel JM, Srijan A, Pitarangsi C, Echeverria P. Trends in antibiotic resistance among diarrheal pathogens isolated in Thailand over 15 years. *Clin Infect Dis.* 1998;26(2):341-5.

[57] Li CC, Chiu CH, Wu JL, Huang YC, Lin TY. Antimicrobial susceptibilities of *Campylobacter jejuni* and *coli* by using E-test in Taiwan. *Scand J Infect Dis.* 1998;30(1):39-42.

[58] Saenz Y, Zarazaga M, Lantero M, Gastanares MJ, Baquero F, Torres C. Antibiotic resistance in *Campylobacter* strains isolated from animals, foods, and humans in Spain in 1997-1998. *Antimicrob Agents Chemother*. 2000;44(2):267-71.

[59] Nelson JM, Chiller TM, Powers JH, Angulo FJ. Fluoroquinolone-resistant *Campylobacter* species and the withdrawal of fluoroquinolones from use in poultry: a public health success story. *Clin Infect Dis*. 2007 Apr 1;44(7):977-80.

[60] Gibreel A, Taylor DE. Macrolide resistance in *Campylobacter jejuni* and *Campylobacter coli*. *J Antimicrob Chemother*. 2006;58(2):243-55.

[61] Cagliero C, Mouline C, Payot S, Cloeckaert A. Involvement of the CmeABC efflux pump in the macrolide resistance of *Campylobacter coli*. *J Antimicrob Chemother*. 2005;56(5):948-50.

[62] Perez-Boto D, Lopez-Portoles JA, Simon C, Valdezate S, Echeita MA. Study of the molecular mechanisms involved in high-level macrolide resistance of Spanish *Campylobacter jejuni* and *Campylobacter coli* strains. *J Antimicrob Chemother*. 2010;65(10):2083-8.

[63] Ouellette M, Gerbaud G, Lambert T, Courvalin P. Acquisition by a Campylobacter-like strain of aphA-1, a kanamycin resistance determinant from members of the family Enterobacteriaceae. *Antimicrob Agents Chemother*. 1987;31(7):1021-6.

[64] Nirdnoy W, Mason CJ, Guerry P. Mosaic structure of a multiple-drug-resistant, conjugative plasmid from *Campylobacter jejuni*. *Antimicrob Agents Chemother*. 2005;49(6):2454-9.

[65] Lehtopolku M, Nakari UM, Kotilainen P, Huovinen P, Siitonen A, Hakanen AJ. Antimicrobial susceptibilities of multidrug-resistant *Campylobacter jejuni* and *C. coli* strains: *in vitro* activities of 20 antimicrobial agents. *Antimicrob Agents Chemother*. 2010;54(3):1232-6.

[66] Aarestrup FM, Engberg J. Antimicrobial resistance of thermophilic *Campylobacter*. *Vet Res*. 2001 May-Aug;32(3-4):311-21.

[67] Tajada P, Gomez-Graces JL, Alos JI, Balas D, Cogollos R. Antimicrobial susceptibilities of *Campylobacter jejuni* and *Campylobacter coli* to 12 beta-lactam agents and combinations with beta-lactamase inhibitors. *Antimicrob Agents Chemother*. 1996;40(8):1924-5.

[68] Gaudreau C, Girouard Y, Gilbert H, Gagnon J, Bekal S. Comparison of disk diffusion and agar dilution methods for erythromycin, ciprofloxacin, and tetracycline susceptibility testing of *Campylobacter coli* and for tetracycline susceptibility testing of Campylobacter jejuni subsp. jejuni. *Antimicrob Agents Chemother*. 2008;52(12):4475-7.

[69] Rodriguez-Avial I, Rodriguez-Avial C, Lopez O, Culebras E, Picazo JJ. In vitro activity of tigecycline (GAR-936) and other antimicrobials against tetracycline- and ciprofloxacin-resistant *Campylobacter* clinical isolates. *Int J Antimicrob Agents*. 2006;27(4):303-6.

[70] Nuorti JP, Niskanen T, Hallanvuo S, Mikkola J, Kela E, Hatakka M, et al. A widespread outbreak of *Yersinia pseudotuberculosis* O:3 infection from iceberg lettuce. *J Infect Dis*. 2004 Mar 1;189(5):766-74.

[71] Stock I, Heisig P, Wiedemann B. Expression of beta-lactamases in *Yersinia enterocolitica* strains of biovars 2, 4 and 5. *J Med Microbiol*. 1999;48(11):1023-7.

[72] Stock I, Wiedemann B. An in-vitro study of the antimicrobial susceptibilities of *Yersinia enterocolitica* and the definition of a database. *J Antimicrob Chemother.* 1999;43(1):37-45.

[73] Bottone EJ. *Yersinia enterocolitica*: the charisma continues. *Clin Microbiol Rev.* 1997;10(2):257-76.

[74] Pham JN, Bell SM, Martin L, Carniel E. The beta-lactamases and beta-lactam antibiotic susceptibility of *Yersinia enterocolitica. J Antimicrob Chemother.* 2000;46(6):951-7.

[75] Capilla S, Ruiz J, Goni P, Castillo J, Rubio MC, Jimenez de Anta MT, et al. Characterization of the molecular mechanisms of quinolone resistance in *Yersinia enterocolitica* O:3 clinical isolates. *J Antimicrob Chemother.* 2004;53(6):1068-71.

[76] Fabrega A, Roca I, Vila J. Fluoroquinolone and multidrug resistance phenotypes associated with the overexpression of AcrAB and an orthologue of MarA in *Yersinia enterocolitica. Int J Med Microbiol.* 2010;300(7):457-63.

[77] Prats G, Mirelis B, Llovet T, Munoz C, Miro E, Navarro F. Antibiotic resistance trends in enteropathogenic bacteria isolated in 1985-1987 and 1995-1998 in Barcelona. *Antimicrob Agents Chemother.* 2000;44(5):1140-5.

[78] Baumgartner A, Kuffer M, Suter D, Jemmi T, Rohner P. Antimicrobial resistance of *Yersinia enterocolitica* strains from human patients, pigs and retail pork in Switzerland. *Int J Food Microbiol.* 2007 Apr 1;115(1):110-4.

[79] Bula CJ, Bille J, Glauser MP. An epidemic of food-borne listeriosis in western Switzerland: description of 57 cases involving adults. *Clin Infect Dis.* 1995;20(1):66-72.

[80] Allerberger F, Wagner M. Listeriosis: a resurgent foodborne infection. *Clin Microbiol Infect.* 2010;16(1):16-23.

[81] Rose WE, Poppens PT. Impact of biofilm on the in vitro activity of vancomycin alone and in combination with tigecycline and rifampicin against *Staphylococcus aureus. J Antimicrob Chemother.* 2009;63(3):485-8.

[82] Zhang Y, Yeh E, Hall G, Cripe J, Bhagwat AA, Meng J. Characterization of *Listeria monocytogenes* isolated from retail foods. *Int J Food Microbiol.* 2007 Jan 1;113(1):47-53.

[83] Bertrand S, Huys G, Yde M, D'Haene K, Tardy F, Vrints M, et al. Detection and characterization of tet(M) in tetracycline-resistant *Listeria* strains from human and food-processing origins in Belgium and France. *J Med Microbiol.* 2005;54(Pt 12):1151-6.

[84] Biavasco F, Giovanetti E, Miele A, Vignaroli C, Facinelli B, Varaldo PE. In vitro conjugative transfer of VanA vancomycin resistance between Enterococci and Listeriae of different species. *Eur J Clin Microbiol Infect Dis.* 1996;15(1):50-9.

[85] Levy SB. Active efflux mechanisms for antimicrobial resistance. *Antimicrob Agents Chemother.* 1992;36(4):695-703.

[86] Charpentier E, Gerbaud G, Jacquet C, Rocourt J, Courvalin P. Incidence of antibiotic resistance in *Listeria* species. *J Infect Dis.* 1995;172(1):277-81.

[87] Morvan A, Moubareck C, Leclercq A, Herve-Bazin M, Bremont S, Lecuit M, et al. Antimicrobial resistance *of Listeria monocytogenes* strains isolated from humans in France. *Antimicrob Agents Chemother.* 2010;54(6):2728-31.

[88] Roberts MC, Facinelli B, Giovanetti E, Varaldo PE. Transferable erythromycin resistance in *Listeria* spp. isolated from food. *Appl Environ Microbiol.* 1996;62(1):269-70.

[89] Godreuil S, Galimand M, Gerbaud G, Jacquet C, Courvalin P. Efflux pump Lde is associated with fluoroquinolone resistance in *Listeria monocytogenes*. *Antimicrob Agents Chemother.* 2003;47(2):704-8.

[90] Poyart-Salmeron C, Carlier C, Trieu-Cuot P, Courtieu AL, Courvalin P. Transferable plasmid-mediated antibiotic resistance in *Listeria monocytogenes*. *Lancet.* 1990 Jun 16;335(8703):1422-6.

[91] Charpentier E, Gerbaud G, Courvalin P. Conjugative mobilization of the rolling-circle plasmid pIP823 from *Listeria monocytogenes* BM4293 among gram-positive and gram-negative bacteria. *J Bacteriol.* 1999;181(11):3368-74.

[92] Charpentier E, Courvalin P. Emergence of the trimethoprim resistance gene dfrD in *Listeria monocytogenes* BM4293. *Antimicrob Agents Chemother.* 1997;41(5):1134-6.

[93] Abrahim A, Papa A, Soultos N, Ambrosiadis I, Antoniadis A. Antibiotic resistance of *Salmonella* spp. and *Listeria* spp. isolates from traditionally made fresh sausages in Greece. *J Food Prot.* 1998;61(10):1378-80.

[94] Klevens RM, Morrison MA, Nadle J, Petit S, Gershman K, Ray S, et al. Invasive methicillin-resistant *Staphylococcus aureus* infections in the United States. *JAMA.* 2007 Oct 17;298(15):1763-71.

[95] Catry B, Van Duijkeren E, Pomba MC, Greko C, Moreno MA, Pyorala S, et al. Reflection paper on MRSA in food-producing and companion animals: epidemiology and control options for human and animal health. *Epidemiol Infect.* 2010;138(5):626-44.

[96] Sakoulas G, Moellering RC, Jr. Increasing antibiotic resistance among methicillin-resistant *Staphylococcus aureus* strains. *Clin Infect Dis.* 2008 Jun 1;46 Suppl 5:S360-7.

[97] Moran GJ, Krishnadasan A, Gorwitz RJ, Fosheim GE, McDougal LK, Carey RB, et al. Methicillin-resistant *S. aureus* infections among patients in the emergency department. *N Engl J Med.* 2006 Aug 17;355(7):666-74.

[98] Monecke S, Kuhnert P, Hotzel H, Slickers P, Ehricht R. Microarray based study on virulence-associated genes and resistance determinants of *Staphylococcus aureus* isolates from cattle. *Vet Microbiol.* 2007 Nov 15;125(1-2):128-40.

[99] de Boer E, Zwartkruis-Nahuis JT, Wit B, Huijsdens XW, de Neeling AJ, Bosch T, et al. Prevalence of methicillin-resistant *Staphylococcus aureus* in meat. *Int J Food Microbiol.* 2009 Aug 31;134(1-2):52-6.

[100] Pu S, Han F, Ge B. Isolation and characterization of methicillin-resistant *Staphylococcus aureus* strains from Louisiana retail meats. *Appl Environ Microbiol.* 2009;75(1):265-7.

[101] Kock R, Harlizius J, Bressan N, Laerberg R, Wieler LH, Witte W, et al. Prevalence and molecular characteristics of methicillin-resistant *Staphylococcus aureus* (MRSA) among pigs on German farms and import of livestock-related MRSA into hospitals. *Eur J Clin Microbiol Infect Dis.* 2009;28(11):1375-82.

[102] Schijffelen MJ, Boel CH, van Strijp JA, Fluit AC. Whole genome analysis of a livestock-associated methicillin-resistant *Staphylococcus aureus* ST398 isolate from a case of human endocarditis. *BMC Genomics.* 2010;11:376.

[103] Weber SG, Gold HS, Hooper DC, Karchmer AW, Carmeli Y. Fluoroquinolones and the risk for methicillin-resistant *Staphylococcus aureus* in hospitalized patients. *Emerg Infect Dis.* 2003;9(11):1415-22.

[104] Kumar R, Yadav BR, Singh RS. Genetic determinants of antibiotic resistance in *Staphylococcus aureus* isolates from milk of mastitic crossbred cattle. *Curr Microbiol.* 2010;60(5):379-86.

[105] Siberry GK, Tekle T, Carroll K, Dick J. Failure of clindamycin treatment of methicillin-resistant *Staphylococcus aureus* expressing inducible clindamycin resistance in vitro. *Clin Infect Dis.* 2003 Nov 1;37(9):1257-60.

[106] Appelbaum PC. The emergence of vancomycin-intermediate and vancomycin-resistant *Staphylococcus aureus*. *Clin Microbiol Infect.* 2006;12 Suppl 1:16-23.

[107] Newell DG, Koopmans M, Verhoef L, Duizer E, Aidara-Kane A, Sprong H, et al. Food-borne diseases - the challenges of 20 years ago still persist while new ones continue to emerge. *Int J Food Microbiol.* 2010 May 30;139 Suppl 1:S3-15.

[108] Songer JG, Trinh HT, Killgore GE, Thompson AD, McDonald LC, Limbago BM. *Clostridium difficile* in retail meat products, USA, 2007. *Emerg Infect Dis.* 2009;15(5):819-21.

[109] Rodriguez-Palacios A, Staempfli HR, Duffield T, Weese JS. *Clostridium difficile* in retail ground meat, Canada. *Emerg Infect Dis.* 2007;13(3):485-7.

[110] Gould LH, Limbago B. *Clostridium difficile* in food and domestic animals: a new foodborne pathogen? *Clin Infect Dis.* 2010 Sep 1;51(5):577-82.

[111] Spigaglia P, Barbanti F, Mastrantonio P, Brazier JS, Barbut F, Delmee M, et al. Fluoroquinolone resistance in *Clostridium difficile* isolates from a prospective study of C. difficile infections in Europe. *J Med Microbiol.* 2008;57(Pt 6):784-9.

[112] Bourgault AM, Lamothe F, Loo VG, Poirier L. In vitro susceptibility of *Clostridium difficile* clinical isolates from a multi-institutional outbreak in Southern Quebec, Canada. *Antimicrob Agents Chemother.* 2006;50(10):3473-5.

[113] Huang H, Weintraub A, Fang H, Nord CE. Antimicrobial resistance in Clostridium difficile. *Int J Antimicrob Agents.* 2009;34(6):516-22.

[114] Cohen SH, Gerding DN, Johnson S, Kelly CP, Loo VG, McDonald LC, et al. Clinical practice guidelines for *Clostridium difficile* infection in adults: 2010 update by the society for healthcare epidemiology of America (SHEA) and the infectious diseases society of America (IDSA). *Infect Control Hosp Epidemiol.* 2010;31(5):431-55.

[115] O'Connor JR, Galang MA, Sambol SP, Hecht DW, Vedantam G, Gerding DN, et al. Rifampin and rifaximin resistance in clinical isolates of *Clostridium difficile*. *Antimicrob Agents Chemother.* 2008;52(8):2813-7.

[116] Baines SD, O'Connor R, Freeman J, Fawley WN, Harmanus C, Mastrantonio P, et al. Emergence of reduced susceptibility to metronidazole in *Clostridium difficile*. *J Antimicrob Chemother.* 2008;62(5):1046-52.

[117] Pelaez T, Cercenado E, Alcala L, Marin M, Martin-Lopez A, Martinez-Alarcon J, et al. Metronidazole resistance in *Clostridium difficile* is heterogeneous. *J Clin Microbiol.* 2008;46(9):3028-32.

[118] Mutlu E, Wroe AJ, Sanchez-Hurtado K, Brazier JS, Poxton IR. Molecular characterization and antimicrobial susceptibility patterns of *Clostridium difficile* strains isolated from hospitals in south-east Scotland. *J Med Microbiol.* 2007;56(Pt 7):921-9.

In: Molecular Typing Methods for TFM
Editors: S. Foley, R. Nayak, T. Johnson et al.

ISBN: 978-1-62100-643-5
© 2012 Nova Science Publishers, Inc.

Chapter 5

RAPID METHODS FOR PATHOGEN DETECTION

Chayapa Techathuvanan and Doris Helen D'Souza

Department of Food Science and Technology
The University of Tennessee
Knoxville, TN, US

ABSTRACT

Culture-based detection methods have long been used as tools for the detection of foodborne pathogens or other food contaminants. To minimize the release of contaminated food commodities to consumers, improved rapid detection assays with high specificity and sensitivity are essential. Rapid detection methods, such as molecular-based assays, immunoassays, and biosensors, have gained popularity and are being developed for use as routine monitoring and screening tools in the food industry. Each of these detection methods have their own strengths and limitations, thus many researchers try to utilize the advantages of one or more techniques to generate robust detection assays for foodborne pathogens. This chapter focuses predominantly on nucleic acid based detection methods, with some information on immunoassays and biosensors. The methods will be described along with a discussion of their advantages, disadvantages, and their current application status in foods.

INTRODUCTION

Culture-based detection of microbial pathogens or contaminants has been used in the food industry for almost a century as a standard microbial diagnostic tool. Although high in sensitivity, it requires several days for completion, and is therefore time-consuming, labor-intensive, and cumbersome. Culture-based detection also presents some difficulties, such as variability in interpretation of some biochemical or morphological tests, as well as the high cost associated with supplies, reagents, and labor [1]. To curb the release of food commodities contaminated with bacterial and/or viral pathogens in the market, improved rapid detection assays for these pathogens with high speed, specificity, and sensitivity are essential. Tremendous efforts have been devoted to develop novel detection technologies with these attributes that are also low in cost and labor requirements to enhance food safety.

In recent years, rapid detection assays, such as molecular-based assays, immunoassays, and biosensors, have gained popularity and are being developed for use as routine monitoring and screening tools in the food industry. As each of these detection methods have their own limitations, many researchers try to overcome their weaknesses by merging the advantages of one or more techniques to come up with a more robust detection assay. Moreover, automated systems have been implemented to improve the practical applications of detection assays for industrial use. Currently, most of the detection methods still require sample preparation and enrichment for the detection of the low number of microorganisms in foods, e.g. cell concentration or sample enrichment, and removal of or minimizing the interference associated with the presence of inhibitors of assay detection, resulting in the extension of assay time. Faced with these challenges, emphasis is placed on improvement of detection sensitivity using simple, economical, and user-friendly procedures along with appropriate sample concentration and sampling strategies. However, detection is dependent on the sample size and the sample being tested. Hence, adequate sample representation and concentration schemes are keys to improve the detection sensitivity of an assay to help facilitate sensitivity and speed of downstream detection.

This chapter will focus mainly on nucleic acid based detection with some information on immunoassays and biosensors, with discussion on their advantages, disadvantages, and their current application status in foods.

NUCLEIC ACID BASED DETECTION

Molecular assays which are based on the specific detection of nucleic acid of foodborne pathogens have gained popularity due to their speed and sensitivity of detection. These methods have been developed and optimized for improved robustness and reliability, as well as for routine detection in foods and the food processing environment, and are discussed below.

Polymerase Chain Reaction (PCR)

The polymerase chain reaction (PCR) was first invented in 1983 by Kary Mullis [2], and was described as a practical application for diagnosis of disease in 1985 by Saiki et al. [3]. PCR is the most widely used oligonucleotide-directed DNA amplification technique that targets and synthesizes specific DNA sequences of a pathogen, resulting in several fold increase in DNA copies [4], similar (or analogous) to a photocopy machine. It is one of the most popular and powerful detection tools studied and currently used in the food industry. The PCR reaction uses a thermostable DNA polymerase so it can withstand the high temperatures associated with thermal PCR cycling. In addition, deoxyribonucleoside triphosphates (dNTPs), selected and specific forward and reverse primers (oligonucleotides) that selectively amplify only the target gene/nucleic acid, buffer, and magnesium chloride are required for amplification of template DNA. Amplification relies on 3 temperature-dependent steps, denaturation of double stranded DNA (at around 90°C), annealing of primers to the target sequence (dependent on primers and target sequence, can be between 50 to 65°C), and extension of complementary DNA strand by the polymerase enzyme (at around 72°C), in a thermal cycler. These three steps are repeated about 30 to 40 times, depending on the length of the amplicon to achieve the desired copy number of target DNA suitable for detection. Amplified products (amplicons) can be detected by using agarose gel electrophoresis after staining with dyes such as ethidium bromide and observing under ultraviolet light. Specific target amplicons are identified by size (sequence length) based on their mobility in the gel in comparison to a standard DNA marker. In the food industry, however, the presence of an amplicon needs to be confirmed using DNA hybridization, restriction digestion, or DNA sequencing, as non-specific products may be formed due to primer binding and amplification from the food matrix components. Therefore, extreme care and caution are used in selecting specific primers that do not cross-react with non-specific targets, or the food matrix. Extensive BLAST searches and pairing are carried out before primers are designed and generated. Various programs from online primer design sites, such as CODEHOP, Gene Fisher, DoPrimer, Primer Selection, Web Primer, PCR Designer, Primo Pro, Primo Degenerate, PCR Primer Design, The Primer Generator, EPRIMER, PRIMO, PrimerQuest, and MethPrimer, and software for personal computer use, including PrimerSelect, DNASIS Max, NetPrimer, Array Designer, GenomePRIDE, OLIGO, Primer Designer, GPRIME, Sarani Gold, Primer Premier, PrimerDesign, and Beacon Designer, are available for primer design and selection [5].

To improve the robustness of nucleic acid amplification assays, including PCR, an internal amplification control (IAC) is recommended in every nucleic acid amplification reaction. In the amplification reaction without IAC, negative results obtained may represent either lack of adequate number of copies of the target sequence, absence of target sequence or false negatives due to the presence of inhibitors from the food matrix, machine malfunction, incorrect reaction mixture, degradation of reagents, or low enzyme activity [6]. False negative results may lead to severe consequences such as contaminated food products being released into the market. Therefore, an IAC is included in the reaction to ensure the presence of an IAC signal when the target is not present to eliminate the possibility of false negatives.

PCR has advantages in being able to detect the presence of viable but non-culturable (VBNC) cells from environmental stress conditions that cannot otherwise be recovered by conventional culture-based detection [7,8]. However, agarose gel electrophoresis based PCR detection has some drawbacks. As the detection involves DNA manipulation with open tubes, possible cross-contamination can occur from the environment or inevitably by the performing technician and lead to false positive results. Therefore, template DNA preparation, as well as amplification and detection rooms are kept separate from each other, to avoid cross-contamination of control and negative tubes. Traditional PCR as a detection method has been applied for the specific and sensitive detection of several foodborne bacteria in different matrices, such as *Salmonella* spp. [9-18], *Listeria monocytogenes* [9], *Escherichia coli.* [14], *Yersinia enterocolitica* [19], *Clostridium botulinum* [20], *Enterobacter sakazakii* [21], and *Campylobacter* spp. [22,23].

Real-time PCR

Bearing the constraints associated with traditional PCR, such as additional time to run the gel followed by amplicon confirmation, as well as possibility of cross-contamination, diagnostic technology has advanced towards using PCR in a real-time format or a quantitative PCR (qPCR). This allows the simultaneous monitoring and detection of amplification by using fluorescence and detection directly as amplification progresses and target amplicons are generated/formed. In these real-time reactions, either non-specific fluorescence dyes, or specific fluorescence probes are incorporated in the reaction to provide the fluorescence signal associated with target amplification. The earlier the fluorescence is detected along with increased signal indicates a larger amount of initial target DNA in the sample. This approach enables the quantification of targets using threshold cycle (C_T), which is the number of PCR cycles where fluorescence is generated greater than the background signal, to estimate the initial number of template copies [24]. Additional advantages of real-time PCR over traditional PCR assays are that the process does not involve the opening of reaction tubes after the initial set up, for agarose gel electrophoresis, therefore, avoiding cross-contamination, with shortened total assay time as further confirmation by DNA hybridization, sequencing, or restriction digestion is not needed.

Real-time PCR Based on Fluorescent Dyes

By incorporation of non-specific fluorescence dyes, such as SYBR Green I, an intercalating dye that non-specifically binds double stranded DNA, the increase in fluorescence is monitored as amplification increases in the PCR assay upon exposure to light of appropriate wavelength. However, product specificity is evaluated after PCR cycling. Melting temperature (T_m) analysis is commonly used for specificity confirmation purposes to distinguish fluorescence detected from primer-dimers or non-specific binding. T_m is a temperature at which 50% of double stranded DNA products are in single stranded form as the temperature is gradually raised to melt the amplicon. The melting profile is specific to each particular product which depends on the length and sequence of DNA, salt, and Mg^{2+} concentration. SYBR Green I-based real-time PCR is relatively inexpensive compared to fluorescent probes, and have been reported for the detection of foodborne pathogenic bacteria that show promise for routine diagnostics (refer to Table 1). Applications of these assays for *Salmonella* detection have been demonstrated in pure culture [25] and in poultry products and poultry environmental samples [26-29]. Fukushima et al. [30] reported the detection of *S. enterica*, *E. coli*, *Y. enterocolitica*, *C. jejuni*, *Vibrio cholera* O139, *V. parahaemolyticus* O3K6, *V. vulnificus*, *Providencia alcalifaciens*, *Aeromonas hydrophila*, *Bacillus cereus*, *Staphylococcus aureus*, and *C. perfringens* by real-time qPCR assay in pure isolates, inoculated food homogenates and natural food samples. As low as 10^1 to 10^3 CFU/g of these tested microorganisms could be detected using the described PCR assay in combination with gradient centrifugation for separation and concentration of cells. SYBR Green I based real-time PCR was also applied to *Bacillus cereus* detection in rice showing detection limits at 10^1 CFU/g when DNA was extracted using commercial kits [31].

Hydrolysis Probes and Real-Time PCR

Fluorescence hydrolysis probes are designed to bind internally to specific target amplified DNA sequences, as amplification proceeds, thereby eliminating the need for further downstream verification of specific amplified products. Typically, probes are labeled with a fluorophore at the 5'end and a quencher at the 3' end, which quenches the fluorescence due to close proximity with the fluorophore, when unbound to target. The increase in fluorescence depends on the hydrolysis of the probes as a result of 5' nuclease activity of *Taq* DNA polymerase enzyme upon the binding of probe to the specific target region during the PCR extension step and thus the generation of a fluorescence signal [32]. However, this method is more expensive when compared to fluorescence dyes, though the cost of labeled probes is now decreasing.

Hydrolysis probes that have been extensively researched include TaqMan® probes used in real-time PCR assays for foodborne pathogen detection [33,34] (Table 1). They have been applied in food matrices, such as for detection of *Salmonella* in meat chicken rinses, fish, and milk [35,36], *V. vulnificus* and *V. cholerae* in oysters [27-39], Shiga toxin producing *E. coli* in bread slices, ground beef, salad green and salad dressing, *L. monocytogenes* in water and milk [40], *C. botulinum* in modified-atmosphere-packaged fish [41] and *Yersinia* in fresh produce, milk, fish, sausages and meats [42,43], as well as pathogen detection in clinical specimens for outbreak tracking purposes [44,45].

Hybridization Probes and Real-Time PCR

Molecular beacons (MBs) are examples of hybridizing probes that have stem-loop structures with nucleic acid sequence specific to the target at the loop region, while the stem comprises of complementary sequences to each other [46]. Similar to TaqMan® probes, a fluorophore is attached to the 5' end and a quencher at the 3'end of the stem [47]. In the absence of target sequence, the MB is in a closed stem-loop form, where the fluorescence is quenched. The MB is able to fluoresce once hybridization occurs as the fluorophore and quencher are separated from each other due to the stronger bonds between the loop region and the target sequence, where the stem is pulled apart and the fluorophore emits fluorescence when excited with light of appropriate wavelength.

The detection sensitivity of real-time PCR assays using MBs are shown in Table 1. In food samples, as few as 2 ± 1 CFU of *S.* Typhimurium after 16-18 h enrichment was observed in 25 g of chicken samples [48]. Similarly, the detection at 4 CFU/25 g of fruit or vegetable samples was shown to be obtained after 16-h enrichment by MB-based real-time PCR [49]. *E. coli* O157:H7 was successfully detected in milk at 10^3 CFU/ml without enrichment; however, the detection limit was not determined by this method [50]. MB-based PCR assays have also been tested in environmental and clinical samples for the detection of *S.* Typhimurium and *S.* Enteritidis [51] and *Mycobacterium avium* subsp. *paratuberculosis* [52].

Table 1. List of Real-time PCR assays for the detection of foodborne pathogens

Microorganism (Target Gene)	IAC	Matrices	Primer/Probe Sequence (5'-3')	Enrichment Media/Time/Temp	Detection Limit	Ref.
SYBR Green I						
Bacillus cereus (*ces*)	Y	Pure culture; Rice	F: CACGCCGAAAGTGATTATACCAA R: CACGATAAAACCACTGAGATAGTG	None	0.06 pg DNA/reaction; 10^1 CFU/g	[31]
				Brain heart broth with 0.1% glucose/4h/37°C	N/A; 10^0 CFU/g	
Enterobacter sakazakii (16S–23S rDNA-ITS)	Y	Pure culture	F: TATAGGTTGTCTGCGAAAGCG R: GTCTTCGTGCTGCGAGTTTG	None	1.8×10^1 CFU/reaction	[204]
		Infant Formula		Modified lauryl sulfate tryptose broth/20 h/44°C and brain-heart infusion broth/5 h/37°C	1.1×10^0 CFU/ 100 g	
Escherichia coli (*tetR*)	N	Pure culture	F: ACAACCCGTAAAACTCGCC R: TTCCAATACGCAACCTAAAG	None	15 DNA copies/reaction	[205]
Escherichia coli O157:H7 (*16S*)	N	Frozen spinach, pasteurized apple juice, and bottled water	Universal bacterial 16S primers (IDT, Coralville, IA)	None	4 CFU/ml	[206]
Campylobacter jejuni (*mapA*)	Y	Feces	F: CTATTTTATTTTTGAGTGCTTGTG R: GCTTTATTTGCCATTTGTTTTATTA	None	3×10^3 CFU/g	[207]
Clostridium botulinum	Y	Pure culture	F: GGGCCTAGAGGTAGCGTARTG R: TCTTYATTTCCAGAAGCATATTT	None	6×10^1 DNA copies/reaction	[208]
Listeria monocytogenes (*hyl*)	N	Biofilms on clean stainless steel Coupons	F: GGGAAATCTGTCTCAGGTGATGT R: CGATGATTTGAACTTCATCTTTTGC	None	6×10^2 CFU/cm^2	[209]

Microorganism (Target Gene)	IAC	Matrices	Primer/Probe Sequence (5'-3')	Enrichment Media/Time/Temp	Detection Limit	Ref.
Salmonella spp. (invA)	N	Pure culture; UHT sterilized whole milk	F: TCGTCATTCCATTACCTACC R: AAACGTTGAAAAACTGAGGA	None	>10^2 CFU/ml; >10^3 CFU/ml	[210]
		Dairy farm lagoon water, and feed/silage samples;		None	10^4 CFU/ml; 10^3 CFU/ml	
				Universal preenrichment Broth/18 h/37°C	10^0 CFU/ml; 10^0 CFU/ml	
Salmonella enterica (invA)	N	Poultry house bioaerosol	F: GTGAAATTATCGCCACGTTCGGGCAA R: TCATCGCACCGTCAAAGGAACC	None	N/A	[211]
Salmonella Enteritidis (sefA)	N	Chicken and turkey	F: GCAGCGGTTACTATTGCAGC R: CTGTGACAGGGACATTTAGCG	Buffered peptone water/24 h/37°C	N/A	[26]
Salmonella Enteritidis (invA)	N	Chicken Iliocecal	F: GTGAAATTATCGCCACGTTCGGGCAA R: TCATCGCACCGTCAAAGGAACC	Tetrathionate broth/18 h/37°C	6 CFU/ml	[27]
Salmonella Enteritidis (invA)	N	Turkey cloacal swab, intestine, gizzard swab, and cecal swab samples	F: GTGAAATTATCGCCACGTTCGGGCAA R: TCATCGCACCGTCAAAGGAACC	Buffered peptone water/18 h/37°C and semisolid modified Rappaport-Vassiliadis Agar/24 h/41.5°C	N/A	[28]
Salmonella Typhimurium, Enteritidis, and Hadar (invA)	N	Chicken skin rinse	F: GTGAAATTATCGCCACGTTCGGGCAA R: TCATCGCACCGTCAAAGGAACC	None	2.2×10^2 CFU/100 ml	[212]
		Spent irrigation water		None	7.5×10^2 CFU/100 ml	
Salmonella Typhimurium (16S rRNA)	N	Pure culture; Tap water; Fishpond water	F: CGGGGAGGAAGGTGTTGTG R: GAGCCCGGGGATTTCACATC	None	100 gene copies/reaction; N/A; N/A	[25]

Table 1. (Continued)

Microorganism (Target Gene)	IAC	Matrices	Primer/Probe Sequence (5'-3')	Enrichment Media/Time/Temp	Detection Limit	Ref.
Salmonella Typhimurium (*invA*)	N	Pure culture; Tap water; Fishpond water	F: GATTCTGGTACTAATGGTGATGATC R: GCCAGGCTATCGCCAATAAC	None; None	2 gene copies/reaction; N/A; N/A	[25]
Serratia marcescens (*gyrB*)	N	Pure culture; Leachate and synthetic building debris	F: AGTGCACGAACAAACTTACAG R: GTCGTACTCGAAATCGGTCACA	None	7.5 fg DNA/reaction; 10^2 CFU/ml or g	[213]
Serratia marcescens (*recA*)	N	Pure culture; Leachate and synthetic building debris	F: CAAGGCGAATGCCTGTAACT R: GAGGATAGGCGCCACATAAA	None	7.5 fg DNA/reaction; 10^2 CFU/ml or g	[213]
Serratia marcescens (*wzm*)	N	Pure culture; Sterile water, leachate, and synthetic building debris	F: GGTCATGCGGGTTCAAATAC R: ATGACCGAGCGTGGAAATAC	None	75 fg DNA/reaction; 10^2 CFU/ml or g	[213]
Staphylococcus aureus (*nuc*)	N	Pure culture	F: GCGATTGATGGTGATACGGTT R: AGCCAAGCCTTGACGAACTAAAGC	None	60 gene copies/μl	[214]
Vibrio vulnificus (*vvh*)	N	Pure culture; Gulf water	F: TTCCAACTTCAAACCGAACTATGA R: ATTCCAGTCGATGCGAATA CGTTG	None; Gulf water with 0.2% Bacto-Peptone /5 h/37°C	1 pg DNA/reaction; 10^2 CFU/ml; 1 CFU/ml	[39]
		Oysters		Gulf water with 0.2% Bacto-Peptone /5 h/37°C	1 CFU/g	

Microorganism (Target Gene)	IAC	Matrices	Primer/Probe Sequence (5'-3')	Enrichment Media/Time/Temp	Detection Limit	Ref.
Yersinia enterocolitica (*16S rRNA*)	N	Pork meat juice	F: GGAATTTAGCAGAGATGCTTTA R: GGACTACGACAGACTTTATCT	N/A	4.2×10^3 CFU/ml	[215]
TaqMan Probe						
Bacillus cereus (*ces*)	Y	Pure culture	F: CGCCGAAAGTGATTATACCAA R: TATGCCCCGTTCTCAAACTG P: FAM-GGGAAAATAACGAGAAATGCA-TAMRA	None	0.6 pg DNA/reaction	[31]
Campylobacter spp. (*16S rRNA*)	Y	Chicken fecal samples	F: CACGTGCTACAATGGCATAT R: GGCTTCATGCTCTCGAGTT P: FAM-CAGAGAACAATCCGAACTGGGACA-BHQ1	Buffered peptone water/5 min/RT	100-150 CFU/ml	[216]
Campylobacter jejuni (*NCTC 11168*)	N	Chicken fecal samples	F: CTGAATTTGATACCTTAAGTGCAG R: CTGAATTTGATACCTTAAGTGCAGC P: FAM-TCTCCTTGCTCATCTTTAGGATAAATTCTTTC ACA-TAMRA	None	2 CFU/reaction	[217]
		Cecal samples		None	25 CFU/reaction	
Campylobacter jejuni (*ORF-C*)	N	Pure culture	F: TTGGTATGGCTATAGGAAACTCTTATAGCT R: CACACCTGAAGTATGAAGTGGTCTAAGT P: FAM-TGGCATATCCTAATTTAAAATTATTTACCAGGA C-TAMRA	None	12 genome equivalents/reaction	[218]
		Milk; Natural milk, natural shellfish, natural raw chicken, natural offal, natural shellfish and natural raw meat		Bolton broth/24 h/37°C, then 24 h/42°C	N/A	
Campylobacter jejuni (*NCTC 11168*)	N	Pure culture	F: CTGAATTTGATACCTTAAGTGCAG R: CTGAATTTGATACCTTAAGTGCAGC P: FAM-TCTCCTTGCTCATCTTTAGGATAAATTCTTTC ACA-TAMRA	None	1 CFU/reaction	[219]

Table 1. (Continued)

Microorganism (Target Gene)	IAC	Matrices	Primer/Probe Sequence (5'-3')	Enrichment Media/Time/Temp	Detection Limit	Ref.
Campylobacter jejuni (*yphC*)	N	Pure culture	F: CATTCTCAAATAGCACTTTTGGTTTT R: GCCCAGCAATGCGTTCA P: FAM-TGCGCATGAGGGCTTTAACGAGC-TAMRA	None	96% (73/76)	[220]
(*gyrA*)			F: AAGATACGGTCGATTTTGTTCA R: CTACAGCTATACCACTTGAACCATTTAATA P: FAM-TGATGGTTCAGAAAGCGAACCTGATGTTTT-TAMRA		96% (73/76)	
Clostridium botulinum (*BoNT/E*)	N	Modified-atmosphere-packaged fish	F: GTGAATCAGCACCTGGACTTTCAG R: GCTGCTTGCACAGGTTTATTGA P: FAM-ATGCACAGAAAGTGCCCGAAGGTGA-TAMRA-p	None	N/A	[41]
Escherichia coli O157:H7 (*eaeA*)	N	Pure culture	F: CCATAATCATTTTATTTAGAGGGA R: GAGAAATAAATTATATTAATAGATCGGA P1: FAM-TTGCTGCAGGATGGGCAACTCTTGA-TAMRA-p P2: FAM-ATGGGCAACTCTTGAGCTTCTGTAA-TAMRA-p P3: FAM-ATTGTCGCTTGAACTGATTTCCTC-TAMRA-p P4: FAM-TAATGTTTATTGTCGCTTGAACTGAT-TAMRA-p	None	≥10^3 CFU/ml (without immunomagnetic separation) ≥10^2 CFU/ml (with immunomagnetic separation)	[34]
		Pure culture		None		
		Ground beef		Modified tryptic soy broth /6 h/37°C	≥10^4 CFU/ml	

Microorganism (Target Gene)	IAC	Matrices	Primer/Probe Sequence (5'-3')	Enrichment Media/Time/Temp	Detection Limit	Ref.
Escherichia coli (stx1)	N	Bread slices; Ground beef; Salad greens; Salad dressing	F: TGTCACATATAAATTATTTCGTTCAACAA R: GCAGTTGATGTCAGAGGGATAGATC P: 6-FAM-AAGCCGTAGATTATTAAACCGCCCTTCCTCT-BHQ1	No enrichment media/16 h/35°C	5,340 CFU/g	[221]
(stx2)			F: CAACGTGTCGCAGCGCT R: AACGCCAGATATGATGAAACCA P: 6-FAM-TCCGGAATGCAAATCAGTCGTCACTCA-BHQ1		5,340 CFU/g	
Escherichia coli (stx1)	N	Pure culture	F: TCTCGACTGCAAAGACGTATGTAGA R: TCCTGATGAAATAGTCTGTAATGGAGTAC P: FAM-TCGCTGAAATGTCATTCGCTCTGCAATA-TAMRA	None	100% (38/38)	[220]
(stx2)			F: ACCCCACCGGCAGTT R: GGTCAAAACGCGCCTGATA P: FAM-TTTTGCTGTGGATATACGAGGGCTTGATGT-TAMRA		89% (40/45)	
(eaeA)			F: TGTTGCTTTGTTTAATTCT(T/C)GATAAGC R: GGAATCGGAGTATAGTTTACACCAA P: FAM-AGTGGAATCCTGGTGCGGC-TAMRA		100% (49/49)	
Listeria monocytogenes (hly)	N	Pure culture	F: CATGGCACCACCAGCATCT R: ATCCGCGTGTTTCTTTTCGA P: FAM-CGCCTGCAAGTCCTAAGACGCCA-TAMRA	None	8 DNA template/reaction	[117]
		Cooked ham			100 CFU/g	
		Raw pork, frankfurter, fermented sausages			10^3 CFU/g	

Table 1. (Continued)

Microorganism (Target Gene)	IAC	Matrices	Primer/Probe Sequence (5'-3')	Enrichment Media/Time/Temp	Detection Limit	Ref.
Listeria monocytogenes (*hlyA*)	N	Pure culture Water Skim milk Whole milk	F: TGCAAGTCCTAAGACGCCA R: CACTGCATCTCCGTGGTATACTAA P: FAM-CGATTTCATCCGCGTGTTTCTTTTCG-TAMRA	None	5-500 CFU/reaction 6-2,000 CFU/reaction 6-6,000 CFU/reaction 6-60 CFU/reaction	[40]
Salmonella enterica (*invA1*) (*invA2*)	N	Pure culture	F: TTCCATTACCTACCTATCTGGTTGATT R: GAACGACCCCATAAACACCAA P: FAM-CCTGATCGCACTGAATATCGTACTGGCG-TAMRA F: AGCGGCGCCAAACCTAA R: AACGACGACCCTTCTTTTCC P: FAM-AGCAAAGGCGAGCAGCCGCTTAGT-TAMRA	None	100% (127/127) 100% (127/127)	[220]
Salmonella (*ttrRSBCA*)	Y	Pure culture; Minced pork	F: CTCACCAGGAGATTACAACATGG R: AGCTCAGACCAAAAGTGACCATC P: 6-FAM-CG+ACGGCG+AG+ACCG-BHQ1	Buffered peptone water/8 h/37°C	N/A; 97%	[35]
Salmonella enterica (*invA*)	N	Pure culture Ground beef, ground pork and raw milk	F: GTGAAATTATCGCCACGTTCGGGCAA R: TCATCGCACCGTCAAAGGAACC	None Buffered peptone water/16 to 18 h/37°C	2 CFU/reaction 2-3 CFU/25 g or ml	[222]
Salmonella enterica and *Salmonella bongori* (*ttrBCA*)	Y	Pure culture Chicken carcass rinses and minced meat	F: CTCACCAGGAGATTACAACATGG R: AGCTCAGACCAAAAGTGACCATC P: FAM-CACCGACGGCGAGACCGACTTT-Dark Quencher	None Buffered peptone water/10 to 20 h/37°C	70% of 10^3 CFU/ml 100% of 10^4 CFU/ml N/A	[36]

Microorganism (Target Gene)	IAC	Matrices	Primer/Probe Sequence (5'-3')	Enrichment Media/Time/Temp	Detection Limit	Ref.
Salmonella Enteritidis (*invA*)	N	Pure culture	N/A	Buffered peptone water/8.4 h/37°C Buffered peptone water/11.6 h/37°C	1 CFU/ml (r*Tth* PCR mixture) 1 CFU/ml (Ampli*Taq* Gold PCR mixture)	[33]
Salmonella Panama (*invA*)	N	Sausage, corn, potato salad, barbecue chicken. cole slaw, pasta salad, brisket, brownie and corn muffin	F: GCGTTCTGAACCTTTGGTAATAA R: CGTTCGGGCAATTCGTTA P: FAM-TGGCGGTGGGTTTTGTTGTCTTCT-TAMRA	None	N/A	[223]
Vibrio cholera (*hlyA*)	N	Pure culture; Oysters; Seawater	F: TGCGTTAAACACGAAGCGAT R: AAGTCTTACATTGTGCTTGGGTCA P: TCAACCGATGCGATTGCCCAAGA	None	>7.0 CFU/ml of reaction mixture; 6-8 CFU g/ml; 10 CFU/ml	[38]
Vibrio parahaemolyticus (*toxR*) (*tdh*)	N	Pure culture	F: CCTTCTATTGAGCAGTGCATTGA R: GTGGCAATCACTTCCACTGGTA P: FAM-CGCTACGTTAAGCACCATGCAGAAGACTC-TAMRA F: CATCTGCTTTTGAGCTTCCATCT R: CTCGAACAACAAACAATATCTCATCA P: FAM-TCCCTTTTCCTGCCCCGGTT-TAMRA	None	100% (41/41) 100% (23/23)	[220]
Vibrio vulnificus (*vvhA*)	N	Pure culture and oysters; Natural oysters	F: TGTTTATGGTGAGAACGGTGACA R: TTCTTTATCTAGGCCCCAAACTTG P: CCGTTAACCGAACCACCCGCAA	None; Artificial seawater/12 to 24 h/30°C	10^2 CFU/ml; N/A	[37]

Table 1. (Continued)

Microorganism (Target Gene)	IAC	Matrices	Primer/Probe Sequence (5'-3')	Enrichment Media/Time/Temp	Detection Limit	Ref.
Vibrio vulnificus (vvhA)	N	Pure culture Oysters	F-vvh785: TTCCAACTTCAAACCGAACTATGAC R-vvh990: ATTCCAGTCGATGCGAATACGTTG P-vvh874: ROX-AACTATCGTGCACGCTTTGGTACCGT-BHQ-2 F-vvh731: CTCACTGGGGCAGTGGCT R-vvh1113: CCAGCCGTTAACCGAACCA F-vvh1059: TGTTTATGGTGAGAACGGTGACA R-vvh1159: TTCTTTATCTAGGCCCCAAACTTG P-vvh1109: FAM-CCGTTAACCGAACCACCCGCAA-BHQ-1	None Gulf water with 0.2% Becto peptone/5 h/37°C	10^3 CFU/ml 1 CFU/g	39
Yersinia enterocolitica (ail)	Y	Pure culture Milk, minced beef, cold-smoked sausage, fish, and Carrots	F: CCCAGTAATCCATAAAGGCTAAC ATAT R: ATGATAACTGGGGAGTAATAGGTTCG P: FAM-TGACCAAACTTATTACTGC CATA-MGB	None Trypticase soy broth with 0.6% yeast extract/18 to 20 h/25°C	10 CFU/reaction (85 fg DNA/reaction) 0.5 to 55 CFU/10 g	[42]
Yersinia pseudotuberculosis (ail)	Y	Pure culture Carrots; Minced beef meat	F: CGTCTGTTAATGTGTATGCGAAG R: GAACCTATCACTCCCCAGTCATTATT P: VIC-CGTGTCAAGGACGATGGGTACAAGTTGG-TAMRA	None Trypticase soy broth with 0.6% yeast extract/18 to 20 h/25°C	0.9 CFU/ml 28 CFU/10 g; 280 CFU/10g	[43]
Molecular Beacon						
Enterotoxigenic Escherichia coli (LT1)	N	Water samples	F: GGCAGGCAAAAGAGAAATGG R: TTGGTCTCGGTCAGATATGTG MB: CACGCCCGGGACTTCGACCTGAAATGTTGGC GTG	Luria-Bertani broth/12 h/37±1°C	2-4 CFU/ml	[224]
Escherichia coli (uidA)	N	Pure culture; Water and fresh produce	F: AGCCAAAAG CCAGACACAGAGT R: CATGACGACCAAAGCCAGTA MB: FAM-GCATCCGGTCAGTGGCAGT-	None; Luria-Bertani broth/18 h/37°C	8×10^3 CFU/ml; 1 CFU/ml	[225]

Microorganism (Target Gene)	IAC	Matrices	DABCYL Primer/Probe Sequence (5'-3')	Enrichment Media/Time/Temp	Detection Limit	Ref.
Escherichia coli O157:H7 (*slt-II*)	N	Skim milk	F: TTAAATGGTACTGCCT R: CAGAGTGGTATAACTGCTGTC MB: N/A	None	10^3 CFU/ml	[50]
Escherichia coli O157:H7 (*rfbE*)	N	Pure culture; Raw milk and apple juice	F1: AAGATTGCGCTGAAGCCTTTG R1: CATTGGCATCGTGTGGACAG F2: AAATATAAAGGTAAATATGTGGAACATTTG G R2: TGGCCTTTAAAATGTAAACAACGGTCAT MB: FAM-CGCTATGGTGAAGGTGGAATGGTTGTCACGA ATAGCG-39-DABCYL	None; Modified *E. coli* broth + novobiocin/6 h/37°C	10^2 CFU/ml; 1 CFU/ml	[226]
Listeria monocytogenes (*hlyA*)	Y	Pure culture; Leaf lettuce and alfalfa sprout	N/A	None; Demi-Fraser broth/24 ± 2 h/30°C	10^2-10^3 CFU/reaction; 4-7 CFU/25 g	[49]
Mycobacterium avium subsp. *paratuberculosis* (*IS900*)	N	Bovine fecal samples	F1: GATCGGAACGTCGGCTGGTCAGG R1: GATCGCCTTGCTCATCGCTGCCG F2: GCAGCTCGACTGCGATGTCATCG R2: GGCAGCGGCTGCTTTATATTCCC MB: TET-CGGA CCGTAACTACCCGCGGCGTGATGGGTCCG-DABCYL	None	1-8 CFU/reaction	[52]
Salmonella (*himA*)	N	Pure culture	F: CGTGCTCTGGAAAACGGTGAG R: CGTGCTGTAATAGGAATATCTTCA MB: FAM-CGCTATCCGGGGGGTAACCCGTAGCG-DABCYL	None	2 CFU/reaction	[46]

Table 1. (Continued)

Microorganism (Target Gene)	IAC	Matrices	Primer/Probe Sequence (5'-3')	Enrichment Media/Time/Temp	Detection Limit	Ref.
Salmonella sp. (*iagA*)	Y	Pure culture; Alfalfa sprouts, cilantro, cantaloupes, and prepacked mixed-salad	N/A	None; Buffered peptone water/16 h/37°C	1-4 CFU/reaction; 4 CFU/25 g	[49]
Salmonella Typhimurium (*iagA*)	Y	Pure culture; Minced chicken	N/A	None; Buffered peptone water/18 h/37°C	1 CFU/reaction; 2 ± 1 CFU/25 g	[48]

F = forward; R = reverse; P = probe; RT = room temperature; ITS = internal transcribed spacer; MB = molecular beacon; TET = tetrachloro-6-carboxyfluorescein-5'; DABCYL = 4-dimethylaminophenylazobenzoic acid-3'; FAM = 6-carboxyfluorescein; TAMRA = tetramethylrhodamine; p = phosphate cap; N/A = not applicable.

Table 2. Reverse-transcriptase PCR (RT-PCR) assays for the detection of foodborne pathogens

Microorganism (Target Gene)	IAC	Matrices	Primer and Probe/Sequence (5'-3')/ Fluorescence Dye	Enrichment Media/Time/Temp	Detection Limit	Reference
Traditional RT-PCR Assay						
Escherichia coli O157:H7 (*slt-II*)	N	Pure culture; Ground beef	TXAF: TTAAATGGGTACTGTCCT TXAR: CAGAGTGGTATAACTGCTGTC	None; Tryptic Soy broth/12h/37°C	1 CFU/g; 1 CFU/g	[58]
			TXBF: TGTTTATGGCGGTTTTATTTG TXBR: ATTATTAAACTGCACTTCAG			
			MK5: TGTAAGCTTAGCCGGACAGAG MK6: CCACGGATCCGGTTATGCCTC			
(*slt-I/II*)			MK1: GGATCCTTTACGATAGACCTTCTCGAC MK2: GGATCCCACATATAAATTATTTCGCTC			
(*tufA*)			TufAF: ACTTCCCGGGCGACGACACTC TufAR: CGCCCGGCATTACCATCTCTAC			
Escherichia coli O157:H7 (*eaeA*)	N	Pure culture	SK1: CCCGAATTCGGCACAAGCATAAGC SK2: CCCGGATCCGTCTCGCCAGTATTCG	None	N/A	[227]
(*rfbE*)			O157AF: AAGATTGGCGTGAAGCCTTTG O157AR: CATTGGCATCGTGTGGACAG		10⁶ CFU	
(*fliC*)			FLIC-F: CCGAATTCATGGCACAAGTCATTAATAC FLIC-R: CCGAATTCTTAACCCTGCAGTAGAGACA		10⁷ CFU	
(*stx1*)			SLTI-F: ACACTGGATGATCTCAGTGG SLTI-R: CTGAATCCCCCTCCATTATG		10⁷ CFU	

Table 2. (Continued)

Microorganism (Target Gene)	IAC	Matrices	Primer and Probe/Sequence (5'-3')/ Fluorescence Dye	Enrichment Media/Time/Temp	Detection Limit	Reference
(stx2)			SLTII-F: CCATGACAACGGACAGCAGTT SLTII-R: CCTGTCAACTGAGCACTTTG		N/A	
(hlyCA)			n-hlyCA: CTTTTGACGTCATGGGGAAGG c-hlyCA: CGAATATTGCAACACCACGTTCAG		N/A	
(16S rRNA)			F: GCGGCCCCTGGACGAA R: GACCGGCTGGCAACAAAGGATAAG		5×10^5 CFU	
Enterococcus faecalis (pbp5)	N	Pure culture	PBP5: CATGCGCAATTAATCGG IS: CATAGCCTGTCGCAAAAC	None	N/A	[228]
Campylobacter spp., Campylobacter jejuni, Campylobacter coli, Campylobacter lari (flaA) (tkt) (cmp)	N	Pure culture and chicken samples	FlaAR651F: CTATGGATGAGCAATTWAAAAT FlaAR652R: CAAGWCCTGTTCCWACTGAAG tktR653F: GCAAACTCAGGACACCCAGG tktR654R: AAAGCATTGTTAATGGCTGC	None	N/A	[229]

Microorganism (Target Gene)	IAC	Matrices	Primer and Probe/Sequence (5'-3')/ Fluorescence Dye	Enrichment Media/Time/Temp	Detection Limit	Reference
256-bp amplicon (putative haem-copper oxidase)			PorAR655F: ATGAAACTAGTTAAACTTAGTTTA PorAR65R: GAATTTGTAAAGAGCTTGAAG BOR657F: AGAACACGCGGACCTATATA BOR658R: CGATGCATCCAGGTAATGTAT			
Clostridium botulinum toxin production (VH toxin gene)	Y	Pure culture	S1F: AGCAAATAGAAAATGAAC S1R: GGAATACTATTATTTA GGGTA	None	N/A	[230]
Listeria monocytogenes (*iap*)	N	Organic waste samples	ELMIAPF: CAAACTGCTAACACAGCTACT ELMIAPR: GCACTTGAATTGCTGTTATTG	None UVM-1 medium/24 h/30°C	10^7 CFU/g <10 CFU/g	[10]
Staphylococcus aureus (*nuc*)	N	Organic waste samples	nuc1: GCGATTGATGGTGATACGGTT nuc2: AGCCAAGCCTTGACGAACTAAAGC	None Ossmer broth/24 h/30°C	10^6 CFU/g <10 CFU/g	[10]
Salmonella spp. (*ompC*)	N	Organic waste samples	S18: ACCGCTAACGCTCGCCTGTAT S19: AGAGGTGGACGGGTTGCTGCCGTT	None Peptone water/20 h/37°C	10^7 CFU/g <10 CFU/g	[10]
Vibrio parahaemolyticus (16S–23S rDNA (Intergenic spacer)) (*rpoS*) (*tdh1, tdh2*)	N	Pure culture and artificial seawater	Vpara-F: GCTGACAAAAACAACAATTTATTGTT Vpara-R: GGAGTTTCGAGTTGATGAAC VrposF: GACAAATGCGTCAGAGACG VrposR1: TCACCACGCAATGCTCTG	None	N/A	[231]

Table 2. (Continued)

Microorganism (Target Gene)	IAC	Matrices	Primer and Probe/Sequence (5'-3')/ Fluorescence Dye	Enrichment Media/Time/Temp	Detection Limit	Reference
(tdh1)			L-tdh: GTAAAGGTGTCTGACTTTTTGAC R-tdh: TGGAATAGAACCTTCATCTTCACC			
(pR72H fragment)			VP21: TGGTTGACATCCTACACATGACTGTG VP22: GGGGATCCCTCAGTACAAAGCCTT VP33: TGCGAATTCGATAGGGTGTTAACC VP32: CGAATCCTTGAACATACGCAGC			
Yersinia enterocolitica (16S rDNA)	N	Organic waste samples	Y.16S-86f: GCGGCAGCGGGAAGTAGTTTA Y.e.eur. 16S-455r: CAATCACAAAGGTTATTAACCTTTATG	None Giolitti-Cantoni broth/24 h/37°C	10^7 CFU/g <10 CFU/g	[10]
Hepatitis A virus	N	Pure culture	BG 7: CCGAAACTGGTTTCAGCTGAGG BG 8: CCTCTGGGTCTCCTTGTACAGC MK 101a: CCGTTTGCCTAGGCTATAGGCTA MK 102a: CAGCTCCATGCTAATCATGGAGT	None	2 PFU/reaction 2 PFU/reaction	[59]
Hepatitis A virus	N	Spring water	Prot-1: CTGGAGAGGTGTGACTGCTG Prot-2: TCCCATGTGGGAAATTCACT Prot-DIG: GTGTGTGGACTCTTGAAATGGA	None	10^{-1} TCID$_{50\%}$/ml	[61]
Hepatitis A virus	N	Shellfish	(+) 2949: TATTTGTCTGTCACAGAACAATCAG (-) 3192: AGGAGGTGGAAGCACTTCATTTGA	None	1,500 RT-PCR$_{50}$ U (27 PFU)	[62]

Microorganism (Target Gene)	IAC	Matrices	Primer and Probe/Sequence (5'-3')/ Fluorescence Dye	Enrichment Media/Time/Temp	Detection Limit	Reference
Hepatitis A virus	N	Pure culture; Green onions	SH-Prot-1: ARTTGGCAGCAATTCTTCAAG SH-Prot-A: ATGGATGCTGGRGTTCTTAC SH-Poly-1: GGCATAGCTGCAGGAAAATT SH-Poly-A: GARTTTACTCAGTGTTCAATGAATGT HAV-F: GTTTTGCTCCTCTTTATCATGCTATG HAV-R: GGAAATGTCTCAGGTACTTTCTTTG	None	10^0 TCID$_{50\%}$; 10^0-10^2 TCID$_{50\%}$ 10^0 TCID$_{50\%}$; 10^2-10^3 TCID$_{50\%}$ 10^2 TCID$_{50\%}$; $\geq 10^3$ TCID$_{50\%}$	[60]
Norovirus GI	N	Shellfish	M5: CACCACCATAAACAGGCTG M3: AGCCTGATAGAGCATTCTTT	None	22.4 RT-PCR$_{50}$U	[62]
Norovirus GII	N	Pure culture; Green onions	SR33: TGTCACGATCTCATCATCACC SR46: TGGAATTCCATCGCCACTGG COG2F: CARGARBCNATGTTYAGRTGGATGAG COG2R: TCGACGCCATCTTCATTCACA Mon431: TGGACIAGRGGICCYAAYCA Mon432: TGGACICGYGGICCYAAYCA Mon433: GAAYCTCATCCAYCTGAACAT Mon434: GAASCGCATCCARCGGAACAT	None	10 RT-PCRU; 100 RT-PCRU 1 RT-PCRU; 1-100 RT-PCRU 1 RT-PCRU; 10^2-10^4 RT-PCRU	[60]
Rotavirus	N	Spring water	Rota-1: GTAAGAAATTAGGTCCAAGAG End 9: GGTCACATCATACAATTCTAATCTAAG Rota-Probe: CAAACTGAGAGAATGATGAGAGTGAATTGG	None	10^{-3} TCID$_{50\%}$/ml	[61]

Table 2. (Continued)

Microorganism (Target Gene)	IAC	Matrices	Primer and Probe/Sequence (5'-3')/ Fluorescence Dye	Enrichment Media/Time/Temp	Detection Limit	Reference
Real-time RT-PCR Assay						
Enterococcus faecalis (16S rRNA)	N	Pure culture	Ec-ssu1'F: GGATAACACTTGGAAACAGG Ec-ssu1R: TCCTTGTTCTTCTCTAACAA SYBR Green I	None	10^{-3} CFU/reaction	[71]
Escherichia coli O157:H7 (*rfbC and fliC*)	N	Pure culture	N/A	None (Filter concentration)	1 CFU/reaction	[7]
		Tap water			3-4 CFU/L	
		River water			7 CFU/L	
VNBC *Escherichia coli* O157:H7 (*rfbC and fliC*)	N	River water	N/A	None (Filter concentration)	50 CFU/L	[7]
Escherichia coli (23S rRNA)	N	Pure culture; Feces	En-lsu3F: TGCCGTAACTTCGGGAGAAGGCA En-lsu3'R: TCAAGGCTCAATGTTCAGTGTC SYBR Green I	None	10^{-1} CFU/reaction; 10^3 CFU/g	[71]
Clostridium perfringens (16S rRNA)	N	Pure culture	PSD7F: CAAAACTACTGAGCTAGAGTACG PSD7R: TAAGATCTCAAGGATCCCAACGGCT SYBR Green I	None	10^{-3} CFU/reaction	[71]
Pseudomonas aeruginosa (16S rRNA)	N	Pure culture; Feces	CIPER-F: AGATGGCATCATCATTCAAC CIPER-R: GCAAGGGATGTCAAGTGT SYBR Green I	None	10^{-3} CFU/reaction; 10^3 CFU/g	[71]
		Human peripheral blood		Brain heart infusion broth/24 h/37°C	2 CFU/ml	

Microorganism (Target Gene)	IAC	Matrices	Primer and Probe/Sequence (5'-3')/ Fluorescence Dye	Enrichment Media/Time/Temp	Detection Limit	Reference
Salmonella enterica (invA)	Y	Spinach, tomatoes, jalapeno, and serrano peppers	invA_176F: CAACGTTTCCTGCGGTACTGT invA_291R: CCCGAACGTGGCGATAATT invA_Tx_208: TX-CTCTTTCGTCTGGCATTATCG ATCAGTACCA-BHQ2	Lactose broth/24 ± 2 h/35 ±2°C	2 CFU/25 g	[66]
Salmonella sp. (invA)	N	Soil and chicken manure	F: ACAGTGCTCGTTTACGACC R: ACTGGTACTGATCGATAAT P: BIOTIN-CTGAGGATTCTGTCAATGTAGAAACGACCCC ATAAACACCAATATCGCCAGTACGATATTC AGTGCGAT	None	5×10^4 cells/g	[232]
Salmonella enterica (invA)	Y	Pure culture	F: CACGCTCTTTCGTCTGGCA R: TACGGTTCCTTTGACGGTGCGA SYBR Green I	None	10^2 CFU/ml	[65,233]
Salmonella enterica (invA)	Y	Inoculated pork chop, pork sausage, and pork carcass rinse; Natural pork carcass rinses, pork carcass swabs, and pork processing surface swabs	F: CACGCTCTTTCGTCTGGCA R: TACGGTTCCTTTGACGGTGCGA SYBR Green I	None; Tetrathionate broth/10 h/37°C; Buffered peptone water/4 h/37°C and tetrathionate broth/12 h/37°C	10^6 CFU/25 g (pork sample) or 500 ml (pork carcass rinse); 10^0-10^1 CFU/25 g (pork sample) or 500 ml (pork carcass rinse); N/A	[111,233]

Table 2. (Continued)

Microorganism (Target Gene)	IAC	Matrices	Primer and Probe/Sequence (5'-3')/ Fluorescence Dye	Enrichment Media/Time/Temp	Detection Limit	Reference
Salmonella enterica (*invA*)	Y	Pure culture;	F: CACGCTCTTTCGTCTGGCA R: TACGGTTCCTTTGACGGTGCGA SYBR Green I	None;	10^6 CFU/ml;	[233]
		Liquid whole egg		None	10^7 CFU/25 ml	
				Tetrathionate broth/6 h/37°C	10^4 CFU/25 ml	
				Tetrathionate broth/12 h/37°C	10^2 CFU/25 ml	
				Tetrathionate broth/16 h/37°C	10^0-10^1 CFU/25 ml	
Salmonella Typhimurium (*invA*)	Y	Lettuce, tomato, jalapeño and serrano peppers	F: CACGCTCTTTCGTCTGGCA R: TACGGTTCCTTTGACGGTGCGA SYBR Green I	None; Buffered peptone water/6 h/37°C	10^6-10^7 CFU/g (pepper) or 25 g (lettuce) or 100 g (tomato); 10^4 CFU/g (pepper), 25 g (lettuce) or 100 g (tomato)	[234]
Salmonella Enteritidis (*sefA*) (*orgC*)	N	Pure culture and raw shell eggs	SEFA-F: GGCTTCGGTATCTGGTGGTGTG SEFA-R: GTCATTAATATTGGCTCCCTGAATA SEFA-P: CCACTGTCCCGTTCGTTGATGGACA ORGC-F: CTTTATGATGCATTCTACCAACGACTG ORGC-R: CCGAATCACCACTGTTAGGA ORGC-P: CGCTTCCTGAGTCAGCCTCTTCTGAAACG	Tissue culture infection/5 h/37°C	10^1 CFU/ml 10^1 CFU/ml	[64]

Microorganism (Target Gene)	IAC	Matrices	Primer and Probe/Sequence (5'-3')/ Fluorescence Dye	Enrichment Media/Time/Temp	Detection Limit	Reference
almonella Typhimurium (16S rRNA)	N	Pure culture	F: CGGGGAGGAAGGTGTTGTG R: GAGCCCGGGGATTTCACATC	None	10^3 RNA copies/reaction	[25]
		Tap water fishpond water			N/A	
Salmonella Typhimurium (invA)	N	Pure culture	F: GATTCTGGTACTAATGGTGATGATC R: GCCAGGCTATCGCCAATAAC	None	20 RNA copies/reaction	[25]
		Tap water fishpond water			N/A	
Salmonella Typhimurium (kdpA)	N	Pure culture	F: GGGCGCTACTGACGCTCAATC R: AGGCTTGCCAGTTGGTATTGG	N/A	N/A	[63]
(proV)			F: GGATTATCCGGCTCGGGTAA R: GAGCGCAAATGACTGGAAGAC			
(proP)			F: TGCCTACGCGTTGGGTAAAG R: CCGTATTTATCGCCGAGCAT			
(rpoS)			F: GTTGGACGGCGACTCAGCTTT R: TTTTACCACCAGACGCAGGTT			
(otsB)			F: TTAACCGTATCCCCGAACTC R: CCGCGAGACGGTCTAACAAC			
(ompC)			F: GCGCCGACATCAACGTATTT R: GCCAACAAAGGCGCAGAACTT			
(gnd)						

Table 2. (Continued)

Microorganism (Target Gene)	IAC	Matrices	Primer and Probe/Sequence (5'-3')/ Fluorescence Dye	Enrichment Media/Time/Temp	Detection Limit	Reference
(lacZ)			F: CAACATCGAAAGCCGTGGTT R: GGCGTTTCGAGGGATTCAA			
(phoA)			F: CACCAGCAGCAGTTTTTCCA R: ATCCAGTGCAGGAGCTCGT			
(16S rRNA)			F: GCGATGCTGCCTCACTGAAT R: TTGCGGATTTGGCGTACAG F: ATTGACGTTACCCGCAGAAGA R: GGGATTTCACATCCGACTTGA SYBR Green I			
Staphylococcus aureus (16S rRNA)	N	Pure culture Human peripheral blood	STPYF: ACGGTCTTGCTGTCACTTATA STPYR2: TACACATATGTTCTTCCCTAATAA SYBR Green I	None Brain heart infusion broth/24 h/37°C	10^{-3} CFU/reaction 2 CFU/ml	[71]
Enterovirus	N	Fresh water and seawater	EV1: GATTGTCACCATAAGCAGC EV2: CCCCTGAATGCGGCTAATC P: FAM-CGGAACCGACTACTTTGGGTGTCCGT-BHQ-P	None	N/A	[74]
Hepatitis A virus (5'NCR)	N	Pure culture; Ground water samples	KH1: ATCTTCCACAAGGGGTAG KH2: CGGCGTTGAATGGTTTT MB: FAM-CTTGCGGGATAGGGTAACAGCGGGGGCA AG-DABCYL	None	1 PFU; 20 PFU/ml	[74]

Microorganism (Target Gene)	IAC	Matrices	Primer and Probe/Sequence (5'-3')/ Fluorescence Dye	Enrichment Media/Time/Temp	Detection Limit	Reference
Hepatitis A virus	N	Pure culture	P1: GTTTTGCTCCTCTTTATCATGCTATG P2: GGAAATGTCTCAGGTACTTTCTTTG P: TCAACAACAGTTTCTACAGA	None	4 x 10^4 CFU/ml	[77]
Hepatitis A virus (VP3-VP1)	N	Shellfish	HAVU2167: GTTTTGCTCCTCTTTACCATGCTATG HAVL2413: GGAAATGTCTCAGGTACTTTCTTTG HAVs2233 (probe): TCAACAACAGTTTCTACAGA	None	20 PFU/g	[78]
Norovirus GI	N	Plasmid Stool samples Shellfish	JJV1F: GCCATGTTCCGITGGATG JJV1R: TCCTTAGACGCCATCATCAT JJV1P: FAM-TGTGGACAGGAGATCGCAATCTC-BHQ	None	10 genome copies/reaction N/A N/A	[80]
Norovirus GII	N	Plasmid Stool samples Shellfish	JJV2F: CAAGAGTCAATGTTTAGGTGGATGAG COG2R: TCGACGCCATCTTCATTCACA RING2-TP: FAM-TGGGAGGGCGATCGCAATCT-BHQ	None	10 genome copies/reaction N/A N/A	[80]
Norovirus GI	N	Stool samples	COG1F: CGYTGGATGCGNTTYCATGA COG1R: CTTAGACGCCATCATCATTYAC RING1(a)-TP: FAM-AGATYGCGATCYCCTGTCCA-TAMRA RING1(b)-TP: FAM-AGATCGCGGTCTCCTGTCCA-TAMRA	None	10 genome copies/reaction	[81]

Table 2. (Continued)

Microorganism (Target Gene)	IAC	Matrices	Primer and Probe/Sequence (5'-3')/ Fluorescence Dye	Enrichment Media/Time/Temp	Detection Limit	Reference
Norovirus GII	N	Stool samples	COG2F: CARGARBCNATGTTYAGRTGGATGAG COG2R: TCGACGCCATCTTCATTCACA RING2-TP: FAM-TGGGAGGGCGATCGCAATCT-TAMRA	None	10 genome copies/reaction	[81]
Norovirus GI	N	Strawberries	GI SCCF: TGGARATGTATGTCCCAGG GI SCCR: CCAACCCARCCATTRTACA TaqMan	None	3.36 RT-PCR units	[83]
Norovirus GII	N	Strawberries	GII SCCF: RGCTNTNGAAATNATGGT GII SCCR: CCRCCNGCATRHCCRTRTACAT TaqMan	None	7.07 RT-PCR units	[83]
Norovirus GI	N	Stool samples	MON 432: TGGACICGYGGICCYAAYCA MON 434: GAASCGCATCCARCGGAACAT SYBR Green I	None	N/A	[84]
Norovirus GII	N	Stool samples	MON 431: TGGACIAGRGGICCYAAYCA MON 433: GGAYCTCATCCAYCTGAACAT SYBR Green I	None	N/A	[84]
Rotavirus (VP6)	N	Stool samples	VP6-F: GACGGVGCRACTACATGGT VP6-R: GTCCAATTCATNCCTGGTGG SYBR Green I	None	N/A	[79]

F = forward; R = reverse; P = probe; MB = molecular beacon; TX = Texas red; R = A or G; Y = C or T; N = any.

Scorpion Probes and Real-Time PCR

Scorpion™ probes, self-quenched hairpin primers, are similar to molecular beacons with a fluorophore and a quenching moiety at the 5' and 3' ends, respectively, with stem-loop configuration and specific loop sequence covalently incorporated into a PCR primer [53]. Scorpion probes are designed to serve simultaneously as a PCR primer and as a molecular beacon [47]. As amplification progresses in PCR, the primer is extended along with target synthesis, the stem-loop unfolds and the loop sequence hybridizes intramolecularly with the amplified target, thus developing fluorescence. Since the 5'-3' exonuclease activity is not necessary for the Scorpion assays, a three-step PCR cycling is usually preferred; however, the probe design and assay optimization are relatively difficult as compared to other assays using fluorescence dyes/probes [54]. Incorporation of Scorpion probes into PCR assays have been shown to efficiently detect *E. coli* O157:H7 in dairy products (raw milk, paneer (soft cheese), and ice cream) [55], *Bacteroides* sp. in water and fecal specimens [56]. Although several real-time PCR assays using Scorpion probes were developed and optimized for specific target detection in clinical studies, such research for the detection of foodborne pathogens in food commodities remains limited.

Reverse-transcriptase PCR

While traditional DNA-based PCR and real-time PCR assays are able to rapidly detect DNA targets with high sensitivity, they cannot distinguish between viable and dead cells. In the food industry when pathogen inactivation measures are typically implemented during food manufacturing, DNA from pathogens can still be present and detected in foods although the cells are killed. Thus, the detection of DNA may lead to misinterpretation of results, when there is a need for the detection of mainly infectious viable cells. In contrast, RNA has a shorter half-life than DNA, therefore, detecting it will indicate the presence of viable cells or recent contamination [57]. In addition, RNA-based amplification assays allow detection of foodborne RNA viruses, which cannot be detected by DNA-based PCR. Several researchers have reported on the use of reverse-transcriptase PCR (RT-PCR) targeting mRNA for the detection of viable foodborne organisms (Table 2). Prior to the regular PCR process, target RNA is reverse-transcribed into cDNA, by using the reverse transcriptase enzyme usually by AMV-Reverse Transcriptase. Then, the PCR steps of DNA amplification are carried out. It is crucial that only RNA be isolated from samples and that DNA carry-over be removed by treatment with RNase-free DNase to avoid false positive results arising from DNA amplification. Burtscher and Wuertz [10] demonstrated the RT-PCR assay for *Salmonella* spp., *L. monocytogenes*, *Y. enterocolitica*, and *S. aureus* detection in inoculated organic waste samples, with detection limits of <10 CFU/g in all tested strains after 20 to 24-h enrichment. Detection limits of 1 CFU/g of Shiga-toxin-producing *E. coli* in ground meat after 12-h enrichment [58] and as few as 1 CFU of *E. coli* O157:H7 in pure culture [7] were reported using RT-PCR. Traditional RT-PCR has been typically used for the detection of foodborne RNA viruses such as hepatitis A virus in pure culture, green onions, spring water, shellfish, and human noroviruses in pure culture, green onions, produce, and shellfish [59-62].

Real-time RT-PCR assays using fluorescence dyes or TaqMan® probes have also been developed for the detection of pathogenic bacteria, including *Salmonella* in pure culture and food matrices such as spinach, tomatoes, jalapeno and serrano peppers, lettuce, pork chop, pork sausage, pork carcass rinse, shell egg, liquid whole egg, water, and environmental samples [25,63-69]. Real-time RT-PCR has also been reported for the detection of *E. coli*, including *E. coli* O157:H7 strain [7,71-72] in pure culture, water samples and clinical samples, *Helicobacter pylori* [73], *Enterococcus faecalis*, *C. perfringens*, and *S. aureus* [71].

Moreover, the epidemiologically significant viral pathogens, including enterovirus in fresh water and seawater [74], hepatitis A virus in pure culture, ground water, and shellfish [75-78], rotavirus in clinical samples [79], human noroviruses in clinical samples, shellfish, and strawberries [80-84], and also avian influenza virus [85] have also been detected using real-time RT-PCR as shown in Table 2.

As indicated earlier, advantages of real-time RT-PCR include speed, sensitivity, and most importantly potential to detect viable cells or recent contamination. However, the initial cost of equipment, as well as skilled labor could limit its use in small scale industries or laboratories.

Multiplex PCR

Multiplex PCR assay targets the simultaneous amplification of more than one gene (or target) in a single reaction with the attempt to reduce time to get results, decrease reagent cost, and labor when compared to conducting numerous separate singleplex PCR assays. It uses several sets of primers, one unique and specific set for each target. It is important that the reaction conditions be optimized to allow for correct annealing of primers and amplification of the different targets. The target amplicons should be of different sizes for ease of differentiation by agarose gel electrophoresis (followed by confirmation) or determination of T_m differences among each target product. The multiplex PCR assay has been successfully applied for foodborne bacterial detection in both DNA-based and RNA-based methods [29,86,87] and demonstrated for the simultaneous detection of *E. coli* O157:H7, *Salmonella*, *S. aureus*, *L. monocytogenes*, and *V. parahaemolyticus*. Simultaneous detection of bacteria of the genus *Listeria*, *L. monocytogenes*, and major serotypes and epidemic clones of *L. monocytogenes* has also been reported by Chen and Knabel [88] as well as for the detection of *E. coli* O157:H7 and *L. monocytogenes* by similar approaches. Wolffs et al. [29] developed a quantitative real-time multiplex PCR assay for *Campylobacter* and *Salmonella* detection in chicken rinses. Thus, as technology advances, detection speed, specificity, and sensitivity are being continuously improved. Even though multiplexing has advantages, the drawback includes decreased sensitivity compared to singleplex reactions. In addition, these PCR based methods require the initial cost of set-up of equipment and training of skilled workers. Therefore, alternate methods that have potential for field deployment and ease of use are being researched.

Table 3. Loop mediated isothermal amplification (LAMP) assay for the detection of foodborne pathogens

Microorganism	Matrices	Target Gene/Primers (5'-3')	Enrichment Media/Time/Temp	Detection Limit	Reference
Traditional LAMP Assay					
Brucella spp.	Pure culture; Infected mice spleens; Infected mice livers; Milk	*BCSP31/* F3: GCTTTACGCAGTCAGACGT B3: GCTCATCCAGCGAAACGC FIP: AGGCGCAAATCTTCCACCTTGCGCCTATTGGGCCTATAAC GG BIP: GGCGACGCTTTACCCGGAAATTCAGGTCTGCGACCGAT LF: CCTTGCCATCATAAAGGCC LB: CGTAAGGATGCAAACATCAA	None	10 fg DNA/tube; 8.2 x 10² CFU/100 mg; 2.0 x 10³ CFU/100 mg, 4.9 x 10⁴ CFU/4.5 ml	[98]
Escherichia coli	Pure culture	LT1/F3: GCCATTATATGCAAATGGCG B3 CCTGCTAAGTGAGCACTTCT FIP: CTCATTATGCCCTCTGGGCAACTCTAGACCCCCAGATGA (F1c+F2) BIP: ATGATCACGCGAGAGGAACACAAAGTGGAAACATATCCG TCA (B1c+B2) LF: AAGACCTCCGGAACGTTTTA LB: ACCGGCTTTGTCAGATATGA ST1/F3: CTCAGGATGCTAAACCAGT B3: CAGAACAAATATAAAGGGGAACTGTT FIP: TCATGCTTTCAGGACCACTTTTATTGAGTCTTCAAAAGAA AAAATCACACT (F1c+F2) BIP: AGTAGCAATTACTGCTGTGAATTGTCCCTTTATATATTAA TAGCACCCG (B1c+B2) LB: GTTGTAATCCTGCTTGT	None	4 CFU/tube 40 CFU/tube	[97]

Table 3. (Continued)

Microorganism	Matrices	Target Gene/Primers (5'-3')	Enrichment Media/Time/Temp	Detection Limit	Reference
Escherichia coli O157 and *Escherichia coli* O26	Ground beef; Alfalfa sprouts	VT1/FIP: GCTCTTGCCACAGACTGCACATTCGTTGACTACTTCTTATCTGG BIP: CTGTGACAGCTGAAGCTTTACGCGAAATCCCCTCTGAATTTGCC F3: GCTATACCACGTTACAGCGTG B3: ACTACTCAACCTTCCCCAGTTC Loop F: AGGTTCCGCTATGCGACATTAAAT VT2/FIP: GCTCTTGATGCATCTCTGGTACACTCACTGGTTTCATCATATCTGG BIP: CTGTCACAGCAGAAGCCTTACGGACGAAATTCTCCCTGTATCTGCC F3: CAGTTATACCACTCTGCAACGTG B3: CTGATTCGCGCCAGTTC Loop F1: TGTATTACCACTGAACTCCATTAACG Loop F2: GGCATTTCCACTAAACTCCATTAACG	Modified *E. coli* broth + novobiocin/20 h/42°C	100% (11.7 CFU/25 g) and 100% (11.7 CFU/25 g) 100% (46.8 CFU/25 g); 100% (10.7 CFU/25 g) and 100% (10.7 CFU/25 g) 100% (42.8 CFU/25 g)	[95]
Escherichia coli O26 or O157	Pure culture; Ground beef; Radish sprouts	VT1/FIP: GCTCTTGCCACAGACTGCACATTCGTTGACTACTTCTTATCTGG BIP: CTGTGACAGCTGAAGCTTTACGCGAAATCCCCTCTGAATTTGCC F3: GCTATACCACGTTACAGCGTG B3: ACTACTCAACCTTCCCCAGTTC Loop F: AGGTTCCGCTATGCGACATTAAAT VT2/FIP: GCTCTTGATGCATCTCTGGTACACTCACTGGTTTCATCATATCTGG	None; Modified *E. coli* broth + novobiocin /18 h/42°C; Modified *E. coli* broth + novobiocin /18 h/42°C	0.7–2.2 CFU/tube; ≤ 5.9–8.9 CFU/25 g; ≤ 20.8–36.8 CFU/25 g	[235]

Microorganism	Matrices	Target Gene/Primers (5'-3')	Enrichment Media/Time/Temp	Detection Limit	Reference
		BIP: CTGTCACAGCAGAAGCCTTACGGACGAAATTCTCCCTGTA TCTGCC F3: CAGTTATACCACTCTGCAACGTG B3: CTGATTCGCGCGCCAGTTC Loop F1: TGTATTACCACTGAACTCCATTAACG Loop F2: GGCATTTCCACTAAACTCCATTAACG			
Campylobacter coli	Human stool samples	CCO0367/CC-FIP: AAGAGATAAACACCATGATCCCAGTCATGAATGAGCTTAC TTTAGC (F1c+F2) CC-BIP: GCGGCAAAGACTTATGATAAAGCTACCGCCATTCCTAAAA CAAG (B1+B2c) CC-F3: TGGGAGCGTTTTTGATCT (F3) CC-B3: AATCAAACTCACCGCCAT (B3c) CC-LF: CCACTACAGCAAAGGTGATG (LFc) CC-LB: CCACGATAGCCTTTATGGA (LB)	None	4.8 x 10³ CFU/g (1.2 CFU/tube)	[104]
Campylobacter jejuni	Human stool samples	CJ0414/CJ-FIP: ACAGCACCGCCACCTATAGTAGAAGCTTTTTTAAACTAGG GC (F1c+F2) CJ-BIP: AGGCAGCAGAACTTACGCATTGAGTTTGAAAAACATTCT ACCTCT (B1+B2c) CJ-F3: GCAAGACAATATTATTGATCGC (F3) CJ-B3: CTTTCACAGGCTGCACTT (B3c) CJ-LF: CTAGCTGCTACTACAGAAACCAC (LFc) CJ-LB: CATCAAGCTTCACAAGGAAA (LB)	None	5.6 x 10³ CFU/g (1.4 CFU/tube)	[104]
Campylobacter jejuni and Campylobacter coli	Chicken meat	CCO0367/CC-FIP: AAGAGATAAACACCATGATCCCAGTCATGAATGAGCTTAC TTTAGC (F1c+F2) CC-BIP: GCGGCAAAGACTTATGATAAAGCTACCGCCATTCCTAAAA CAAG (B1+B2c) CC-F3: TGGGAGCGTTTTTGATCT (F3) CC-B3: AATCAAACTCACCGCCAT (B3c) CC-LF: CCACTACAGCAAAGGTGATG (LFc)	Preston broth with 5% lysed horse blood/22 to 24 h/ 42°C	98.5% (67/68; 7.9 CFU/tube of C. jejuni and 3.8 CFU/tube of C. coli)	[236]

Table 3. (Continued)

Microorganism	Matrices	Target Gene/Primers (5'-3')	Enrichment Media/Time/Temp	Detection Limit	Reference
Cryptosporidium parvum	Pure culture	CC-LB: CCACGATAGCCTTTATGGA (LB) gp60/F3: TCGCACCAGCAAATAAGGC B3: GCCGCATTCTTCTTTTGGAG FIP: ACCCTGGCTACCAGAAGCTTCAGAACTGGAGACGCAGAA BIP: GGCCAAACTAGTGCTGCTTCCCGTTTCGGTAGTTGCGCCTT	None	400 fg template/µl	[105]
Cryptosporidium parvum oocysts	Oocyst suspensions; Fecal and water samples	gp60/F3: TCGCACCAGCAAATAAGGC B3: GCCGCATTCTTCTTTTGGAG FIP: ACCCTGGCTACCAGAAGCTTCAGAACTGGAGACGCAGAA BIP: GGCCAAACTAGTGCTGCTTCCCGTTTCGGTAGTTGCGCCTT	None	0.1–1 oocysts; 100% (25/25)	[105]
Salmonella spp.	Pure culture	*invA*/FIP: CCCAGATCCCGCATTGTTGAT-TTTT-CCGCCCCATATTATCGCTAT (F1c+F2) BIP: GACCATCACCAATGGTCAGCA-TTTT-TTGGCGGTATTTCGGTGGG (B1c+B2) F3: GTTCAACAGCTGCGTCATGA B3: CGCTATTGCCGGCATCATTA	None	100 fg template/tube	[94]
Salmonella enterica	Liquid eggs	N/A	Buffered peptone water/20 h/37°C	<1 CFU/g	[92]
Salmonella enterica	Pure culture	*invA*/FIP: GACGACTGGTACTGATCGATAGTTTTCAACGTTTCCTGC GG BIP: CCGGGTGAAATTATCGCCACACAAAACCCACCGCCAGG F3: GGCGATATTGGTGTTTATGGGG B3: AACGATAAACTGGACCACGG Loop F: GACGAAAGAGCGTGGTAATTAAC Loop B: GGGGCAATTCGTTATTGGCGATAG	None	>2.2 CFU/tube	[91]

Microorganism	Matrices	Target Gene/Primers (5'-3')	Enrichment Media/Time/Temp	Detection Limit	Reference
O9 *Salmonella*	Pure culture; Chicken cecal droppings (spiked cecals); Chicken cecal droppings (spiked chickens)	IS-FIP: GTAGGGCAGTAGGCAGCATATTCTGCACAACATTCTGCTT CCAG IS-BIP: GTAAGTATCCCGCATAATCGTGCCGCATAGCGATCTCCTT CGTTG IS-F3: AACTCGACACACTCATCTTCGG IS-B3: CACAGTGATGATCTGATGCTCAG IS-LF: AATTGTGTGAATGGAAAAACGTACG IS-LB: CACATTTAGAGATCATCCGGCATAA	None; Hajna tetrathionate (HTT) broth/24 h/41.5°C; HTT broth/24 h/41.5°C	10³ CFU/ml; 6.1 x 10¹ CFU/g; 95.8% (11/12)	[93]
Staphylococcus aureus	Pure culture	*spa*/FIP: GCTCTTCGTTTAAGTTAGGCATGTT-TGCGCAACAAATAAGTTCA BIP: AAGTCTTAAAGACGATCCAAGCC-TTCGGGTGCTTGAGATTCG LB: AGCACTAACGTTTTAGGTGAAGC F3: AATGACTCTCAAGCTCCAA B3: CTTTGTTGAAATTGTTGTCAGC *mecA*/FIP: GGTCTTTCTGCATTCCTGGAATAAT-AGAAGATGGTATGTGGAAGT BIP: AGAAACGTGGTAAAATTTTAGACCGA-CCTAATCTCATATGTGTTCCTGT F3: CATTGATCGCAACGTTCAA B3: AGATACAATTCTTTGGAACGATG	None	10³ copies/tube 10² copies/tube	[102]
Staphylococcus aureus	Pure culture	*sea*/SEA FIP: GATCCAACTCCTGAACAGTTACAATACAGTACCTTTGGAA ACG (F1c-F2) SEA BIP: CTGATGTTTTGATGGGAAGGTTCCGAAGGTTCTGTAGA AGT (B1-B2c) SEA F3: TCAATTTATGGCTAGACGGT (F3) SEA B3: CTTGAGCACCAAATAAATCG (B3c)	None	2.3 CFU/tube	[101]

Table 3. (Continued)

Microorganism	Matrices	Target Gene/Primers (5'-3')	Enrichment Media/Time/Temp	Detection Limit	Reference
		SEA LB: AGAGGGGATTAATCGTGTTTCA (LB)			
		seb/SEB FIP:			
		CACCAAATAGTGACGAGTTAGGTAAGACGTACAAACTAA			
		TAAGAAAAGG (F1c-F2)			
		SEB BIP:			
		ACTCTATGAATTTAACAACTCGCCTTGTCATACCAAAAGC			
		TATTCTCA (B1-B2c)			
		SEB F3: GTTCGGGTATTTGAAGATGG (F3)		30.2 CFU/tube	
		SEB B3: TTGGTCAAATTTATCTCCTGG (B3c)			
		SEB LF: TCTAATTCTTGAGCAGTCA (LFc)			
		SEB LB: ATGAAACGGGATATATTAAATTTAT (LB)			
		sec/SEC FIP:			
		TCCTTCATGTTTTGTTATTCCTCCAAGATAATGTAGGTAAA			
		GTTACAGGT (F1c-F2)			
		SEC BIP:			
		ACCACTTTGATAATGGGAACTTACATTTGCACTTCAAAAG		≤6.9 CFU/tube	
		AAATTGTG (B1-B2c)			
		SEC F3: TGTAAACTGCTATTTTTCATCCA (F3)			
		SEC B3: CTTTTATGTCTAGTTCTTGAGCT (B3c)			
		SEC LB: TGTACTTATAAGAGTTTATGAAAAT (LB)			
		sed/SED FIP:			
		CGCTGTATTTTCCTCCGAGAGTGCGCTATTTGCAAAAGG			
		AT (F1c-F2)			
		SED BIP: AGAGTTTGATTCTTCTGATGGGTCTTA		38 CFU/tube	
		TTCGTAATTGTTTTCGGGAA (B1-B2c)			
		SED F3: ACAAGAATTAGATGCACAAGC (F3)			
		SED B3: TGAAGGTGCTCTGTGGAT (B3c)			
		SED LB: TGATTTATTTGATGTTAAGGGGTG (LB)			

Microorganism	Matrices	Target Gene/Primers (5'-3')	Enrichment Media/Time/Temp	Detection Limit	Reference
Vibrio parahaemolyticus	Pure culture; Oysters	*toxR*/F3: TTGGATTCCACGCGTTAT B3: CGTTCAATGCACTGCTCA FIP: TGAGATTCCGCAGGGTTTGTAA TTATTTTTGGCACTATTACTACCG BIP: GTTCCGTCAGATTGGTGAGTATC TAGAAGGCAACCAGTTGTT Loop: AGAACGTACCAGTGATGACACC	None	47-470 CFU/tube; 1.1 × 10⁵ CFU/g	[99]
Vibrio parahaemolyticus	Shrimps	*tdh*/Tdh-FIP: GTACCTGACGTTGTGAATACTGATTGTCTCTGACTTTTGGA CAAAC Tdh-BIP: TGACATCCTACACGACTGTGAACACTTATAGCCAGACACC GC Tdh-F3: AGATATTGTTTGTTGTTCGAGAT Tdh-B3: AACACAGCAGAATGACCG Tdh-LF: GTACGGTTTTCTTTTTACATTACG Tdh-LB: AAGACTATACAATGGCAGCG *trh1*/Trh1-FIP: AGGCTTGTTTTTTCTGATTTTGTGACTACACAATGGCTGCT CT Trh1-BIP: TCTTCTGTTAGTGATTTCGTTGGTTTTCATCCAAATACGTT ACACT Trh1-F3: GCGCCTATATGACGGTAA Trh1-B3: ACATTGACGAAATATTCTGGC Trh1-LF: AGACCGTTGARAGGCC *trh2*/Trh2-FIP: CCGATTGACCGTATACATCTTTGTTGTGGAGGACTATTGG ACAA Trh2-BIP: TCAAAGTGGTTAAGCGCCTATATGCCATSTTTATAACCAG AAAGAGC	Alkaline peptone water/overnight/36°C	0.8 CFU/tube (AQ3815 strain [*tdh*⁺]) 21.3 CFU/tube (AQ4037 strain [*trh1*⁺]) 5.0 CFU/tube (AT4 strain [*trh2*⁺])	[100]

Table 3. (Continued)

Microorganism	Matrices	Target Gene/Primers (5'-3')	Enrichment Media/Time/Temp	Detection Limit	Reference
		Trh2-F3: CATCAATACCTTTCCTTCTCC Trh2-B3: GCTTGTTTCTCTGATTTGTG Trh2-LF: TGGTTTTCTTTTATGKTTCGGT Trh2-LB: ATGGTCAYAACTATACRATGGC			
Vibrio parahaemolyticus	Pure culture; Shrimps	*tlh/*Tlh-FIP: ATGTTTTTAAATGAAACG GAGCTCCGGCAAAAAACGAAGATGGT (F1c+F2) Tlh-BIP: ACGTCGCAAAACGTTATCCGGCGAAGAACGTAAATGTCTG (B1+B2c) Tlh-F3: AGCTACTCGAAAGATGATCC (F3) Tlh-B3: GGTTGTATGAGAAGGGATTG (B3c) Tlh-LF: ACCAGTAGCCGTCAATG (LFc) Tlh-LB: TTAGATTTGGCGAACGAGA (LB)	None	5.3 x 10² CFU/ml (2.0 CFU/tube); 5.3 x 10² CFU/g (2.0 CFU/tube)	[103]
Yersinia enterocolitica	Pure culture; Pork meat	*gyrB/*Y-BIP: CCGGTTTGATCGGTTTCGCCCACTTA CAAGATGGGTGTGCC Y-FIP: GTGCGTTTCTGGCCGAGCTTGCAGA CGTTTTGCCAGGATT Y-B3: CGCCGTGAAGGTAAAGTTCA Y-F3: CAGAGTT-CAGGAACGACAGC	None; Peptone sorbit bile enrichment Broth/48 h/25°C	65 CFU/ml; N/A	[237]
Yersinia pseudotuberculosis	Pure culture	*inv/*F3: CTCGTCGCGTGATTTCTCC B3: GATCTACCCCGACAGTGAGT FIP: CCAGTTGTGGGAGTGCAGGTAACTATAAAG AGCGCCCAGCC BIP: CACCGGTGAGCGTGTTGCTTTGTGTAATTGA TCCCGGCAGT LF: CATTCGCGCAAATCC LB: GCAACGCAACCCTTATGC	N/A	10⁰ CFU/tube	[238]

Microorganism	Matrices	Target Gene/Primers (5'-3')	Enrichment Media/Time/Temp	Detection Limit	Reference
RT-LAMP Assay					
Salmonella Typhimurium	Pure culture	*invA*/ FIP: GACGACTGGTACTGATCGATAG TTTTTCAACGTTTCCTGCGG BIP:	None	10^1 CFU/ml	111
	Pork chops	CCGGTGAAATTATCGCCACACAAAACCCACGCCAGG F3: GGCGATATTGGTGTTTATGGGG B3: AACGATAAACTGGACCACGG FLoop: GACGAAAGAGCGTGGTAATTAAC BLoop: GGGCAATTCGTTATTGGCGATAG	Tetrathionate broth (TTB)/10 h/37°C	10^2 CFU/25 g	
	Pork sausage		TTB/10 h/37°C	10^2 CFU/25 g	
	Natural pork chop, ground pork, and pork sausage		BPW/4 h/37°C and tetrathionate broth/12 h/37°C	N/A	
Salmonella enterica	Natural pork carcass rinses, pork carcass swabs	*invA*/ FIP: GACGACTGGTACTGATCGATAG TTTTTCAACGTTTCCTGCGG BIP: CCGGTGAAATTATCGCCACACAAAACCCACGCCAGG F3: GGCGATATTGGTGTTTATGGGG B3: AACGATAAACTGGACCACGG FLoop: GACGAAAGAGCGTGGTAATTAAC BLoop: GGGCAATTCGTTATTGGCGATAG	BPW/4 h/37°C and tetrathionate broth/12 h/37°C	N/A	[69]
Norovirus GI	Fecal specimens	F3: CCRGGNTGGCARGCNATGTT B3: CCAACCCARCCATTRTACA FIP1: F1C, CATTTACGAATTCGGGGCAGG; F2, CGCTGGATGCGNTTCCATGA FIP2: F1C, CATTTACAAAATCGGGCAGG; F2, CGCTGGATGCGNTTCCATGA BIP1: B1C, GATGGCGTCTAAGGACGC; B2, AGCTGTRTTTGCCTCTGGWAC BIP2: B1C, GATGGCGTCTAAGGACGC; B2, AGCWGTATTAACCTCCGGYAC LF1: AGATYGCGATCYCCTGTCCA LF2: AGATTGCGATCTCCTGCCCA LF3: AGCTCGCGGTCTCTCTGTCCA	None	10^2 copies/tube	[106]

Table 3. (Continued)

Microorganism	Matrices	Target Gene/Primers (5'-3')	Enrichment Media/Time/Temp	Detection Limit	Reference
Norovirus GII	Fecal specimens	F3: GGNMTGGANTTTTAYGTGCCMAG B3: CCRCCNGCATRHCCRTRTACAT FIP1: F1C, GGGAGCMAGATTGCGATCGC; F2, GAGBCNATGTTYAGRTGGAT FIP2: F1C, GGGAGCMAGATTGCGATCGC; F2, GAGCCCATGTTCAGRTGGAT FIP3: F1C, GGGAGCGAGATTGCGATCGC; F2, GAGTCAATGTTYAGGTGGAT BIP1: B1C, TGTGAATGAAGATGGCGTCG; B2,	None	10³ copies/tube	[106]
		CTCATTRTTRRVTCTCTGGBACGAG BIP2: B1C, TGTGAATGAAGATGGCGTCG; B2, CTCATTRTTGCYCTCTGGYACGAG BIP3: B1C, TGTGAATGAAGATGGCGTCG; B2, CTCATTGTTGAYCTCTGGKACGAG BIP4: B1C, TGTGAATGAAGATGGCGTCG; B2, CTCATTRTTACTTTCTGGCACGAG LF1: GTGCTCARATCWGARAACCTC LF2: GTGCTGAGGTCWGARAATCTC LF3: GTGCTCAAATCTGAGAATCTC LF4: GTGCTCAAGTCTGAGAAYCTC			
Hepatitis A virus	Pure culture	F3: GCATGGAGCTGTAGGAGTCT B3: CACTCAAATGCATCCACTGGA FIP: ACCCGTAGCCTACCTCTTGTGG-TGTTGGAACGTCACCTTG (F1c+F2) FIP03I: ACCCGTAGCCTACCCCTTGTGG-TGTTTGGGACGTCGCCTTG BIP: TTGGATAGGGTAACAGCGGCG-CTCCGGCGTTGAATG (B1C+B2) F loop: TGAAAGCCAAGTTAACACTG B loop: GATATTGGTGAGTTGTTAAGAC	None	0.4–0.8 FFU/tube	[110]

Microorganism	Matrices	Target Gene/Primers (5'-3')	Enrichment Media/Time/Temp	Detection Limit	Reference
Hepatitis E virus	Fecal, liver and bile samples	F3: T^{5175}GGAGATG CCACCATGGCGCTCTCG^{5198} B3: A^{5445}CGCCAAGCGGA GCCGAGTGGAC^{5423} FIP: A^{5296}CCGCCGCTGCGCGCCGCCC^{5279}C^{5213}TGCTCTTCGTGCTTCT GCCTATGCTGC^{5240} BIP: G^{5303}GTGGTTTCTGGGGTGACCGGTT^{5326}C^{5376}C GAAGGGGTTGGTTGGATGAATATAGG^{5349} LOOP-F: C^{5273}GACGGCCAGACGGCTGACC^{5254} LOOP-B: G^{5320}ATTCTCAGCCCTTCGCCCTCC^{5342}	N/A	0.045 fg (9 copies)/tube	[108]

*The forward inner primer (FIP) consisted of the F1 complementary sequence and the F2 direct sequence, the back inner primer (BIP) consisted of the B1 direct sequence and the B2 complementary sequence.

F1c, sequence complementary to F1; F2c, sequence complementary to F2; B3c, sequence complementary to B3; LFc, sequence complementary to LF.

Table 4. Nucleic acid sequence–based amplification (NASBA) for the detection of foodborne pathogens

Microorganism	Matrices	Target Gene/Primer and Probe Sequence (5'-3')	Enrichment Media/Time/Temp	Detection Sensitivity	Reference
Campylobacter jejuni	Pure culture; Poultry products, dairy products, red meats and vegetables	P1 OT1118: AATTCTAATACGACTCACTATAGGGAGAGAGTGTGAC TGATCATCCTCTCA P2 OT1547: GACAACAGTTGGAAACGACTGCTAATA Probe 031559: CTGCTTAACACAAGTTGAGTAGG	None; Preston broth/18 h/42°C	3×10^1 CFU/ml; 1-1,000 CFU/10 g	[118,239]
Listeria monocytogenes	Pure culture; Chicken breast meat, shrimps, soft cheese, minced meat (port/beef), dry sausage, mushrooms, radish, and raw milk	P1 OT1683: TCAAATCATCATGCCCCTTA P2 OT16116: AATTCl-AATACGACTCACTATAGGGAGAGAGGCGAGITGCA GC Probe OT1682: GCTAATCCCATAAAACTAT	None; Modified Fraser broth/24 h/30°C and phosphate buffered Listeria enrichment broth/24 h/30°C	2×10^5 CFU/ml; 1-100 CFU/25 g	[119]
Listeria monocytogenes	Pure culture; Liquid milk; Milk powder; Egg powder; Ice cream; Cheeses	*hlyA*/P1: AATTCTAATACGACTCACTAT AGGGAGATAACCTTTTCTTGGCGGCACA P2: GTCCTAAGACGCCAATCGAA Capture probe: CAAGGATTGGATTACAATAAAAACAATGTATTAG TATACCACGGAGATGCAGTGAC	None; Modified listeria enrichment broth/48 h/30°C	500 CFU/reaction 0.2 CFU/g; 0.7 CFU/g; 1.8 CFU/g; 0.2 CFU/g; 0.5-62 CFU/g	[115]
Mycobacterium avium subsp. paratuberculosis	Human and bovine fecal samples	MAP57F: CAACGACGACCAAGACGA MAP57R: AATTCTAATACGACTCACTATAGGGAGAAGGAGC AAACCGATCACGACA MAP57MB: FAM-CGATCGCTGATGAAACCGAGCTCGTCGATCG-DABCYL Af2: CGATGCAACGCGAAGAAC Ar: GGTTGGCCCCGGCAGTCT MBl: HEX-CGCAGGAACGTGCAGAGATGTGCGCCCCTGCG-DABCYL	None	N/A	[117]

Microorganism	Matrices	Target Gene/Primer and Probe Sequence (5'-3')	Enrichment Media/Time/Temp	Detection Sensitivity	Reference
		IAC F: AATTCTAATACGACTCACTATAGGGAGAAAGGCAA CGACGACCAAGACGACGATGCAACGCG IAC R: AGCAAACCGATCACGACACAGGTTGGCCCCGGCAGT CT			
Salmonella Enteritidis	Pure culture	*dnaK*/SDnaK1: AATTCTAATACGACTCACTATAGGGAGAGGCAGT CGGTTCGTTGATG SDnaK2: GATGCAAGGTCGCATATGAGCTTGATGTGAAAGG TCAGA	None	10^1 CFU/reaction	[114,240]
	Cake, chocolate, infant formula, macaroni, non-fat dry milk and red pepper		Lactose broth, brilliant green water or skim milk/8 h/35°C	10^2–10^1 CFU/25 g	
	Liquid whole egg		Buffered peptone water/16 h/37°C	2.8 CFU/25 g	
Vibrio cholerae	Pure culture; Environmental water	*hlyA*/Pvc55-1 *hlyA*: AATTCTAATACGACTCACTATAGGGAATCTCTTCC GTCCGATCAA Pvc56-2 *hlyA*: TGATGCTGAAGGTCAAGCAG MBvc10-*hlyA*: CCGATCTCAGAAAGGCTTATGGGGTGGATCGG	None	5×10^5 CFU/ml; $\leq 5 \times 10^5$ CFU/ml (*hlyA*)	[116]
				50 CFU/ml; $\leq 5 \times 10^3$ CFU/ ml (*tcpA*)	
		tcpA/Pvc62-1 *tcpA*: AATTCTAATACGACTCACTATAGGGCGCTGAGACC ACACCCATA Pvc60-2 *tcpA*: GAAGAAGTTTGTAAAAGAAGAACACG MBvc11-*tcpA*: CCGATCAGAAAACCGGTCAAGAGGGTGATCGG		500 CFU/ml; $\leq 5 \times 10^5$ CFU/ ml (*ctxA*)	
				50 CFU/ml; $\leq 5 \times 10^3$ CFU/ ml (*groEL*)	

Table 4. (Continued)

Microorganism	Matrices	Target Gene/Primer and Probe Sequence (5'-3')	Enrichment Media/Time/Temp	Detection Sensitivity	Reference
		ctxA/Pvc64-1 *ctxA*: AATTCTAATACGACTCACTATAGGGAGAAGGTGG GTGCAGTGGCTATAACA Pvc61-2 *ctxA*: TGATCATGCAAGAGGAACTCA MBvc-12 *ctxA*: CCGATCTTGTTAGGCACGATGATGGAGATCGG *groEL*/Pvc65-1 *groEL*: AATTCTAATACGACTCACTATAGGGATGATGTTGC CCACGCTAGA Pvc66-2 *groEL*: GGTTATCGCTGCGGTAGAAG MBvc13-*groEL*: CCGATCCTGTCTGTACCTTGTGCCGAGATCGG *toxR*/Pvc69-1 *toxR*: AATTCTAATACGACTCACTATAGGGCGGAACCGTT TTGACGTATT Pvc72-2 *toxR*: CTCGCAATGATTTGCATGAC MBvc14-*toxR*: CCGATCTTAACCCAAGCCATTTCGACGATCGG		500 CFU/ml; $\leq$ 5 x 10^5 CFU/ml (*toxR*)	
Enterovirus	Clinical samples	EV/P1.3: AATTCTAATACGACTCACTATAGGGCACGGATGG CCAATCCA P2.2: GATGCAAGGTCGCATATGAGGGTGTGAAGAGCCT ATTGAG WT EV Probe: Biotin–CTCCGGCCCCTGAAT GCGGGCTAAT IC-probe: Biotin-GCAAAGTATCATCCCTCCAG	None	96%	[124]

Microorganism	Matrices	Target Gene/Primer and Probe Sequence (5'-3')	Enrichment Media/Time/Temp	Detection Sensitivity	Reference
Enterovirus	Water samples	EV/ P1.3: AATTCTAATACGACTCACTATAGGGCACCGGATGG CCAATCCA P2.2: GATGCAAGGTCGCATATGAGGGTGTGAAGAGCCT ATTGAG WT EV Probe: Biotin–CTCCGGCCCCTGAAT GCGGGCTAAT IC-probe: Biotin-GCAAAGTATCATCCCTCCAG	None	N/A	[125]
Hepatitis A virus	Pure culture; Lake water	5' NCR/UC1: AATGGATCCGTAGGA GTCTAAATTGGGGA T7KH2: AATTCTAATACGACTCACTAT AGGGAGACGGCGTTGAATGGTTTTT MB: 6-FAM: CTTGCGGGATAGGGTAAC AGCGGCGGCGCAAG-DABCYL	None (with combination of immunomagnetic separation)	1 PFU; 10 PFU	[241]
Hepatitis A virus	Pure culture	P1: GTTTTGCTCCTCTTTATCATGCTATG T7P2: AATTCTAATACGACTCACTATAGGGAGGAGAAAT GTCTCAGGTACTTTCTTTG P probe: TCAACAACAGTTTCTACAGA BB1: CAGATTGGCTTACTACACA T7BB2: AATTCTAATACGACTCACTATAGGGAGGACACATGCA ACTCCAAATCTGT	None	0.4 ng RNA/reaction or 2 PFU/reaction (4 x 10^2 PFU/ml) (P and BB primers); 4 ng/ml (HPA primers); 40 ng/ml (AD primers) ≤ 10^6 PFU/ml (BB primers)	[77,120]
	Waste water	BB probe: GATTGATCTGTGCTATGGTTCCTGGTGACC		≤ 10^8 PFU/3 cm^2 (BB primers)	
	Lettuce	HPA: GGCAGACATTGAGGAAGAGC T7HPA: AATTCTAATACGACTCACTATAGGGAGGAGATGGTCAC CAGGAACCATAGC HPA probe:		≤ 10^8 PFU/3 cm^2 (BB primers)	
	Blueberry				

Table 4. (Continued)

Microorganism	Matrices	Target Gene/Primer and Probe Sequence (5'-3')	Enrichment Media/Time/Temp	Detection Sensitivity	Reference
		CTGAGGTTGGATCACACCAGGTTGAACCTT AD: TCTTCAACCTCTAATCCTCCTC T7AD: AATTCTAATACGACTCACTATAGGGAGAGTCTTGT CACCCAAACCATC AD probe: CCGTTGATACTCCTTGGGTAGAGAAGGAGT			
Hepatitis A virus Norovirus GI Norovirus GII	Stool samples; Lettuce; Sliced deli turkey	BB1: GATGCAAGGTCGCATATGAGCAGATTGGCTTACTA CACA BB2: AATTCTAATACGACTCACTATAGGGAGACATGCA ACTCCAAATCTGT BB probe: Biotin- GATTGATCTGTGCTATGGTTCCTGGTGACC NVP1: AATTCTAATACGACTCACTATAGGGAGAAGGATCT CATCATCACCATA NVP2b: GATGCAAGGTCGCATATGAGATACCACTATGATG CAGATTA NVP2a: GATGCAAGGTCGCATATGAGGAATTCCATCGCCC ACTGGCT NVG1a: Biotin-ACAGGCCTATCACCGATGT NVG1b: Biotin-ACTGGCTTATCACCTGATGT NVG1c: Biotin-TATCACCTGATGTTATACAATCC NVG2a: Biotin-GTCCCCTGACATCATACAGGCT NVG2b: Biotin-ACAGGACTAGGCCCCGACAT NVG2c: Biotin-TCAGGTCTCTCACCAGAT	None	2×10^{-2} PFU/reaction; 2×10^{1} PFU/9 cm^2; 2 $\times 10^{3}$ PFU/9 cm^2 (Hepatitis A virus) 2×10^{-2} PDU/reaction; 2×10^{1} PDU/9 cm^2; 2 $\times 10^{1}$ PDU/9 cm^2 (Norovirus GI) 2×10^{-2} PDU/reaction; 2×10^{0} PDU/9 cm^2; 2 $\times 10^{0}$ PDU/9 cm^2 (Norovirus GII)	[121]

Microorganism	Matrices	Target Gene/Primer and Probe Sequence (5'-3')	Enrichment Media/Time/Temp	Detection Sensitivity	Reference
Norovirus GI and GII	Fecal samples; Shellfish	JV12: AGCCAGTGGGCGATGGAATTC JV13: AATTCTAATACGACTCACTATAGGGAATCATCATC ACCATAGAAAGAG PI: TCNGAAATGGATGTTGG (N=A/T/C/G) JV12: AGCCAGTGGGCGATGGAATTC JV13: AATTCTAATACGACTCACTATAGGGAATCATCATC ACCATAGAAAGAG PII: AGCCAGTGGGCGATGGAATTC	None	5 pg RNA/ml; 100 pg RNA/1.5 g	[122]
Norovirus GII	Clinical samples	NVP1: AATTCTAATACGACTCACTATAGGGAGACTCATCA TCACCATA NVPa: AATTCCATCGCCCACTGGCT NVG2a: Biotin-GTCCCCTGACATCATACAGGCT NVG2b: Biotin-ACAGGACTAGGCCCGACAT NVG2c: Biotin-TCAGGTCTCTCACCAGAT	None	N/A	[123]
Norovirus GII	Clinical samples; Lettuce; Sliced turkey	JJV2F: CAAGAGTCAATGTTTAGGTGGATGAG COG2R: AATTCTAATACGACTCACTATAGGGAGATCGACGC CATCTTCATTCACA SafI-MB: FAM-CCAAGCGGAGGGCGATCGCAATCTGGGCTTG-DABCYL	None	N/A	[123]

Table 4. (Continued)

Microorganism	Matrices	Target Gene/Primer and Probe Sequence (5'-3')	Enrichment Media/Time/Temp	Detection Sensitivity	Reference
Noroviruses (GGI.2, GGI.3, GGI.4, GGI.6, GGII, GGIIb, GGIIc, GGIId, GGII.1, GGII.2, GGII.3, GGII.4, and GGII.7)	River water	JV12Y: ATACCACTATGATGCAGAYTA T7-JV13i: AATTCTAATACGACTCACTATAGGGAGAAGGTCAT CATCACCATAGAAIGAG Ni: GAATTCCATCGCCCACTGGCT T7-Ni: AATTCTAATACGACTCACTATAGGGAGAAGGAGC CAGTGGGCGATGGAATTC SR48/50/52: GTGAACAGYATAAAYCAYTGG T7-SR48/50/52: AATTCTAATACGACTCACTATAGGGAGAAGGATC CCARTGRTTTATRCTGTTCAC MBNVG2.1: FAM- CGATCGGTCCCCTGACATCATACAGGCTCGATCG-DABSYL MBNVG2.2: FAM- CGATCGACAGGACTAGGCCCGACACGATCG-DABSYL MBNVG2.4: FAM-CGATCG TCAGGTCTCTCACCAGATGTT CGATCG-DABSYL MBNVG1.1: FAM-CGATCGACAGGCCTATCACCGA CGATCG-DABSYL MBNVG1.2: FAM- CGTCACTGGCTTATCACCTGATGTGACG-DABSYL MBNVG1.3: FAM- CGATCGTATCACCTGATGTTATACAATCC CGATCG-DABSYL MBGGIc: FAM- GCGATGGAIGTTGGIGACTAIGTCATCGC- DABSYL MBGGIi: FAM-CGATCGGAAITCCATCICCCAITG CGATCG-DABSYL MBUK3: FAM-	None	N/A	[126]

Microorganism	Matrices	Target Gene/Primer and Probe Sequence (5'-3')	Enrichment Media/Time/Temp	Detection Sensitivity	Reference
		CGTCCCTGACATCATACAGGCTGGGACG-DABCYL MBJV5: FAM-CGATGCTCACCAGAGGTTGTCCAAGCGCATCG-DABSYL			[107]
Norovirus GI and GII	Oysters	G1F3N1: CCAGGYTGGCAGGCCATGTT G1F3N2: CCTGGKTGGCAGGCCATGTT G1F3N3: CCCGGCTGGCAGCCCATGTT G1F3N4: CCAGGRTGGCARGCCATGTT G1F3N5: CCGGGTTGGCAGGCAATGTT G1F3N6: CCAGGTTGGCAGGCTATATT G2F3N1: GGCATGGATTTCTCACGTGCCCA G2F3N2: GGRATGGATTTTTACGTGCCAA G2F3N3: GGRATGGATTTYTATGTGCCRA G2F3N4: GGMATGGATTTTTACGTGCCCA G2F3N5: GGTCTGGARTTTTATGTGCCCA AATTCTAATACGACTCACTATAGGGAGAGCCAAC CCARCCATTRTACA G2B3IT7: AATTCTAATACGACTCACTATAGGGAGAGCCRCCN GCATRHCCRTRTACA	None	N/A	
Rotavirus	Pure culture	*Gene 9*/Rota-l: GTAAGAAATTAGGTCCAAGAG Rota-2+T7: AATTCTAATACGACTCACTATAGGGAGAGGTCAC ATCGAACAATTC Rota-probe: CAAACTGAGAGAGAAATGAATGAGAGTGAATTGG	None	40 PFU/ml (0.2 PFU/reaction)	[120]

MB = molecular beacon; DABSYL = 4-dimethylaminoazobenzene-4'-sulfonyl; DABCYL = 4-dimethylaminophenylazobenzoic acid-3'; FAM = 6-carboxyfluorescein; TAMRA = tetramethylrhodamine; HEX = hexachloro-6-carboxyfluorescein; N/A = not applicable

Isothermal Amplification

Small scale industries and processors often need hand-held or portable devices that do not require skill, labor, or expensive equipment for routine or rapid and sensitive detection of pathogens. Therefore, amplification techniques have been developed for DNA or RNA amplification under isothermal conditions, where only one temperature is required and a simple water-bath can be used without the need for expensive thermocyclers. Some of the isothermal methods include loop-mediated isothermal amplification (LAMP), transcription mediated amplification (TMA), nucleic acid sequence-based amplification (NASBA), signal mediated amplification of RNA technology, strand displacement amplification (SDA), rolling circle amplification, isothermal multiple displacement amplification, helicase-dependent amplification, single primer isothermal amplification, and circular helicase-dependent amplification. Some of these techniques have been researched for foodborne application and are discussed below.

Loop-Mediated Isothermal Amplification (LAMP)

LAMP is a novel nucleic acid amplification assay that is rapid, specific, relatively simple and easy to perform. First described by Notomi et al. in 2000, this assay relies on an autocycling strand displacement DNA synthesis performed by the *Bst* DNA polymerase large fragment [89]. It also requires 4 to 6 sequence specific primers that recognize 4 to 6 distinct regions on the target gene that allows for accurate and specific pathogen detection [90]. The assay requires only one temperature (60-65°C) in a water-bath, eliminating the need for expensive thermocycling equipment. As nucleic acid is amplified, insoluble magnesium pyrophosphate is formed. Therefore, the increase in turbidity can be observed either visually or by a hand-held turbidimeter. Moreover, the incorporation of fluorescence dyes or probes along with a fluorometer may aid in the quantification and ease of LAMP assay detection. However, the current limitation of the LAMP-based assay is that only external positive and negative controls can be used to determine the success of the amplification reaction and the elimination of false negatives and false positives. Ideally, similar to PCR-based methods, the incorporation of an IAC in the reaction mixture is recommended. Thus, the development and optimization of an appropriate IAC is warranted. The DNA-based LAMP assay has been applied for the detection of *Salmonella* [91-94], *E. coli* O157, O26, and other enterotoxigenic strains [95-97], *Brucella* spp. [98], *V. parahaemolyticus* [94,99,100], *S. aureus* [101,102], *V. cholerae* [103], *Campylobacter* spp. [103,104], and *Cryptosporidium* [105] in pure culture as well as from food products (Table 3).

Similar to PCR, LAMP can be developed into a reverse-transcriptase LAMP (RT-LAMP) assay, targeting RNA, by isolating RNA instead of DNA and using an additional reverse transcription step before amplification. The RT-LAMP assay has been used for detection of pathogens in food, food processing environment and clinical samples for foodborne viruses [106-110] and bacteria such as *Salmonella* [69,111], refer to Table 3. Likewise, multiplexing can also be achieved by optimization of the LAMP assay for detecting two or more targets, such as the simultaneous detection of *V. parahaemolyticus* and related *Vibrio* species targeting the *tdh*, *trh*1, and *trh*2 genes [100], along with using various fluorophores for real-time detection.

Nucleic Acid Sequence-Based Amplification (NASBA)

Although PCR coupled to initial reverse transcription can be used for the detection of target RNA to provide information on viable cells, NASBA can be employed as an alternative transcription-based RNA amplification method that is carried out at isothermal conditions, typically 41°C. NASBA was first described by Guatelli et al. in 1990 [112], that involves the use of 3 different enzymes; reverse transcriptase, RNaseH and T7 RNA polymerase, and 2 primers (one containing the bacteriophage T7 promoter sequence at its 5' end). It can rapidly amplify target RNA sequences by more than 10^8-fold, in a water-bath within 90 min [113]. This assay reportedly can also overcome the drawback of RT-PCR without the interference of carry-over DNA, as NASBA theoretically and typically does not detect any background genomic double stranded DNA due to the absence of a denaturation step. Another advantage is that NASBA does not require a thermocycler. NASBA has been optimized for the detection of several foodborne bacterial and viral pathogens (Table 4). The mRNA-based NASBA to detect *Salmonella enterica* targeting the *dnaK* gene, was applied to food samples [114], with detection sensitivities of 10^2-10^1 CFU/25 g in fresh meats, poultry, fish, ready-to-eat salads or bakery products after 18-h enrichment. Moreover, NASBA or a multiplex NASBA has been used for the detection of other foodborne bacteria, such as *L. monocytogenes*, *V. cholerae*, *C. jejuni* and *M. avium* [115-119], and several foodborne viruses, including hepatitis A virus, human noroviruses, rotavirus, enteroviruses [77,107,119-126], and avian influenza virus [127].

Other Isothermal Amplification Methods

Rolling circle amplification (RCA), developed over the last few decades, is an isothermal enzymatic process for DNA synthesis. The reaction uses DNA polymerases, such as Φ29 DNA polymerase, Sequenase™, Klenow and Vent™ exo-enzymes, or *Bst* DNA polymerase large fragment [128], to continuously amplify a short circular single-stranded DNA template by using a single DNA primer to obtain an end product that is hundreds of thousands (10^5) of nucleotides in length with repetitive sequence units that are complementary to the circular DNA template [129]. In RCA, more than billion-fold amplification (10^9) can be achieved within 1–2 h [128]. In addition, the incorporation of a circularizable oligonucleotide probe allows the RCA to target sequence as both ends of the probe can be ligated thus eliminating the need for a reverse transcription step [130]. Microorganisms such as *E. coli* K-12 and O157:H7 [131,132], and *L. monocytogenes* [133] have been detected by RCA assays showing their effectiveness in nucleic acid amplification and detection.

Strand-displacement amplification (SDA) is a DNA amplification method that is based on nicking an unmodified strand of DNA using restriction enzymes, such as *Bso*BI, and replicating the 3' end at the nick using a 5'-3' exonuclease-deficient DNA polymerase enzyme to displace the downstream DNA strand [134,135]. Once these processes are repeated, single-stranded DNA is continuously generated. SDA has been tested for the detection and identification of microbial pathogens such as *E. coli* O157:H7, as well as a RT-SDA assay targeting mRNA in *M. tuberculosis* [134]. Although an isothermal condition is required for the reaction, initial heating is necessary for DNA denaturation.

Helicase-dependent amplification (HDA) is an isothermal assay utilizing a helicase enzyme to produce single-stranded DNA templates for primer hybridization [136]. Then, the primer extension is carried out by DNA polymerase. Helicase unwinds the duplex DNA enzymatically without the need for heat denaturation of DNA. Various HDA methods have been proposed with different advantages and drawbacks, including an ambient temperature HDA using *E. coli* UvrD helicase, a thermostable HDA using *Tte*-UvrD helicase, a circular HDA (cHDA) using T7 gp4B DNA helicase, and a primase-based whole genome amplification (pWGA) using T7 gp4 DNA helicase-primase [137].

These isothermal amplification methods have high potential to be powerful tools for foodborne pathogen detection. Although, these assays have been tested for the detection of bacterial pathogens in pure culture in laboratory conditions and in some clinical samples [138], their application in food matrices is currently very limited.

Microarrays

Microarray technology has gained increasing interest from researchers to identify target genes. This approach involves the use of specific oligonucleotide probes immobilized on a solid substrate, such as glass, and hybridization of target DNA sequences labeled to the immobilized probes [139]. The detection is based on monitoring of the increase in fluorescence due to the binding of DNA and substrates. Up to hundreds of thousands of oligonucleotide probes can be used in a single array (high density microarray) to increase the power of identification. A reported multi-pathogen identification microarray containing 53,660 pathogen probes was successfully demonstrated for high confidence identification of 18 pathogenic prokaryotes, eukaryotes and viruses, with the limit of detection as little as 10 fg of DNA in samples, below what could be detected by PCR [140]. Additionally, an oligonucleotide array incorporating 13,000 elements representing selected strains of hepatitis A virus (HAV), human coxsackieviruses A and B (CVA and CVB), genogroups I and II of human norovirus (NV), and human rotavirus (RV) gene segments 3,4,10, and 11 was shown to have advantage over PCR due to its ability to identify closely related strains [141]. DNA oligonucleotide arrays have also been tested for the detection of *Arcobacter* and *Campylobacter* isolates from retail chicken samples [142], where *A. butzleri*, *C. coli*, and *C. jejuni* were specifically identified by the assay. These researchers suggested from their validation experiments that this DNA microarray has a detection sensitivity threshold of approximately 10,000 *C. jejuni* cells, which needs to be improved when compared to nucleic acid amplification assays. Therefore, before microarrays can be applied in routine settings, several limitations such as detection sensitivity, cross-reactivity with food matrices, inhibitory substance removal from food matrices, volume reduction and sample concentration and purification need to be addressed. Besides, the cost and skill required to perform these assays need to be considered as well. A more in-depth coverage of microarrays is provided in Chapter 13.

IMMUNOLOGICAL DETECTION

The principle of immunological assays is based on the interaction between antigen and antibody and can typically be used with the specific characterized microorganisms (known antigen and its associated antibody) and also with their physiological responses to stress [143]. These methods include radioimmunoassay (RIA), enzyme immunoassay (EIA), enzyme linked immunosorbent assay (ELISA), enzyme-linked fluorescent assay (ELFA), immune electron microscopy (IEM), immunomagnetic separation (IMS), lateral flow immunodiffusion (LFI), bioluminescent enzyme immunoassay (BEIA), immunochromatography (ICG), enzyme-linked immunomagnetic chemiluminescence (ELIMCL), immuno-precipitation assay, and immunoagglutination. Though the immunoassay based methods are generally highly specific, the drawbacks include low detection sensitivity, and are based on the affinity of the antibody to the pathogen or toxin. Other drawbacks include potential interference from contaminants (in the food matrix) to the assay, as well as specificity to a particular target that may not be able to detect other closely related pathogens [144]. A pre-enrichment step is typically required prior to immunological detection. Moreover, it has been reported that the identification of target microorganisms using these assays can be difficult to confirm in some cases [145].

Immunological detection methods have been reported for the detection of foodborne pathogens, including *E. coli* O157:H7 [146-149], *Salmonella* spp. [146,148,150], *L. monocytogenes* [146,148,151,152], *Campylobacter* spp. [153,154], *Shigella* [155], and *Fusarium* sp. [156], and toxins, including *Staphylococcal* enterotoxins [157-159], and zearalenone [160]. Several automated machines and test kits have been developed and are commercially available, such as the VIDAS SLM™ (bioMérieux) for *Salmonella* ELFA assay, and the TECRA™ ELISA kit (TECRA, Australia) for *Salmonella* spp., *Listeria* spp., and *E. coli* O157:H7, respectively. The VIDAS system has been tested for potential application of *Salmonella* detection in food and food environmental samples [161,162]. The system found to detect as low as 5.0×10^0 CFU/ml of *Salmonella* in the samples with reported specificity to be 0.98, and sensitivity to be 1.0 (no false-negatives) [162].

FLOW CYTOMETRY

Flow cytometry (FCM) is a technique used for the detection of microorganisms without culturing or enrichment, that are suspended in a stream of fluid followed by electronic detection. Fluorescent stains, such as SYTO dyes, fluorogenic substrates, fluorescently-labeled antibodies or oligonucleotide probes are used prior to the FCM analysis using a flow cytometer for the detection of target-specific fluorescence signals. With specific staining, FCM allows the detection and discrimination of live and dead cells [163,164] and can distinguish between reproductively viable, metabolically active, intact, and permeabilized microorganisms [164-166]. FCM has been tested for its competency for viable culturable, viable non-culturable, and nonviable cell differentiation [163]. The detection of *E. coli* O157:H7, *P. aeruginosa*, *S. aureus*, *S.* Typhimurium, and *Shigella flexneri* by FCM have been reported for pure culture and food samples, such as milk [163,164,167].

Table 5. Different techniques for foodborne pathogen detection by biosensors

Pathogen	Biosensor Approach	Assay time	Detection Limit	References
B. cereus	Conductometric electrochemistry	6 min	35 to 88 CFU/ml	[170]
B. cereus	Impedimetric electrochemistry	N/A	N/A	[242]
C. botulinum	Bidiffractive grating biosensor (BDG)	N/A	N/A	[243]
C. jejuni	Amperometric electrochemistry	30 min	50 cells/ml	[174]
E. coli	Resonant mirror detection	N/A	N/A	[244]
E. coli	Optical method using laser beam	N/A	45 cells	[245]
E. coli	Bioluminescence	1 to 2 h	$<10^3$ cells	[246, 247]
E. coli	Amperometric electrochemistry	30 min	50 cells/ml	[174]
E. coli	Potentiometric electrochemistry	1.5 h	10 cells/ml	[248]
E. coli	Impedimetric electrochemistry	N/A	10^1 to 10^7 CFU/ml	[249]
E. coli	Bioluminescence	N/A	N/A	[250]
E. coli O157:H7	Evanescent wave	4 h	3 to 30 CFU/ml	[251]
E. coli O157:H7	Diffuse reflectance spectroscopy	45 min	5×10^5 to 5×10^8 cells/ml	[252]
E. coli O157:H7	Quantum dots	N/A	10^6 cells/ml	[253]
E. coli O157:H7	Chemiluminescence	30 min	10^2 to 10^5 CFU/ml	[254]
E. coli O157:H7	Chemiluminescence enzyme immunoassay	24 h	10^1 to 10^2/g	[255]
E. coli O157:H7	Bacteriophage-based bioluminescene	4 h	10 CFU/ml	[256]
E. coli O157:H7	Amperometric electrochemistry	6 to 10 min	81 to 78 CFU/ml	[257]
E. coli O157:H7	Amperometric electrochemistry	2 h	6×10^2 cells/ml	[258]
E. coli O157:H7	Amperometric electrochemistry	30 min	100 cells/ml	[259]
E. coli O157:H7	Amperometric electrochemistry	35 min	50 cells/ml	[260]
E. coli O157:H7	Conductometric electrochemistry	10 min	7.9×10^1 CFU/ml	[257]
E. coli O157:H7	Turbidimetry (based on the optical density measurements)	N/A	N/A	[261]
E. coli O157:H7	Imaging ellipsometry (IE)	N/A	10^3 to 10^7 CFU/ml	[262]

Pathogen	Biosensor Approach	Assay time	Detection Limit	References
E. coli O157:H7	Fluorescence microscopy	N/A	10^2 CFU/ml	[262]
E. coli O157:H7	Chemiluminescent immunoassay	N/A	10^4 to 10^5 CFU/ml	[148]
E. coli O157:H7 heat-hided	Potentiometric electrochemistry	45 min	7.1×10^2 cells/ml	[263]
E. coli O157:H7 live	Amperometric electrochemistry	30 min	2.5×10^4 cells/ml	
E. coli O157:H7, no enrichment	Amperometric electrochemistry	15 min	1.6×10^1 to 7.2×10^7 CFU/ml	[264]
E. coli O157:H7, with enrichment		6 h	8.0×10^0 to 8.0×10^1 CFU/ml	
Francisella tularensis	Bidiffractive grating biosensor (BDG)	N/A	N/A	[243]
L. monocytogenes	Amperometric electrochemistry	30 min	10 cells/ml	[174]
L. monocytogenes	Chemiluminescent immunoassay	N/A	10^4 to 10^5 CFU/ml	[148]
L. monocytogenes	Impedimetric electrochemistry	N/A	N/A	[242, 265]
L. monocytogenes	Automated optical method	24 h	10–50 cells each in 25 g sample (milk, shell eggs, fresh and ready-to-eat meats or raw chicken)	[266]
Legionella pneumophila	Imaging ellipsometry (IE)	N/A	10^3 to 10^7 CFU/ml	[262]
Ricin toxin	Bidiffractive grating biosensor (BDG)	N/A	N/A	[243]
S. aureus	Turbidimetry (based on the optical density measurements)	N/A	N/A	[261]
S. aureus enterotoxin B	Bidiffractive grating biosensor (BDG)	N/A	N/A	[243]

Table 5. (Continued)

Pathogen	Biosensor Approach	Assay time	Detection Limit	References
S. Typhimurium	Imaging ellipsometry (IE)	N/A	10^3 to 10^7 CFU/ml	[262]
S. Typhimurium	Chemiluminescent immunoassay	N/A	10^4 to 10^5 CFU/ml	[148]
S. Typhimurium	Optic interferometer	12 h	10^5 CFU/ml	[267]
S. Typhimurium	Amperometric electrochemistry	2.5 h	1.09×10^3 CFU/ml	[268]
S. Typhimurium	Amperometric electrochemistry	2 h	5×10^3 cells/ml	[269]
S. Typhimurium	Impedimetric electrochemistry	2.2 h	5.4×10^5 CFU/ml	[270]
S. Typhimurium	Impedimetric electrochemistry	9.3 h	4.8 CFU/ml	[270]
Salmonella	Bioluminescence	N/A	N/A	[250]
Salmonella	Amperometric electrochemistry	35 min	50 cells/ml	[260]
Salmonella	Surface-enhanced infrared absorption spectroscopy	N/A	N/A	[271, 272]
Salmonella	Bacteriophage-based bioluminescene	1–3 h	10^8 CFU/ml	[273]
Salmonella	Amperometric electrochemistry	6 h	1 to 5 CFU/ml	[274]
Salmonella spp.	Conductometric electrochemistry	10 min	7.9×10^1 CFU/ml	[257]
Salmonella spp.	Automated optical method	24 h	10–50 cells each in 25 g sample (milk, shell eggs, fresh and ready-to-eat meats or raw chicken)	[266]
Septicemia/toxemia (septox) in chickens	Near-infrared spectroscopy	N/A	N/A	[275]
V. parahaemolyticus	Cyclic voltammetric Electrochemistry	N/A	7.374×10^4 CFU/ml	[276]
Y. enterocolitica	Turbidimetry (based on the optical density measurements)	N/A	N/A	[261]
Y. enterocolitica	Imaging ellipsometry (IE)	N/A	10^3 to 10^7 CFU/ml	[262]
Y. enterocolitica	Chemiluminescent immunoassay	N/A	10^4 to 10^5 CFU/ml	[148]

Adapted from Velusamy et al., 2010 (Reference [168]).

BIOSENSORS

Biosensors are analytical devices based on the combination of biological responses with a signal, which may be optical, electrochemical, thermometric, piezoelectric, magnetic or micromechanical, for use in detection. The specificity of biosensors relies on bioreceptors that selectively bind the specific target [168] such as antibody/antigen [178], biomimetic materials (synthetic bioreceptors) [179] or bacteriophages [180,181]. Once the target binds to bioreceptor, a biological signal is produced, amplified and then recorded by a detector. Due to its ease of automation and rapid response, biosensors have been broadly researched and applied for detection of microorganisms in environmental and food samples. Lai et al. [182] reported that an electrochemical E-DNA detection method could rapidly identify the sequence-specific PCR products (without the need for purification) of the *gyrB* gene of *S.* Typhimurium with as few as 90 gene copies. This sensor showed no response (no cross-reactivity) to the *gyrB* genes of *E. coli* or various *Shigella* species. Silbert et al. [179] successfully developed and applied the chromatic polymer polydiacetylene sensor for bacterial detection, including *S.* Typhimurium, *Bacillus cereus*, *E. coli* K-12 strains C600, C600 pMRInv, and MC4100, and *E. coli* BL, in pure culture, food samples, and for screening of antibiotic resistant bacteria. The quantitative and simultaneous detection of 4 selected species of bacteria, *E. coli* O157:H7, *S.* Typhimurium, *L. monocytogenes*, and *C. jejuni*, using an 8-channel surface plasmon resonance (SPR) sensor was reported to be achieved with detection limits as low as 3.4×10^3 CFU/ml [183]. Representative studies of foodborne pathogen detection using biosensors are shown in Table 5. Progress continues to be made for the application of biosensors in routine diagnostics.

LAB-ON-A-CHIP

Research on Lab-on-a-chip (LOC) systems has been advancing continuously over the last few years towards the goal of obtaining a portable, hand-held device for contaminant screening. The use of microfabrication and microfluidics allows the detection of target microorganisms in a small scale setting enabling faster detection time with less sample and reagent quantity, and lower fabrication costs. The LOC is an extensive development of the Micro Total Analysis Systems (µTAS) concept which allows completion of different laboratory functions on a chip [184]. The system involves microfabrication of micropumps for flow control, assembly and interfacing development for substrate bonding on a surface material (such as poly(dimethyl siloxane) (PDMS), poly(methyl methacrylate) (PMMA), or other biocompatible and biological materials), optical integration for target detection, and flowsensors and fluidic processors [184,185]. Thus, the rapid, specific and sensitive laboratory assays, such as PCR and RT-PCR, can be miniaturized into on-a-chip systems [185-188]. However, further research is still needed before these systems can be used in the field testing due to the challenges associated with complex food matrices/particles that may interfere with signal intensity and fluid transportation. The concepts for integrated microfluid treatments for analysis systems including sample preparation, target separation and concentration, as well as removal of inhibitors are therefore very critical. It remains hopeful that this technology will continue to advance for routine applications.

VIABLE VS. NON-VIABLE CELL DETECTION

Several detection methods such as mRNA based NASBA and reverse-transcriptase-based nucleic acid amplification methods (RT-PCR and RT-LAMP assays) have been used for live cells detection [67-69,111,114,116,189]. More recently however, nucleic acid dyes for viability measurement coupled to DNA-based amplification assays has gained significant interest. Studies have shown that nucleic acid dyes, such as ethidium monoazide (EMA) and propidium monoazide (PMA), can reduce the PCR signal from the DNA of dead cells as these chemicals can only enter dead cells and bind to their DNA, and block amplification [190,191]. EMA treatment has been tested for live cells detection in combination with PCR assays for several foodborne bacteria, including *L. monocytogenes* [190-193], *C. jejuni* [192], *E. coli* O157:H7, *S.* Typhimurium [190], *S.* Senftenberg, *Clostridium perfringens* [191], *V. vulnificus* [194], *Micrococcus luteus*, *M. avium*, *S. aureus*, *Serratia marcescens* [190] and *Legionella* spp. [195]. However, EMA has shown some evidence of permeating into membranes and reacting with DNA in live microorganisms as well, resulting in a loss of PCR signal from live cells [192]. PMA is a chemical that has been proposed as a non-membrane-permeating intercalating dye [190]. Therefore, DNA of live cells with intact membranes should not be susceptible to PMA treatment, as the dye cannot penetrate the cells or strongly bind the double stranded DNA to prevent DNA amplification. Moreover, PMA has been used to distinguish between infectious and noninfectious enteric viruses with RNA genomes, including coxsackievirus, poliovirus, echovirus, and Norwalk virus [196]. Although the detection of live foodborne pathogens has been successfully shown in pure culture [164,190,197-200], studies of pathogen detection application in food, environmental and clinical samples are still limited [191,201-203] and need further investigation. This is another area of interest to the food industry where significant strides in live cell detection in foods for routine analysis are perceived to be made in the near future.

FUTURE PERSPECTIVES

It is clear that each individual detection technique described has its own advantages and limitations. Therefore, the trend of integrating two or more emerging technologies is expanding in order to enhance assay performance with added benefits of overcoming the existing drawbacks. Several rapid foodborne pathogen detection techniques have been developed and some are commercially available as kits and equipments. Although these rapid assays propose several advantages such as speed, less labor, and high specificity and sensitivity, validation of these assays still remains a challenge. Before detection methods can officially be employed for use, standardization of methods for their accuracy, specificity, reproducibility, and robustness is crucial. This includes the absence of false positive and false negative detection by the assay as it could result in large safety impacts or unnecessary costly recalls of food items. Moreover, cost effective and user-friendly assays, as well as the ability to transfer the technologies to the field for on-site testing/monitoring would allow the food industry to easily adopt these new tools for routine use. Thus, development and application of microfluidics and microfabrication approaches are significantly important to the on-going field of foodborne pathogen detection. While many challenges are being overcome, there still remains a lot of room for improvement in the field of pathogen detection, including sample preparation and concentration, in addition to the final detection with improved signal amplification and improved assay sensitivity.

REFERENCES

[1] Tomás, D., Rodrigo, A., Hernández M. & Ferrús, M. (2009). Validation of real-time PCR and enzyme-linked fluorescent assay-based methods for detection of *Salmonella* spp. in chicken feces samples. *Food Analytical Methods, 2,* 180–189.

[2] Mullis, K. B. (1990). The unusual origin of the polymerase chain reaction. Scientific American, 262, 56-65.

[3] Saiki, R. K., Scharf, S., Faloona, F., Mullis, K. B., Horn, G. T., Erlich, H. A. & Arnheim, N. (1985). Enzymatic amplification of beta-globin genomic sequences and restriction site analysis for diagnosis of sickle cell anemia. *Science, 230,* 1350-1354.

[4] Kang, J., Lee, M. S. & Gorenstein, D. G. (2005). The enhancement of PCR amplification of a random sequence DNA library by DMSO and betaine: Application to in vitro combinatorial selection of aptamers. *Journal of Biochemical and Biophysical Methods, 64,* 147-151.

[5] Abd-Elsalam K. A. (2003). Bioinformatic tools and guideline for PCR primer design. *African Journal of Biotechnology, 2,* 91-95.

[6] Hoorfar, J., N. Cook, B. Malorny, M. Wagner, D. De Medici, A. Abdulmawjood, and P. Fach. 2003. Making Internal Amplification Control Mandatory for Diagnostic PCR. *Journal of Clinical Microbiology.* 41, 5835.

[7] Liu, Y., Gilchrist, A., Zhang, J. & Li, X-F. (2008). Detection of viable but nonculturable *Escherichia coli* O157:H7 bacteria in drinking water and river water. *Applied and Environmental Microbiology, 74,* 1502–1507.

[8] Fakhr, M. K., McEvoy, J. M., Sherwood, J. S. & Logue, C. M. (2006). Adding a selective enrichment step to the iQ-CheckTM real-time PCR improves the detection of *Salmonella* in naturally contaminated retail turkey meat products. *Letters in Applied Microbiology, 43,* 78–83.

[9] Burtscher, C., Fall, P. A., Wilderer, P. A. & Wuertz, S. (1999). Detection of *Salmonella* spp. and *Listeria monocytogenes* in suspended organic waste by nucleic acid extraction and PCR. *Applied and Environmental Microbiology, 65,* 2235–2237.

[10] Burtscher, C. & Wuertz, S. (2003). Evaluation of the use of PCR and reverse transcriptase PCR for detection of Pathogenic bacteria in biosolids from anaerobic digestors and aerobic composters. *Applied and Environmental Microbiology*, 69, 4618–4627.

[11] Ferretti, R., Mannazzu, I., Cocolin, L., Comi, G. & Clementi, F. (2001). Twelve-hour PCR-based method for detection of *Salmonella* spp. in food. *Applied and Environmental Microbiology, 67,* 977–978.

[12] Guo, X., Chen, J., Beuchat, L. R. & Brackett, R. E. (2000). PCR detection of *Salmonella enterica* serotype Montevideo in and on raw tomatoes using primers derived from hilA. *Applied and Environmental Microbiology, 66,* 5248–5252.

[13] Löfström, C., Knutsson, R., Axelsson, C. E. & Rådström, P. (2004). Rapid and specific detection of *Salmonella* spp. in animal feed samples by PCR after culture enrichment. *Applied and Environmental Microbiology, 70*, 69–75.

[14] Naravaneni, R. & Jamil, K. (2005). Rapid detection of food-borne pathogens by using molecular techniques. *Journal of Medical Microbiology, 54*, 51–54.

[15] Pathmanathan, S. G., Cardona-Castro, N., Sánchez-Jiménez, M. M., Correa-Ochoa, M. M., Puthucheary, S. D. & Thong, K. L. (2003). Simple and rapid detection of *Salmonella* strains by direct PCR amplification of the hilA gene. *Journal of Medical Microbiology, 52*, 773–776.

[16] Perera, K. & Murray, A. (2008). Development of a PCR assay for the identification of *Salmonella enterica* serovar Brandenburg. *Journal of Medical Microbiology, 57*, 1223–1227.

[17] Sánchez-Jiménez, M. M. & Cardona-Castro, N. (2004). Validation of a PCR for diagnosis of typhoid fever and salmonellosis by amplification of the hilA gene in clinical samples from Colombian patients. *Journal of Medical Microbiology, 53*, 875–878.

[18] Singer, R. S., Cooke, C. L., Maddox, C. W., Isaacson, R. E. & Wallace, R. L. (2006). Use of pooled samples for the detection of *Salmonella* in feces by polymerase chain reaction. *Journal of Veterinary Diagnostic Investigation, 18*, 319–325.

[19] Kapperud, G., Vardund, T., Skjerve, E., Hornes, E. & Michaelsen, T. E. (1993). Detection of pathogenic *Yersinia enterocolitica* in foods and water by immunomagnetic separation, nested polymerase chain reactions, and colorimetric detection of amplified DNA. *Applied and Environmental Microbiology, 59*, 2938-2944.

[20] Fach, P., Perelle, S., Dilasser, F., Grout, J., Dargaignaratz, C., Botella, L., Gourreau, J-M., Carlin, F., Popoff, M. R. & Broussolle, V. (2002). Detection by PCR–enzyme-linked immunosorbent assay of *Clostridium botulinum* in fish and environmental samples from a coastal area in Northern France. *Applied and Environmental Microbiology, 68*, 5870–5876.

[21] Nair, M. K. M. & Venkitanarayanan, K. S. (2006). Cloning and sequencing of the ompA gene of *Enterobacter sakazakii* and development of an ompA-targeted PCR for rapid detection of *Enterobacter sakazakii* in infant formula. *Applied and Environmental Microbiology, 72*, 2539–2546.

[22] Lübeck, P. S., Cook, N., Wagner, M., Fach, P. & Hoorfar, J. (2003b). Toward an international standard for PCR-based detection of food-borne thermotolerant *Campylobacters*: Validation in a multicenter collaborative trial. *Applied and Environmental Microbiology, 69*, 5670–5672.

[23] Lübeck, P. S., Wolffs, P., On, S. L. W., Ahrens, P., Rådström, P. & Hoorfar, J. (2003a). Toward an international standard for PCR-based detection of food-borne thermotolerant *Campylobacters*: Assay development and analytical validation. *Applied and Environmental Microbiology, 69*, 5664–5669.

[24] Klein, D. (2002). Quantification using real-time PCR technology: applications and limitations. *Trends in Molecular Medicine, 8*, 257-260.

[25] Fey, A., Eichler, S., Flavier, S., Christen, R., Hofle, M. G. & Guzman, C. A. (2004). Establishment of a real-time PCR-based approach for accurate quantification of bacterial RNA targets in water, using *Salmonella* as a model organism. *Applied and Environmental Microbiology, 70*, 3618–3623.

[26] De Medici, D., Croci, L., Delibato, E., Pasquale, S. D., Filetici, E., & Toti, L. (2003). Evaluation of DNA extraction methods for use in combination with SYBR Green I real-time PCR to detect *Salmonella enterica* serotype Enteritidis in poultry. *Applied and Environmental Microbiology,* 69, 3456–3461.

[27] Eyigor, A., Carli, K. T. & Unal, C. B. (2002). Implementation of real-time PCR to tetrathionate broth enrichment of *Salmonella* detection in poultry. *Letters in Applied Microbiology,* 34, 37–41.

[28] Temelli, S., S. Kahya, Eyigor, A. & Carli, K. T. (2010): Incidence of *Salmonella* Enteritidis in chicken layer flocks in Turkey: Results by real-time polymerase chain reaction and International Organization for Standardization culture methods. *Poultry Science,* 89, 1406-1410.

[29] Wolffs, P. F. G., Glencross, K., Norling, B. & Griffiths, M. W. (2007). Simultaneous quantification of pathogenic *Campylobacter* and *Salmonella* in chicken rinse fluid by a flotation and real-time multiplex PCR procedure. *International Journal of Food Microbiology,* 117, 50–54.

[30] Fukushima, H., Katsube, K., Hata, Y., Kishi, R. & Fujiwara, S. (2007). Rapid separation and concentration of food-borne pathogens in food samples prior to quantification by viable-cell counting and real-time PCR. *Applied and Environmental Microbiology,* 73, 92-100.

[31] Fricker, M., Messelhäußer, U., Busch, U., Scherer, S. & Ehling-Schulz, M. (2007). Diagnostic real-time PCR assays for the detection of emetic *Bacillus cereus* strains in foods and recent food-borne outbreaks. *Applied and Environmental Microbiology,* 73, 1892–1898.

[32] Tyagi, S. & Kramer, F. R. (1996). Molecular beacons: probes that fluoresce upon hybridization. *Nature Biotechnology,* 14, 303–308.

[33] Knutsson, R., Löfström, C., Grage, H., Hoofar, J. & Rådström, P. (2002). Modeling of 5'nuclease real-time responses for optimization of a high-throughput enrichment PCR procedure for *Salmonella enterica. Journal of Clinical Microbiology*, 40, 52–60.

[34] Oberst, R. D., Hays, M. P., Bohra, L. K., Phebus, R. K., Yamashiro, C. T., Paszko-Kolva, C., Flood, S. J., Sargeant, J. M. & Gillespie, J. R. (1998). PCR-based DNA amplification and presumptive detection of *Escherichia coli* O157:H7 with an internal fluorogenic probe and the 5' nuclease (TaqMan) assay. *Applied and Environmental Microbiology,* 64, 3389–3396.

[35] Josefsen, M. H., Krause, M., Hansen, F. & Hoorfar, J. (2007). Optimization of a 12-hour TaqMan PCR-based method for detection of *Salmonella* bacteria in meat. *Applied and Environmental Microbiology,* 73, 3040-3048.

[36] Malorny, B., Paccassoni, E., Fach, P., Bunge, C., Martin, A. & Helmuth, R. (2004). Diagnostic Real-Time PCR for Detection of *Salmonella* in Food. *Applied and Environmental Microbiology,* 70, 7046-7052.

[37] Campbell, M. S. & Wright, A. C. (2003). Real-time PCR analysis of *Vibrio vulnificus* from oysters. *Applied and Environmental Microbiology,* 69, 7137-7144.

[38] Lyon, W. J. (2001). TaqMan PCR for Detection of *Vibrio cholerae* O1, O139, non-O1, and non-O139 in pure cultures, raw oysters, and synthetic seawater. *Applied and Environmental Microbiology,* 67,. 4685–4693.

[39] Panicker, G. & Bej, A. K. (2005). Real-time PCR detection of *Vibrio vulnificus* in oysters: Comparison of oligonucleotide primers and probes targeting *vvhA*. *Applied and Environmental Microbiology,* 71, 5702-5709.

[40] Nogva, K. R., Naterstad, K., Holck, A. & Lillehaug, D. (2000a). Application of 5'-nuclease PCR for quantitative detection of *Listeria monocytogenes* in pure cultures, water, skim milk, and unpasteurized whole milk. *Applied and Environmental Microbiology,* 66, 4266-4271.

[41] Kimura, B., Kawasaki, S., Nakano, H. & Fujii, T. (2001). Rapid, quantitative PCR monitoring of growth of *Clostridium botulinum* type E in modified-atmosphere-packaged fish. *Applied and Environmental Microbiology*, 67, 206-216.

[42] Lambertz, S. T., Nilsson, C., Hallanvuo, S. & Lindblad, M. (2008a). Real-time PCR method for detection of pathogenic *Yersinia enterocolitica* in food. *Applied and Environmental Microbiology,* 74, 6060-6067.

[43] Lambertz, S. T., Nilsson, C. & Hallanvuo, S. (2008b). TaqMan-based real-time PCR method for detection of *Yersinia pseudotuberculosis* in Food. *Applied and Environmental Microbiology,* 74, 6465–6469.

[44] Schuurman, T., de Boer, R. F., van Zanten, E., van Slochteren, K. R., Scheper, H. R., Dijk-Alberts, B. G., Möller, A. V. M. & Kooistra-Smid, A. M. D. (2007a). Feasibility of a molecular screening method for detection of *Salmonella enterica* and *Campylobacter jejuni* in a routine community-based clinical microbiology laboratory. *Journal of Clinical Microbiology,* 45, 3692-3700.

[45] Schuurman, T., Roovers, A., van der Zwaluw, W. K., van Zwet, A. A., Sabbe, L. J. M., Mirjam, A., Kooistra-Smid, D. & van Duynhoven, Y. T. H. P. (2007b). Evaluation of 5'-nuclease and hybridization probe assays for the detection of shiga toxin-producing *Escherichia coli* in human stools. *Journal of Clinical Microbiology,* 70, 406-415.

[46] Chen, W., Martinez, G. & Mulchandani, A. (2000). Molecular beacons: A real-time polymerase chain reaction assay for detecting *Salmonella*. *Analytical Biochemistry,* 280, 166–172.

[47] Broude, N. E. (2005). Molecular beacons and other hairpin probes. *Encyclopedia of diagnostic genomics and proteomics.* New York, NY: Marcel Dekker Inc.

[48] Patel, J. R., Bhagwat, A. A., Sanglay, G. C. & Solomon, M. B. (2006). Rapid detection of *Salmonella* from hydrodynamic pressure-treated poultry using molecular beacon real-time *PCR. Food Microbiology,* 23, 39–46.

[49] Liming, S. H. & Bhagwat, A. A. (2004). Application of a molecular beacon—real-time PCR technology to detect *Salmonella* species contaminating fruits and vegetables. *International Journal of Food Microbiology,* 95, 177– 187.

[50] McKillip, J. L. & Drake, M. (2000). Molecular beacon polymerase chain reaction detection of *Escherichia coli* O157:H7 in milk. *Journal of Food Protection,* 63, 855–859.

[51] Hadjinicolaou, A. V., Demetriou, V. L., Emmanuel, M. A., Kakoyiannis, C. K. & Kostrikis, L. G. (2009). Molecular beacon-based real-time PCR detection of primary isolates of *Salmonella* Typhimurium and *Salmonella* Enteritidis in environmental and clinical samples. *BMC Microbiology,* 9, 1-14.

[52] Fang, Y., Wu, W-H., Pepper, J. L., Larsen, J. L., Marras, S. A. E., Nelson, E. A., Epperson, W. B. & Christopher-Hennings, J. (2002). Comparison of real-time, quantitative PCR with molecular beacons to nested PCR and culture methods for

detection of *Mycobacterium avium* subsp. *paratuberculosis* in bovine fecal samples. *Journal of Clinical Microbiology*, 40, 287–291.

[53] Kutyavin, I. V. (2010). New approach to real-time nucleic acids detection: folding polymerase chain reaction amplicons into a secondary structure to improve cleavage of Förster resonance energy transfer probes in 5'-nuclease assays. *Nucleic Acids Research*, 38, e29.

[54] Pestana, E. A., Belak, S., Diallo, A., Crowther, J. R. & Viljoen, G. J. 2010. Early, Rapid and Sensitive Veterinary Molecular Diagnostics - Real Time PCR Applications. Dordrecht, NL: Springer Science+Business Media.

[55] Singh, J., Batish, V. K. & Grover, S. (2009a). A scorpion probe–based real-time PCR assay for detection of *E. coli* O157:H7 in dairy products. *Foodborne Pathogens and Disease*, 6, 395-400.

[56] Stricker, A. R., Wilhartitz, I., Farnleitner, A. H. & Mach, R. L. (2008). Development of a Scorpion probe-based real-time PCR for the sensitive quantification of *Bacteroides* sp. ribosomal DNA from human and cattle origin and evaluation in spring water matrices. *Microbiological Research*, 163, 140—147.

[57] Maurer, J. J. 2006. The Mythodology of PCR: A Warning to the Wise. In: J. J. Maurer (Ed.), PCR Methods in Foods. New York, NY, Springer Science+Bussiness Media, Inc.

[58] McIngvale, S. C., Elhanafi, D. & Drake, M. A. (2002). Optimization of reverse transcriptase PCR to detect viable shiga-toxin-producing *Escherichia coli*. *Applied and Environmental Microbiology*, 68, 799–806.

[59] Bhattacharya, S. S., Kulka, M., Lampel, K. A., Cebula, T. A. & Goswami, B. B. (2004). Use of reverse transcription and PCR to discriminate between infectious and non-infectious hepatitis A virus. *Journal of Virological Methods*, 116, 181–187.

[60] Guévremont, E., Brassard, J., Houde, A., Simard, C. & Trottier, Y. L. (2006). Development of an extraction and concentration procedure and comparison of RT-PCR primer systems for the detection of hepatitis A virus and norovirus GII in green onions. *Journal of Virological Methods*, 134, 130–135.

[61] Brassard, J., Seyer, K., Houde, A., Simard, C. & Trottier, Y. L. (2005). Concentration and detection of hepatitis A virus and rotavirus in spring water samples by reverse transcription-PCR. *Journal of Virological Methods*, 123, 163–169.

[62] Kingsley, D. H. & Richards, G. P. (2001). Rapid and efficient extraction method for reverse transcription-PCR detection of hepatitis A and Norwalk-like viruses in shellfish. *Applied and Environmental Microbiology*, 67, 4152–4157.

[63] Balaji, B., O'Connor, K., Lucas, J. R., Anderson, J. M. & Csonka, L. N. (2005). Timing of induction of osmotically controlled genes in *Salmonella enterica* Serovar Typhimurium, determined with quantitative real-time reverse transcription-PCR. *Applied and Environmental Microbiology*, 71, 8273–8283.

[64] Day, J. B., Basavanna, U. & Sharma, S. K. (2009). Development of a cell culture method to isolate and enrich *Salmonella enterica* serotype enteritidis from shell eggs for subsequent detection by real-time PCR. *Applied and Environmental Microbiology*, 75, 5321–5327.

[65] D'Souza, D. H., Critzer, F. J. & Golden, D. A. (2009). Real-time reverse-transcriptase-PCR (RT-PCR) for the rapid detection of *Salmonella* using invA primers. *Foodborne Pathogens and Disease*, 6, 1097-1106.

[66] González-Escalona, N., Hammack, T. S., Russell, M., Jacobson, A. P., De Jesús, A. J., Brown, E. W. & Lampel, K. A. (2009). Detection of live *Salmonella* sp. cells in produce by TaqMan-based quantitative reverse transcriptase real-time PCR targeting invA mRNA. *Applied and Environmental Microbiology, 75*, 3714-3720.

[67] Miller, N. D., Draughon, F. A. & D'Souza, D. H. (2010a). Real-time reverse-transcriptase PCR for *Salmonella* Typhimurium detection from jalapeño and serrano peppers. *Foodborne Pathogens and Disease, 7*, 367-373.

[68] Techathuvanan, C., Draughon, F. A. & D'Souza, D. H. (in press a). Real-time reverse-transcriptase polymerase chain reaction for the rapid and sensitive detection of *Salmonella* Typhimurium from pork. Foodborne Pathogens and Disease, in press.

[69] Techathuvanan, C., Draughon, F. A. & D'Souza, D. H. (in press b). Comparison of RT-PCR, loop-mediated isothermal amplification, and culture-based assays for *Salmonella enterica* detection from pork processing environments. *Journal of Food Protection*, in press.

[70] Fitzmaurice, J., Glennon, M., Duffy, G., Sheridan, J. J., Carroll, C. & Maher, M. (2004). Application of real-time PCR and RT-PCR assays for the detection and quantitation of VT 1 and VT 2 toxin genes in *E. coli* O157:H7. *Molecular and Cellular Probes, 18*, 123–132.

[71] Matsuda, K., Tsuji, H., Asahara, T., Kado, Y. & Nomoto, K. (2007). Sensitive quantitative detection of commensal bacteria by rRNA-targeted reverse transcription-PCR. *Applied and Environmental Microbiology, 73*, 32–39.

[72] Sheridan, G. E. C., Masters, C. I., Shallcross, J. A. & Mackey, B. M. (1998). Detection of mRNA by reverse transcription-PCR as an indicator of viability in *Escherichia coli* cells. *Applied and Environmental Microbiology, 64*, 1313–1318.

[73] Rokbi, B., Seguin, D., Guy, B., Mazarin, V., Vidor, E., Mion, F., Cadoz, M. & Quentin-Millet, M-J. (2001). Assessment of Helicobacter pylori gene expression within mouse and human gastric mucosae by real-time reverse transcriptase PCR. *Infection and Immunity, 69*, 4759–4766.

[74] Fuhrman, J. A., Liang, X. & Noble, R. T. (2005). Rapid detection of enteroviruses in small volumes of natural waters by real-time quantitative reverse transcriptase PCR. *Applied and Environmental Microbiology, 71*, 4523–4530.

[75] Abd El Galil, K. H., El Sokkary, M. A., Kheira, S. M., Salazar, A. M., Yates, M. V., Chen, W. & Mulchandani, A. (2004). Combined immunomagnetic separation–molecular beacon–reverse transcription-PCR assay for detection of hepatitis A virus from environmental samples. *Applied and Environmental Microbiology, 70*, 4371–4374.

[76] Costafreda, M. I., Bosch, A. & Pintó, R. M. (2006). Development, evaluation, and standardization of a real-time TaqMan reverse transcription-PCR assay for quantification of hepatitis A virus in clinical and shellfish samples. *Applied and Environmental Microbiology, 72*, 3846–3855.

[77] Jean, J., Blais, B., Darveau, A. & Fliss, I. (2001). Detection of hepatitis A virus by the nucleic acid sequence-based amplification technique and comparison with reverse transcription-PCR. *Applied and Environmental Microbiology, 67*, 5593–5600.

[78] Legeay, O., Caudrelier, Y., Cordevant, C., Rigottier-Gois, L. & Lange, M. (2000). Simplified procedure for detection of enteric pathogenic viruses in shellfish by RT-PCR. *Journal of Virological Methods, 90*, 1–14.

[79] Kang, G., Iturriza-Gomara, M., Wheeler, J. G., Crystal, P., Monica, B., Ramani, S., Primrose, B., Moses, P. D., Gallimore, C. I., Brown, D. W. & Gray, J. (2004). Quantitation of group A rotavirus by real-time reverse-transcription-polymerase chain reaction: Correlation with clinical severity in children in South India. *Journal of Medical Virology*, 73, 118–122.

[80] Jothikumar, N., Lowther, J. A., Henshilwood, K., Lees, D. N., Hill, V. R. & Vinjé, J. (2005). Rapid and sensitive detection of noroviruses by using TaqMan-based one-step reverse transcription-PCR assays and application to naturally contaminated shellfish samples. *Applied and Environmental Microbiology*, 71, 1870–1875.

[81] Kageyama, T., Kojima, S., Shinohara, M., Uchida, K., Fukushi, S., Hoshino, F. B., Takeda, n. & Katayama, K.. (2003). Broadly reactive and highly sensitive assay for Norwalk-like viruses based on real-time quantitative reverse transcription-PCR. *Journal of Clinical Microbiology*, 41, 1548–1557.

[82] Lowther, J. A., Henshilwood, K. & Lees, D. N. (2008). Determination of norovirus contamination in oysters from two commercial harvesting areas over an extended period, using semiquantitative real-time reverse transcription PCR. *Journal of Food Protection*, 71, 1427-1433.

[83] Park, Y-B., Cho, Y-H., Jee, Y-M. & Ko, G-P. (2008). Immunomagnetic separation combined with real-time reverse transcriptase PCR assays for detection of norovirus in contaminated food. *Applied and Environmental Microbiology*, 74, 4226–4230.

[84] Richards, G. P., Watson, M. A., Fankhauser, R. L. & Monroe, S. S. (2004). Genogroup I and II noroviruses detected in stool samples by real-time reverse transcription-PCR using highly degenerate universal primers. *Applied and Environmental Microbiology*, 70, 7179–7184.

[85] Slomka, M. J., Pavlidis, T., Banks, J., Shell, W., McNally, A., Essen, S. & Brown, I. H. (2007). Validated H5 Eurasian real-time reverse transcriptase-polymerase chain reaction and its application in H5N1 outbreaks in 2005-2006. *Avian Diseases*, 51, 373-377.

[86] Nordstrom, J. L., Vickery, M. C. L., Blackstone, G. M., Murray, S. L. & DePaola, A. (2007). Development of a multiplex real-time PCR assay with an internal amplification control for the detection of total and pathogenic *Vibrio parahaemolyticus* bacteria in oysters. *Applied and Environmental Microbiology*, 73, 5840–5847.

[87] Kim, J. S., Lee, G. G., Park, J. S., Jung, Y. H., Kwak, H. S., Kim, S. B., Nam, Y. S. & Kwon, S. T. (2007a). A novel multiplex PCR assay for rapid and simultaneous detection of five pathogenic bacteria: *Escherichia coli* O157:H7, *Salmonella*, Staphylococcus aureus, Listeria monocytogenes, and Vibrio parahaemolyticus. *Journal of Food Protection*, 70, 1656–1662.

[88] Chen, Y. & Knabel, S. J. (2007). Multiplex PCR for simultaneous detection of bacteria of the genus *Listeria, Listeria monocytogenes*, and major serotypes and epidemic clones of *L. monocytogenes*. *Applied and Environmental Microbiology*, 73, 6299–6304.

[89] Notomi, T., Okayama, H., Masubuchi, H., Yonekawa, T., Watanabe, K., Amino, N. & Hase, T. (2000). Loop-mediated isothermal amplification of DNA. *Nucleic Acids Research*, 28, E63.

[90] Salehi, T. Z., Mahzounieh, M. & Saeedzadeh, A. 2005. Detection of InvA gene in isolated *Salmonella* from broilers by PCR method. *International Journal of Poultry Science*, 4, 557-559.

[91] Hara-Kudo, Y., Yoshino, M., Kojima, T. & Ikedo, M. (2005). Loop-mediated isothermal amplification for the rapid detection of *Salmonella*. *FEMS Microbiology Letters,* 253, 155–161.

[92] Ohtsuka, K., Yanagawa, K., Takatori, K. & Hara-Kudo, Y. (2005). Detection of *Salmonella enterica* in naturally contaminated liquid eggs by loop-mediated isothermal amplification, and characterization of *Salmonella* isolates. *Applied and Environmental Microbiology,* 71, 6730–6735.

[93] Okamura, M., Ohba, Y., Kikuchi, S., Suzuki, A., Tachizaki, H., Takehara, K., Ikedo, M., Kojima, T. & Nakamura, M. (2008). Loop-mediated isothermal amplification for the rapid, sensitive, and specific detection of the O9 group of *Salmonella* in chickens. *Veterinary Microbiology,* 132, 197–204.

[94] Wang, L., Shi, L., Alam, M. J., Geng, Y. & Li, L. (2008). Specific and rapid detection of foodborne *Salmonella* by loop-mediated isothermal amplification method. *Food Research International,* 41, 69–74.

[95] Hara-Kudo, Y., Konishi, N., Ohtsuka, K., Hiramatsu, R., Tanaka, H., Konuma, H. & Takatori, K. (2008). Detection of verotoxigenic *Escherichia coli* O157 and O26 in food by plating methods and LAMP method: A collaborative study. *International Journal of Food Microbiology,* 122, 156–161.

[96] Hill, J., Beriwal, S., Chandra, I., Paul, V. K., Kapil, A., Singh, T., Wadowsky, R. M., Singh, V., Goyal, A., Jahnukainen, T., Johnson, J. R., Tarr, P. I. & Vats, A. (2008). Loop-Mediated Isothermal Amplification Assay for Rapid Detection of Common Strains of *Escherichia coli. Journal of Clinical Microbiology,* 46, 2800–2804.

[97] Yano, A., Ishimaru, R. & Hujikata, R. (2007). Rapid and sensitive detection of heat-labile I and heat-stable I enterotoxin genes of enterotoxigenic *Escherichia coli* by loop-mediated isothermal amplification. *Journal of Microbiological Methods*, 68, 414–420.

[98] Ohtsuki, R., Kawamoto, K., Kato, Y., Shah, M. M., Ezaki, T. & Makino, S-I. 2007. Rapid detection of *Brucella* spp. by the loop-mediated isothermal amplification method. *Journal of Applied Microbiology,* 104, 1815–1823.

[99] Chen, S. & Ge, B. (2010). Development of a toxR-based loop-mediated isothermal amplification assay for detecting *Vibrio parahaemolyticus. BMC Microbiology,* 10, 41.

[100] Yamazaki, W., Kumeda, Y., Misawa, N., Nakaguchi, Y. & Nishibuchi, M. (2010). Development of a loop-mediated isothermal amplification assay for sensitive and rapid detection of the *tdh* and *trh* genes of *Vibrio parahaemolyticus* and related *Vibrio* species. *Applied and Environmental Microbiology,* 76, 820–828.

[101] Goto, M., Hayashidani, H., Takatori, K. & Hara-Kudo, Y. (2007). Rapid detection of enterotoxigenic *Staphylococcus aureus* harbouring genes for four classical enterotoxins, SEA, SEB, SEC and SED, by loop-mediated isothermal amplification assay. *Letters in Applied Microbiology,* 45, 100–107.

[102] Misawa, Y., Yoshida, A., Saito, R., Yoshida, H., Okuzumi, K., Ito, N., Okada, M., Moriya, K. & Koike, K. (2007). Application of loop-mediated isothermal amplification technique to rapid and direct detection of methicillin-resistant *Staphylococcus aureus* (MRSA) in blood cultures. *Journal of Infection and Chemotherapy,* 13, 134–140.

[103] Yamazaki, W., Ishibashi, M., Kawahara, R. & Inoue, K. (2008b). Development of a loop-mediated Isothermal amplification assay for sensitive and rapid detection of *Vibrio parahaemolyticus. BMC Microbiology,* 8, 163.

[104] Yamazaki, W., Taguchi, M., Ishibashi, M., Kitazato, M., Nukina, M., Misawa, N. & Inoue, K. (2008a). Development and evaluation of a loop-mediated isothermal amplification assay for rapid and simple detection of *Campylobacter jejuni* and *Campylobacter coli*. *Journal of Medical Microbiology,* 57, 444–451.

[105] Karanis, P., Thekisoe, O., Kiouptsi, K., Ongerth, J., Igarashi, I. & Inoue, N. (2007). Development and preliminary evaluation of a loop-mediated isothermal amplification procedure for sensitive detection of *Cryptosporidium* oocysts in fecal and water samples. *Applied and Environmental Microbiology,* 73, 5660–5662.

[106] Fukuda, S., Takao, S., Kuwayama, M., Shimazu, Y. & Miyazaki, K. (2006). Rapid detection of norovirus from fecal specimens by real-time reverse transcription–loop-mediated isothermal amplification assay. *Journal of Clinical Mircobiology,* 44, 1376–1381.

[107] Fukuda, S., Sasaki, Y. & Seno, M. (2008). Rapid and sensitive detection of norovirus genomes in oysters by a two-step isothermal amplification assay system combining nucleic acid sequence-based amplification and reverse transcription–loop-mediated isothermal amplification assays. *Applied and Environmental Microbiology,* 74, 3912–3914.

[108] Lan, X., Yang, Li, B. Y., Yin, X. P., Li, X. R. & Liu, J. X. (2009). Reverse transcription–loop-mediated isothermal amplification assay for rapid detection of hepatitis E virus. *Journal of Clinical Microbiology,* 47, 2304–2306.

[109] Postel, A., Letzel, T., Frischmann, S., Grund, C., Beer, M. & Harder, T. (2010). Evaluation of two commercial loop-mediated isothermal amplification assays for detection of avian influenza H5 and H7 hemagglutinin genes. *Journal of Veterinary Diagnostic and Investigation,* 22, 61–66.

[110] Yoneyama, T., Kiyohara, T., Shimasaki, N., Kobayashi, G., Ota, Y., Notomi, T., Totsuka, A. & Wakita, T. (2007). Rapid and real-time detection of hepatitis A virus by reverse transcription loop-mediated isothermal amplification assay. *Journal of Virological Methods,* 145, 162–168.

[111] Techathuvanan, C., Draughon, F. A. & D'Souza, D. H. (2010b). Loop-mediated isothermal amplification (LAMP) for the rapid and sensitive detection of *Salmonella* Typhimurium from pork. *Journal of Food Science,* 75, M165-M172

[112] Fox, J. D., Han, S., Samuelson, A., Zhang, Y., Neale, M. L. & Westmoreland, D. (2002) Development and evaluation of nucleic acid sequence based amplification (NASBA) for diagnosis of enterovirus infections using the NucliSens® Basic kit. *Journal of Clinical Virology,* 24, 117–130.

[113] Compton, J. (1991) Nucleic acid sequence-based amplification. *Nature,* 350, 91–92.

[114] D'Souza, D. H. & Jaykus, L-A. (2003). Nucleic acid sequence based amplification for the rapid and sensitive detection of *Salmonella enterica* from foods. *Journal of Applied Microbiology,* 95, 1343–1350.

[115] Blais, B. W., Turner, G., Sooknanan, R. & Malek, L. T. (1997). A Nucleic Acid Sequence-Based Amplification System for Detection of *Listeria monocytogenes* hlyA Sequences. *Applied and Environmental Microbiology,* 63, 310–313.

[116] Fykse, E. M., Skogan, G., Davies, W., Olsen, J. S. & Blatny, J. M. (2007). Detection of *Vibrio cholerae* by real-time nucleic acid sequence-based amplification. *Applied and Environmental Microbiology,* 73, 1457–1466.

[117] Rodríguez-Lázaro, D., D'Agostino, M., Pla, M. & Cook, N. (2004). Construction strategy for an internal amplification control for real-time diagnostic assays using nucleic acid sequence-based amplification: Development and clinical application. *Journal of Clinical Microbiology,* 42, 5832–5836.

[118] Uyttendaele, M., Schukkink, R., van Gemen, B. & Debevere, J. (1995a). Detection of *Campylobacter jejuni* added to foods by using a combined selective enrichment and nucleic acid sequence-based amplification (NASBA). *Applied and Environmental Microbiology,* 61, 1341–1347.

[119] Uyttendaele, M., Schukkink, R., van Gemen, B. & Debevere, J. (1995b). Development of NASBA®, a nucleic acid amplification system, for identification of *Listeria monocytogenes* and comparison to ELISA and a modified FDA method. *International Journal of Food Microbiology,* 27, 77-89.

[120] Jean, J., Blais, B., Darveau, A. & Fliss, I. (2002). Simultaneous detection and identification of hepatitis A virus and rotavirus by multiplex nucleic acid sequence-based amplification (NASBA) and microtiter plate hybridization system. *Journal of Virological Methods,* 105, 123–132.

[121] Jean, J., D'Souza, D. H. & Jaykus, L-A. (2004). Multiplex nucleic acid sequence-based amplification for simultaneous detection of several enteric viruses in model ready-to-eat foods. *Applied and Environmental Microbiology,* 70, 6603–6610.

[122] Kou, X., Wu, Q., Zhang, J. & Fan, H. (2006). Rapid detection of noroviruses in fecal samples and shellfish by nucleic acid sequence-based amplification. *Journal of Microbiology,* 44, 403-408.

[123] Lamhoujeb, S., Fliss, I., Ngazoa, S. E. & Jean, J. (2008). Evaluation of the persistence of infectious human noroviruses on food surfaces by using real-time nucleic acid sequence-based amplification. *Applied and Environmental Microbiology,* 74, 3349–3355.

[124] Landry, M. L., Garner, R. & Ferguson, D. (2003). Rapid enterovirus RNA detection in clinical specimens by using nucleic acid sequence-based amplification. *Journal of Clinical Microbiology,* 41, 346–350.

[125] Rutjes, S. A., Italiaander, R., van den Berg, H. H. J. L., Lodder, W. J. & de Roda Husman, A. M. (2005). Isolation and detection of enterovirus RNA from large-volume water samples by using the NucliSens miniMAG System and real-time nucleic acid sequence-based amplification. *Applied and Environmental Microbiology,* 71, 3734–3740.

[126] Rutjes, S. A., van den Berg, H. H. J. L., Lodder, W. J. & de Roda Husman, A. M. (2006). Real-time detection of noroviruses in surface water by use of a broadly reactive nucleic acid sequence-based amplification assay. *Applied and Environmental Microbiology,* 72, 5349–5358.

[127] Lau, L. T., Banks, J., Aherne, R., Brown, I. H., Dillon, N., Collins, R. A., Chan, K. Y., Fung, Y. W., Xing, J. & Yu, A. C. H. (2004). Nucleic acid sequence-based amplification methods to detect avian influenza virus. *Biophysical Research Communications,* 313, 336–342.

[128] Demidov, V. V. (2002). Rolling-circle amplification in DNA diagnostics: the power of simplicity. *Expert Review of Molecular Diagnostics,* 2, 542-548.

[129] Zhao, W., Ali, M. M., Brook, M. A. & Angew, Y. L. (2008). Rolling circle amplification: Applications in nanotechnology and biodetection with functional nucleic acids. *Angewandte Chemie International Edition,* 47, 6330 – 6337.

[130] Zhang, D., Wu, J., Ye, F., Feng, T., Lee, I. & Yin, B. (2006). Amplification of circularizable probes for the detection of target nucleic acids and proteins. *Clinica Chimica Acta,* 363, 61–70.

[131] Inoue, J., Shigemori, Y. & Mikawa, T. (2006). Improvements of rolling circle amplification (RCA) efficiency and accuracy using Thermus thermophilus SSB mutant protein. *Nucleic Acids Research,* 34, e69.

[132] Nelson, J. R., Cai, Y. C., Giesler, T. L., Farchaus, J. W., Sundaram, S. T., Ortiz-Rivera, M., Hosta, L. P., Hewitt, P. L., Mamone, J. A., Palaniappan, C. & Fuller, C. W. (2002). TempliPhi, phi29 DNA polymerase based rolling circle amplification of templates for DNA sequencing. *Biotechniques,* Suppl, 44-47.

[133] Murakami, T., Sumaoka, J. & Komiyama, M. (2009). Sensitive isothermal detection of nucleic-acid sequence by primer generation–rolling circle amplification. *Nucleic Acids Research,* 37, e19.

[134] Ge, B., Larkin, C., Ahn, S., Jolley, M., Nasir, M., Meng, J. & Hall, R. H. (2002). Identification of *Escherichia coli* O157:H7 and other enterohemorrhagic serotypes by EHEC-hlyA targeting, strand displacement amplification, and fluorescence polarization. *Molecular and Cellular Probes,* 16, 85–92.

[135] Walker, G. T., Fraiser, M. S., Schram, J. L., Little, M. C., Nadeau, J. G. & Malinowski, D. P. (1992). Strand displacement amplification—an isothermal, in vitro DNA amplification technique. *Nucleic Acids Research,* 20, 1691–1696.

[136] Vincent, M., Xu, Y. & Kong, H. (2004). Helicase-dependent isothermal DNA amplification. *European Molecular Biology Organization Reports,* 5, 795-800.

[137] Jeong, Y. J., Park, K. & Kim, D. E. (2009). Isothermal DNA amplification in vitro: the helicase-dependent amplification system. *Cellular and Molecular Life Science,* 66, 3325–3336.

[138] Piersimoni, C. & Scarparo, C. (2003). Relevance of commercial amplification methods for direct detection of *Mycobacterium tuberculosis* complex in clinical samples. *Journal of Clinical Microbiology,* 41, 5355–5365.

[139] Dolan, P. L., Wu, Y., Ista, L. K., Metzenberg, R. L., Nelson, M. A. & Lopez, G. P. (2001). Robust and efficient synthetic method for forming DNA microarrays. *Nucleic Acids Research,* 29, e107.

[140] Wilson, W. J., Strout, C. L., DeSantis, T. Z., Stilwell, J. L., Carrano, A. V. & Andersen, G. L. (2002). Sequence-specific identification of 18 pathogenic microorganisms using microarray technology. *Molecular and Cellular Probes,* 16, 119–127.

[141] Ayodeji, M., Kulka, M., Jackson, S. A., Patel, I., Mammel, M., Cebula, T. A. & Goswami, B. B. (2009). A Microarray Based Approach for the Identification of Common Foodborne Viruses. *The Open Virology Journal,* 3, 7-20.

[142] Quiñónes, B., Parker, C. T., Janda, Jr., J. M., Miller, W. G. & Mandrell, R. E. (2007). Detection and genotyping of *Arcobacter* and *Campylobacter* isolates from retail chicken samples by use of DNA oligonucleotide arrays. *Applied and Environmental Microbiology,* 73, 3645–3655.

[143] Hahm, B. K. & Bhunia, A. K. (2006). Effect of environmental stresses on antibody-based detection of *Escherichia coli* O157: H7, *Salmonella enterica* serotype Enteritidis and Listeria monocytogenes. *Journal of Applied Microbiology,* 100, 1017–1027.

[144] Meng, J. H. & Doyle, M. P. (2002). Introduction. Microbiological food safety. *Microbes and Infect,* 4, 395–397.

[145] Gorski, L. & Csordas, A. 2010. Molecular detection: Principles and methods. In: Liu D. (Ed.), Molecular detection of foodborne pathogens. (pp. 1-20). Boca Raton, FL: CDC Press.

[146] Chen, C. S. & Durst, R. A. (2006). Simultaneous detection of *Escherichia coli* O157: H7, *Salmonella* spp. and *Listeria monocytogenes* with an array-based immunosorbent assay using universal protein G-liposomal nanovesicles. Talanta, 69, 232–238.

[147] Gehring, A. G., Irwin, P. L., Reed, S.A. & Tu, S. I. (2006). Enzyme-linked immunomagnetic chemiluminescence incorporating anti-H7 and anti-O157 antibodies for the detection of *Escherichia coli* O157: H7. *Journal of Rapid Methods and Automation in Microbiology,* 14, 349–361.

[148] Magliulo, M., Simoni, P., Guardigli, M., Michelini, E., Luciani, M., Lelli, R. & Roda, A. (2007). A rapid multiplexed chemiluminescent immunoassay for the detection of *Escherichia coli* O157: H7, *Yersinia* enterocolitica, *Salmonella* typhimurium, and *Listeria monocytogenes* pathogen bacteria. *Journal of Agricultural and Food Chemisrty,* 55, 4933–4939.

[149] Sunwoo, H. H., Wang, W. W. & Sim, J. S. (2006). Detection of *Escherichia coli* O157:H7 using chicken immunoglobulin Y. *Immunology Letters,* 106, 191–193.

[150] Schneid, A. D., Rodrigues, K. L., Chemello, D., Tondo, E. C., Ayub, M. A. Z. & Aleixo, J. A. G. (2006). Evaluation of an indirect ELISA for the detection of *Salmonella* in chicken meat. *Brazilian Journal of Microbiology*, 37, 350–355.

[151] Churchill, R. L. T., Lee, H. & Hall, J. C. (2006). Detection of *Listeria monocytogenes* and the toxin listeriolysin O in food. *Journal of Microbiological Methods,* 64, 141–170.

[152] Hibi, K., Abe, A., Ohashi, E., Mitsubayashi, K., Ushio, H., Hayashi, T., Ren, H. & Endo, H. (2006). Combination of immunomagnetic separation with flow cytometry for detection of *Listeria monocytogenes. Analytica Chimica Acta,* 573, 158–163.

[153] Borck, B., Stryhn, H., Ersboll, A. K. & Pedersen, K. (2002). Thermophilic *Campylobacter* spp. in turkey samples: evaluation of two automated enzyme immunoassays and conventional microbiological techniques. *Journal of Applied Microbiology,* 92, 574–582.

[154] Hochel, I., Slavickova, D., Viochna, D., Skvor, J. & Steinhauserova, I. (2007). Detection of *Campylobacter* species in foods by indirect competitive ELISA using hen and rabbit antibodies. *Food and Agricultural Immunology,* 18, 151–167.

[155] Warren, B. R., Parish, M. E. & Schneider, K. R. (2006). Shigella as a foodborne pathogen and current methods for detection in food. *Critical Review in Food Science and Nutrition,* 46, 551–567.

[156] Meirelles, P. G., Ono, M. A., Ohe, M. C. T., Maroneze, D. M., Itano, E. N., Garcia, G. T., Sugiura, Y., Ueno, Y., Hirooka, E. Y. & Ono, E. Y. S. (2006). Detection of Fusarium sp. contamination in corn by enzyme-linked immunosorbent assay. *Food and Agricultural Immunology,* 17, 79–89.

[157] Bennett, R.W. (2005). Staphylococcal enterotoxin and its rapid identification in foods by enzymelinked immunosorbent assay-based methodology. *Journal Food Protection,* 68, 1264–1270.

[158] Jechorek, R. P. & Johnson, R. L. (2008). Evaluation of the VIDAS® staph enterotoxin II (SET 2) immunoassay method for the detection of Staphylococcal enterotoxins in selected foods: collaborative study. *Journal of AOAC International,* 91, 164–173.

[159] Schlosser, G., Kacer, P., Kuzma, M., Szilagyi, Z., Sorrentino, A., Manzo, C., Pizzano, R., Malorni, L. & Pocsfalvi, G. (2007). Coupling immunomagnetic separation on magnetic beads with matrix-assisted laser desorption ionization-time of flight mass spectrometry for detection of staphylococcal enterotoxin B. *Applied and Environmental Microbiology,* 73, 6945–6952.

[160] Kawamura, O. & Emoto, A. (2006). Production of monoclonal antibodies against zearalenone. Kagawa Daigaku Nogakubu Gakujutsu Hokoku, 58, 7-11.

[161] Walker, R. L., Kinde, H., Anderson, R. J. & Brown, A. E. (2001). Comparison of VIDAS enzyme-linked fluorescent immunoassay using Moore swab sampling and conventional culture method for *Salmonella* detection in bulk tank milk and in-line milk filters in California dairies. *International Journal of Food Microbiology,* 67, 123-129.

[162] Yeh, K. S., Tsai, C. E., Chen, S. P. & Liao, C. W. (2002). Comparison between VIDAS automatic enzyme-linked fluorescent immunoassay and cultural method for *Salmonella* recovery from pork carcass sponge samples. *Journal of Food Protection,* 65, 1656-1659.

[163] Gunasekera, T. S., Attfield, P. V. & Veal. D. A. (2000). A flow cytometry method for rapid detection and enumeration of total bacteria in milk. *Applied and Environmental Microbiology,* 66, 1228–1232.

[164] Khan, M. M. T., Pyle, B. H. & Camper, A. K. (2010). Specific and rapid enumeration of viable but nonculturable and viable-culturable gram-negative bacteria by using flow cytometry. *Applied and Environmental Microbiology,* 76, 5088–5096.

[165] Nebe-von Caron, G., Stephens, P. & Badley, R. A. (1998). Assessment of bacterial viability status by flow cytometry and single cell sorting. *Journal of Applied Microbiology,* 84, 988–998.

[166] Nebe-von-Caron, G., Stephens, P. J., Hewitt, C. J., Powell, J. R. & Badley, R. A. (2000). Analysis of bacterial function by multi-colour fluorescence flow cytometry and single cell sorting. *Journal of Microbiological Methods,* 42, 97–114.

[167] Berney, M., Hammes, F. & Bosshard, F. (2007). Assessment and interpretation of bacterial viability by using the LIVE/DEAD BacLight kit in combination with flow cytometry. *Applied and Environmental Microbiology,* 73, 3283–3290.

[168] Velusamy, V., Arshak, K., Korostynska, O., Oliwa, K. & Adley, C. (2010). An overview of foodborne pathogen detection: In the perspective of biosensors. *Biotechnology Advances,* 28, 232–254.

[169] Guntupalli, R., Hu, J., Lakshmanan, R. S., Huang, T. S., Barbaree, J. M. & Chin, B. A. (2007). A magnetoelastic resonance biosensor immobilized with polyclonal antibody for the detection of *Salmonella* typhimurium. *Biosensor and Bioelectronics,* 22, 1474–1479.

[170] Pal, S., Alocilja, E. C. & Downes, F. P. (2007). Nanowire labeled direct-charge transfer biosensor for detecting *Bacillus* species. *Biosensor and Bioelectronics,* 22, 2329–2336.

[171] Subramanian, A., Irudayaraj, J. & Ryan, T. (2006). A mixed self-assembled monolayer-based surface plasmon immunosensor for detection of *E. coli* O157: H7. *Biosensor and Bioelectronics,* 21, 998-1006.

[172] Tokarskyy, O. & Marshall, D. L. (2008). Immunosensors for rapid detection of *Escherichia coli* O157:H7 —perspectives for use in the meat processing industry. *Food Microbiology,* 25, 1-12.

[173] Waswa, J., Irudayaraj, J. & DebRoy, C. (2007). Direct detection of *E. coli* O157: H7 in selected food systems by a surface plasmon resonance biosensor. *LWT-Food Science and Technology,* 40, 187–192.

[174] Chemburu, S.,Wilkins, E. & Abdel-Hamid, I. (2005). Detection of pathogenic bacteria in food samples using highly-dispersed carbon particles. *Biosensor and Bioelectronics,* 21, 491–499.

[175] Chen, S. H., Wu, V. C. H., Chuang, Y. C. & Lin, C. S. (2008). Using oligonucleotide-functionalized Au nanoparticles to rapidly detect foodborne pathogens on a piezoelectric biosensor. *Journal of Microbiological Methods,* 73, 7-17.

[176] Lermo, A., Campoy, S., Barbe, J., Hernandez, S., Alegret, S. & Pividori, M. (2007). In situ DNA amplification with magnetic primers for the electrochemical detection of food pathogens. *Biosensor and Bioelectronics,* 22, 2010–2017.

[177] Steichen, M., Decrem, Y., Godfroid, E. & Buess-Herman, C. (2007). Electrochemical DNA hybridization detection using peptide nucleic acids and [Ru(NH3)(6)](3+) on gold electrodes. *Biosensor and Bioelectronics,* 22, 2237–2243.

[178] Zhao, J. X., Jedlicka, S. S., Lannu, J. D., Bhunia, A. K. & Rickus, J. L. (2006). Liposome-doped nanocomposites as artificial-cell-based biosensors: detection of listeriolysin O. *Biotechnology Progress,* 22, 32–37.

[179] Silbert, L., Ben Shlush, I., Israel, E., Porgador, A., Kolusheva, S. & Jelinek, R. (2006). Rapid chromatic detection of bacteria by use of a new biomimetic polymer sensor. *Applied and Environmental Microbiology,* 72, 7339–7344.

[180] Singh, A., Glass, N., Tolba, M., Brovko, L., Griffiths, M. & Evoy, S. (2009b). Immobilization of bacteriophages on gold surfaces for the specific capture of pathogens. *Biosensor and Bioelectronics,* 24, 3645–3651.

[181] Xie, F., Yang, H., Li, S., Shen, W., Wan, J., Johnson, M. L., Wikle, H. C., Kim, D-J. & Chin, B. A. (2009). Amorphous magnetoelastic sensors for the detection of biological agents. *Intermetallics,* 17, 270–273.

[182] Lai, R. Y., Lagally, E. T., Lee, S-H., Soh, H. T., Plaxco, K. W. & Heeger, A. J. (2006). Rapid, sequence-specific detection of unpurified PCR amplicons via a reusable, electrochemical sensor. *Proceedings of National Academy of Sciences,* 103, 4017–4021.

[183] Taylor, A. D., Ladd, J., Yu, Q. M., Chen, S. F., Homola, J. & Jiang, S. Y. (2006). Quantitative and simultaneous detection of four foodborne bacterial pathogens with a multi-channel SPR sensor. *Biosensor and Bioelectronics,* 22, 752–758.

[184] West, J., Becker, M., Tombrink, S. & Manz, A. (2008). Micro total analysis systems: latest achievements. *Analytical Chemistry,* 80, 4403-4419.

[185] Beer, N. R., Wheeler, E. K., Lee-Houghton, L., Watkins, N., Nasarabadi, S., Hebert, N., Leung, P., Arnold, D. W., Bailey, C. G. & Colston, B. W. (2008). On-chip single-copy real-time reverse-transcription PCR in isolated picoliter droplets. *Analytical Chemistry,* 80, 1854-1858.

[186] Chen, L., West, J., Auroux, P.-A., Manz, A. & Day, P. J. R. (2007). Ultrasensitive PCR and real-time detection from human genomic samples using a bi-directional flow micro-reactor. *Analytical Chemistry*, 79, 9185-9190.

[187] Toriello, N. M., Lui, C. N. & Mathies, R. A. (2006). Multichannel reverse transcription-polymerase chain reaction microdevice for rapid gene expression and biomarker analysis. *Analytical Chemistry*, 78, 7997-8003.

[188] Wang, H., Chen, J., Zhu, L., Shadpour, H., Hupert, M. L. & Soper, S. A. (2006). Continuous flow thermal cycler microchip for DNA cycle sequencing. *Analytical Chemistry*, 78, 6223-6231.

[189] Simpkins, S. A., Chan, A. B., Hays, J., Pöpping, B. & Cook, N. (2000). An RNA transcription-based amplification technique (NASBA) for the detection of viable *Salmonella enterica*. *Letters in Applied Microbiology*, 30, 75-79.

[190] Nocker, A., Cheung, C. Y. & Camper, A. K. (2006). Comparison of propidium monoazide with ethidium monoazide for differentiation of live vs. dead bacteria by selective removal of DNA from dead cells. *Journal of Microbiological Methods*, 67, 310–320.

[191] Wagner, A. O., Malin, C., Knapp, B. A. & Illmer, P. (2008). Removal of free extracellular DNA from environmental samples by ethidium monoazide and propidium monoazide. *Applied and Environmental Microbiology*, 74, 2537–2539.

[192] Flekna, G., Štefanič, P., Wagner, M., Smulders, F. J. M., Možina, S. S. & Hein, I. (2007). Insufficient differentiation of live and dead *Campylobacter jejuni* and *Listeria monocytogenes* cells by ethidium monoazide (EMA) compromises EMA/real-time PCR. *Research in Microbiology*, 158, 405-412.

[193] Pan, Y. & Breidt, Jr., F. (2007). Enumeration of viable *Listeria monocytogenes* cells by real-time PCR with propidium monoazide and ethidium monoazide in the presence of dead cells. *Applied and Environmental Microbiology*, 73, 8028–8031.

[194] Wang, S. & Levin, R.E. (2006). Discrimination of viable *Vibrio vulnificus* cells from dead cells in real-time PCR. *Journal of Microbiological Methods*, 64, 1–8.

[195] Chang, B., Sugiyama, K., Taguri, T., Amemura-Maekawa, J., Kura, F. & Watanabe, H. (2009). Specific detection of viable Legionella cells by combined use of photoactivated ethidium monoazide and PCR/real-time PCR. *Applied and Environmental Microbiology*, 75, 147–153.

[196] Parshionikar, S., Laseke, I. & Fout, G. S. (2010). Use of propidium monoazide in reverse transcriptase PCR to distinguish between infectious and noninfectious enteric viruses in water samples. *Applied and Environmental Microbiology*, 76, 4318–4326.

[197] Nocker, A., Sossa, K. E. & Camper, A. K. (2007). Molecular monitoring of disinfection efficacy using propidium monoazide in combination with quantitative PCR. *Journal of Microbiological Methods*, 70, 252–260.

[198] Nocker, A., Mazza, A., Masson, L., Camper, A. K. & Brousseau, R. (2009). Selective detection of live bacteria combining propidium monoazide sample treatment with microarray technology. *Journal of Microbiological Methods*, 76, 253–261.

[199] Pan, Y., Breidt, Jr., F. & Kathariou, S. (2009). Competition of *Listeria monocytogenes* serotype 1/2a and 4b strains in mixed-culture biofilms. *Applied and Environmental Microbiology*, 75, 5846–5852.

[200] Rawsthorne, H., Dock, C. N. & Jaykus, L. A. (2009). PCR-based method using propidium monoazide to distinguish viable from nonviable *Bacillus subtilis* spores. *Applied and Environmental Microbiology*, 75, 2936–2939.

[201] Brescia, C. C., Griffin, S. M., Ware, M. W., Varughese, E. A., Egorov, A. I. & Villegas, E. N. (2009). *Cryptosporidium* propidium monoazide-PCR, a molecular biology-based technique for genotyping of viable *Cryptosporidium* oocysts. *Applied and Environmental Microbiology*, 75, 6856–6863.

[202] Josefsen, M. H., Löfström, C., Hansen, T. B., Christensen, L. S., Olsen, J. E. & Hoorfar, J. (2010). Rapid quantification of viable *Campylobacter* bacteria on chicken carcasses, using real-time PCR and propidium monoazide treatment, as a tool for quantitative risk assessment. *Applied and Environmental Microbiology*, 76, 5097–5104.

[203] Wahman, D. G., Wulfeck-Kleier, K. A. & Pressman, J. G. (2009). Monochloramine disinfection kinetics of Nitrosomonas europaea by propidium monoazide quantitative PCR and Live/Dead BacLight methods. *Applied and Environmental Microbiology*, 75, 5555–5562.

[204] Liu, Y., Cai, X., Zhang, X., Gaob, Q., Yang, X., Zheng, Z., Luo, M. & Huang, X. (2006). Real time PCR using TaqMan and SYBR Green for detection of Enterobacter sakazakii in infant formula. *Journal of Microbiological Methods*, 65, 21–31.

[205] Morsczeck, C., Langendörfer, D. & Schierholz, J. M. J. (2004). A quantitative real-time PCR assay for the detection of tetR of Tn10 in *Escherichia coli* using SYBR Green and the Opticon. *Biochemmical and Biophysical Methods*, 59, 217–227.

[206] Desai, P. T., Walsh, M. K. & Weimer, B. C. (2008). Solid-Phase Capture of Pathogenic Bacteria by Using Gangliosides and Detection with Real-Time PCR. *Applied and Environmental Microbiology*, 74, 2254–2258.

[207] Inglis, G. D. & Kalischuk, L. D. (2004). Direct quantification of *Campylobacter jejuni* and *Campylobacter* lanienae in feces of cattle by real-time quantitative PCR. *Applied and Environmental Microbiology*, 70, 2296–2306.

[208] Fenicia, L., Anniballi, F., De Medici, D., Delibato, E. & Aureli, P. (2007). SYBR Green real-time PCR method to detect Clostridium botulinum type A. *Applied and Environmental Microbiology*, 73, 2891–2896.

[209] Guilbaud, M., de Coppet, P., Bourion, F., Rachman, C., Prévost, H. & Dousset, X. (2005). Quantitative detection of *Listeria monocytogenes* in biofilms by real-time PCR. *Applied and Environmental Microbiology*, 71, 2190–2194.

[210] Nam, H-M., Srinivasan, V., Gillespie, B. E., Murinda, S. E. & Oliver, S. P. (2005). Application of SYBR green real-time PCR assay for specific detection of *Salmonella* spp. in dairy farm environmental samples. *International Journal of Food Microbiology*, 102, 161–171.

[211] Fallschissel, K., Kämpfer, P. & Jäckel, U. (2009). Direct detection of *Salmonella* cells in the air of livestock stables by real-time PCR. *Annals of Occupational Hygiene*, 53, 859–868.

[212] Wolffs, P. F. G., Glencross, K., Thibaudeau, R. & Griffith, M. W. (2006). Direct quantitation and detection of Salmonellae in biological samples without enrichment, using two-step filtration and real-time PCR. *Applied and Environmental Microbiology*, 72, 3896–3900.

[213] Saikaly, P. E., Barlaz, M. A. & de los Reyes III, F. L. (2007). Development of quantitative real-time PCR assays for detection and quantification of surrogate

biological warfare agents in building debris and leachate. *Applied and Environmental Microbiology, 73,* 6557–6565.

[214] Hein, I., Lehner, A., Rieck, P., Klein, K., Brandl, E. & Wagner, M. (2001). Comparison of different approaches to quantify *Staphylococcus aureus* cells by real-time quantitative PCR and application of this technique for examination of cheese. *Applied and Environmental Microbiology, 67,* 3122–3126.

[215] Wolffs, P., Knutsson, R., Norling, B. & Radstrom, P. (2004). Rapid quantification of *Yersinia enterocolitica* in pork samples by a novel sample preparation method, flotation, prior to real-time PCR. *Journal of Clinical Microbiology, 42:* 1042-1047.

[216] Lund, M., Nordentoft, S., Pedersen, K. & Madsen, M. (2004). Detection of *Campylobacter* spp. in chicken fecal samples by real-time PCR. *Journal of Clinical Microbiology, 42,* 5125–5132.

[217] Rudi, K., Høidal, H. K., Katla, T., Johansen, B. K., Nordal, J. & Jakobsen, K. S. (2004). Direct real-time PCR quantification of *Campylobacter jejuni* in chicken fecal and cecal samples by integrated cell concentration and DNA purification. *Applied and Environmental Microbiology, 70,* 790–797.

[218] Sails, A. D., Fox, A. J., Bolton, F. J., Wareing, D. R. A. & Greenway, D. L. A. (2003). A real-time PCR assay for the detection of *Campylobacter jejuni* in foods after enrichment culture. *Applied and Environmental Microbiology, 69,* 1383–1390.

[219] Nogva, H. K., Bergh, A., Holck, A. & Rudi, K. (2000b). Application of the 5'-nuclease PCR assay in evaluation and development of methods for quantitative detection of *Campylobacter jejuni*. *Applied and Environmental Microbiology, 66,* 4029–4036.

[220] Iijima, Y., Asako, N. T., Aihara, M. & Hayashi, K. (2004). Improvement in the detection rate of diarrhoeagenic bacteria in human stool specimens by a rapid real-time PCR assay. *Journal of Medical Microbiology, 53,* 617–622.

[221] Heller, L.C., Davis, C. R., Peak, K. K., Wingfield, D., Cannons, A. C., Amuso, P. T. & Cattani, J. (2003). Comparison of methods for DNA isolation from food samples for detection of shiga toxin-producing *Escherichia coli* by real-time PCR. *Applied and Environmental Microbiology, 69,* 1844-1846.

[222] Chen, S., Yee, A., Griffiths, M., Larkin, C., Yamashiro, C. T., Behari, R., Paszko-Kolva, C., Rahn, K. & De Grandis, S. A. (1997). The evaluation of a fluorogenic polymerase chain reaction assay for the detection of *Salmonella* species in food commodities. *International Journal of Food Microbiology, 35,* 239-250.

[223] Daum, L. T., Barnes, W. J., McAvin, J. C., Neidert, M. S., Cooper, L. A., Huff, W. B., Gaul, L., Riggins, W. S., Morris, S., Salmen, A. & Lohman, K. L. (2002). Real-time PCR detection of *Salmonella* in suspect foods from a gastroenteritis outbreak in Kerr County, Texas. *Journal of Clinical Microbiology, 40,* 3050–3052.

[224] Ram, S., Vajpayee, P. & Shanker, R. (2008). Rapid culture-independent quantitative detection of enterotoxigenic *Escherichia coli* in surface waters by real-time PCR with molecular beacon. *Environmental Science and Technology, 42,* 4577–4582.

[225] Sandhya, S., Chen, W. & Mulchandani, A. (2008). Molecular beacons: A real-time polymerase chain reaction assay for detecting *Escherichia coli* from fresh produce and water. *Analytica Chimica Acta, 614,* 208–212.

[226] Fortin, N. Y., Mulchandani, A. & Chen, W. (2001). Use of real-time polymerase chain reaction and molecular beacons for the detection of *Escherichia coli* O157:H7. *Analytical Biochemistry, 289,* 281–288.

[227] Yaron, S. &Matthews, K. R. (2002). A reverse transcriptase-polymerase chain reaction assay for detection of viable *Escherichia coli* O157:H7: Investigation of specific target genes. *Journal of Applied Microbiology*, 92, 633-640.

[228] Lleò, M. M., Pierobon, S., Tafi, M. C., Signoretto, C. & Canepari, P. (2000). mRNA detection by reverse transcription-PCR for monitoring viability over time in an *Enterococcus faecalis* viable but nonculturable population maintained in a laboratory microcosm. *Applied and Environmental Microbiology*, 66, 4564–4567.

[229] Sung, K. D., Stern, N. J. & Hiett, K. L. (2004). Relationship of messenger RNA reverse transcriptase-polymerase chain reaction signal to *Campylobacter* spp. viability. *Avian Diseases*, 48, 254-262.

[230] McGrath, S., Dooley, J. S. & Haylock, R. W. (2000). Quantification of *Clostridium botulinum* toxin gene expression by competitive reverse transcription-PCR. *Applied and Environmental Microbiology*, 2000, p. 1423–1428 Vol. 66, No. 4

[231] Coutard, F., Pommepuy, M., Loaec, S. & Hervio-Heath, D. (2005). mRNA detection by reverse transcription–PCR for monitoring viability and potential virulence in a pathogenic strain of *Vibrio parahaemolyticus* in viable but nonculturable state. *Journal of Applied Microbiology*, 98, 951–961

[232] Jacobsen, C. S. & Holben, W. E. (2007). Quantification of mRNA in *Salmonella* sp. seeded soil and chicken manure using magnetic capture hybridization RT-PCR. *Journal of Microbiological Methods*, 69, 315–321.

[233] Techathuvanan, C., Draughon, F. A. & D'Souza, D. H. (2010a). Real-time reverse-transcriptase polymerase chain reaction for the rapid and sensitive detection of *Salmonella* Typhimurium from pork. *Journal of Food Protection*, 73, 507-514.

[234] Miller, N. D., Davidson, P. M. & D'Souza, D. H. (in press). Real-time reverse-transcriptase PCR for *Salmonella* Typhimurium detection from lettuce and tomatoes. *LWT-Food Science and Technology*, Accepted.

[235] Hara-Kudo, Y., Nemoto, J., Ohtsuka, K., Segawa, Y., Takatori, K., Kojima, T. & Ikedo, M. (2007). Sensitive and rapid detection of Vero toxin-producing *Escherichia coli* using loop-mediated isothermal amplification. *Journal of Medical Microbiology*, 56, 398–406.

[236] Yamazaki, W., Taguchi, M., Kawai, T., Kawatsu, K., Sakata, J., Inoue, K. & Misawa, N. (2009). Comparison of loop-mediated isothermal amplification assay and conventional culture methods for detection of *Campylobacter jejuni* and *Campylobacter coli* in naturally contaminated chicken meat samples. *Applied and Environmental Microbiology*, 75, 1597–1603.

[237] Gao, H., Lei, Z., Jia, J., Wang, S., Chen, Y., Sun, M. & Liang, C. (2009). Application of loop-mediated isothermal amplification for detection of *Yersinia enterocolitica* in pork meat. *Journal of Microbiological Methods*, 77, 198–201.

[238] Horisaka, T., Fujita, K., Iwata, T., Nakadai, A., Okatani, A. T., Horikita, T., Taniguchi, T., Honda, E., Yokomizo, Y. & Hayashidani, H. (2004). Sensitive and specific detection of *Yersinia pseudotuberculosis* by loop-mediated isothermal amplification. *Journal of Clinical Microbiology*, 42, 5349–5352.

[239] Uyttendaele, M., Schukkink, R., van Gemen, B. & Debevere, J. (1994). Identification of *Campylobacter jejuni*, *Campylobacter coli* and *Campylobacter* lari by the nucleic acid amplification system NASBA. *Journal of Applied Bacteriology*, 77, 694-701.

[240] Cook, N., Ellison, J., Kurdziel, A.S., Simpkins, S. & Hays, J.P. (2002). A nucleic acid sequence-based amplification method to detect *Salmonella enterica* serotype Enteritidis strain PT4 in liquid whole egg. *Journal of Food Protection,* 65, 1177–1178.

[241] Abd El Galil, K. H., El Sokkary, M. A., Kheira, S. M., Salazar, A. M., Yates, M. V., Chen, W. & Mulchandani, A. (2005). Real-Time Nucleic Acid Sequence-Based Amplification Assay for Detection of Hepatitis A Virus. *Applied and Environmental Microbiology,* 71, 7113–7116.

[242] Susmel, S., Guilbault, G. G. & O'Sullivan, C. K. (2003). Demonstration of labeless detection of food pathogens using electrochemical redox probe and screen printed gold electrodes. *Biosensor and Bioelectronics,* 18, 881–889.

[243] O'Brien, T., Johnson, L. H., Aldrich, J. L., Allen, S. G., Liang, L. T., Plummer, A. L., Krak, S. J. & Boiarski, A. A. (2000). The development of immunoassays to four biological threat agents in a bidiffractive grating biosensor. *Biosensor and Bioelectronics,* 14, 815–828.

[244] Kiba, A, K. Toyoda, K. Yoshioka, K. Tsujimura, H. Takahashi and Y. Ichinose et al., A pea NTPase, PsAPY1, recognizes signal molecules from microorganisms, *J Gen Plant Pathol* 72 (2006), pp. 238–246

[245] Acharya, G., Chang, C. L. & Savran, C. (2006). An optical biosensor for rapid and label-free detection of cells. *Journal of American Chemical Society,* 128, 3862–3863.

[246] Frank, L., Markova, S., Remmel, N., Vysotski, E. & Gitelson, I. (2007). Bioluminescent signal system: Bioluminescence immunoassay of pathogenic organisms. *Luminescence,* 22, 215–220.

[247] Lehtinen, J., Jarvinen, S., Virta, M. & Lilius, E. M. (2006). Real-time monitoring of antimicrobial activity with the multiparameter microplate assay. *Journal of Microbiolgical Methods,* 66, 381–389.

[248] Ercole, C., Del Gallo, M., Mosiello, L., Baccella, S. & Lepidi, A. (2003). *Escherichia coli* detection in vegetable food by a potentiometric biosensor. *Sensors and Actuators B: Chemical,* 91, 163–168.

[249] Munoz-Berbel, X., Vigues, N., Jenkins, A. T. A., Mas, J. & Munoz, F. J. (2008). Impedimetric approach for quantifying low bacteria concentrations based on the changes produced in the electrode-solution interface during the pre-attachment stage. *Biosensor and Bioelectronics,* 23, 1540–1546.

[250] Blasco, R., Murphy, M. J., Sanders, M. F. & Squirrell, D. J. (1998). Specific assays for bacteria using phage mediated release of adenylate kinase. *Journal of Applied Microbiology,* 84, 661–666.

[251] Varkey, S., Cannons, A. C. & Lim, D. V. (2002). Enhanced detection of DNA fragments with an evanescent biosensor using a signal amplification system. Abstract, *American Society for Microbiology General Meeting,* 102, 145.

[252] Rahman, S., Lipert, R. J. & Porter, M. D. (2006). Rapid screening of pathogenic bacteria using solid phase concentration and diffuse reflectance spectroscopy. *Analytica Chimca Acta,* 569, 83–90.

[253] Hahn, M. A., Keng, P. C. & Krauss, T. D. (2008). Flow cytometric analysis to detect pathogens in bacterial cell mixtures using semiconductor quantum dots. *Analytical Chemistry,* 80, 864–872.

[254] Mathew, F. P., Alagesan, D. & Alocilja, E. C. (2004). Chemiluminescence detection of Escherichia coli in fresh produce obtained from different sources. *Luminescence,* 19, 193–198.

[255] Kovacs, H. D. & Rasky, K. (2001). Testing of a chemiluminescence enzyme immunoassay for selective detection of E. coli O157 from ground beef samples. *Acta Veterinaria Hungarica,* 49, 377–383.

[256] Brigati, J. R., Ripp, S. A., Johnson, C. M., Iakova, P. A., Jegier, P. & Sayler, G. S. (2007). Bacteriophage-based bioluminescent bioreporter for the detection of Escherichia coli O157:H7. *Journal of Food Protection,* 70, 1386–1392.

[257] Muhammad-Tahir, Z. & Alocilja, E. C. (2004). A disposable biosensor for pathogen detection in fresh produce samples. *Biosystem Engineering,* 88, 145–151.

[258] Ruan, C., Wang, H. & Li, Y. (2002). A bienzyme electrochemical biosensor coupled with immunomagnetic separation for rapid detection of *Escherichia coli* O15:H7 in food samples. *Transactions of ASAE,* 45, 249–255.

[259] Abdel-Hamid, I., Ivnitski, D., Atanasov, P. & Wilkins, E. (1999a). Flow-through immunofiltration assay system for rapid detection of *E. coli* O157: H7. *Biosensor and Bioelectronics,* 14, 309–316.

[260] Abdel-Hamid, I., Ivnitski, D., Atanasov, P. & Wilkins, E. (1999b). Highly sensitive flow-injection immunoassay system for rapid detection of bacteria. *Analytica Chimica Acta,* 399, 99-108.

[261] Barco-Alcala, E., Garcia-Gimeno, R. M., Castillejo-Rodriguez, A. M. & Zurera-Cosano, G. (2000). Turbidimetry as a fast method to determine microorganisms in foods. *Alimentaria,* 37, 109–112.

[262] Choi, J-W. & Oh, B-K. (2008). Optical detection of pathogens using protein chip. *Advanced Environmental Monitoring,* 4, 348–362.

[263] Gehring, A. G., Patterson, D. L. & Tu, S. I. (1998). Use of a light-addressable potentiometric sensor for the detection of *Escherichia coli* O157:H7. *Analytical Biochemistry,* 258, 293–298.

[264] Varshney, M., Yang, L. J., Su, X. L. & Li, Y. B. (2005). Magnetic nanoparticle-antibody conjugates for the separation of *Escherichia coli* O157:H7 in ground beef. *Journal of Food Protection,* 68, 1804–1811.

[265] Tully, E., Higson, S. P. & Kennedy, R. O. (2008). The development of a 'labeless' immunosensor for the detection of *Listeria monocytogenes* cell surface protein, Internalin B. *Biosensor and Bioelectronics,* 23, 906–912.

[266] Peng, H. & Shelef, L. A. (2001). Automated simultaneous detection of low levels of Listeriae and Salmonellae in foods. *International Journal of Food Microbiology,* 63, 225–233.

[267] Seo, K. H., Brackett, R. E., Hartman, N. F. & Campbell, D. P. (1999). Development of a rapid response biosensor for detection of *Salmonella typhimurium*. *Journal of Food Protection,* 62, 431–437.

[268] Yang, L. J., Ruan, C. M. & Li, Y. B. (2001). Rapid detection of *Salmonella typhimurium* in food samples using a bienzyme electrochemical biosensor with flow injection. *Journal of Rapid Methods and Automation in Microbiology,* 9, 229–240.

[269] Che, Y. H., Yang, Z. P., Li, Y. B., Paul, D. & Slavik, M. (1999). Rapid detection of *Salmonella typhimurium* using an immunoelectrochemical method coupled with

immunomagnetic separation. *Journal of Rapid Methods and Automation in Microbiology,* 7, 47–59.

[270] Yang, L. J., Li, Y. B., Griffis, C. L. & Johnson, M. G. (2004). Interdigitated microelectrode (IME) impedance sensor for the detection of viable *Salmonella typhimurium. Biosensor and Bioelectronics,* 19, 1139–1147.

[271] Brown, C. W., Li Y., Seelenbinder, J. A., Pivarnik, P., Rand, A. G., Letcher, S. V., Gregory, O. J. &Platek, M. J. (1998). Immunoassays based on surface-enhanced infrared absorption spectroscopy. *Analytical Chemistry,* 70, 2991–2996.

[272] Seelenbinder, J. A., Brown, C. W., Pivarnik, P. & Rand, A. G. (1999). Colloidal gold filtrates as metal substrates for surface-enhanced infrared absorption spectroscopy. *Analytical Chemistry,* 71, 1963–1966.

[273] Chen, J. & Griffiths, M. W. (1996). Salmonella detection in eggs using Lux(+) bacteriophages. *Journal of Food Protection,* 59, 908–914.

[274] Brooks, J. L., Mirhabibollahi, B. & Kroll, R. G. (1992). Experimental enzyme-linked amperometric immunosensors for the detection of *Salmonella*s in foods. *Journal of Applied Bacteriology,* 73, 189–196.

[275] Dey, B. P., Chen, Y. R., Hsieh, C. & Chan, D. E. (2003). Detection of septicemia in chicken livers by spectroscopy. *Poultry Science,* 82, 199–206.

[276] Zhao, G. Y., Xing, F. F. & Deng, S. P. (2007). A disposable amperometric enzyme immunosensor for rapid detection of *Vibrio parahaemolyticus* in food based on agarose/nano-Au membrane and screen-printed electrode. *Electrochemical Communications,* 9, 1263–1268.

SECTION II. MOLECULAR TYPING METHODS

In: Molecular Typing Methods for TFM
Editors: S. Foley, R. Nayak, T. Johnson et al.

ISBN: 978-1-62100-643-5
© 2012 Nova Science Publishers, Inc.

Chapter 6

SUBTYPING OF BACTERIAL FOODBORNE PATHOGENS: PHENOTYPIC METHODS AND AN INTRODUCTION TO MOLECULAR METHODS

Steven L. Foley[1], Aaron M. Lynne[2], Rajesh Nayak[1], Sanjay K. Shukla[3] and Timothy J. Johnson[4]

[1] Division of Microbiology
National Center for Toxicological Research
U.S. Food and Drug Administration
Jefferson, AR, US
[2] Department of Biological Sciences
Sam Houston State University
Huntsville, TX, US
[3] Center for Human Genetics
Marshfield Clinic Research Foundation
Marshfield, WI, US
[4] Department of Veterinary and Biomedical Sciences
College of Veterinary Medicine
University of Minnesota
St. Paul, MN, US

ABSTRACT

This chapter provides a brief introduction to molecular subtyping methods that will be covered in the following chapters and provide a more in-depth review of the phenotypic methods that have been used to characterize bacteria. While the phenotypic methods, such as serotyping, phage typing, antimicrobial susceptibility testing and multilocus enzyme electrophoresis (MLEE), are not the major focus of this book, they do provide the foundation on which the molecular typing methods have been developed and they play an important role in the molecular typing schemes used for bacterial pathogens.

Therefore the first section of the chapter reviews these phenotypic methods, including some of the more recent advancements, and the remainder of the chapter introduces the molecular typing methods that will be featured in this section of the book.

INTRODUCTION

The following chapters (Chapters 7-13) in the book will focus on the different molecular typing methods that are currently available for the characterization of bacterial foodborne pathogens. In this chapter, we provide a brief introduction to molecular subtyping methods and provide an overview of some of the phenotypic methods that have been used to characterize bacteria. These methods are not a major focus of the book; however they are the foundation on which the molecular typing methods, such as multilocus enzyme electrophoresis (MLEE) and multilocus sequence typing (MLST), have been developed. Others play an important role in the molecular typing schemes used for bacterial pathogens. For example, serotyping is an important step in the characterization of *Salmonella* and is typically carried out before molecular subtyping. Some of these "traditional" phenotypic methods have also been undergoing improvements, which will be discussed in this chapter.

An understanding of how foodborne pathogens are disseminated through production and processing environments into our foods is important to help develop strategies to limit future contamination. To gain this understanding, it is important to identify the sources of pathogens and determine the factors that affect the spread of these organisms through the food supply chain. The identification of source and distribution patterns for foodborne pathogens relies on strong epidemiological skills that are supported by different phenotypic and molecular tools. The identification of common phenotypic and genotypic profiles, coupled with an epidemiological link, can be used for effective source tracking. These typing methods serve to augment epidemiological investigations that are used in microbial source tracking.

In the evaluation of the different typing methods, a number of characteristics must be taken into account, including the discriminatory power, reproducibility of results, ability to return useable results, time to results, cost, and ability to effectively analyze the results [1, 2]. When typing methods are evaluated for these characteristics, it becomes clear that there is no single typing method that maximally meets all these characteristics. For example, whole genome sequencing of an isolate can provide a high level of discrimination (the ability to separate non-related strains), likely typeability (the technique generates an interpretable result for each strain typed) and reproducibility, yet still remains prohibitive for routine typing due to relatively high costs, time requires and the large amount of data processing and analysis needed to return a result. The following chapters in this section of the book are dedicated to in-depth reviews of the different molecular typing techniques and should provide the reader with a good foundation for future projects that utilize these typing methods.

PHENOTYPIC METHODS

Prior to the development and refinement of molecular typing methods, identification and characterization of microorganisms were based on comparisons of bacterial phenotypes. The initial presumptive identification of microorganisms occurred through the use of a series of selective and differential media to isolate the particular bacterium. These approaches utilize some of the inherent differences among organisms to utilize and ferment unique carbohydrate sources for growth, to survive under specific "harsh" growth conditions (e.g. high salt concentrations, presence of specific antimicrobials or dyes), and growth under different temperature and oxygen level conditions to narrow down the likely identity of a particular bacterium [3]. Once the species of the isolated organism is presumptively identified, its identity is further confirmed by biochemical testing, which utilizes a series of tests to determine the abilities of the microorganism to ferment different carbohydrates and break down specific amino acids and other compounds to determine the identity based on a cumulative biochemical profile. Because of their importance in species identification, several miniaturized manual test systems such as API-20E^{TM} strips (bioMerieux, Inc., Hazelwood, MO), Enterotube II^{TM} system (BD Diagnostics, Sparks, MD), RapID^{TM} System (Remel, Lenexa, KS) and automated systems including Vitek^{TM} (bioMerieux), Biolog^{TM} (Biolog, Inc., Hayward CA) and Phoenix^{TM} (BD Diagnostics) have been developed to rapid identify bacteria based on their biochemical profiles. The specific microorganisms can be further characterized by phenotypic methods, including serotyping, phage typing, antimicrobial susceptibilities, and MLEE. Most phenotypic methods have been in use for many decades and still have utility today. Some have undergone refinements over recent years to improve their utility and others have served as the basis for more modern molecular typing methods.

Serotyping

Once the species of bacteria has been identified, further differentiation is often desired. Foodborne pathogens, such as *Salmonella* and *Escherichia coli*, are often serotyped. For *Salmonella*, serotyping was historically used to separate isolates into distinct species. This led to a genus with well over 2000 separate species [4]. With the advent of more modern genetic testing, it was found that the various serotypes (serovars) were for the most part highly related, thus the taxonomy was reworked such that are presently only two species, *S. enterica* and *S. bongori* [4], with over 2,500 identified serotypes. The serotype of a particular strain remains the main descriptor of the organism. Organizations, such as the Centers for Disease Control and Prevention (CDC), European Food Safety Authority (EFSA) and World Health Organization (WHO) report on the number of infections by *Salmonella* serotype; for example, the number of *S. enterica* serovar Enteritidis cases in a given year reported to the CDC [5]. Once the serotype is identified, various molecular typing methods are performed and evaluated in the context of that serotype. Because of the continued utility and role of serotyping in source tracking schemes for *Salmonella*, a number of researchers have been working to develop more rapid and efficient methods to identify *Salmonella* serovars. Some of these methods are briefly described below.

Traditional serotyping methodologies utilize variability in the somatic (O) and flagellar (H) surface antigens to group strains into their respective serotypes [6]. To carry out *Salmonella* serotyping for O antigens, bacterial cells are suspended in ethanol and heat treated, which inactivates the H antigens [7]. The ethanol is removed and the O antigen preparation suspended in a phenol-saline solution. Initially the alcohol-treated antigens are tested against a mixture of antisera that will identify the O group of the strain. The vast majority (98-99%) of *Salmonella* fall into O serogroups A, B, C_1, C_2, D or E. The antigen and antisera are mixed on a glass slide and observed for agglutination within a minute of mixing. The reactions are scored based on their agglutination profiles, ranging from no agglutination (-) to complete clumping (4+). Partial clumping is scored from +/-, for very slight agglutination, up to 3+, for 75% agglutination. Occasionally, cross-agglutination can occur due to overlap in antigens in the different serogroups. In such cases, antiserum for a single antigen is used to identify the serogroup [7].

Once the O group is determined, the next stage is the H antigen determination [7]. H antigens are prepared by mixing bacteria grown in broth culture with a formalin-saline solution. The H antigen suspension is combined with a specific mixture of H antisera in a tube and incubated in a water bath at 48-50°C for up to an hour. The reactions are read at 15, 30 and 60 minutes and scored on the negative to 4+ scale. The choice of H antisera to test the antigens is based on the previously determined O group; certain H antigens are commonly associated with different O groups. This selective approach limits the number of tests needed to carry out the serotyping. In some strains, the H antigens can undergo phase variation, in which flagellar expression is altered leading to different antigenic conformations [8]. Most strains that undergo phase variation have two phases (including most *Salmonella* serotypes) and are referred to as diphasic, however typically only one phase is detected at a time and additional procedures need to be done to reverse the phase and allow identification of the second phase. The strains that do not undergo phase variation are termed monophasic. Under certain circumstances, testing with individual H antigens is required to distinguish between strains with similar antigenic properties (the details are beyond the introductory scope of the chapter, but the interested reader is referred to the work of Brenner and McWhorter-Murlin [7]).

The overall serotype is determined by a combination of the agglutination profiles for the O and H antigens according to the modified Kauffmann-White scheme for naming serotypes [9]. For example, the antigenic formula for *Salmonella* serovar Typhimurium is 1,4,5,12:i:1,2; the "1,4,5,12" is the antigenic formula for O serogroup B strains, the "i:1,2" refers to the H antigens and that the flagella have undergone phase variation and are recognized by both the i antiserum (phase 1) and the 1,2 antisera (phase 2). In addition to *Salmonella*, serotyping is important for identifying particular groups in different species, including *Campylobacter* and *Escherichia coli* [10-12]. For example, in *E. coli* there are a number of serotypes that are associated with specific types of disease, including *E. coli* O157:H7, which is defined by its recognition by the O157 and H7 antisera and is associated with severe gastrointestinal illness, kidney problems and sometimes death. Other O types, including O26, O45, O111, O103, O121, and O145 can also encode shiga toxins and have been associated with human disease as well [13].

Serotyping is a labor and resource-intensive process, requiring specialized and costly sets of antisera to carry out analyses. Thus, most serotyping is done at reference labs, where there are well trained staffs and ample volume to cover the costs of reagents. Because of these limitations, a number of researchers have been working to develop alternative ways to "serotype" isolates using molecular techniques. Most of the molecular methods focus on the detection of differences in the *rfb* gene cluster, associated with the O antigen biosynthesis, and the *fliC* and *fliB* genes, associated with the H antigens [14]. While these are the targets of most molecular serotyping methodologies, many different approaches have been developed to utilize these targets to determine serotype, including conventional and real time PCR-based methods, microarrays and bead-based systems [12, 15-21].

Antimicrobial Susceptibility Testing (AST)

The results of antimicrobial susceptibility testing (AST) can be used to distinguish among different foodborne pathogens through a comparison of antimicrobial resistance profiles. While AST can be used to characterize isolates, it should be pointed out that often the identification of antimicrobial resistant pathogens from patients or other sources is a reason to conduct microbial source tracking studies to gain a better understanding of the sources that may have contributed to the development of resistance. Because of the potential importance of antimicrobial resistance among foodborne pathogens, Chapter 4 in this book is dedicated to this topic. The value of AST as a microbial source tracking tool lies in the fact that there are often differences in the types of antimicrobials used in different animal production operations or by healthcare providers that may affect the resistance profiles of different bacteria. For example, a number of studies have used differential antimicrobial resistance profiles to track fecal pollution by *E. coli* from human and animal sources [22-24]. Based on the presence of specific resistance phenotypes associated with particular sources, the investigators can focus the search for the sources of contamination on those most likely to contribute to the observed patterns. Typically, AST results are used in conjunction with other molecular methods to further identify the sources because of the potential for overlap of resistance profiles in different environments [25]. Among clinical isolates, AST is also important to aid clinicians in choosing proper therapies. The data taken together can provide insights into trends in antimicrobial resistance in a particular population.

For use as a phenotyping method, it is extremely important that the proper methods are carried out to ensure that the results are uniformly interpreted and are reproducible. Extensive work has been done by organizations such as the Clinical and Laboratory Standards Institute (CLSI) to standardize and validate methods for conducting AST [26]. These methods involve standardized media, initial bacterial inoculum levels, incubation conditions, quality control strains and interpretive criteria to determine whether an isolate is susceptible, intermediate or resistant to the particular antimicrobial tested [27]. A number of methods can be used to perform AST and they vary in the ease of performance and amount of data provided. Probably the simplest to perform is the Kirby-Bauer disk diffusion method [28], which indicates whether an isolate is susceptible, intermediate or resistant (SIR) to a particular antimicrobial. However, it does not determine the minimal inhibitory concentration (MIC) of the antimicrobial. The disk diffusion method involves preparing a standardized dilution of the bacterial strain being tested and thoroughly streaking a suspension across the surface of an appropriate medium (such as Mueller-Hinton agar). After streaking, paper disks impregnated with a known antimicrobial concentration are placed on the surface of the agar and the plates are incubated under standardized conditions [29]. After incubation, the zones of inhibition

(Figure 1) are measured and compared to standard interpretation criteria to determine the SIR status [27].

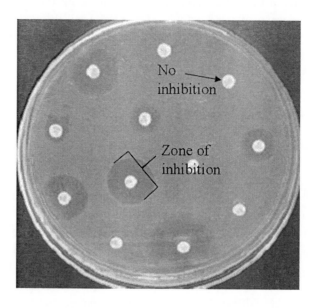

Figure 1. Mueller-Hinton agar plate showing the results of antimicrobial susceptibility testing using disk the diffusion (Kirby-Bauer) methods In interpreting the results, the zone of inhibition is measured and compared to standardized interpretive guidelines to determine whether the strain is susceptible, intermediate or resistant to the antimicrobial present in the paper disk at the center of the zone. The plate also shows several disks where there is no inhibition, indicating that the bacterial isolate is resistant to those antimicrobials.

There are additional methods that provide more quantitative data about the MIC for a particular antimicrobial, including the broth dilution, agar dilution methods and certain agar diffusion methods. For foodborne pathogens, including *Salmonella* and *E. coli*, the broth microdilution methods are commonly employed. As with the disk diffusion, a standardized inoculum is prepared and dispensed into the wells of a microtiter plate that contains a range of antimicrobial dilutions (Figure 2). Often the plates are manufactured by commercial companies with dehydrated antimicrobials in the plate that are hydrated upon addition of the inoculum. The plates are incubated under standardized conditions and then observed for growth in the wells. The well with the lowest concentration of a particular antimicrobial that lacks visible growth is defined as the MIC (Figure 2). The MIC value is compared to the standardized interpretive criteria and the SIR status is determined [26]. In the agar dilution method, an aliquot of the standardized inoculum is plated onto a series of media containing different concentrations of antimicrobials (Figure 3). After incubation, the plates are removed and observed to determine the MIC value, which is used to determine whether the isolate is SIR. To increase the throughput and testing efficiency, multiple bacterial strains can be tested on the same set of plates using a plate replicator. The plate replicator has a series of pins that pick up a standardized amount of inoculum from the wells of a multi-well plate and dispense it on each of the test plates in a common pattern [30]. Additionally, certain agar diffusion methods can be used to determine an MIC. One such method is the Epsilometer test (Etest, bioMerieux), in which test strips with a gradient of antimicrobial concentrations are placed on a bacterial streaked plate prepared similarly to the disk diffusion plate. After incubation, the plates are read and the antimicrobial concentration at the point where the growth intersects the test strip is used to determine the MIC (see Figure 4). With all AST methodologies, it is important to include the proper quality control strains with accepted interpretation ranges to ensure that the data are valid, which will allow comparison among isolates from various sources.

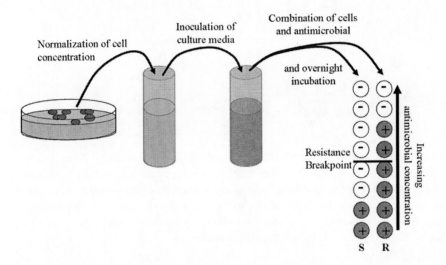

Figure 2. Schematic of the basic methods used to carry out broth dilution antimicrobial susceptibility testing. The minimal inhibitory concentration (MIC) value for a particular drug can be determined by finding the minimal concentration (dilution) of antimicrobial that inhibits growth of the bacteria. If the MIC value is higher than a defined breakpoint, the strain is resistant to that particular antimicrobial agent.

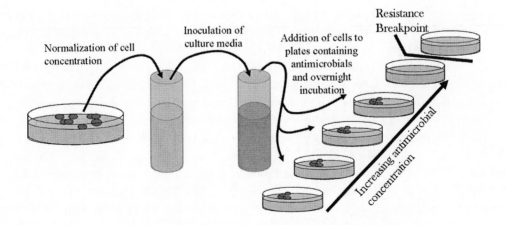

Figure 3. Schematic of the basic methods used to carry out agar dilution antimicrobial susceptibility testing. The MIC value for a particular drug can be determined by finding the minimal concentration (dilution) of antimicrobial present in the selection plates that inhibits growth of the bacteria. If the MIC value is higher than a defined breakpoint, the strain is resistant to that particular antimicrobial agent.

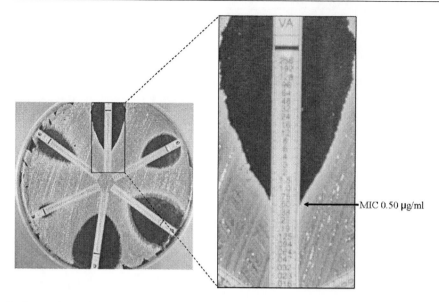

MIC 0.50 µg/ml

Figure 4. Test plate showing the results of antimicrobial susceptibility testing agar diffusion Epsilometer test (E-test) methods. The E-test strip has a gradient of antimicrobial concentrations from top (higher) to bottom (lower). The MIC value is determined by examining the point where bacterial growth intersects the test strip. In the test shown in the enlarged panel, the MIC is determined to be 0.50 µg/ml. MIC results are compared to standardized interpretive guidelines to determine whether the strain is susceptible, intermediate or resistant to the antimicrobial.

Phage Typing

Another phenotyping method that has had a long history of use is phage typing. Phage typing utilizes the selective ability of bacteriophages to infect and lyse specific bacterium [31]. Bacterial infection is mediated by the presence of specific phage receptors, present on the cell surface, that allow binding of complementary phages. If the phage binds to the appropriate surface receptor, the phage will infect the bacterium and cause cell lysis [32]. Phage-induced lysis appears as plaques, or zones of clearing, within a lawn of bacteria on an agar plate. The assignment of the particular phage type is based on whether or not specific typing phages are able to lyse the bacterial cells [33]. The sources of the phages in a particular typing scheme originate from multiple sources, including direct isolation of phages from wild type lysogenic bacterial strains and environmental sources (e.g. water and wastewater) [34], and through the adaptation of previously isolated phages to bacterial culture systems.

There are phage typing schemes for a number of bacterial foodborne pathogens including *Campylobacter* and *E. coli* [10, 11, 35]; however, they are widely used for *Salmonella*, especially for serovars Typhimurium and Enteritis isolates. Phage typing has been useful in the identification of *S.* Typhimurium Definitive Type 104 (DT104) isolates. DT104 strains cause severe gastrointestinal illness and are typically resistant to multiple antibiotics [35]. Also, phage typing differentiates *S.* Enteritidis isolates involved in disease with those from different sources [33]. Certain *S.* Enteritidis phage types have historically been more common in one geographical area than in others. In the US, phage type (PT) 8 has been the most commonly detected, while in Europe, PT 4 is most common [36]. One of the major limitations of phage typing is that the maintenance of stocks of biologically active phages is labor intensive. Hence, phage typing is mostly done in reference laboratories, where specially trained personnel maintain the necessary phage stocks [37]. Also, there are limited numbers of available phages for bacterial subtypes, as many bacterial trains are untypeable by phage typing, which limits widespread application of this method to distinguish bacterial strains [38].

Multilocus Enzyme Electrophoresis (MLEE)

Another method that has historically been used for typing bacteria is MLEE. MLEE relies on amino acid sequence variation among conserved cellular enzymes, which upon separation produce characteristic electrophoresis profiles that can be compared among strains. Enzyme mobility variation is associated with amino acid sequence variation that leads to changes in the protein's electrostatic charge and thus migration in an electric field. Most of these cellular enzymes are encoded by housekeeping genes, which tend to be highly conserved within a genus [39]. For the procedure, multiple water-soluble enzymes are separated in starch or cellulose acetate gels and are detected using enzyme-specific stains. The multi-enzyme pattern creates unique profiles for distinct strains that are referred to as electrophoretic types, which allow for statistical inferences to be made about the genetic relatedness of the strains typed [39]. Overall, the methods are best used for evaluating changes on an evolutionary scale rather than an epidemiological time scale due to the conserved nature of the enzyme targets. Also, MLEE has largely been replaced by multilocus sequence typing (MLST) which is discussed extensively in Chapter 9. MLST, which utilizes DNA sequencing of multiple housekeeping genes, is less time consuming, more reproducible and more portable than MLEE.

MOLECULAR TYPING METHODS

In addition to the phenotypic methods for bacterial characterization, a number of molecular typing methods can be used to characterize microbial pathogens. These can generally be broken down into three major groups: those that utilize restriction of the bacterial DNA, those that rely on PCR amplification of targets in the bacterial genome, and those that are based on the sequencing of specific genetic targets.

As we begin to look at the molecular subtyping methods, it is beneficial to look at some of the historical advances in our understanding of infectious disease transmission that have led to our current state of the art technologies. These advances date back to the time before the common era, when certain philosophers believed that living, yet invisible creatures were the cause of many human diseases [40]. It was not until Antony van Leeuwenhoek developed the microscope in the late 17th century that bacteria could be visualized [41]. This technological innovation led to advances in bacteriology that have relevance to the modern use of molecular subtyping for tracking foodborne pathogens. Some early advances dealt with pathogen transmission. For example, in the 1840s, Ignaz Semmelweis discovered that physicians were transmitting pathogens from cadavers to mothers in hospital maternity wards and that steps could be implemented to break the cycle of pathogen transmission [40]. Around the same time, John Snow used epidemiological techniques to identify that the source of a major cholera outbreak in London was a common water pump used by many citizens [42]. As the understanding of infectious diseases continued to grow, in 1884 Robert Koch, a German physician, published what are now know as Koch's postulates, which are used to confirm that a particular pathogen is the cause of the disease observed [43]. Subsequently, a large number of discoveries were made during the late nineteenth century and early twentieth century identifying specific bacterial species that were the causative agents of some of the major infectious diseases [40].

A number of key genetics discoveries also laid the ground work for the development of molecular subtyping. Some of these discoveries were related to the horizontal gene transfer among bacteria that can lead to microbial diversity, including the discovery of transformation by Griffith in 1928, the description of conjugation by Lederberg and Tatum in 1946 and the findings of Hershey and Chase in 1952 that bacteriophages inject DNA into bacterial hosts [44, 45]. Watson and Crick, describing the structure of DNA in 1953, paved the way for molecular biology discoveries [46]. In 1970, Smith and Wilcox discovered restriction endonucleases [47], which provide the basis for the restriction analysis techniques described in this book (PFGE, ribotyping, AFLP, etc.). Then in 1977, Sanger and colleagues developed a technique for DNA sequencing [48], which has played a key role in molecular typing techniques, such as multilocus sequence typing (MLST), single nucleotide polymorphism (SNP) typing and the early whole genome sequencing efforts. The polymerase chain reaction (PCR), developed by Kary Mullis in 1983 [49], led to a number of advances in molecular subtyping including the amplification-based methods, along with the MLST, amplified fragment length polymorphism (AFLP) and multiple locus variable number tandem repeat analysis (MLVA). Many of these methods are discussed extensively in the following chapters, but in the following paragraphs we present a brief overview of these methods to set the stage.

Restriction-Based Methods

Bacterial pathogens each have a genetic backbone that is made up of a single circular chromosome (with a few exceptions) and often a number of plasmids. Isolates that are more closely related have more similar genetic sequences; thus by utilizing methods that can identify specific genetic differences among bacterial strains, we can gain insights into their relatedness. In one set of approaches, termed restriction fragment length polymorphism (RFLP) analysis, the bacterial genomic DNA is digested with specific restriction enzymes, the bands are separated, and the resulting fragments are analyzed. The sizes and numbers of the fragments can be used to distinguish between non-clonal isolates. A number of issues need to be taken into account for the restriction analysis of whole genomes, due to their size and the technical limitations of separation and visualization technologies. The restriction of a bacterial genome with a frequent-cutting enzyme, followed by separation using traditional agarose electrophoresis, will result in an irresolvable smear that cannot be analyzed.

To get around these limitations, a number of different approaches have been employed. One is to use a rare-cutting restriction enzyme (e.g., *XbaI*) to produce a manageable number of fragments, followed by electrophoresis using specialized conditions that will allow separation of fragments too large for normal electrophoresis. This is the approach utilized in pulsed-field gel electrophoresis (PFGE) [50], the topic of Chapter 7. Another approach is to use more frequent cutting restriction enzymes, which generate a very large number of fragments, and utilize methods to reduce the number of fragments visually detected and analyzed. In amplified fragment length polymorphism (AFLP) analysis, a relatively limited number of fragments are amplified by PCR techniques that minimize the number of fragments that are detected. These fragments are typically fluorescently labeled at the PCR step, and separated in a capillary-based DNA sequencer to generate a restriction profile that can be evaluated to determine relatedness among isolates [51, 52]. Alternatively, the large number of fragments can be separated by traditional electrophoresis, with the fragments then transferred to a membrane and Southern blotted with probes for specific repetitive elements present in the bacterial chromosome. Probably the most common technique using this approach is ribotyping, in which the ribosomal RNA (rRNA) gene sequences are detected [53]. Another method that can be used is called optical mapping which gives a high-resolution and ordered restriction map of a bacterial genome. AFLP, ribotyping and optical mapping are discussed in greater detail in Chapter 8. In addition to chromosomal DNA, plasmid DNA can be the target of restriction analysis. These genetic elements are significantly smaller than the chromosome, thus their restriction fragments can be separated, visualized and analyzed by traditional gel electrophoresis [54]. Chapter 3 examines many of the important aspects about plasmids.

Amplification-Based Methods

Another approach for molecular subtyping is the use of PCR to amplify targets within bacteria that will provide a means to distinguish isolates. As with RFLP analyses, there are a number of different PCR-subtyping approaches that target different genetic elements in the bacteria. In random amplified polymorphic DNA PCR (RAPD-PCR), the PCR primers used are random sequence primers. When two primers bind in close proximity, they amplify the sequence between them, creating variably sized amplicons that are detected following electrophoresis [55]. Another approach is to utilize PCR primers that target sets of repeated DNA sequences that occur throughout the genomes of many bacterial species. In repetitive element PCR (Rep-PCR), when PCR primers recognize sites close enough together, they amplify the intervening regions of DNA, resulting in multiple amplicons that can be detected following separation [56]. Both Rep-PCR and RAPD-PCR are discussed in greater detail in Chapter 11. Instead of amplifying unknown intervening sequences, another method that utilizes repetitive elements in the bacterial genome is variable number of tandem repeat (VNTR) analysis. With VNTR, loci with known tandem repeats are identified and primers are designed for the flanking regions to amplify the repeat regions. Often the numbers of direct repeats in these regions are polymorphic among less related strains, and thus will have different size amplicons, following PCR [57, 58]. Typically, multiple VNTR loci are amplified using different fluorescently labeled primers and the reactions are separated using an automated DNA sequencer. In multilocus VNTR analysis (MLVA), the number of repeats for each locus is determined and compared to identify potential relationships among strains [59]. VNTR and MLVA are discussed in Chapter 10. Another approach utilizing PCR is to target specific sets of genes and develop a profile based on the presence or absence of the genes [60]. PCR amplification profiling as a subtyping method is discussed in Chapter 12. A potential modification of this method is to screen for the presence of multiple genes using microarrays to get detailed presence/absence profiles for gene sets. This approach is discussed in Chapter 13, which focuses on the utility of microarray analysis.

DNA Sequencing-Based Methods

With an increasing ability to carry out DNA sequencing, subtyping methods have been developed to directly examine differences in DNA sequences. One such method is multilocus sequence typing (MLST), in which multiple housekeeping genes that are predicted to have relatively conserved sequences are sequenced and compared for nucleotide base changes. For most pathogens, common sets of loci are sequenced and the results are uploaded to on-line databases that define the allele type for each gene. Each of the alleles provides a sequence type, which is used to compare isolates [61]. Another approach is to examine the strains for single nucleotide polymorphisms (SNPs) at a series of specific loci to determine if there are base pair changes that would provide information about isolate relatedness [62]. Because SNP examines specific loci, there are a number of detection options other than direct sequencing (such as real time PCR and mass spectroscopy) that can be used for SNP detection [63]. MLST and other sequence typing-based methods are described in Chapter 9. As next generation sequencing technologies become more accessible and less expensive, it is likely that whole genome sequencing may become a viable option for the molecular subtyping of bacteria.

DISCLAIMER

The use of trade names is for identification purposes only, and does not imply endorsement by the U.S. Food and Drug Administration or the U.S. Department of Health and Human Services. The views presented in this manuscript do not necessarily reflect those of the FDA.

REFERENCES

[1]   Foley SL, Zhao S, Walker RD. Comparison of molecular typing methods for the differentiation of *Salmonella* foodborne pathogens. *Foodborne Pathog Dis.* 2007 Fall;4(3):253-76.

[2]   van Belkum A, Tassios PT, Dijkshoorn L, Haeggman S, Cookson B, Fry NK, et al. Guidelines for the validation and application of typing methods for use in bacterial epidemiology. *Clin Microbiol Infect.* 2007;13 Suppl 3:1-46.

[3]   Zimbro M, Powers D, Miller S, Wilson J, Johnson J. Difco & BBL Manual. BD *Diagnostic Systems;* 2006.

[4]   Brenner FW, Villar RG, Angulo FJ, Tauxe R, Swaminathan B. Salmonella nomenclature. *J Clin Microbiol.* 2000;38(7):2465-7.

[5]   Centers for Disease Control and Prevention. *Salmonella* Surveillance: Annual Summary, 2006. Atlanta, GA: Centers for Disease Control and Prevention; 2008

[6]   Voogt N, Wannet WJ, Nagelkerke NJ, Henken AM. Differences between national reference laboratories of the European community in their ability to serotype *Salmonella* species. *Eur J Clin Microbio lInfect Dis.* 2002;21(3):204-8.

[7]   Brenner FW, McWhorter-Murlin AC. Identification and Serotyping of *Salmonella.* Atlanta Centers for Disease Control and Prevention; 1998.

[8]   Lederberg J, Iino T. Phase Variation in *Salmonella. Genetics.* 1956;41(5):743-57.

[9]   Brenner F. Modified Kauffmann-White scheme. Atlanta, GA: Centers for Disease Control and Prevention; 1998.

[10] Frost JA, Kramer JM, Gillanders SA. Phage typing of *Campylobacter jejuni* and *Campylobacter coli* and its use as an adjunct to serotyping. *Epidemiol Infect.* 1999;123(1):47-55.

[11] Barrett TJ, Lior H, Green JH, Khakhria R, Wells JG, Bell BP, et al. Laboratory investigation of a multistate food-borne outbreak of *Escherichia coli* O157:H7 by using pulsed-field gel electrophoresis and phage typing. *J Clin Microbiol.* 1994;32(12):3013-7.

[12] Terai A, Yamamoto S, Mitsumori K, Okada Y, Kurazono H, Takeda Y, et al. *Escherichia coli* virulence factors and serotypes in acute bacterial prostatitis. *Int J Urol.* 1997;4(3):289-94.

[13] Brooks JT, Sowers EG, Wells JG, Greene KD, Griffin PM, Hoekstra RM, et al. Non-O157 Shiga toxin-producing *Escherichia coli* infections in the United States, 1983-2002. *J Infect Dis.* 2005 Oct 15;192(8):1422-9.

[14] Yoshida C, Franklin K, Konczy P, McQuiston JR, Fields PI, Nash JH, et al. Methodologies towards the development of an oligonucleotide microarray for determination of *Salmonella* serotypes. *J Microbiol Methods.* 2007;70(2):261-71.

[15] Fitzgerald C, Collins M, van Duyne S, Mikoleit M, Brown T, Fields P. Multiplex, bead-based suspension array for molecular determination of common *Salmonella* serogroups. *J Clin Microbiol.* 2007;45(10):3323-34.

[16] Wattiau P, Van Hessche M, Schlicker C, Vander Veken H, Imberechts H. Comparison of classical serotyping and PremiTest assay for routine identification of common *Salmonella enterica* serovars. *J Clin Microbiol.* 2008;46(12):4037-40.

[17] Wattiau P, Weijers T, Andreoli P, Schliker C, Veken HV, Maas HM, et al. Evaluation of the Premi Test *Salmonella*, a commercial low-density DNA microarray system intended for routine identification and typing of Salmonella enterica. *Int J Food Microbiol.* 2008 Apr 30;123(3):293-8.

[18] Leader BT, Frye JG, Hu J, Fedorka-Cray PJ, Boyle DS. High-throughput molecular determination of *Salmonella enterica* serovars by use of multiplex PCR and capillary electrophoresis analysis. *J Clin Microbiol.* 2009;47(5):1290-9.

[19] Cai HY, Lu L, Muckle CA, Prescott JF, Chen S. Development of a novel protein microarray method for serotyping *Salmonella enterica* strains. *J Clin Microbiol.* 2005;43(7):3427-30.

[20] Peterson G, Gerdes B, Berges J, Nagaraja TG, Frye JG, Boyle DS, et al. Development of microarray and multiplex polymerase chain reaction assays for identification of serovars and virulence genes in *Salmonella enterica* of human or animal origin. *J Vet Diagn Invest.* 2010;22(4):559-69.

[21] Kim S, Frye JG, Hu J, Fedorka-Cray PJ, Gautom R, Boyle DS. Multiplex PCR-based method for identification of common clinical serotypes of *Salmonella enterica* subsp. enterica. *J Clin Microbiol.* 2006;44(10):3608-15.

[22] Carroll SP, Dawes L, Hargreaves M, Goonetilleke A. Faecal pollution source identification in an urbanizing catchment using antibiotic resistance profiling, discriminant analysis and partial least squares regression. *Water Res.* 2009;43(5):1237-46.

[23] Whitlock JE, Jones DT, Harwood VJ. Identification of the sources of fecal coliforms in an urban watershed using antibiotic resistance analysis. *Water Res.* 2002;36(17):4273-82.

[24] Wiggins BA. Discriminant analysis of antibiotic resistance patterns in fecal streptococci, a method to differentiate human and animal sources of fecal pollution in natural waters. *Appl Environ Microbiol.* 1996;62(11):3997-4002.

[25] Foley SL, White DG, McDermott PF, Walker RD, Rhodes B, Fedorka-Cray PJ, et al. Comparison of subtyping methods for *Salmonella enterica* serovar Typhimurium from food animal sources. *J Clin Microbiol.* 2006;44(10):3569-77.

[26] NCCLS. Performance Standards for Antimicrobial Susceptibility Testing; Twelfth Informational Supplement (M100-S12). (M100-S12) ed. Wayne, PA: National Committee for Clinical Laboratory Standards; 2002.

[27] NCCLS. Performance standards for antimicrobial disk and diffusion susceptibility testing for bacteria isolated from animals; approved standard-second edition (M31-A2). Wayne, PA: National Committee for Clinical Laboratory Standards; 2002.

[28] Bauer AW, Kirby WM, Sherris JC, Turck M. Antibiotic susceptibility testing by a standardized single disk method. *Am J Clin Pathol.* 1966;45(4):493-6.

[29] Wistreich G. Microbiology Laboratory-Fundamentals and Applications. 2 ed. Upper Saddle River, NJ: Pearson Education; 2003.

[30] Cockerill FR, 3rd. Conventional and genetic laboratory tests used to guide antimicrobial therapy. *Mayo Clin Proc.* 1998;73(10):1007-21.

[31] Schmieger H. Molecular survey of the *Salmonella* phage typing system of Anderson. *JBacteriol.* 1999 1999/03//;181(5):1630-5.

[32] Snyder L, Champness W. Molecular Genetics of Bacteria. 1 ed. Washington, D.C.: ASM Press; 1997.

[33] Hickman-Brenner FW, Stubbs AD, Farmer JJ, III. Phage typing of *Salmonella enteritidis* in the United States. *J Clin Microbiol.* 1991;29(12):2817-23.

[34] Ward LR, de Sa JD, Rowe B. A phage-typing scheme for *Salmonella enteritidis*. *Epidemiol Infect.* 1987;99(2):291-4.

[35] Humphrey T. Salmonella Typhimurium definitive type 104. A multi-resistant *Salmonella*. *Int J Food Microbiol.* 2001;67(3):173-86.

[36] Altekruse S, Koehler J, Hickman-Brenner F, Tauxe RV, Ferris K. A comparison of *Salmonella enteritidis* phage types from egg-associated outbreaks and implicated laying flocks. *Epidemiol Infect.* 1993;110(1):17-22.

[37] Arbeit RD, Murray PR, Baron EJ, Pfaller MA, Tenover FC, Yolken RH. Laboratory Procedures for the Epidemiologic Analysis of Microorganisms. *Manual of Clinical Microbiology.* Washington, D.C.: ASM Press; 1995. p. 190-208.

[38] Amavisit P, Markham PF, Lightfoot D, Whithear KG, Browning GF. Molecular epidemiology of *Salmonella* Heidelberg in an equine hospital. *Vet Microbiol.* 2001;80(1):85-98.

[39] Selander RK, Caugant DA, Ochman H, Musser JM, Gilmour MN, Whittam TS. Methods of multilocus enzyme electrophoresis for bacterial population genetics and systematics. *Appl Environ Microbiol.* 1986;51(5):873-84.

[40] Prescott LM, Harley JP, Klein DA. Microbiology. Dubuque, IA: McGraw-Hill Higher Education; 2005.

[41] Dobell C. Antony van Leeuwenhoek and his "little animals". New York: Harcourt, Brace and Company; 1932.

[42] Centers for Disease Control and Prevention. 150th Anniversary of John Snow and the pump handle. *MMWR Morb Mortal Wkly Rep.* 2004 Sep 3;53(34):783.

[43] Falkow S. Molecular Koch's postulates applied to bacterial pathogenicity--a personal recollection 15 years later. *Nat Rev Microbiol.* 2004;2(1):67-72.

[44] O'Connor C. Isolating Hereditary Material: Frederick Griffith, Oswald Avery, Alfred Hershey, and Martha Chase. *Nature Education.* 2008;1:1.

[45] Lederberg J, Tatum EL. Gene recombination in *Escherichia coli. Nature.* 1946 Oct 19;158(4016):558.

[46] Watson JD, Crick FH. The structure of DNA. *Cold Spring Harb Symp Quant Biol.* 1953;18:123-31.

[47] Roberts RJ. How restriction enzymes became the workhorses of molecular biology. *Proc Natl Acad Sci U S A.* 2005 Apr 26;102(17):5905-8.

[48] Sanger F, Nicklen S, Coulson AR. DNA sequencing with chain-terminating inhibitors. *Proc Natl Acad Sci U S A.* 1977;74(12):5463-7.

[49] Bartlett JM, Stirling D. A short history of the polymerase chain reaction. *Methods Mol Biol.* 2003;226:3-6.

[50] Schwartz DC, Cantor CR. Separation of yeast chromosome-sized DNAs by pulsed field gradient gel electrophoresis. *Cell.* 1984;37(1):67-75.

[51] Mueller UG, Wolfenbarger LL. AFLP genotyping and fingerprinting. *Trends Ecol Evolut* 1999;14(10):389-94.

[52] Bonin A, Ehrich D, Manel S. Statistical analysis of amplified fragment length polymorphism data: a toolbox for molecular ecologists and evolutionists. *Mol Ecol.* 2007;16(18):3737-58.

[53] Ling JM, Lo NW, Ho YM, Kam KM, Hoa NT, Phi LT, et al. Molecular methods for the epidemiological typing of *Salmonella enterica* serotype Typhi from Hong Kong and Vietnam. *J Clin Microbiol.* 2000;38(1):292-300.

[54] Nauerby B, Pedersen K, Dietz HH, Madsen M. Comparison of Danish isolates of *Salmonella enterica* serovar Enteritidis PT9a and PT11 from hedgehogs (*Erinaceus europaeus*) and humans by plasmid profiling and pulsed-field gel electrophoresis. *J Clin Microbiol.* 2000;38(10):3631-5.

[55] Welsh J, McClelland M. Fingerprinting genomes using PCR with arbitrary primers. *Nucleic Acids Res.* 1990;18(24):7213-8.

[56] Versalovic J, Koeuth T, Lupski JR. Distribution of repetitive DNA sequences in eubacteria and application to fingerprinting of bacterial genomes. *Nucleic Acids Res.* 1991;19(24):6823-31.

[57] van Belkum A, Melchers WJ, Ijsseldijk C, Nohlmans L, Verbrugh H, Meis JF. Outbreak of amoxicillin-resistant *Haemophilus influenzae* type b: variable number of tandem repeats as novel molecular markers. *J Clin Microbiol.* 1997;35(6):1517-20.

[58] Hyytia-Trees E, Smole SC, Fields PA, Swaminathan B, Ribot EM. Second generation subtyping: a proposed PulseNet protocol for multiple-locus variable-number tandem repeat analysis of Shiga toxin-producing *Escherichia coli* O157 (STEC O157). *Foodborne Pathog Dis.* 2006 Spring;3(1):118-31.

[59] Lindstedt BA, Vardund T, Aas L, Kapperud G. Multiple-locus variable-number tandem repeats analysis for genetic fingerprinting of pathogenic bacteria. *Electrophoresis.* 2005;26:2567-82.

[60] David DE, Lynne AM, Han J, Foley SL. Evaluation of virulence factor profiling in the characterization of veterinary *Escherichia coli* isolates. *Appl Environ Microbiol.* 2010;76(22):7509-13.

[61] Enright MC, Spratt BG. Multilocus sequence typing. *Trends Microbiol.* 1999;7(12):482-7.

[62] Cebula TA, Jackson SA, Brown EW, Goswami B, LeClerc JE. Chips and SNPs, bugs and thugs: a molecular sleuthing perspective. *J Food Prot.* 2005;68(6):1271-84.

[63] Foley SL, Lynne AM, Nayak R. Molecular typing methodologies for microbial source tracking and epidemiological investigations of Gram-negative bacterial foodborne pathogens. *Infect Genet Evol.* 2009;9(4):430-40.

In: Molecular Typing Methods for TFM
Editors: S. Foley, R. Nayak, T. Johnson et al.

ISBN: 978-1-62100-643-5
© 2012 Nova Science Publishers, Inc.

Chapter 7

PULSED-FIELD GEL ELECTROPHORESIS ANALYSIS OF BACTERIAL FOODBORNE PATHOGENS

Mary E. Stemper[1], Steven L. Foley and Sanjay K. Shukla[3]

[1] Division of Laboratory Medicine
Marshfield Clinic
Marshfield, WI, US
[2] Division of Microbiology
National Center for Toxicological Research
US Food and Drug Administration
Jefferson, AR, US
[3] Center for Human Genetics
Marshfield Clinic Research Foundation
Marshfield, WI, US

ABSTRACT

Pulsed-field gel electrophoresis (PFGE) is the most common molecular typing technique used in the investigation of bacterial foodborne infections. The PFGE procedure involves cutting the genomic DNA with a rare-cutting restriction enzyme and separating the fragments separated using specialized electrophoresis conditions. The resultant patterns are compared to one another to determine the similarity of isolates. In disease investigations, when isolates from ill patients share common PFGE profiles and a strong epidemiological link with isolates from a potential source, it provides convincing evidence of the likely source of contamination. PFGE is widely utilized for the molecular subtyping of many foodborne pathogens because of its high level of standardization and its ability to separate among un-related isolates. This chapter examines the basics of PFGE, along with the procedures involved in PFGE analysis and examines the utility of PFGE for genotyping bacterial foodborne pathogens.

INTRODUCTION

Bacterial foodborne pathogens have a significant impact on public health; therefore the ability to identify the sources of bacterial contamination of foods is important to benefit human health and well-being. A number of typing tools have been used to link those that are ill to likely sources of infection during epidemiological investigations. Pulsed-field gel electrophoresis (PFGE) is the most common molecular typing technique used in the investigation of bacterial foodborne infections. With PFGE, genomic DNA is cut and the fragments separated to create patterns that are compared to determine how similar isolates are to one another. If in conjunction with a strong epidemiological link, a common PFGE profile is detected among a potential source and ill person, it provides strong evidence of the likely source of illness. In fact, PFGE is considered the gold standard technique for genotyping many foodborne pathogens because of a high level of standardization and its ability to separate among un-related isolates.

Because the results of PFGE analysis aids in determining potential epidemiological linkages, public health officials are able to make science-based decisions to reduce the transmission of pathogens through the food supply. This ability to track foodborne pathogens is due in part to the fact that PFGE results are highly reproducible because of standardized methods, which can be shared between multiple laboratories. For many foodborne pathogens, standardized methods and uniform standards have been developed though the PulseNet program headquartered at U.S. Centers for Disease Control and Prevention (CDC) [1]. While PFGE is a gold standard typing method, it is not without its disadvantages: the procedure is somewhat labor-intensive, typically requiring between 48-72 hours to go from an isolate to PFGE profile, and does require some specialized equipment and technical expertise to complete the methods. This chapter will explore in depth the basics of PFGE, provide a detailed look at the procedures involved in PFGE analysis and examine its relative utility for genotyping a number of bacterial foodborne pathogens.

Background

PFGE analysis is based on the restriction of the whole bacterial genome with a rare cutting enzyme to generate a relatively small number of DNA fragments, compared to other restriction fragment length polymorphism (RFLP) analyses. While other RFLP methods typically rely on Southern blotting to visualize a small percentage of the restriction fragments, PFGE utilizes specialized electrophoresis techniques that are able to separate very large DNA fragments which can be visualized. The profiles of the separated fragments are compared to make determinations about the relatedness of particular bacterial isolates. PFGE has been used successfully to genotype bacterial foodborne pathogens from a number of species including, *Campylobacter* spp., *Escherichia coli*, *Listeria* spp., *Salmonella enterica*, *Vibrio* spp., and *Yersinia* spp. [2, 3]. PFGE protocols for these foodborne pathogens are available through PulseNet (www.cdc.gov/pulsenet/protocols.htm).

While the method steps are described in detail below, the basic procedure involves embedding whole bacterial cells in agarose prior to cell lysis and DNA restriction. By embedding whole cells in agarose plugs and then extracting the genomic DNA, the genomic

DNA is spared potential mechanical shearing associated with pipetting intact chromosome. This provides improved profile resolution as the fragments generated are due to the restriction digestion rather than sheering. The restriction fragments generated are often very large, which creates separation problems for traditional electrophoresis, thus during PFGE, the polarity of the electric field is switched at regular intervals during electrophoresis, allowing separation DNA fragments of up to 800 kb [4, 5]. To facilitate analysis of the profiles, each gel contains multiple size standards spread across the lanes for normalization of banding profiles within the same gel and to other gels run with the same size standards [6]. The use of "universal" size standard coupled with standardized PFGE protocols has facilitated the development of national and international typing programs for foodborne pathogens, such as PulseNet-USA and PulseNet-Europe, that allow for increased disease surveillance and outbreak detection [7-9]. Ultimately one of the goals of using PFGE for foodborne pathogens is to identify the likely sources of contamination that leads to human illness that will allow for a rapid response to minimize the impact on human health. To this end, PFGE has provides an important tool for public health.

Overview of the PFGE Methodology

PFGE has been valuable for molecular typing due to its ability to separate a large range of sizes of DNA fragments from approximately 20 to 100 kb in size. This ability to separate very large DNA fragments distinguishes PFGE from traditional electrophoresis and is vital to its utility for molecular typing. Pulsed-field gel electrophoresis was first described by Schwartz and Cantor in 1984. The technique makes use of an alternating electric field to separate DNA fragments through a gel matrix. The basic PFGE technique has gone through a number of refinements over the years, the most notable of which is the development of the "contour-clamped homogeneous electric field" (CHEF) separation techniques. The CHEF electrophoresis unit utilizes 24 electrodes positioned in a hexagonal contour around the agarose gel. This configuration allows the operator to use or develop a separation program that switches the current between different electrodes at set intervals to allow the DNA to migrate through the gel in a cross pattern at 120° angles. This non-linear separation facilitates improved separation of larger DNA molecules observed with PFGE.

To carry out the procedure, cells are grown overnight, collected and suspended in a buffer at a standardized cell concentration. The cells are then added to melted agarose and placed into plug molds. Once solidified, the bacterial containing plugs are incubated with lysis enzymes and detergents to break open the cells releasing the DNA within the plugs, thereby minimizing mechanical shearing of the DNA. The residual cellular debris is removed from the plugs by a series of washes and DNA that remains in the plug is restricted with a rare-cutting endonuclease. The plug is placed in an agarose gel and the DNA fragments separated under alternating electric field conditions. As the larger fragments migrate, they move slowly because they recoil and realign as the electrical field is alternated, conversely, the smaller fragments more easily move through the agarose matrix and thus migrate more rapidly. Following completion of electrophoresis, the gels are stained and the image captured for analysis. Typically each gel contains multiple size standards that allow for normalization of samples across the gel and to allow for comparison to samples from other gels with the same size standard as well.

GENERALIZED PFGE PROCEDURE

This section provides a detail description of the different steps used to carry out PFGE. This generalized protocol has been adapted from some previously described techniques [10-13]. While the basic protocol described is applicable to many organisms, the baseline information will be for the Gram-negative enteric organisms with noted variations for other pathogens as well. Many of the pathogen specific variations to the generalized protocol are described in Table 1.

Table 1. Optimal conditions for specific foodborne pathogens based on current literature[a]

Organism	Plug preparation and Lytic enzymes[a]	Lysis Buffer[b]	Restriction Enzymes
Escherichia coli *Salmonella enterica* *Shigella sp.*	Harvest cells from ON growth on BAP, resuspend, add proteinase K and 1% Gold agarose containing 1% SDS	ESP	*Xba*I, *Bln*I or *Spe*I
Klebsiella sp.	Harvest cells from ON growth on BAP, resuspend, add proteinase K and 1% Gold agarose containing 1% SDS	ESP	*Xba*I
Listeria monocytogenes	Harvest cells from ON growth in BHI or LB, resuspend, add lysozyme and 1% Gold agarose	ESP	*Asc*I, or *Apa*I
Campylobacter sp.	Harvest cells from ON growth on HIB in microaerophilic conditions, resuspend, add proteinase K and 1% Gold agarose containing 1% SDS	ESP	*Sma*I or *Kpn*I
Yersinia sp.	Harvest cells from ON growth on BAP, resuspend, add proteinase K and 1% Gold agarose containing 1% SDS	ESP	*Asc*I or *Not*I
Staphylococcus aureus	Harvest cells from ON growth on BAP, resuspend, add lysostaphin and 1% Gold agarose	EC and ESP	*Sma*I
Coagulase-negative *Staphylococcus*	Harvest cells from ON growth in BHI or LB, resuspend, add lysostaphin, lysozyme and 1% Gold agarose	EC and ESP	*Sma*I

Organism	Plug preparation and Lytic enzymesa	Lysis Bufferb	Restriction Enzymes
Enterococcus sp.	Harvest cells from ON growth in BHI or LB, resuspend, add lysozyme, mutanolysin and 1% Gold agarose	EC and ESP	*Sma*I
Clostridium difficile	Harvest cells from ON growth in BHI in anaerobic conditions, resuspend, add Lysostaphin, lysozyme and 1% Gold agarose containing 1% SDS	EC and ESP	*Sma*I[c]

[a] ON = overnight, BAP = blood agar plate, BHI=brain heart infusion plate, HIB = heart infusion with rabbit blood, LB = Luria broth, SDS= sodium dodecyl sulfate, ADC = acid-albumin-dextrose-catalase.

[b] EC = EC buffer (6 mM Tris Cl, 1.0 M NaCl, 0.1 M EDTA, 0.5% Brij 58, 0.2% deoxycholate, 0.5% Sarkosyl [pH 7.5]), ESP=Proteinase K buffer (50 mM Tris, 50 mM EDTA [pH 8.0], 1% Sarkosyl, and 100 µg/ml proteinase K).

[c] Running buffer containing 200 uM thiourea minimizes degradation of DNA during the electrophoresis.

Note: References for the pathogen specific PFGE procedures include: Arbeit et al., 1990 (*E. coli*) [41]; Bannerman et al., 1995 (*S. aureus*) [10]; Barrett et al., 1994 (*E. coli*) [42]; CDC PulseNet, (multiple) (www.cdc.gov/pulsenet/protocols.htm); Donabedian et al., 1992 (*Enterococcus*) [43]; Fawley and Wilcox, 2002 (*C. difficile*) [44]; Graves and Swaminathan, 2001 (*L. monocytogenes*)[45]; Halpin et al., 2010 (*L. monocytogenes*)[46]; Hansen et al., 2002 (*Klebsiella*) [47]; Kato et al., 1994 (*C. difficile*) [48]; Klaassen et al., 2002 (*C. difficile*) [49]; Kristjánsson et al., 1994 (*C. difficile*) [50]; Macfarlane et al., 1999 (*S. aureus*) [51]; McDougal et al., 2003 (*S. aureus*) [52]; Reed et al., 2007 (*S. aureus*) [14]; Saken et al., 1994 (*Yersinia* spp.) [44] ; Samore et al., 1997 (*C. difficile*) [53]; Tenover et al., 1994 (multiple) [54].

Growth and Harvesting of Cells

In preparation for PFGE, it is important to have a pure culture of the organisms to be typed. Thus, a single colony of the isolate is inoculated on a rich medium, such as 5% sheep blood agar plate and incubated overnight at 37°C in ambient conditions. The next day a cell suspension is produced by selecting several colonies from the plate with a sterile cotton swab and suspending them in a 5 ml culture tube containing 2 ml of cell suspension buffer (0.1 M Tris Cl, 0.15 M NaCl, 0.1 M EDTA). The size of the culture tube and volume of suspension buffer can be adjusted as needed for the instrument used to determine the cell density. The turbidity of the cell suspension is adjusted until it reaches approximately 15% transmittance (20% for organisms like *S. aureus*) using a Vitek colorimeter (bioMerieux, Durham, NC). Alternatively the turbidity can be adjusted using a Microscan Turbidity Meter (Dade Behring Inc, Deerfield, IL; desired turbidity reading of 0.48-0.52) or in a spectrophotometer measuring absorbance at 610 nm (desired absorbance of 1.3-1.4). Regardless of method used, the optimal cell density is approximately 1×10^9 cells/ml. An important element of PFGE is the proper use of a size standard to allow for intra and inter gel comparisons of isolates. Most often this standard is prepared from a bacterial reference strain that is prepared and processed along with the test strains. This approach provides both a reliable size standard as well as an added quality control to evaluate the efficacy of the PFGE procedures. Some of the most commonly used strains are *Salmonella enterica* ser. Braenderup H9812 (ATCC# BAA-644) digested with *Xba*I [6] for Gram-negative foodborne pathogens and *S. aureus* NCTC 8325 digested with *Sma*I [14] for staphylococci.

Plug Preparation

Following cell concentration adjustment, 400 µl aliquots of each the cell suspensions are added to 2 ml microcentrifuge tubes and combined with cell-lysis enzymes (Table 1). For example, with *Salmonella* and *E. coli,* 20 µl of 20 mg/ml proteinase K is added to each tube to begin lysis. Each cell suspension is then mixed 400 µl of molton 1% Seakem Gold agarose (Lonza # 50150) made with TE buffer (10 mM Tris HCl, 1 mM EDTA [pH 8.0]) and 1% sodium dodecyl sulfate (SDS) and quickly dispensed into plug molds. After solidifying, the plugs are removed from the molds and plugs for each sample are transferred to a 50 ml conical tube containing 5 ml of cell lysis buffer (CLB, for *Salmonella*: 50 mM Tris, 50 mM EDTA [pH 8.0], 1 % Sarkosyl, and 0.1 mg/ml proteinase K). The tubes are placed in a 54°C shaking water bath and incubated for at least 2 hours, up to overnight, with vigorous shaking (~150 rpm). Next, the CLB is removed and the plugs are washed twice with 10 ml of sterile water that has been heated to 50°C. During each wash, the tubes are placed into a 50°C water bath and vigorously shaken for 10 min. Following the water washes, the cellular debris in the plugs is removed by four washes in 10 ml TE buffer (10 mM Tris, 1.0 mM EDTA [pH 8.0] for 10-15 minutes each at 50°C with shaking. Following the washes, the plugs can be stored at 4°C in TE buffer or prepared for restriction digestion.

Restriction Digestion

To start the restriction process, 200 µl of the appropriate restriction buffer (varies depending on the enzyme used and is typically supplied with the enzyme) is added to a 1.5 mL microcentrifuge tube for each sample. To this buffer is added an approximately 3 x 5 mm section of the plug containing the sample DNA. Since most molds are larger than the desired size, the plugs can be cut using a scalpel or single edged razor blade. The plug in the restriction buffer is incubated at the optimum enzyme activity temperature for 15-30 minutes. After incubation, the buffer is carefully removed to avoid damaging the plug and 200 µl of a restriction enzyme mixture, made by combining the desired restriction enzyme at an optimal concentration with the appropriate restriction buffer, is added to each tube and the digestion is allowed to proceed for at least 2 hours up to overnight. For foodborne pathogens like *Salmonella, E. coli* and *Shigella*, the primary enzyme used is *Xba*I, followed by *Avr*II. A list of the most commonly used restriction enzymes is provided in Table 1. Since typically not all of the plug is used in the restriction process, the remainder of a plug can be stored at 4°C in TE buffer and digested with other enzymes if needed during the disease investigation. The ability to digest the sample with multiple enzymes may be important if following initial digestion, the PFGE patterns from two or more isolates are indistinguishable and there is epidemiological evidence that may suggest that the isolates may not be directly linked to one another. The second enzyme digestion can help determine whether the strains are truly indistinguishable or not.

Preparing and Loading the Agarose Gel

Towards the end of the restriction digest, a 1% Seakem Gold agarose gel in 0.5 X strength TBE buffer (0.89 M Tris, 0.89 M boric acid, 20 mM EDTA pH 8.0) is prepared by heating the mixture until all of the agarose is dissolved. Because there are different sized gel casting stands, the volume of agarose solution needed will vary accordingly. The gel casting stand is prepared by placing the running platform in the bottom of the casting stand and tightening the end screws so there are no gaps. It is important that the gel is cast on a level surface to ensure uniform thickness, if not on a level surface adjust the sides of the casting stand to level the unit. The comb is then added to the casting stand towards the top of the gel in the appropriate grooves and the molten agarose can then be poured into the casting stand. The gel is allowed to fully solidify before removing the comb. Next, the digested plugs are removed from their respective tubes and positioned in the wells of the gel against the front wall of the well. Once the plugs are placed, each of the wells are topped off by pipetting molten agarose into the wells to seal the plugs into position. Alternatively, the plugs can be loaded in the casting stand prior to pouring the gel. With this method, the plugs are placed on the running platform adjacent to the front of the comb and then the molten agarose is added to the casting stand locking the plugs into place. Once the gel is solidified, the comb is removed and the wells backfilled with agarose. With either method of plug placement, it is important to space multiple reference strain plugs across each gel (for example. in lanes 1, 5, 10, and 15 of a 15 well gel), these are important for the normalization step of the analysis to compensate for any variability in migration across the gel.

Electrophoresis

Gel electrophoresis is carried out in pulsed-field unit such as BioRad's CHEF Mapper or CHEF DR-III systems. In these systems, 2 liters of 0.5X TBE buffer is prepared and added to the electrophoresis chamber and the buffer is continually circulated through a chiller unit to cool the buffer to 14°C, which is the temperature used during the run. The gel and attached running platform are removed from the casting stand and placed into the running frame within the electrophoresis chamber (Figure 1A). The electrophoresis running conditions are programmed into the controller module based on organism specific running conditions. Some of the parameters that are programmed include the initial and final switch time (in seconds), which set the conditions for switching the electric field directions, the length of run (in hours), and voltage (per centimeter of the gel). For *Salmonella, E. coli* and *Shigella*, the parameters for running a include an initial switch time of 2.16 seconds, a final switch of 63.8 seconds (for *Salmonella*) or 54.17 seconds (for *E. coli* and *Shigella*) and a run length of 18 hours at 6V/cm [13].

Gel Imaging

At the end of the run, the gel needs to be stained to visualize the banding patterns present for each sample. The most commonly used staining dye remains ethidium bromide, which works well, but is a known mutagen and needs to be handled with care and disposed of properly. Other newer stains such as Lonza GelStar® Nucleic Acid Gel Stain (Cambrex Bio Science Rockland, Inc.) and Sybr Safe (Invitrogen, Carlsbad, CA) also work to stain PFGE gels. For ethidium bromide staining, the gel is typically stained for 30 minutes with an ethidium bromide solution (1 µg/ml) with mild shaking. Following staining, the gel is placed in water for at least 15-30 minutes to remove the background stain and the gel is visualized under ultra-violet light and the image captured using a digital photodocumentation system (Figure 1B). The gel image is saved as an image file by the respective systems and often converted to a *.tif image for analysis in a fingerprint software program.

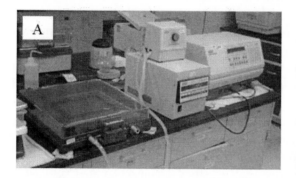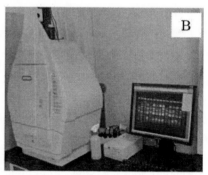

Figure 1. Running and visualizing the PFGE gel: A. gel electrophoresis using a CHEF unit, on the left is the running chamber, in the middle is the chiller (bottom) and recirculating pump (top) and the unit controller on the right; and B. imaging the DNA patterns in the PFGE gel using a digital photo-documentation system.

Fingerprint and Cluster Analysis

There are a number of software programs that can be used for gel image analysis, including GelCompar II (Applied Maths, Kortrijk, Belgium), FPQuest (BioRad), IMAGE (http://www.sanger.ac.uk/resources/software/image/), and BioNumerics (Applied Maths), which is likely the most widely used program. Since BioNumerics is likely the most common program for the analysis of PFGE banding patterns (and is functionally very similar to GelCompar II and FPQuest), the following description of the analysis steps is based on BioNumerics. The gel image is imported into the selected BioNumerics database as a .tif image. If the image is the first PFGE gel processed in a particular database, a new PFGE experiment will need to be created, which defines the type of files being analyzed. Once the experiment is set up, the gel images are analyzed in four steps, which are described below. In Step 1 - "Strips – defining the lanes", the portion of the gel to be analyzed is selected and the lane finding feature is used to define the individual lanes in the selected area of the gel. Adjustments can be made to parameters such as the lanes thickness, spot removal, and initial image optimization to improve analysis.

In Step 2 - "Curves – calculating the densitometric curves", the gel image quality is optimized by a spectral analysis for background subtraction and noise filtering. Step 3 - "Normalization – adjusting lanes with respect to a reference", is one of the most important steps of the analysis because it normalizes the lanes to the reference strain profiles that are distributed across the gel (Figure 2). Initially the reference system is defined during the first gel that is analyzed in a particular experiment. In most cases the reference pattern is derived from a standard strain, such as *S.* Braenderup H9812 digested with *Xba*I, which has fragments of approximately 1135, 669, 453, 398, 337, 310, 244, 217, 139, 105, 78, 55, 33, 29, and 20.5 kbp. Once the internal reference system is set up for the particular experiment type, all future gels are normalized to this standard, which facilitates cross-gel comparison of profiles. When subsequent gels are run under the same conditions with the same reference strains, the band patterns can be normalized to the reference system so that PFGE patterns can be compared to others in the database, even if they were run at different times.

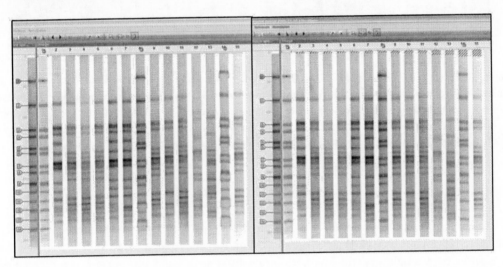

Figure 2. The normalization of PFGE patterns to the internal reference system during analysis in BioNumerics software. The green bands mark the fragments of the reference strain and indicate the downward shift that all lanes will undergoe to align with the internal reference system. Panel A shows pre-normalization *Xba*I digested PFGE patterns of *Salmonella enterica* serovar Heidelberg isolates PFGE patterns and Panel B shows the normalized patterns.

Once the gel has been normalized to the reference standards, the final step is Step 4 - "Bands- defining bands and quantification". In this step, the software automatically searches the various lanes for bands based on user define search criteria. In many cases, the results should be manually verified to ensure that proper band calling occurred. If needed, misidentified bands can be removed or added as required. Once the bands have been properly called in the gel, the results are saved and lane images are linked to their corresponding entries in the associated BioNumerics database. Phylogenetic analysis can be carried out based on the respective PFGE patterns to determine the likelihood that a particular isolate is associated with a potential outbreak. For this analysis, the isolates to be examined are selected and compared to one another using one of a number of different comparison algorithms. These algorithms are described in more detail in a later chapter on "Phylogentic Analysis of Molecular Typing Data". The most commonly used comparison algorithms are the Dice coefficient and unweighted pair group method-using averages (UPGMA) analysis with a band position tolerance of about 1.2-1.5% and an optimization of 1%. The results of the analyses are typically shown graphically in a dendrogram which shows the percent similarity of the isolates (Figure 3).

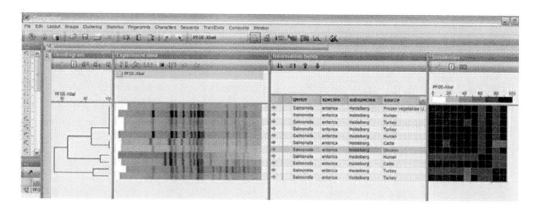

Figure 3. A dendrogram analysis of *Xba*I digested PFGE patterns of *Salmonella enterica* serovar Heidelberg isolates in BioNumerics software. The restricted DNA patterns were compared using the dice coefficient and unweighted pair group of arithmetic averages (UPGMA) method. The dendrogram shows the percent similarity on the far left, followed by the PFGE images and corresponding identification fields. A color-based similarity matrix is shown on the far right.

Interpretation

Criteria have been developed to aid in the determination of genetic relatedness between the bacterial isolates by PFGE [15, 16]. According to Tenover et al. (1995), bacterial isolates that differ by a single genetic event, reflected by 2 to 3 band differences, are defined as "closely related." Isolates with 2 genetic differences (4 to 6 band differences) are "possibly related," while those isolates with ≥3 genetic differences (≥7 band differences) compared with outbreak strains are considered "different or unrelated" [16]. However, these criteria are applicable to smaller, local studies with limited genetic variability among isolates [3]. More recently, it was proposed by researchers at the U.S. Centers for Disease Control and Prevention (CDC) that the "Tenover" criteria were not generally applicable in all foodborne outbreak investigations since they did not adequately account for differences associated with genetic events such as horizontal gene transfer [15]. The newer criteria put forth by the CDC take into account the background history of the species/serotype of isolates that are under investigation rather than just the number of bands in the DNA profiles and the location of origin. According to Barrett et al. (2006), the reproducibility of the PFGE method for a specific bacterium, the quality of the PFGE gel (sharp, clear bands free of partial digestion artifacts), the variability of the organism being subtyped and the prevalence of pattern should be considered in interpreting the results. Moreover, isolates displaying "indistinguishable" patterns (with no genetic differences and differences in the number of DNA fragments) should be included in the detection of infection clusters, and the variable patterns (with 2 to 3 band differences) could be accepted if the outbreak persists for a longer period of time or if the spread of infection involves person to person contact [15]. The interpretation criteria are routinely used in the U.S. by PulseNet and other federal and state public health laboratories [13, 15].

Troubleshooting

Because there are a number of steps and reagents that are involved in the PFGE procedure, there are multiple factors that affect the quality of PFGE gels. Some of the factors that can alter the quality of PFGE result from the correct preparation of reagents, proper handling and storage of enzymes, use of ultra-purified water and clean glassware, and maintenance of the PFGE equipment. Additionally, poor gel results may be the result of inadequate cell lysis, insufficient washing of the plugs or incomplete DNA digestion in the plugs. To solve problems with incomplete lysis of the cells, the length of the lysis time can be increased; likewise the concentration of lysing enzymes can be increased. If the washing of the plugs is not thorough enough, it is possible that residual proteinases will remain which can inhibit restriction enzyme digestion, leading to incomplete cutting and fuzzy restriction pattern. By increasing the number and length of washes, the problem of residual proteases can be minimized providing a sharper band profile. Shadow or ghost bands in a gel are typically due to incomplete restriction digestion of the DNA in the plugs. The problem is typically resolved by making sure that optimal digestion conditions are followed, including not having too high a cell density, utilizing appropriate incubation times and temperature for the enzyme used and ensuring that plugs are fully submerged in the restriction enzyme mixture. Additionally, some products resolve with heavy smearing in the lanes. This problem is typically due to DNA degradation during the sample preparation. One of the ways to minimize the potential for the smearing is to include thiourea in the electrophoresis running buffer, which often aids in pattern resolution. Problems with gel running and staining can also lead to problems with image interpretation. If the gel is poured on a non-level surface, differential gel thickness can lead to uneven staining or lanes that do not run straight, thus it is important that the casting is level when the gel is poured and the running platform is placed securely in the running frame of the electrophoresis unit. If the PFGE unit is not properly maintained and serviced, consequences such as damaged or thin electrodes can also lead to gels not running straight due to electrical problems in the different field orientations.

PFGE IN PRACTICE FOR FOODBORNE PATHOGENS

PFGE has been used successfully to type a number of bacterial foodborne pathogens. A number of PFGE protocols for specific pathogens are available at the PulseNet website (http://www.cdc.gov/pulsenet/protocols.htm), including *Campylobacter jejuni*, *E. coli* O157:H7, *Listeria*, *Salmonella*, *Shigella* and *Vibrio cholerae*. When PFGE has been compared to other molecular typing methods for bacterial foodborne pathogens, the technique is often considered one of the best typing methods.

A number of studies have utilized PFGE to characterize *Salmonella* serovars at different points along the food production continuum including those isolated from the farm, processing facilities, ready to eat foods and ill human patients themselves [17-19]. Because PFGE is often considered the "gold standard" molecular typing technique, there have been a number of studies that have used PFGE to benchmark other molecular typing methods. Multilocus sequence typing (MLST) has been compared to PFGE by a number of researchers with mixed results. Fakhr et al. (2005) reported that PFGE was better at separating non-clonal isolates when MLST was done using four housekeeping genes [20]. In contrast, Kotetishvili et al. (2002) found that PFGE was inferior to MLST with a different set of four genes [21]. Others have found that PFGE and MLST have similar discriminatory ability, however within the analysis; the isolates do not always cluster similarly. In other words, MLST was able in many instances to distinguish among isolates in an apparently clonal PFGE cluster and PFGE able to separate isolates in a single sequence type [22]. When PFGE was compared to amplified fragment length polymorphism (AFLP) analysis, the discriminatory abilities were generally quite similar [23, 24] or AFLP was more discriminatory [25]. When PFGE was compared to multilocus variable number of tandem repeat analysis (MLVA), MLVA was shown to have greater ability to distinguish between *Salmonella* isolates [26-28]. It is important to note that each of these *Salmonella* studies above was generally done with single enzyme PFGE. As additional enzymes are used in the analysis, the discriminatory ability of PFGE increases, allowing for better separation of non-clonal *Salmonella* isolates [29].

In addition to subtyping *Salmonella,* PFGE has been used for the investigation *E. coli* O157:H7 outbreaks and pathogen surveillance [8, 30]. In studies comparing PFGE to other *E .coli* O157:H7 typing methods, PFGE has generally been one of the more discriminatory methods. Foley et al. (2004) found the PFGE was better able to distinguish *E .coli* O157:H7 isolates than MLST and PCR-based typing methods. Conversely, Hyytia-Trees et al. (2006) and Pei et al. (2008) found MLVA to be more discriminatory than PFGE for distinguishing among *E. coli* isolates [31, 32].

For *Campylobacter*, PFGE has continually demonstrated its ability as one of the best molecular typing methods for these pathogens [33, 34]. There has been some concern about which restriction enzyme is most optimal for *Campylobacter* PFGE typing. The current recommended enzyme in the PulseNet program for *C. jejuni* is *Sma*I [12], however Sails et al. (2003) reported that DNA from some *Campylobacter* isolates were not able to be efficiently digested by *Sma*I to resolve adequate profiles [34]. Additionally, Michaud et al. (2001) found that the *Kpn*I restricted plugs provided better discrimination than *Sma*I digested plugs [35]. While not as well studied as some of the foodborne pathogens, PFGE has also proved useful for typing *Shigella* spp. [36-38] and *Y. enterocolitica* isolates [39, 40].

CONCLUSIONS AND FUTURE DIRECTIONS

PFGE has been a typing method that has enjoyed widespread acceptance for the use in genotyping bacterial foodborne pathogens and will likely continue to play a major role into the foreseeable future. This longevity is due in part to its relatively good ability to distinguish between non-clonal isolates and due to the current public health infrastructure invested in the technology. In the United States, all States and many municipalities are able to conduct PFGE typing and report the results to the PulseNet program. Each of these laboratories have invested in the specialized equipment needed to carry out and analyze PFGE results in a highly standardized fashion, which has allowed for significant data sharing that has facilitated the detection of widespread outbreaks of foodborne illness. It is likely that there will be future refinements to the methods. For example, it was realized for some serovars of *Salmonella* that analyzing isolates after only *Xba*I digestion likely led to over interpretation of clonality. Thus when many isolates initially believed to be clonal were typed using an additional enzyme, such as *Bln*I/*Avr*II, they were found to be different. This has led to the recommendation to use multiple enzymes for typing certain foodborne pathogens. Additionally, there have been updates to the analysis criteria used by CDC to characterize the relatedness of isolates (described above in the text) due to a better understanding of the variable genetic diversity of certain pathogens.

While PFGE is likely to be important into the future, there is work ongoing to develop new typing methods that will provide improved discrimination in a shorter amount of time. As the cost of whole genome sequencing comes down and the sequence analysis tools are improved, there will likely be the day in which genome sequencing replaces PFGE as the gold standard typing method. A present, the sequencing approach is not feasible due to equipment costs, reagent costs and technical hurdles, thus in the interim PFGE will continue to play a vital role as a tool for the molecular epidemiology of bacterial foodborne pathogens.

DISCLAIMER

The use of trade names is for identification purposes only, and does not imply endorsement by the U.S. Food and Drug Administration or the U.S. Department of Health and Human Services. The views presented in this manuscript do not necessarily reflect those of the FDA.

REFERENCES

[1]   Swaminathan B, Barrett TJ, Hunter SB, Tauxe RV. PulseNet: the molecular subtyping network for foodborne bacterial disease surveillance, United States. *Emerg Infect Dis.* 2001;7(3):382-9

[2]   Foley SL, Zhao S, Walker RD. Comparison of molecular typing methods for the differentiation of *Salmonella* foodborne pathogens. *Foodborne Pathog Dis.* 2007 Fall;4(3):253-76.

[3]   Olive DM, Bean P. Principles and applications of methods for DNA-based typing of microbial organisms. *J Clin Microbiol.* 1999;37(6):1661-9.

[4]   Lukinmaa S, Nakari UM, Eklund M, Siitonen A. Application of molecular genetic methods in diagnostics and epidemiology of food-borne bacterial pathogens. *APMIS.* 2004 Nov-Dec;112(11-12):908-29.

[5]   van Belkum A, Tassios PT, Dijkshoorn L, Haeggman S, Cookson B, Fry NK, et al. Guidelines for the validation and application of typing methods for use in bacterial epidemiology. *Clin Microbiol Infect.* 2007;13 Suppl 3:1-46.

[6]   Hunter SB, Vauterin P, Lambert-Fair MA, Van Duyne MS, Kubota K, Graves L, et al. Establishment of a universal size standard strain for use with the PulseNet standardized

pulsed-field gel electrophoresis protocols: converting the national databases to the new size standard. *J Clin Microbiol.* 2005;43(3):1045-50.

[7]   Gerner-Smidt P, Hise K, Kincaid J, Hunter S, Rolando S, Hyytia-Trees E, et al. PulseNet USA: a five-year update. *Foodborne Pathog Dis.* 2006 Spring;3(1):9-19.

[8]   Gerner-Smidt P, Scheutz F. Standardized pulsed-field gel electrophoresis of Shiga toxin-producing *Escherichia coli*: the PulseNet Europe Feasibility Study. *Foodborne Pathog Dis.* 2006 Spring;3(1):74-80.

[9]   Swaminathan B, Gerner-Smidt P, Ng LK, Lukinmaa S, Kam KM, Rolando S, et al. Building PulseNet International: an interconnected system of laboratory networks to facilitate timely public health recognition and response to foodborne disease outbreaks and emerging foodborne diseases. *Foodborne Pathog Dis.* 2006 Spring;3(1):36-50.

[10]   Bannerman TL, Hancock GA, Tenover FC, Miller JM. Pulsed-field gel electrophoresis as a replacement for bacteriophage typing of *Staphylococcus aureus*. *J Clin Microbiol.* 1995;33(3):551-5.

[11]   Maslow JN, Mulligan ME, Arbeit RD. Molecular epidemiology: application of contemporary techniques to the typing of microorganisms. *Clin Infect Dis.* 1993;17(2):153-62.

[12]   Ribot EM, Fitzgerald C, Kubota K, Swaminathan B, Barrett TJ. Rapid pulsed-field gel electrophoresis protocol for subtyping of *Campylobacter jejuni*. *J Clin Microbiol.* 2001;39(5):1889-94.

[13]   Ribot EM, Fair MA, Gautom R, Cameron DN, Hunter SB, Swaminathan B, et al. Standardization of pulsed-field gel electrophoresis protocols for the subtyping of *Escherichia coli* O157:H7, *Salmonella*, and *Shigella* for PulseNet. *Foodborne Pathog Dis.* 2006 Spring;3(1):59-67.

[14]   Reed KD, Stemper ME, Shukla SK. Pulsed-field gel electrophoresis of MRSA. *Methods Mol Biol.* 2007;391:59-69.

[15]   Barrett TJ, Gerner-Smidt P, Swaminathan B. Interpretation of pulsed-field gel electrophoresis patterns in foodborne disease investigations and surveillance. *Foodborne Pathog Dis.* 2006;3(1):20-31.

[16]   Tenover FC, Arbeit RD, Goering RV, Mickelsen PA, Murray BE, Persing DH, et al. Interpreting chromosomal DNA restriction patterns produced by pulsed-field gel electrophoresis: criteria for bacterial strain typing. *J Clin Microbiol.* 1995;33(9):2233-9.

[17]   Kam KM, Luey KY, Chiu AW, Law CP, Leung SF. Molecular characterization of *Salmonella enterica* Serotype Typhi isolates by pulsed-field gel electrophoresis in Hong Kong, 2000-2004. *Foodborne Pathog Dis.* 2007 Spring;4(1):41-9.

[18]   Nayak R, Stewart T, Wang RF, Lin J, Cerniglia CE, Kenney PB. Genetic diversity and virulence gene determinants of antibiotic-resistant *Salmonella* isolated from preharvest turkey production sources. *Int J Food Microbiol* 2004 Feb 15;91(1):51-62.

[19]   Aktas Z, Day M, Kayacan CB, Diren S, Threlfall EJ. Molecular characterization of *Salmonella* Typhimurium and *Salmonella* Enteritidis by plasmid analysis and pulsed-field gel electrophoresis. *Int J Antimicrob Agents.* 2007;30(6):541-5.

[20]   Fakhr MK, Nolan LK, Logue CM. Multilocus sequence typing lacks the discriminatory ability of pulsed-field gel electrophoresis for typing *Salmonella enterica* serovar Typhimurium. *J Clin Microbiol.* 2005;43(5):2215-9.

[21] Kotetishvili M, Stine OC, Kreger A, Morris JG, Jr., Sulakvelidze A. Multilocus sequence typing for characterization of clinical and environmental *Salmonella* strains. *J Clin Microbiol.* 2002;40(5):1626-35.

[22] Foley SL, White DG, McDermott PF, Walker RD, Rhodes B, Fedorka-Cray PJ, et al. Comparison of subtyping methods for *Salmonella enterica* serovar Typhimurium from food animal sources. *J Clin Microbiol.* 2006;44(10):3569-77.

[23] Lindstedt BA, Heir E, Vardund T, Kapperud G. Fluorescent amplified-fragment length polymorphism genotyping of *Salmonella enterica* subsp. *enterica* serovars and comparison with pulsed-field gel electrophoresis typing. *J Clin Microbiol.* 2000 2000;38(4):1623-7.

[24] Tamada Y, Nakaoka Y, Nishimori K, Doi A, Kumaki T, Uemura N, et al. Molecular typing and epidemiological study of *Salmonella enterica* serotype Typhimurium isolates from cattle by fluorescent amplified-fragment length polymorphism fingerprinting and pulsed-field gel electrophoresis. *J Clin Microbiol.* 2001;39(3):1057-66.

[25] Desai M, Threlfall EJ, Stanley J. Fluorescent amplified-fragment length polymorphism subtyping of the *Salmonella enterica* serovar Enteritidis phage type 4 clone complex. *J Clin Microbiol.* 2001;39(1):201-6.

[26] Pedersen-Gulrud K, Boxrud D, Medus C, Besser J, Bartkus J. Comparison of milti-locus variable number tandem repeat analysis (MLVA) and pulsed-field gel electrophoresis (PFGE) for surveillence of *Salmonella* Typhimurium. Abstract from the 2006 PulseNet Meeting, Miami, FL. 2006.

[27] Boxrud D, Pedersen-Gulrud K, Medus C, Besser J, Lyszkowicz E, Barlkus JM. Comparison of multiple-locus variable number tandem repeat analysis, pulsed-field gel electrophoresis and phage typing for *Salmonella enterica* serotype Enteritidis. Abstract from the International Meeting on Microbial Epidemiological Markers (IMMEM7), Victoria, BC Canada. 2006;82B.

[28] Torpdahl M, Sorensen G, Lindstedt BA, Nielsen EM. Multiple locus variable number of tandem repeats: improved surveillance and outbreak detection of human *Salmonella* Typhimurium infections. Abstract from the 2006 PulseNet Meeting, Miami, FL. 2006.

[29] Brown EW, Keys C. Pulsed-Field Gel Electrophoresis is a Poor Evolutionary Indicator in *Salmonella*. Abstract from the 2006 ASM General Meeting, Orlando, FL. 2006.

[30] Proctor ME, Kurzynski T, Koschmann C, Archer JR, Davis JP. Four strains of *Escherichia coli* O157:H7 isolated from patients during an outbreak of disease associated with ground beef: importance of evaluating multiple colonies from an outbreak-associated product. *J Clin Microbiol.* 2002;40(4):1530-3.

[31] Hyytia-Trees E, Smole SC, Fields PA, Swaminathan B, Ribot EM. Second generation subtyping: a proposed PulseNet protocol for multiple-locus variable-number tandem repeat analysis of Shiga toxin-producing *Escherichia coli* O157 (STEC O157). *Foodborne Pathog Dis.* 2006 Spring;3(1):118-31.

[32] Pei Y, Terajima J, Saito Y, Suzuki R, Takai N, Izumiya H, et al. Molecular characterization of enterohemorrhagic *Escherichia coli* O157:H7 isolates dispersed across Japan by pulsed-field gel electrophoresis and multiple-locus variable-number tandem repeat analysis. *Jpn J Infect Dis.* 2008;61(1):58-64.

[33] Nielsen EM, Engberg J, Fussing V, Petersen L, Brogren CH, On SL. Evaluation of phenotypic and genotypic methods for subtyping *Campylobacter jejuni* isolates from humans, poultry, and cattle. *J Clin Microbiol.* 2000;38(10):3800-10.

[34] Sails AD, Swaminathan B, Fields PI. Utility of multilocus sequence typing as an epidemiological tool for investigation of outbreaks of gastroenteritis caused by *Campylobacter jejuni. J Clin Microbiol.* 2003;41(10):4733-9.

[35] Michaud S, Menard S, Gaudreau C, Arbeit RD. Comparison of SmaI-defined genotypes of *Campylobacter jejuni* examined by KpnI: a population-based study. *J Med Microbiol.* 2001;50(12):1075-81.

[36] Kariuki S, Muthotho N, Kimari J, Waiyaki P, Hart CA, Gilks CF. Molecular typing of multi-drug resistant *Shigella dysenteriae* type 1 by plasmid analysis and pulsed-field gel electrophoresis. *Trans R Soc Trop Med Hyg.* 1996 Nov-Dec;90(6):712-4.

[37] Soldati L, Piffaretti JC. Molecular typing of *Shigella* strains using pulsed field gel electrophoresis and genome hybridization with insertion sequences. *Res Microbiol.* 1991;142(5):489-98.

[38] Talukder KA, Dutta DK, Albert MJ. Evaluation of pulsed-field gel electrophoresis for typing of *Shigella dysenteriae* type 1. *J Med Microbiol.* 1999;48(8):781-4.

[39] Buchrieser C, Weagant SD, Kaspar CW. Molecular characterization of *Yersinia enterocolitica* by pulsed-field gel electrophoresis and hybridization of DNA fragments to ail and pYV probes. *Appl Environ Microbiol.* 1994;60(12):4371-9.

[40] Saken E, Roggenkamp A, Aleksic S, Heesemann J. Characterisation of pathogenic *Yersinia enterocolitica* serogroups by pulsed-field gel electrophoresis of genomic NotI restriction fragments. *J Med Microbiol.* 1994;41(5):329-38.

[41] Arbeit RD, Arthur M, Dunn R, Kim C, Selander RK, Goldstein R. Resolution of recent evolutionary divergence among *Escherichia coli* from related lineages: the application of pulsed field electrophoresis to molecular epidemiology. *J Infect Dis.* 1990;161(2):230-5.

[42] Barrett TJ, Lior H, Green JH, Khakhria R, Wells JG, Bell BP, et al. Laboratory investigation of a multistate food-borne outbreak of *Escherichia coli* O157:H7 by using pulsed-field gel electrophoresis and phage typing. *J Clin Microbiol.* 1994;32(12):3013-7.

[43] Donabedian SM, Chow JW, Boyce JM, McCabe RE, Markowitz SM, Coudron PE, et al. Molecular typing of ampicillin-resistant, non-beta-lactamase-producing *Enterococcus faecium* isolates from diverse geographic areas. *J Clin Microbiol.* 1992;30(11):2757-61.

[44] Fawley WN, Wilcox MH. Pulsed-field gel electrophoresis can yield DNA fingerprints of degradation-susceptible *Clostridium difficile* strains. *J Clin Microbiol.* 2002;40(9):3546-7.

[45] Graves LM, Swaminathan B. PulseNet standardized protocol for subtyping *Listeria monocytogenes* by macrorestriction and pulsed-field gel electrophoresis. *Int J Food Microbiol.* 2001 Apr 11;65(1-2):55-62.

[46] Halpin JL, Garrett NM, Ribot EM, Graves LM, Cooper KL. Re-evaluation, optimization, and multilaboratory validation of the PulseNet-standardized pulsed-field gel electrophoresis protocol for *Listeria monocytogenes. Foodborne Pathog Dis.* 2010;7(3):293-8.

[47] Hansen DS, Skov R, Benedi JV, Sperling V, Kolmos HJ. *Klebsiella* typing: pulsed-field gel electrophoresis (PFGE) in comparison with O:K-serotyping. *Clin Microbiol Infect.* 2002;8(7):397-404.

[48] Kato H, Kato N, Watanabe K, Ueno K, Ushijima H, Hashira S, et al. Application of typing by pulsed-field gel electrophoresis to the study of *Clostridium difficile* in a neonatal intensive care unit. *J Clin Microbiol.* 1994;32(9):2067-70.

[49] Klaassen CH, van Haren HA, Horrevorts AM. Molecular fingerprinting of *Clostridium difficile* isolates: pulsed-field gel electrophoresis versus amplified fragment length polymorphism. *J Clin Microbiol.* 2002;40(1):101-4.

[50] Kristjansson M, Samore MH, Gerding DN, DeGirolami PC, Bettin KM, Karchmer AW, et al. Comparison of restriction endonuclease analysis, ribotyping, and pulsed-field gel electrophoresis for molecular differentiation of *Clostridium difficile* strains. *J Clin Microbiol.* 1994;32(8):1963-9.

[51] Macfarlane L, Walker J, Borrow R, Oppenheim BA, Fox AJ. Improved recognition of MRSA case clusters by the application of molecular subtyping using pulsed-field gel electrophoresis. *J Hosp Infect.* 1999;41(1):29-37.

[52] McDougal LK, Steward CD, Killgore GE, Chaitram JM, McAllister SK, Tenover FC. Pulsed-field gel electrophoresis typing of oxacillin-resistant *Staphylococcus aureus* isolates from the United States: establishing a national database. *J Clin Microbiol.* 2003;41(11):5113-20.

[53] Samore M, Killgore G, Johnson S, Goodman R, Shim J, Venkataraman L, et al. Multicenter typing comparison of sporadic and outbreak *Clostridium difficile* isolates from geographically diverse hospitals. *J Infect Dis.* 1997;176(5):1233-8.

[54] Tenover FC, Arbeit R, Archer G, Biddle J, Byrne S, Goering R, et al. Comparison of traditional and molecular methods of typing isolates of *Staphylococcus aureus*. J Clin Microbiol. 1994;32(2):407-15.

In: Molecular Typing Methods for TFM
Editors: S. Foley, R. Nayak, T. Johnson et al.

ISBN: 978-1-62100-643-5
© 2012 Nova Science Publishers, Inc.

Chapter 8

OTHER RESTRICTION-BASED TYPING METHODS

Steven L. Foley[1], Rajesh Nayak[1],
Sanjay K. Shukla[2] and Mary E. Stemper[3]

[1] Division of Microbiology
National Center for Toxicological Research
US Food and Drug Administration
Jefferson, AR, US
[2] Center for Human Genetics
Marshfield Clinic Research Foundation
Marshfield, WI, US
[3] Division of Laboratory Medicine
Marshfield Clinic
Marshfield, WI, US

ABSTRACT

Multiple genotyping methods have been developed to distinguish individual organisms from one another. The primary target for these molecular subtyping methods has been the bacterial chromosome, which has DNA sequence variability between non-clonal bacteria. Several typing methods have exploited the potential sequence variability in restriction enzyme recognition sites and/or variability in the size of DNA segments between the recognition sites to distinguish bacteria from one another. When restriction enzymes cut the bacterial DNA at specific locations, the resultant fragments are separated by electrophoresis and visualized to determine a strain-specific profile that can be used for subtyping. These methods are termed restriction fragment length polymorphism (RFLP) methods. Among the more common RFLP techniques are pulsed-field gel electrophoresis (PFGE), ribotyping, amplified fragment length polymorphisms (AFLP), RFLP-PCR and plasmid analysis. This chapter focuses on these RFLP methods, with the exception of PFGE, which is covered extensively in Chapter 7, providing an overview and description of the basic techniques for each of the methods.

INTRODUCTION

The investigation of foodborne illnesses have traditionally relied upon phenotypic analyses of bacterial pathogens, such as biochemical tests for species identification, serotyping and phage typing for taxonomic classification. As scientists have gained a better understanding of the genetics and molecular biology of bacterial species, additional genotyping methods have been developed that can distinguish individual organisms from one another and delineate an outbreak to a potential source. One of the key targets for these genotypic measures has been the bacterial chromosome, which has variability in the DNA sequence in non-clonal bacteria. A number of typing methods have utilized this variability based upon the restriction sites or cutting of the bacterial DNA at specific locations. These fragments are separated by electrophoresis and visualized, either by direct staining or after identification of a subset of the fragments using PCR or DNA hybridization labeling techniques. This chapter focuses on the RFLP methods except pulsed-field gel electrophoresis (PFGE) which is discussed in Chapter 7.

RESTRICTION FRAGMENT LENGTH POLYMORPHISM (RFLP) ANALYSIS

Because each bacterial species have unique DNA sequences, methods have been developed to take advantage of sequence differences to distinguish strains from each other. This has been accomplished by digesting the bacterial chromosome with restriction enzymes, separating the DNA fragments using electrophoresis and visualizing the differences in number and size of the fragments generated (Figure 1). The differences in the number and positions of restriction sites within the bacterial genome, as well as many differences in the sequence between the restrictions sites, can be detected with RFLP analysis. There are multiple approaches to carryout RFLP analyses, these approaches attempt to optimize the restriction frequency, separation parameters and analysis methods. Ideally, RFLP procedures would use a frequent cutting enzyme coupled to a high resolution separation technology that would generate a set of restriction fragments that detects small variations between strains. Unfortunately, this ideal situation does not exist due to technological hurdles and the characteristics of the bacterial genome. For example, an enzyme such as *Pst*I, which recognizes the sequence CTGCAG, occurs on average every 4^6 (4096) base pairs in a bacterial genome and the *Salmonella enterica* serovar Typhimurium LT2 genome has 4,857,432 bases [1]. Therefore, digesting this strain with *Pst*I is predicted to produce over 1000 restriction fragments (1186 by random probability and 1031 detected by *in silico* analysis). When separated by agarose gel electrophoresis, the resultant DNA profiles are an irresolvable smear that is impossible to interpret and distinguish bacterial isolates [2]. Other separation methods, such as capillary electrophoresis, mass spectroscopy and certain liquid chromatography methods are also unable to resolve the fragments due to the large sizes of some fragments. Therefore, alternative approaches need to be utilized for RFLP analysis to be effective. These approaches include using rare cutting restriction enzymes along with specialized electrophoresis methods to separate the resultant large fragments (PFGE), using specialized restriction and imaging approaches (optical mapping) [3] or by using frequent cutting restriction enzymes coupled with techniques to limit the number of fragments are actually detected (ribotyping and amplified fragment length polymorphism [AFLP] analysis).

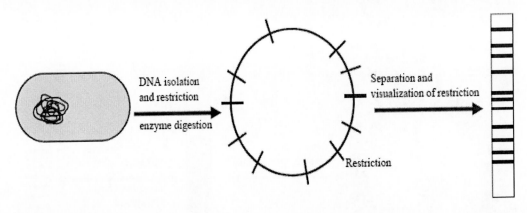

Figure 1. Schematic of the basic restriction fragment length polymorphism (RFLP) analysis.

RIBOTYPING

One of the more commonly used RFLP-based methods is ribotyping, which relies on the detection of ribosomal RNA (rRNA) gene sequences in restriction fragments following digestion of genomic DNA with a frequent cutting enzyme (Figure 2) [4]. The genomes of bacterial foodborne pathogens typically contain multiple copies of the *rrn* operon, which encodes the 5S, 16S and 23S rRNA. The gene sequences in the *rrn* operon are well conserved, while the DNA sequences adjacent to the operons are less conserved [5]. When the genomic DNA from a strain is cleaved with a restriction enzyme, ran on a gel, transferred to a nylon membrane, and hybridized with a labeled probe that recognizes the rRNA sequence, it will produce a characteristic banding pattern. Because of the conserved nature of the *rrn* operon sequence in a specific species, the hybridization probes recognize and bind to the target sequences. However, the flanking regions of DNA do not have the conservation of sequence that the *rrn* operons have and differences in the DNA sequences within an isolate can be determined [5]. Thus, when there are genetic changes in the region adjacent to the rRNA sequence that alter the electrophoretic mobility of the fragment, it will be recognized following incubation with the rRNA probe [4]. These changes typically result in distinct patterns that can be used to discriminate between foodborne pathogens.

Ribotyping has a major advantage in that the results can be efficiently reproduced. This is especially true with automated systems, where most of the procedural steps are robotically controlled reducing the chance for user error or inter-operator variability. The data generated can be compared to existing databases to gain information about the strain being typed. The system also generates relatively few bands, which makes analysis easier [6]. In addition, the discriminatory power of ribotyping can be improved by treating the bacterial isolates with additional enzymes to generate additional banding profiles [7].

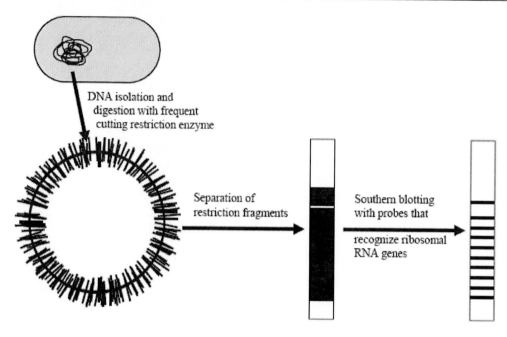

Figure 2. Schematic of the basic ribotyping methods.

A drawback of ribotyping arises from the limited number of *rrn* operons within some species or serotypes [5]. The number of rRNA genes needs to be high enough for the test to be maximally effective at distinguishing between organisms. Additionally for genetic differences to be detected by ribotyping, the mutation or a genetic change must be within a fragment that contains the rRNA probe recognition sites. If outside the fragments, the genetic difference will not be detected [4]. Additionally, if using an automated system, the test can be more expensive than other typing tests, which may be a major concern when dealing with a large number of isolates. Conversely, the manual methods are quite labor intensive, prone to inter-scientist variability and have a fairly slow turnaround time, which can limit their utility when time is important [4].

Basic Methodology for Ribotyping

As with most restriction-based methods, the procedure for ribotyping begins with the isolation of total DNA from the strains being tested. Typically bacterial cells are lysed with enzymes such as proteinase K or lysozyme and detergents such as sodium dodecyl sulfate (SDS) or Tween-80 and the DNA is extracted using methods such as phenol:chloroform extraction and ethanol precipitated [4, 8, 9]. The DNA is then digested using appropriate restriction endonucleases (Table 1), and the fragments are loaded into the wells of an agarose gel and electrophoretically separated. Following electrophoresis, the DNA from the gel is transferred to nylon membrane by Southern blotting and hybridized with probes specific for either the 16S rRNA or a combination of 16S and 23S rRNA genes (Table 1). Commonly the probes are labeled with digoxigenin (DIG), that allows for colorimetric detection following treatment with anti-DIG antibodies conjugated to alkaline phosphatase and an appropriate chromogenic substrate [4]. Alternatively, radio-labeled probes can be used to detect the rRNA genes. The probes used recognize the highly conserved portions of the rRNA genes.

Esteban et al. [10], Ling et al. [11] and Liebana et al. [12] provide in-depth methods for manual ribotyping of *Salmonella*, and the following paragraphs describe a protocol based on these papers. Five ml cultures of *Salmonella* are grown in brain heart infusion broth and incubated overnight at 37°C. The next day, the cells are pelleted by centrifugation and washed with TE buffer (10 mM Tris, 1 mM EDTA), pelleted again and suspended in a lysis solution containing 555 µl of TE buffer, 12 µl of RNase (10 mg/ml), 30 µl of 10% SDS, and 3 µl of proteinase K (20 mg/ml). The suspension is incubated at 55°C for 1 hour and the DNA extracted once with equal volumes of phenol, followed by two extractions with phenol-chloroform-isoamyl alcohol (25:24:1) and finally one extraction with chloroform-isoamyl alcohol (24:1). Following the extractions the aqueous phase is transferred to a fresh tube and 16 µl of NaCl and two volumes of absolute alcohol are added and the mixture incubated overnight at -70°C. The next day, the DNA is centrifuged and the pellet washed with 70% ethanol and suspended in 90 µl of TE buffer.

For the restriction digestion, 4 µg of the DNA template is incubated with 10 U of *Eco*RI (or other enzyme, see Table 1) and the corresponding buffer for 16 hours at 37°C. Following enzyme digestion, the restriction fragments are separated in a 25-cm long, 0.8% agarose gel prepared with tris-acetate EDTA [13] buffer at 45 volts for 20 hours at 14°C. DIG-labeled DNA size standards should be included interspaced in some of the wells of the gel to allow for later sizing and normalization. The DNA from the gel is transferred to positively charged nylon membranes using a vacuum blotter (or other available means of Southern transfer) according to the manufacturer's instructions. Following transfer, the membranes are rinsed in 2X SSC buffer (1X SSC contains 0.15 M NaCl, 0.015 M sodium citrate) and allowed to dry before UV cross-linking the DNA to the membrane as directed by the manufacturer. For blotting with a DIG-labeled *rrnB* probe (prepared by labeling the amplified *rrnB* gene sequence with DIG-High prime kit [Roche Diagnostics, Indianapolis, IN]), the membranes are pre-hybridized and hybridized according to the manufacturer. Following overnight hybridization, the blots are washed with a solution of 2X SSC and 0.1 % SDS, followed by 2 washes with 0.1X SSC and 0.1 % SDS. The DIG-labeled products are recognized by a detection kit containing an anti-DIG antibody conjugated to alkaline phosphatase and chemiluminescent substrate (Roche). The developed blots are visualized and digitized for comparative analysis.

In addition to the manual methods, ribotyping can be largely automated with the RiboPrinter Microbial Characterization System (Qualicon, Inc., Wilmington, DE). With the RiboPrinter, the profile is easily exported to analysis programs such as BioNumerics (Applied Maths, Sint-Martens-Latem, Belgium) for comparison and cluster analysis. Overall, ribotyping seems to have the most utility for pathogens, such as *Listeria* and *Salmonella*, while the discriminatory ability is not high enough for typing *E. coli* or *Campylobacter* species [4]. Please refer to reviews by Pavlic and Griffiths [4] and Bouchet et al. [5] for more detailed information on ribotyping.

Table 1. Conditions used for ribotyping of bacterial foodborne pathogens

Species	Number of rrn Operons[a]	Restriction Enzymes	Probe Target(s)	Manual/ RiboPrinter	Comment	References
Salmonella	7	*PvuII*	16S rRNA	RiboPrinter		[6]
		EcoRI	16S rRNA	RiboPrinter		[83]
		EcoRI, HindII, SmaI, Sau3AI, HaeIII, XhoI	rRNA (included 5S, 16S and 23S)	Manual	*EcoRI* provided the best results	[10]
		PstI and SphI	*rrnB*	Manual		[84]
		PstI, ClaI or *KpnI*	16S-23S rRNA	Manual	*PstI and ClaI* produced best patterns	[11]
Escherichia coli	7	*HindIII*	16S rRNA	RiboPrinter		[85]
		EcoRI or *HindIII*	*rrnB*	Manual	*Ecol* provided a higher level of discrimination	[86]
Campylobacter spp.	3	*PstI*	16S rRNA	Riboprinter	Very few bands generated due to small number of *rrn* operons.	[87]
Listeria monocytogenes	6	*EcoRI*	*rrnB*	Manual		[9]
		EcoRI or *PvuII*	16S rRNA	RiboPrinter		[7]

[a] number obtained from the manuscript by Bouchet et al (2008) [5].

INSERTIONAL SEQUENCES (IS) – RFLP

Another set of methods that uses Southern blotting to minimize the number of bands that are visualized following RFLP analysis is insertion sequence (IS)–RFLP, which relies on targets other than the rRNA genes to identify restriction fragments. For typing some *Salmonella* serovars, the IS*200* sequences in the genome have been probed instead of the rRNA genes [14, 15]. The IS*200* sequences are approximately 700 base pairs long and found randomly throughout the genome of many *Salmonella* strains. Threlfall and colleagues (1993) found that IS*200* typing worked well to discriminate certain antimicrobial resistant strains of *Salmonella* from those that were susceptible [16]. A major drawback for routine typing of *Salmonella* is that not all strains contain the IS*200* sequences, thus making this typing ineffective in distinguishing bacterial strains [15]. IS-RFLP schemes have also been developed for *Yersinia*, which contain a 708-base pair IS element that shares 85% sequence similarity with the IS*200* from *Salmonella* isolates [17]. In addition to the IS*200*-like elements, Leclercq et al. [18] developed a set of IS-RFLP methods that utilized three IS elements (IS*100*, IS*285* and IS*1541*) to characterize *Y. pestis* strains. This study found that the three target IS-RFLP distinguished *Y. pestis* isolates based on their geographical origin.

OPTICAL MAPPING

One of the more recent methods to be developed based on the restriction digestion of the bacterial chromosome is a technique called optical mapping. Optical mapping uses restriction digestion coupled to specialized DNA separation and visualization to obtain high resolution and ordered restriction maps of bacterial genomes [19, 20]. Optical mapping has potential strengths when compared to the more commonly used genotyping techniques, such as PFGE and MLST; methods which have advanced epidemiological and evolutionary studies of bacterial pathogens, yet have some limitations. For example, with PFGE the number of high molecular DNA fragments analyzed and compared among strains is generally in the 15 to 30 range and the banding profiles are based only on the molecular mass of the restriction fragments and do not identify their ordered location within the bacterial genome; these factors limit the information gathered on types of genetic events that contribute to observed banding pattern differences. With MLST, typically seven housekeeping genes are partially sequenced and analyzed for genetic polymorphisms to determine their genetic relatedness (see Chapter 9). Because MLST examines a limited number of genetic loci, the presence of insertions, deletions, or duplications outside of the loci that contribute to genetic diversity will go undetected.

A key strength of optical mapping is its ability to generate ordered restriction maps of the bacterial genome (Figure 3), which is extremely useful in the detection of macro-level changes in the genome including insertions, deletions, inversions, and duplications, when compared to sequenced reference genomes for a particular pathogen [3, 19, 21-23]. These genetic events can be used to compare pathogens potentially associated with a foodborne disease outbreak to help define whether the pathogens have identical or very similar restriction profiles which may indicate a common source [19]. In preparing to carry out optical mapping, many of the initial sample preparation steps are similar to PFGE; however the subsequent steps diverge in the way in which the DNA is separated, restricted and analyzed. The restriction digestion steps are followed by fluorescent labeling of the DNA fragments, imaging and assembly of the restriction map of the genome using software developed by the OpGen Inc. (Madison, WI). Optical mapping was initially used to characterize the genomes of several bacteria including *Deinococcus radiodurans* [24], *Yersinia pestis* [25], *Rhodobacter sphaeroides* [26], and *Rhodospirillum rubrum* [22]. More recently, the techniques have also been used to characterize a number of bacterial species associated with foodborne illnesses such as *E. coli* [19, 21, 23], *Salmonella* [3, 27], *Staphylococcus aureus* [28], and *Mycobacterium avium* subspecies *paratuberculosis* [29]. The following section will provide information on the methods to carry out optical mapping based largely on the methods described by Zhou et al [20]; however pathogen-specific differences (restriction enzymes, digestions times, etc.) for each of the organisms are described in the associated references above.

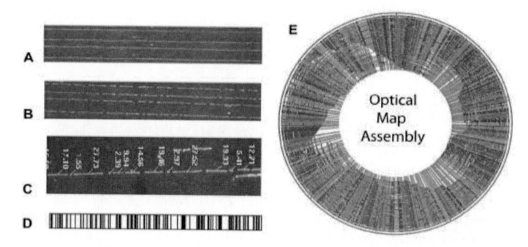

Figure 3. Creation of an optical map. (A) Presence of linearized DNA molecules on a glass chip. (B) *In situ* digested DNA molecules seen as gaps in the linear DNA molecules. (C) Visualization of a single digested and YoYo-1 stained DNA molecule. (D) Representation of a linear ordered restriction map of a bacterial genome in a bar coded form. (E) Circular representation of an optical map. Figure reprinted from Shukla et al. [64] with permission from the American Society for Microbiology.

Basic Methodology for Optical Mapping

Bacterial cells are grown overnight in a non-selective broth medium and the samples processed as described for PFGE (Chapter 7), with an aliquot of each strain being embedded into low melt agarose [20]. Bacterial lysis and agarose plug washing is carried out as described for PFGE to isolate the bacterial genomic DNA [30]. Following DNA isolation, the agarose plugs are melted at 70°C and digested with β-agarase to free the DNA from the plugs. The samples are centrifuged to remove supercoiled plasmid DNA and a Lambda bacteriophage size standard is added to the DNA [20]. The high molecular weight genomic DNA molecules are immobilized on a derivatized cover slip impregnated with micron-sized capillaries. The DNA spreads through the capillary channels due to capillary action and the positive charges on the cover slip surface (Figure 3A). Next, the cover slips are overlaid with a thin coating of acrylamide that polymerizes on the glass surface, sealing in the linear DNA molecules. After washing, the linearized DNA samples are then subjected to *in situ* digestion with a suitable restriction enzyme that will generate anywhere from 300 to 500 restriction fragments (Figure 3B). For example, Saunders et al. [3] used the restriction enzyme *Nco*I to digest a collection of *Salmonella* isolates to explore their genetic diversity.

The *in situ* digested DNA molecules are stained with a fluorescent dye, such as YOYO-1, and imaged with a fluorescence microscope connected to a high resolution camera to capture the restriction fragment patterns of the individual channels (Figure 3C). Because multiple high molecular weight DNA molecules are immobilized prior to digestion, the restriction fragments of the digested molecules from the individual channels are aligned with one another in a similar fashion as DNA sequence assembly is done to generate the whole genome restriction map (Figure 3D) [20]. This process of image capture, analyses and assembly is carried out using the optical mapping computer program (OpGen, Inc.). The end result of the process is a highly ordered restriction map of the whole bacterial genome (Figure 3E), which can be compared among strains to indentify genetic differences. The comparative genomics analyses can be done by the OpGen's MapSolver program. The software program uses an algorithm which aligns pairs of restriction maps according to a model that incorporates differences in fragment sizing, enzyme cut variability and the potential loss of small fragments from the maps. Strains with better matching alignments have higher scores in the algorithm. Likewise, the consensus restriction maps of multiple isolates can be compared to one another and subjected to phylogenetic and cluster analyses to determine the similarity among strains based on their optical maps [23]. Optical mapping has also been an important tool to assist in bacterial genome sequence assembly [31], closure of sequence gaps [25] and determining DNA methylation profiles [32]. Saunders et al. [3] have shown that optical mapping has aided in distinguishing variation in genomes associated with antimicrobial resistance and prophage content of *Salmonella*. Optical mapping does have some potential considerations in that it requires specialized instrumentation (such as the Argus[TM] Optical Mapping System, OpGen, Inc.) or sending samples to core facilities, such as at OpGen, for mapping [3, 31]. The per sample costs are also currently higher than many of the other molecular typing methods [31]; however as the technology becomes more widely adopted, the costs will likely continue to decrease, potentially making optical mapping a viable option for routine molecular subtyping of foodborne pathogens in the future. In addition, while the mapping results often identify the sites of genetic variability, site specific sequencing is often required to determine the identity of genomic changes such as any novel insertions, deletions or duplications.

AMPLIFIED FRAGMENT LENGTH POLYMORPHISMS (AFLP)

Amplified fragment length polymorphisms (AFLP) analysis is an RFLP method that utilizes restriction digestion with two enzymes coupled with PCR amplification to selectively generate fingerprints to distinguish bacterial strains (Figure 4) [33]. As with ribotyping, the initial restriction digestion will lead a large set of DNA fragments to analyze. With AFLP, the reduction of fragments for analysis is achieved by selectively amplifying a percentage of the original fragments. Adapter DNA that have a PCR primer recognition site and complementary sequence to the restriction fragment overhangs are ligated to the ends of the DNA [34]. The PCR primers are designed such that they recognize the adapter sequences plus an additional base or two beyond the restriction enzyme recognition site. The addition of the extra selective base(s) helps to further reduce the number of fragments amplified by a factor of four, because for efficient annealing and amplification, the primer needs to be complementary to the "unknown" base(s) [33]. Following amplification, the reaction products are separated by electrophoresis and the profiles compared to one another. One of the more common adaptations is to use a fluorescently labeled PCR primer and to separate the reactions in an automated DNA sequencer, which gives very good resolution of the amplified fragments [35].

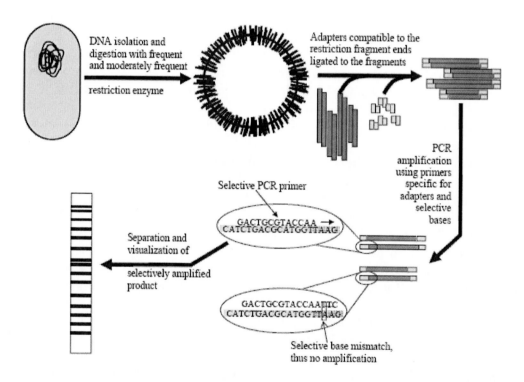

Figure 4. Schematic of the basic amplified fragment length polymorphism (AFLP) analysis.

Overall, AFLP is a strong discriminatory method to differentiate bacteria strains [34]. This technique combines restriction analysis with PCR amplification to increase the signal of the restriction fragments, thus only a small amount of DNA is required for analysis. Because the technique relies both on restriction digestion and PCR amplification, it is also discussed in Chapter 11, which focuses on the PCR-amplification-based methods of subtyping. This technique also allows for simultaneous screening of a large number of isolates through the use of an automated DNA sequencer [36]. This automation also assists in the analysis of the profiles because the data generated is fairly easily converted to forms that can be analyzed with programs like BioNumerics or Excel (Microsoft, Redmond, WA) [35]. A prior knowledge of the bacterial DNA sequence is not required and the fragments that are generated represent a wide range of different locations throughout the bacterial genome, giving a relatively good coverage of the genome to identify inter-strain differences [34]. Enhanced typing can be accomplished through the optimal selection of restriction enzymes and number of selective bases to include in the primers. Some of the potential drawbacks of AFLP include that it can be more labor intensive than other typing methods [35]. The reaction products are typically separated with an automated sequencer, thus laboratories without access to the proper equipment will not be able to perform this technique [37]. Additionally for discrimination among strains, mutation or variation of the gene sequence that distinguish strains needs to occur within the sequence that is amplified or in the restriction site in order to be detected [38].

Basic Methodology for AFLP

Bacterial pure cultures are grown overnight on a non-selective media using standard conditions. Following incubation, genomic DNA is extracted from the organisms either using commercially available kits (such as those available through Qiagen (Valencia, CA), Promega (Madison, WI), etc.) or by methods that have been shown to be effective for the lysis and DNA isolation for the species of pathogen being tested [34, 35]. One method for isolating bacterial genomic DNA using phenol-chloroform-isoamyl alcohol is described above in the section on ribotyping. The DNA is typically alcohol precipitated and treated with 25 µl of DNase-free RNase (0.25 mg/ml) to degrade residual RNA [34]. The isolated DNA is restricted with enzymes, such as *Eco*RI and *Mse*I. These two enzymes are commonly used, however for bacteria with genomes with unusual G+C content, other enzymes may need to be used if the number of restriction sites for certain enzymes is too low. Ideally, one of the enzymes used is a moderately frequent cutter, often having a six base-pair recognition site and the other a more frequent cutter, often with a four base-pair recognition site [34]. A typical restriction reaction would include approximately 1 µg template DNA, 10 U of the each selected enzymes and an appropriate buffer and the mixture incubated at 37˚C for 1 hour [33, 34].

Following restriction, short DNA adapter sequences containing PCR primer target sites and sequence complementary to the overhangs generated at the restriction enzyme sites are ligated to the corresponding ends of the restriction fragments. See Figure 4 for examples of adapters for *Eco*RI and *Mse*I restricted products. The double stranded adapter sequences contain target sequences to which a portion of the PCR primer will bind during selective amplification. Additionally, they block the restriction sites, which prevent the fragments from potentially ligating to one another [34]. Rare cutters like *Eco*RI, are used at a final concentration of 0.04 µM, while frequent cutters like *Mse*I are used at 0.4 µM [34]. The adaptors are ligated using 1 U of T4 DNA ligase and incubated for 3 hours at 37˚C [33]. Following adaptor ligation, the DNA is precipitated and washed as described above and stored -20˚C prior to the PCR reactions.

PCR reactions are carried out from primers that recognize templates in the adapter, restriction site and additional unknown base(s) within the fragment. See Figure 5 for examples of primers for the *Eco*RI and *Mse*I adapters. Additionally, Table 2 in Chapter 11 provides recommended restriction enzymes, adapter sequences and PCR primer sequences for many of the prominent bacterial foodborne pathogens. The inclusion of the additional one to three nucleotides on the 3′-end of the primers functions to reduce the number of fragments that are amplified during the PCR reactions. Initial PCR amplification are carried out under stringent conditions, thus if there is a mismatch between primer and binding site, amplification will not occur efficiently. Subsequent rounds of PCR are carried out under less stringent conditions. For example, Janssen et al. [34] reported initial amplification at annealing temperature of at 65°C; this temperature was dropped by 0.7°C for each of the next 11 cycles and stayed at 56°C for the final 12 cycles. Because of this PCR strategy, for each additional selective base added to the primers, the number of fragments amplified is reduced by a factor of four [39]. Additionally, one of the primers can be fluorescently- or radio-labeled to help facilitate selective detection of the amplified products following separation [33, 40]. Through an optimization of restriction enzyme selection and primer design, the experiments can be such that there are an optimum number of fragments are amplified for separation and analysis [33]. Commercial kits are available from Applied Biosystems (Carlsbad, CA), Invitrogen (Carlsbad, CA) and LI-COR (Lincoln, NE) to carryout AFLP. These kits provide adapters, an assortment of primer options with different selective bases and the reagents to separate the products using an automated DNA sequencer [40].

```
EcoRI Adapter
5-CTCGTAGACTGCGTACC
        CATCTGACGCATGGTTAA-5

EcoRI Primer^A
5-GACTGCGTACCAATTCNNN


MseI Adapter
5-GACGATGAGTCCTGAG
        TACTCAGGACTCAT-5

MseI Primer^A
5-GATGAGTCCTGAGTAANNN

^AN are the selective bases that can be added to the primers
```

Figure 5. Example adapters and selective primers for *Eco*RI and *Mse*I digestions during AFLP analysis [33].

Depending on the approach taken, the PCR products will either be separated using agarose gel, polyacrylamide gel or capillary electrophoresis. While the use of agarose gel electrophoresis is likely the most simple way to separate products, the resolution of the products is not as good as the other methods [38]. Large format polyacrylamide gels, such as those used for manual sequencing, were initially used quite extensively for separation and analysis because they provided a long format to separate product and gave fairly high resolution results [33, 34]. More recently the separation is typically done using capillary DNA sequencers with fragment analysis software [35, 40]. In automated systems, primers used for AFLP PCR reactions are labeled with a fluorescent tags, such as 6-FAM, ROX, JE or TAMRA [39]. This fluorescent-AFLP approach has allowed for enhanced throughput and ease of analysis. In a run, standards can be incorporated in each reaction mix to allow for normalization of results and the results can easily be imported into analysis programs to carryout cluster analysis [35]. The analysis of fingerprint data is covered extensively in Chapter 14 of this book. AFLP has been successfully utilized for molecular typing studies in a number of species of bacterial foodborne pathogens including *Campylobacter, Salmonella, E. coli, Shigella* and *Yersinia spp.* (Chapter 11 and [37, 41-44].

RFLP-PCR

This set of methods also combines RFLP and PCR, but varies from AFLP in that PCR amplification occurs first followed by the digestion of the amplicon with a frequent cutting enzyme. The restriction fragments are separated and the profiles compared to one another [45, 46]. The sequences that are typically targeted for analysis have regions of conserved sequence that bracket a region that is more variable. This allows the primers to bind efficiently and selectively amplify a product, and provides a polymorphic target for the restriction enzymes to cut to produce potentially variable band patterns [47]. Following PCR and restriction, the DNA fragments are separated by agarose gel electrophoresis and stained with an intercalating dye like ethidium bromide and visualized [48]. One of the more common applications of RFLP-PCR is the analysis of the flagellin genes (*flaA* and/or *flaB*) in *Campylobacter* spp. The *flaA* gene is amplified using specific primers to generate a 1725-bp PCR product, which is then restricted with the restriction enzyme *Dde*I [49]. After separation, the DNA banding patterns compared among strains to identify diversity. The flagellin genes have been shown to have regions with a fair amount of variation which allows the differential DNA fingerprint profiles following restriction digest [50]. For *Salmonella* RFLP-PCR, the analysis of *fliC* gene is able to discriminate *S. enterica* serovar Gallinarium isolates [51], but has demonstrated limited success for other *Salmonella* serovars [52].

PLASMID ANALYSIS

Plasmid DNA analyses can be carried out by profiling the number and size of plasmids present in a bacterial strain, by whole plasmid sequencing, by PCR amplification profiling for certain plasmid-associated genetic factors (replicon typing, antimicrobial resistance and/or virulence genes) or by restriction digestion and subsequent analysis of the resultant plasmid profiles [53-56]. The information presented here will focus on the plasmid isolation and profiling based on plasmid size and number, and the restriction analysis of plasmids. These were among the first genotypic methods that were used to type enteric foodborne pathogens [57, 58]. Plasmids are extra-chromosomal, circular DNA molecules that are present in cytoplasm of many bacterial cells. Plasmids replicate separately from the bacterial chromosome allowing for variable number of copies of plasmid DNA in bacteria. During cell division, plasmids are distributed to the daughter cells, thus bacteria from the same clonal lineage often share the same cohort of plasmids. However, plasmids can be gained or lost during the life of a bacterium, so over a long period of time the plasmid profiles may shift in bacteria of a common origin [59]. Strains of bacteria can harbor multiple plasmids, as long as the plasmids have different origins of replication and partitioning systems. Multiple plasmids that have the same origin of replication and plasmid partitioning sequences generally do not coexist in the same cell due to "plasmid incompatibility" (discussed in more detail in Chapter 3) [60]. In general, plasmids confer selective advantages to host bacteria, as many carry genes for resistance to antimicrobial agents and disinfectants, nutrient acquisition and virulence [61]. Additionally, many plasmids carry genes that encode secretion systems that will allow for the plasmid to transfer copies of itself to other bacterial strains [62]. Because of the selective advantages that plasmids provide to bacteria, it is often important to characterize their genetics and understand their distribution in the microbial populations, especially since many plasmids are known to transverse species barriers [54].

Methodology for Plasmid Analysis

Several procedures have been developed to selectively isolate plasmid DNA from the chromosomal DNA [63-66]. In addition a large number of commercial vendors have developed kits to isolate plasmids. These kits often have trade offs; there are mini-prep kits that can isolate smaller plasmids (<50 kb) in a short amount of time, while other kits that are more labor intensive, can isolate larger amounts of plasmid DNA, including plasmids approaching 200 kb in size. For most of the kits, a defined amount of bacterial culture is grown overnight and the cells are harvested, either by scraping from a culture plate or by centrifugation if grown in broth culture. The bacterial cells are suspended in buffers provided by the kit and the plasmid extraction occurs in a stepwise fashion. Because there are a large number of options in commercial kits, it is prudent to identify the goals of the study and what are the isolation requirements as far as the sizes of plasmids that are expected to be isolated and amount of product needed for downstream applications.

In case of manual plasmid extraction, there have been a number of approaches taken to separate chromosomal DNA and cellular debris from plasmid DNA, including gentle bacterial lysis followed by cesium chloride-ethidium bromide (CsCl-EtBr) density gradient centrifugation [66], boiling the lysate to denature the chromosome prior to density gradient centrifugation [65], treatment with salt and SDS to precipitate chromosomal DNA and proteins [67] and alkaline-SDS treatment to selective degrade the chromosomal DNA [64]. The CsCl-EtBr density gradient centrifugation is often quite labor intensive and utilize chemicals that are known mutagens [68]. Following the initial purification steps, the plasmid DNA is typically further purified by dialysis (in the cases of CsCl-EtBr density centrifugation) or phenol-chloroform extraction [69], followed by precipitation with salt and alcohol to concentrate the plasmid DNA. One of the more commonly used methods for plasmid isolation is described by Kado and Liu (1981), which will be described in a greater detail below [63].

For Gram-negative organisms, such as *E. coli* and *Salmonella*, 3 ml of bacterial cells are grown overnight in LB broth at 37°C with shaking. The next day, bacterial cells are pelleted and suspended in 1 ml of 1X Tris-acetate EDTA solution and the cells lysed by the addition of 2 ml of SDS-alkaline lysis solution (SDS, 3% w/v and 50 mM Tris [pH. 12.6]). The suspension is heated at 55°C for 20 minutes in a water bath, followed by extraction with 2 volumes of phenol-chloroform solution (1:1). The tubes are shaken to emulsify the mixture prior to centrifugation at 4,300 x g for 15 minutes at 4°C. The aqueous (upper) phase containing the plasmid is transferred to a tube for storage and further analysis [63]. The plasmid preparation can be analyzed by agarose gel electrophoresis to determine quality and yield. If the DNA needs to be concentrated, the plasmids can be precipitated using sodium acetate and ethanol [63]. Many of the miniprep kits that are available also rely on some variation of the alkaline lysis procedures [68, 70].

For basic plasmid analysis to determine the size and number of plasmids present in a particular strain, the plasmids are separated by gel electrophoresis alongside molecular weight standards such as the BacTracker supercoiled ladder (Epicentre, Madison, WI) or plasmids extracted from strains with known plasmid sizes such as *E. coli* 39R861 and V517 [71]. The plasmids from the samples are compared to the size standard used to define plasmid profiles [72]. One of the potential limitations of this approach is that plasmids in different conformations (supercoiled, nicked or open circle) will tend to migrate at different rates, therefore a single plasmid could be responsible for multiple bands on the gel, which would confound the interpretation [2]. Additionally, some of the large plasmids (>100 kb or so) often do not separate well with conventional electrophoresis due to their large sizes, therefore distinctly different plasmids with similar sizes may be considered the same. Similarly if a strain has smaller plasmids of very similar size, they will migrate at similar rates and show up as a single band on a gel.

A potential approach to overcome some of the limitations of plasmid profiling is to digest the isolated plasmids with a restriction enzyme, such as *Hin*dIII, and carry out RFLP analysis on the plasmid DNA [73]. The restricted DNA is linear, thus there is not a problem with differential migration rates due to plasmid conformation. Also, similar sized, yet different plasmids will have distinct profiles and the overlapping plasmids will likely resolved if they have restriction sites in unique regions. A potential drawback can occur if the plasmids lack adequate restriction sites, then the restriction analysis will not work well and alternative enzymes will need to be chosen. Plasmid profile analysis and plasmid RFLP analysis have been used extensively to characterize foodborne pathogens, including *Salmonella* [74-76], *E. coli* [77, 78], *Yersinia* [79, 80] and *Shigella* [81, 82].

CONCLUSIONS

This chapter looked at many of the methods besides PFGE that rely on restriction analysis of DNA to develop characteristics fingerprint profiles. The RFLP-based methods will likely continue to play a key role in the characterization of certain bacterial foodborne pathogens. In the future, it is likely that efforts to improve the utility of RFLP will focus on the development of improved methods for the detection of highly informative regions of the bacterial genome and decreasing the time it takes to go from pathogen isolation to molecular typing result.

DISCLAIMER

The use of trade names is for identification purposes only, and does not imply endorsement by the U.S. Food and Drug Administration or the U.S. Department of Health and Human Services. The views presented in this manuscript do not necessarily reflect those of the FDA.

REFERENCES

[1]   McClelland M, Sanderson KE, Spieth J, Clifton SW, Latreille P, Courtney L, et al. Complete genome sequence of *Salmonella enterica* serovar Typhimurium LT2. *Nature.* 2001;413(6858):852-6.

[2]   Olsen JE, Brown DJ, Skov MN, Christensen JP. Bacterial typing methods suitable for epidemiological analysis. Applications in investigations of salmonellosis among livestock. *Vet Q.* 1993;15(4):125-35.

[3]   Saunders MP, Wu G, Abuoun M, Pan Z, Anjum M, Woodward MJ. Optical genetic mapping defines regions of chromosomal variation in serovars of *S. enterica* subsp. *enterica* of concern for human and animal health. *Epidemiol Infect.* 2010;22:1-10.

[4]   Pavlic M, Griffiths MW. Principles, applications, and limitations of automated ribotyping as a rapid method in food safety. *Foodborne Pathog Dis.* 2009;6(9):1047-55.

[5]   Bouchet V, Huot H, Goldstein R. Molecular genetic basis of ribotyping. *Clin Microbiol Rev.* 2008;21(2):262-73.

[6]   Bailey JS, Fedorka-Cray PJ, Stern NJ, Craven SE, Cox NA, Cosby DE. Serotyping and ribotyping of *Salmonella* using restriction enzyme *Pvu*II. *J Food Prot.* 2002;65(6):1005-7.

[7]   Gendel SM, Ulaszek J. Ribotype analysis of strain distribution in *Listeria monocytogenes*. *J Food Prot.* 2000;63(2):179-85.

[8]   Regnault B, Grimont F, Grimont PA. Universal ribotyping method using a chemically labelled oligonucleotide probe mixture. *Res Microbiol.* 1997;148(8):649-59.

[9]   Graves LM, Swaminathan B, Reeves MW, Wenger J. Ribosomal DNA fingerprinting of *Listeria monocytogenes* using a digoxigenin-labeled DNA probe. *Eur J Epidemiol.* 1991;7(1):77-82.

[10] Esteban E, Snipes K, Hird D, Kasten R, Kinde H. Use of ribotyping for characterization of *Salmonella* serotypes. *J Clin Microbiol.* 1993;31(2):233-7.

[11] Ling JM, Lo NW, Ho YM, Kam KM, Hoa NT, Phi LT, et al. Molecular methods for the epidemiological typing of *Salmonella enterica* serotype Typhi from Hong Kong and Vietnam. *J Clin Microbiol.* 2000;38(1):292-300.

[12] Liebana E, Garcia-Migura L, Breslin MF, Davies RH, Woodward MJ. Diversity of strains of *Salmonella enterica* serotype enteritidis from English poultry farms assessed by multiple genetic fingerprinting. *J Clin Microbiol.* 2001;39(1):154-61.

[13] Campbell EA, Korzheva N, Mustaev A, Murakami K, Nair S, Goldfarb A, et al. Structural mechanism for rifampicin inhibition of bacterial RNA polymerase. *Cell.* 2001;104(6):901-12.

[14] Olsen JE, Skov MN, Angen O, Threlfall EJ, Bisgaard M. Genomic relationships between selected phage types of *Salmonella enterica* subsp. *enterica* serotype Typhimurium defined by ribotyping, IS200 typing and PFGE. *Microbiology.* 1997;143 (Pt 4):1471-9.

[15] Millemann Y, Gaubert S, Remy D, Colmin C. Evaluation of IS200-PCR and comparison with other molecular markers To trace *Salmonella enterica* subsp. *enterica* serotype Typhimurium bovine isolates from farm to meat. *J Clin Microbiol.* 2000;38(6):2204-9.

[16]   Threlfall EJ, Torre E, Ward LR, Rowe B, Gibert I. Insertion sequence IS200 can differentiate drug-resistant and drug-sensitive *Salmonella typhi* of Vi-phage types E1 and M1. *J Med Microbiol.* 1993;39(6):454-8.

[17]   Odaert M, Berche P, Simonet M. Molecular typing of *Yersinia pseudotuberculosis* by using an IS200-like element. *J Clin Microbiol.* 1996;34(9):2231-5.

[18]   Leclercq AJ, Torrea G, Chenal-Francisque V, Carniel E. 3 IS-RFLP: a powerful tool for geographical clustering of global isolates of *Yersinia pestis. Adv Exp Med Biol.* 2007;603:322-6.

[19]   Kotewicz ML, Jackson SA, LeClerc JE, Cebula TA. Optical maps distinguish individual strains of *Escherichia coli* O157:H7. *Microbiology.* 2007;153(Pt 6):1720-33.

[20]   Zhou S, Kile A, Bechner M, Place M, Kvikstad E, Deng W, et al. Single-molecule approach to bacterial genomic comparisons via optical mapping. *J Bacteriol.* 2004;186(22):7773-82.

[21]   Lim A, Dimalanta ET, Potamousis KD, Yen G, Apodoca J, Tao C, et al. Shotgun optical maps of the whole *Escherichia coli* O157:H7 genome. *Genome Res.* 2001;11(9):1584-93.

[22]   Reslewic S, Zhou S, Place M, Zhang Y, Briska A, Goldstein S, et al. Whole-genome shotgun optical mapping of *Rhodospirillum rubrum. Appl Environ Microbiol.* 2005;71(9):5511-22.

[23]   Schwan WR, Briska A, Stahl B, Wagner TK, Zentz E, Henkhaus J, et al. Use of optical mapping to sort uropathogenic *Escherichia coli* strains into distinct subgroups. *Microbiology.* 2010 Jul;156(Pt 7):2124-35.

[24]   Lin J, Qi R, Aston C, Jing J, Anantharaman TS, Mishra B, et al. Whole-genome shotgun optical mapping of *Deinococcus radiodurans. Science.* 1999;285(5433):1558-62.

[25]   Zhou S, Deng W, Anantharaman TS, Lim A, Dimalanta ET, Wang J, et al. A whole-genome shotgun optical map of *Yersinia pestis* strain KIM. *Appl Environ Microbiol.* 2002;68(12):6321-31.

[26]   Zhou S, Kvikstad E, Kile A, Severin J, Forrest D, Runnheim R, et al. Whole-genome shotgun optical mapping of *Rhodobacter sphaeroides* strain 2.4.1 and its use for whole-genome shotgun sequence assembly. *Genome Res.* 2003;13(9):2142-51.

[27]   Petersen RF, Litrup E, Larsson JT, Torpdahl M, Sorensen G, Muller L, et al. Molecular characterization of *Salmonella* Typhimurium highly successful outbreak strains. *Foodborne Pathog Dis.* 2011;8(6):655-61.

[28]   Shukla SK, Kislow J, Briska A, Henkhaus J, Dykes C. Optical mapping reveals a large genetic inversion between two methicillin-resistant *Staphylococcus aureus* strains. *J Bacteriol.* 2009;191(18):5717-23.

[29]   Wu CW, Schramm TM, Zhou S, Schwartz DC, Talaat AM. Optical mapping of the *Mycobacterium avium* subspecies *paratuberculosis* genome. *BMC Genomics.* 2009;10:25.

[30]   Schwartz DC, Cantor CR. Separation of yeast chromosome-sized DNAs by pulsed field gradient gel electrophoresis. *Cell.* 1984;37(1):67-75.

[31]   Latreille P, Norton S, Goldman BS, Henkhaus J, Miller N, Barbazuk B, et al. Optical mapping as a routine tool for bacterial genome sequence finishing. *BMC Genomics.* 2007;8:321.

[32]   Ananiev GE, Goldstein S, Runnheim R, Forrest DK, Zhou S, Potamousis K, et al. Optical mapping discerns genome wide DNA methylation profiles. *BMC Mol Biol.* 2008;9:68

[33]   Vos P, Hogers R, Bleeker M, Reijans M, van de Lee T, Hornes M, et al. AFLP: a new technique for DNA fingerprinting. *Nucleic Acids Res.* 1995;23(21):4407-14.

[34]   Janssen P, Coopman R, Huys G, Swings J, Bleeker M, Vos P, et al. Evaluation of the DNA fingerprinting method AFLP as an new tool in bacterial taxonomy. *Microbiology.* 1996;142(Pt 7):1881-93.

[35]   Scott F, Threlfall J, Stanley J, Arnold C. Fluorescent amplified fragment length polymorphism genotyping of *Salmonella* Enteritidis: a method suitable for rapid outbreak recognition. *Clin Microbiol Infect.* 2001;7(9):479-85.

[36]   Grady R, Desai M, O'Neill G, Cookson B, Stanley J. Genotyping of epidemic methicillin-resistant *Staphylococcus aureus* phage type 15 isolates by fluorescent amplified-fragment length polymorphism analysis. *J Clin Microbiol.* 1999;37(10):3198-203.

[37]   Tamada Y, Nakaoka Y, Nishimori K, Doi A, Kumaki T, Uemura N, et al. Molecular typing and epidemiological study of *Salmonella enterica* serotype Typhimurium isolates from cattle by fluorescent amplified-fragment length polymorphism fingerprinting and pulsed-field gel electrophoresis. *J Clin Microbiol.* 2001;39(3):1057-66.

[38]   Mueller UG, Wolfenbarger LL. AFLP genotyping and fingerprinting. *Trends Ecol Evolut* 1999;14(10):389-94.

[39]   Savelkoul PH, Aarts HJ, de Haas J, Dijkshoorn L, Duim B, Otsen M, et al. Amplified-fragment length polymorphism analysis: the state of an art. *J Clin Microbiol* 1999;37(10):3083-91.

[40]   Applied Biosystems. AFLP Microbial Fingerprinting Protocol. Foster City, CA: *Applied Biosystems;* 2010.

[41]   Sirisriro T, Sethabutr O, Mason C, Talukder KA, Venkatesan MM. An AFLP-based database of *Shigella flexneri* and *Shigella sonnei* isolates and its use for the identification of untypeable *Shigella* strains. *J Microbiol Methods.* 2006;67(3):487-95.

[42]   Duim B, Wassenaar TM, Rigter A, Wagenaar J. High-resolution genotyping of *Campylobacter* strains isolated from poultry and humans with amplified fragment length polymorphism fingerprinting. *Appl Environ Microbiol.* 1999;65(6):2369-75.

[43]   Boghenbor KK, On SL, Kokotovic B, Baumgartner A, Wassenaar TM, Wittwer M, et al. Genotyping of human and porcine *Yersinia enterocolitica, Yersinia intermedia*, and *Yersinia bercovieri* strains from Switzerland by amplified fragment length polymorphism analysis. *Appl Environ Microbiol.* 2006;72(6):4061-6.

[44]   Fearnley C, On SL, Kokotovic B, Manning G, Cheasty T, Newell DG. Application of fluorescent amplified fragment length polymorphism for comparison of human and animal isolates of *Yersinia enterocolitica. Appl Environ Microbiol.* 2005;71(9):4960-5.

[45]   Foley SL, Zhao S, Walker RD. Comparison of molecular typing methods for the differentiation of *Salmonella* foodborne pathogens. *Foodborne Pathog Dis.* 2007;4(3):253-76.

[46]   Nayak R, Stewart T, Nawaz M, Cerniglia C. In vitro antimicrobial susceptibility, genetic diversity and prevalence of UDP-glucose 4-epimerase (galE) gene in

Campylobacter coli and *Campylobacter jejuni* from Turkey production facilities. *Food Microbiol.* 2006;23(4):379-92.

[47] Mohran ZS, Guerry P, Lior H, Murphy JR, el Gendy AM, Mikhail MM, et al. Restriction fragment length polymorphism of flagellin genes of *Campylobacter jejuni* and/or *C. coli* isolates from Egypt. *J Clin Microbiol.* 1996;34(5):1216-9.

[48] Olive DM, Bean P. Principles and applications of methods for DNA-based typing of microbial organisms. *J Clin Microbiol.* 1999;37(6):1661-9.

[49] Harrington CS, Moran L, Ridley AM, Newell DG, Madden RH. Inter-laboratory evaluation of three flagellin PCR/RFLP methods for typing *Campylobacter jejuni* and *C. coli*: the CAMPYNET experience. *J Appl Microbiol.* 2003;95(6):1321-33.

[50] Harrington CS, Thomson-Carter FM, Carter PE. Evidence for recombination in the flagellin locus of *Campylobacter jejuni*: implications for the flagellin gene typing scheme. *J Clin Microbiol.* 1997;35(9):2386-92.

[51] Kwon HJ, Park KY, Yoo HS, Park JY, Park YH, Kim SJ. Differentiation of *Salmonella enterica* serotype gallinarum biotype pullorum from biotype gallinarum by analysis of phase 1 flagellin C gene (*fliC*). *J Microbiol Methods.* 2000;40(1):33-8.

[52] Dauga C, Zabrovskaia A, Grimont PA. Restriction fragment length polymorphism analysis of some flagellin genes of *Salmonella enterica*. *J Clin Microbiol.* 1998;36(10):2835-43.

[53] Johnson TJ, Wannemuehler YM, Johnson SJ, Logue CM, White DG, Doetkott C, et al. Plasmid replicon typing of commensal and pathogenic *Escherichia coli* isolates. *Appl Environ Microbiol.* 2007;73(6):1976-83.

[54] Fricke WF, McDermott PF, Mammel MK, Zhao S, Johnson TJ, Rasko DA, et al. Antimicrobial resistance-conferring plasmids with similarity to virulence plasmids from avian pathogenic *Escherichia coli* strains in *Salmonella enterica* serovar Kentucky isolates from poultry. *Appl Environ Microbiol.* 2009;75(18):5963-71.

[55] Kaldhone P, Nayak R, Lynne AM, David DE, McDermott PF, Logue CM, et al. Characterization of *Salmonella enterica* serovar Heidelberg from turkey-associated sources. *Appl Environ Microbiol.* 2008 Aug;74(16):5038-46.

[56] Foley SL, Lynne AM. Food animal-associated *Salmonella* challenges: pathogenicity and antimicrobial resistance. *J Anim Sci.* 2008;86(14 Suppl):E173-87.

[57] Schaberg DR, Tompkins LS, Falkow S. Use of agarose gel electrophoresis of plasmid deoxyribonucleic acid to fingerprint Gram-negative bacilli. *J Clin Microbiol.* 1981, 1981;13(6):1105-8.

[58] Mayer LW. Use of plasmid profiles in epidemiologic surveillance of disease outbreaks and in tracing the transmission of antibiotic resistance. *Clin Microbiol Rev.* 1988;1(2):228-43.

[59] Summers DK. The Biology of Plasmids. 1 ed. Oxford: Blackwell Science; 1996.

[60] Helsinki D. Introduction to plasmids: a selective view of their history. In: Funnell B, Phillips G, editors. *Plasmid Biology.* Washington, DC: ASM Press; 2004. p. 1-21.

[61] Threlfall EJ, Frost JA, Ward LR, Rowe B. Plasmid profile typing can be used to subdivide phage-type 49 of *Salmonella* typhimurium in outbreak investigations. *Epidemiol Infect.* 1990;104(2):243-51.

[62] Fricke WF, Welch TJ, McDermott PF, Mammel MK, LeClerc JE, White DG, et al. Comparative genomics of the IncA/C multidrug resistance plasmid family. *J Bacteriol.* 2009;191(15):4750-7.

[63] Kado CI, Liu ST. Rapid procedure for detection and isolation of large and small plasmids. *J Bacteriol.* 1981;145(3):1365-73.

[64] Birnboim HC, Doly J. A rapid alkaline extraction procedure for screening recombinant plasmid DNA. *Nucleic Acids Res.* 1979;7(6):1513-23.

[65] Holmes DS, Quigley M. A rapid boiling method for the preparation of bacterial plasmids. *Anal Biochem.* 1981;114(1):193-7.

[66] Clewell DB, Helinski DR. Supercoiled circular DNA-protein complex in *Escherichia coli*: purification and induced conversion to an opern circular DNA form. *Proc Natl Acad Sci U S A.* 1969;62(4):1159-66.

[67] Hirt B. Selective extraction of polyoma DNA from infected mouse cell cultures. *J Mol Biol.* 1967;26(2):365-9.

[68] Promega. DNA purification. Protocols and Applications Guide. Madison, WI: Promega; 2009.

[69] Wang Z, Rossman TG. Large-scale supercoiled plasmid preparation by acidic phenol extraction. *Biotechniques.* 1994;16(3):460-3.

[70] Engebrecht J, Heilig JS, Brent R. Preparation of bacterial plasmid DNA. *Curr Protoc Immunol.* 2001;10-3.

[71] Olsen JE. Molecular typing of *Salmonella*. In: Wray C, Wray A, editors. *Salmonella* in Domestic Animals. U.K.: CAB International; 2000. p. 429-43.

[72] Nauerby B, Pedersen K, Dietz HH, Madsen M. Comparison of Danish isolates of *Salmonella enterica* serovar enteritidis PT9a and PT11 from hedgehogs (*Erinaceus europaeus*) and humans by plasmid profiling and pulsed-field gel electrophoresis. *J Clin Microbiol.* 2000;38(10):3631-5.

[73] Foley SL, Walker R. Methods of differentiation among bacterial foodborne pathogens. Beier RC, Pillai SD, Phillips TD, Ziprin RL, editors. Ames, IA: Iowa State University; 2005.

[74] Nayak R, Stewart T, Wang RF, Lin J, Cerniglia CE, Kenney PB. Genetic diversity and virulence gene determinants of antibiotic-resistant *Salmonella* isolated from preharvest turkey production sources. *Int J Food Microbiol* 2004;91(1):51-62.

[75] Threlfall EJ, Bhat MB, Sharma KB. Genetic analysis of plasmids coexisting in *Salmonella newport* isolated from a salmonellosis outbreak in Delhi. *Indian J Med Res.* 1982;76:358-63.

[76] Aktas Z, Day M, Kayacan CB, Diren S, Threlfall EJ. Molecular characterization of *Salmonella* Typhimurium and *Salmonella* Enteritidis by plasmid analysis and pulsed-field gel electrophoresis. *Int J Antimicrob Agents.* 2007;30(6):541-5.

[77] Johnson JR, Sannes MR, Croy C, Johnston B, Clabots C, Kuskowski MA, et al. Antimicrobial drug-resistant *Escherichia coli* from humans and poultry products, Minnesota and Wisconsin, 2002-2004. *Emerg Infect Dis.* 2007;13(6):838-46.

[78] Domingue G, Willshaw GA, Smith HR, Perry N, Radford D, Cheasty T. DNA-based subtyping of verocytotoxin-producing *Escherichia coli* (VTEC) O128ab:H2 strains from human and raw meat sources. *Lett Appl Microbiol.* 2003;37(6):433-7.

[79] Capilla S, Goni P, Rubio MC, Castillo J, Millan L, Cerda P, et al. Epidemiological study of resistance to nalidixic acid and other antibiotics in clinical *Yersinia enterocolitica* O:3 isolates. *J Clin Microbiol.* 2003;41(10):4876-8.

[80] Garcia JA, Dominguez L, Larsen JL, Pedersen K. Ribotyping and plasmid profiling of *Yersinia ruckeri*. *J Appl Microbiol.* 1998;85(6):949-55.

[81] Liu PY, Lau YJ, Hu BS, Shyr JM, Shi ZY, Tsai WS, et al. Analysis of clonal relationships among isolates of *Shigella sonnei* by different molecular typing methods. *J Clin Microbiol.* 1995;33(7):1779-83.

[82] Gebre-Yohannes A, Drasar BS. Molecular epidemiology of plasmid patterns in *Shigella flexneri* types 1-6. *Epidemiol Infect.* 1991;107(2):321-34.

[83] Oscar TP. Identification and characterization of *Salmonella* isolates by automated ribotyping. *J Food Prot.* 1998;61(5):519-24.

[84] Liebana E, Guns D, Garcia-Migura L, Woodward MJ, Clifton-Hadley FA, Davies RH. Molecular typing of *Salmonella* serotypes prevalent in animals in England: assessment of methodology. J Clin Microbiol. 2001;39(10):3609-16.

[85] Casarez EA, Pillai SD, Mott JB, Vargas M, Dean KE, Di Giovanni GD. Direct comparison of four bacterial source tracking methods and use of composite data sets. *J Appl Microbiol.* 2007;103(2):350-64.

[86] Alos JI, Lambert T, Courvalin P. Comparison of two molecular methods for tracing nosocomial transmission of *Escherichia coli* K1 in a neonatal unit. *J Clin Microbiol.* 1993;31(7):1704-9.

[87] Rosef O, Johnsen G, Stolan A, Klaeboe H. Similarity of *Campylobacter lari* among human, animal, and water isolates in Norway. *Foodborne Pathog Dis.* 2008;5(1):33-9.

In: Molecular Typing Methods for TFM
Editors: S. Foley, R. Nayak, T. Johnson et al.

ISBN: 978-1-62100-643-5
© 2012 Nova Science Publishers, Inc.

Chapter 9

MULTILOCUS SEQUENCE TYPING AND OTHER SEQUENCE-BASED METHODS TO CHARACTERIZE FOODBORNE PATHOGENS

Mohamed K. Fakhr[1], Aneesa Noormohamed[1] and Steven L. Foley[2]

[1] Department of Biological Science
The University of Tulsa
Tulsa, OK, US
[2] Division of Microbiology
National Center for Toxicological Research
U.S. Food and Drug Administration
Jefferson, AR, US

ABSTRACT

Advances in DNA sequencing methods have enabled scientists to better understand the genetics of bacterial pathogens. Bacterial genomes are diverse due to genetic recombination, mutations or horizontal gene transfer between bacteria and phages. Most genotyping methods rely on the indirect detection the sequence variability, such as differences in the sizes of PCR products or restriction fragments, whereas multilocus sequence typing (MLST), single nucleotide polymorohisms (SNP) analysis and whole genome sequencing rely on the direct comparison of DNA sequences to determine the relationship between different bacterial strains. This chapter explores the different sequence-based methods, MLST and SNP analysis in detail, providing an introduction to the methods, along with the basic procedures and how these methods have been used for typing bacterial foodborne pathogens.

INTRODUCTION

With the advent of DNA sequencing methods, researchers have been able to gain a great deal of knowledge about the genetics of bacterial pathogens. What was discovered is that microbial genomes are quite diverse due in large part to genetic recombination, mutations or horizontal gene transfer between bacteria and phages. This diversity among bacterial genomes allows bacteria to have different functional attributes which are exploited by the phenotypic methods of characterization and serve as the targets for the various genotyping methods described throughout this book. Most of the genotyping methods rely on indirect methods to detect the sequence variability, such as differences in the size of PCR products or restriction fragments, whereas the predominant methods described in this chapter, multilocus sequence typing (MLST) and single nucleotide polymorohism (SNP) analysis rely on the direct detection of differences between the DNA sequences to determine the relationship between different bacterial strains. MLST relies on the comparison of DNA sequences of multiple, typically fairly conserved, loci within the bacterial genome to determine a particular sequence type for an isolate. With SNP analysis, sequence differences in specific base pairs are detected and can be used to generate SNP profiles that can be compared to other strains in a subtyping scheme. Whole genome sequencing (WGS) also relies on the detection of nucleotide changes. The potential for using WGS for subtyping has evolved with the advent of next generation sequencing platforms that allow for the relatively rapid generation of large volumes of sequence data. However to date, WGS has not been widely used for molecular subtyping of bacterial pathogens, thus it is not covered extensively in this chapter. The use of WGS for subtyping is discussed in the section of Chapter 16 that focuses on the future direction of molecular subtyping.

MULTILOCUS SEQUENCE TYPING

Background

Multilocus sequence typing (MLST) is a molecular subtyping method in which multiple regions of the bacterial genome are sequenced and the resultant nucleotide sequences are compared for base changes [1, 2]. MLST follows in the footsteps of the phenotypic method multilocus enzyme electrophoresis (MLEE). MLEE characterizes isolates based on the detection of variation in the amino acid sequences of the water-soluble enzymes rather than the genes themselves [3]. These changes in the amino acids lead to mobility differences in the proteins during electrophoresis that can be detected after staining. For MLST, the choice of which genes/loci to sequence is an important consideration. The loci sequenced need to have some level of genetic diversity, bracketed by stable sequences for primer binding. The targets for MLST sequencing have traditionally been housekeeping genes, which are required for basic cellular function. The genes are typically present is all members of a particular species and are not under a strong selective pressure that can lead to rapid changes within the sequence or PCR priming sites. These housekeeping genes typically display adequate diversity to identify distinct alleles for the different strains, especially when examining diversity over a longer term periods of time [1, 4]. However, for epidemiological investigations it may be essential to detect greater sequence diversity to distinguish between closely related strains. In these cases, the inclusion of genes that are under greater selective pressure (virulence, antimicrobial resistance, stress response, etc.) in an MLST scheme may be valuable as they may be more polymorphic [1, 5]. When MLST has been adapted to study the diversity of virulence genes rather than housekeeping genes, the typing method can be referred to as multi-virulence-locus sequence typing (MVLST) [6, 7]. With MVLST, researchers/ clinicians are typically able to get a higher discriminatory power than regular MLST and also better observe the local epidemiology of the organisms being studied [7, 8]. In other instances, researchers have added antimicrobial resistance genes to their MLST scheme, which also increases the discriminatory power and the reproducibility of the MLST scheme [9, 10].

Table 1. MLST Databases

Organism	Website/database	Applications	References
Campylobacter jejuni and *C. coli*	http://pubmlst.org/campylobacter	Epidemiological surveillance of foodborne infections, population structure analysis	[3]
Escherichia coli	http://mlst.ucc.ie/mlst/dbs/Ecoli http://www.shigatox.net/ecmlst/cgi-bin/scheme http://www.pasteur.fr/recherche/genop ole/PF8/mlst/EColi.html*	Examination of the evolution of virulence	[3, 13]
Listeria monocytogenes	http://www.pasteur.fr/recherche/genop ole/PF8/mlst/Lmono.html*	Epidemiological surveillance	[3]
Salmonella enterica	http://mlst.ucc.ie/mlst/dbs/Senterica	-	[3]
Vibrio parahaemolyticus	http://www.pasteur.fr/mlst	population structure, source grouping	[46, 47]
Vibrio vulnificus	http://pubmlst.org/vvulnificus	population structure, microbial evolution	[48, 49]

MLST typically involves the sequencing of 450 to 500 bp fragments of internal sequences of seven housekeeping genes [11]. In some protocols, fewer genes have been used and have provided adequate discrimination [12], however the inclusion of the additional loci increase the discriminatory power of the MLST scheme [9]. The sequencing data from each of the loci are combined to determine the sequence type (ST) for a particular strain. A ST is determined based on the pattern of specific alleles of the individual loci sequenced (Figure 1). Allele types are assigned based on a comparison to large MLST datasets, which are typically available online. If a sequence for a locus had previously been detected, then the corresponding allele number is assigned to the strain. If a novel sequence is detected then the locus is given a new allele number. When all of the alleles for a strain are defined, they are used to define the strain's ST. If different strains have common ST, they are said to be clonal by MLST [2]. The process of MLST analysis is described later in this chapter.

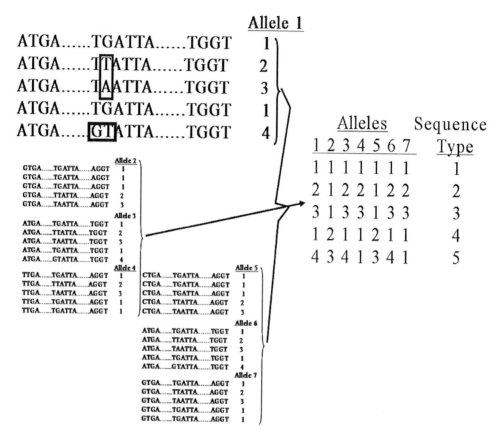

Figure 1. Diagram of the principals of MLST. Different loci are sequenced and compared for differences within the sequence. Each unique sequence is assigned as a separate allele type. In the top portion of the figure, those nucleotides which are different from the first sequence are identified with a box and are used to define the distinct alleles. The allele types for each isolate are combined and compared and based on the allele profile sequence types are defined. Each unique set of allele defines a new sequence type.

For many of the foodborne pathogens there are internet accessible MLST databases (Table 1) that provide standardized protocols and user interfaces to submit data for analyses, which facilitates the rapid exchange of MLST results [11]. With these databases, the locus-specific sequences are uploaded to the databases and allele types are assigned based on the sequenced in dataset. MLST data can be analyzed in a variety of ways including by comparing the allelic profiles of the individual strains or by comparing the raw sequencing data. The choice of the best analysis approach is dependant on the predominant cause of sequence diversity (recombination versus mutations). These topics are discussed in detail below.

Table 2. MLST PCR and sequencing primers, PCR reaction conditions and product sizes

Locus	Primer Type	Primer Sequence	Annealing Temp. °C	Amplicon size*	Locus size	Reference
Campylobacter jejuni[A]						
aspA	PCR Forward	AGTACTAATGATGCTTATCC	50	899	477	[27]
	PCR Reverse	ATTTCATCAATTTGTTCTTTGC				
	Seq. Forward	CCAACTGCAAGATGCTGTACC				
	Seq. Reverse	TTAATTTGCGGTAATACCATC				
glnA	PCR Forward	TAGGAACTTGGCATCATATTACC	50	1262	477	[27]
	PCR Reverse	TTGGACGAGCTTCTACTGGC				
	Seq. Forward	CATGCAATCAATGAAGAAAC				
	Seq. Reverse	TTCCATAAGCTCATATGAAC				
gltA	PCR Forward	GGGCTTGACTTCTACAGCTACTTG	50	1012	402	[27]
	PCR Reverse	CCAAATAAAGTTGTCTTGGACGG				
	Seq. Forward	GTGGCTATCCTATAGAGTGGC				
	Seq. Reverse	CCAAAGCCACCAATACCTG				
glyA	PCR Forward	GAGTTAGAGCGTCAATGTGAAGG	50	816	507	[27]
	PCR Reverse	AAACCTCTGGCAGTAAGGGC				
	Seq. Forward	AGCTAATCAAGGTGTTTATGCGG				
	Seq. Reverse	AGGTGATTATCCGTTCCATCGC				
tkt	PCR Forward	GCAAACTCAGGACACCCAGG	50	1102	459	[27]
	PCR Reverse	AAAGCATTGTTAATGGCTGC				
	Seq. Forward	GCTTAGCAGATATTTTAAGTG				
	Seq. Reverse	AAGCCTGCTTGTTCTTTGGC				
pgm	PCR Forward	TACTAATAATATCTTAGTAGG	50	1150	498	[27]
	PCR Reverse	CACAACATTTTCATTTCTTTTC				
	Seq. Forward	GGTTTTAGATGTGGCTCATG				
	Seq. Reverse	TCCAGAATAGCGAAATAAGG				
uncA	PCR Forward	ATGGACTTAAGAATATTATGGC	50	1120	489	[27]
	PCR Reverse	ATAAATTCCATCTTCAAATTCC				
	Seq. Forward	TGTTGCAATTGGTCAAAAGC				
	Seq. Reverse	TGCCTCATCTAAATCACTAGC				

[A]http://pubmlst.org/campylobacter/mlst-info/cjejuni/cjejuni-info.shtml

Table 2. (Continued)

Locus	Primer Type	Primer Sequence	Annealing Temp. °C	Amplicon size*	Locus size	Reference
Campylobacter coli[B]						
aspA	PCR & Seq. For.	CAACTTCAAGATGCAGTACC	50		477	[28]
	PCR & Seq. Rev.	ATCTGCTAAAGTATGCATTGC				
glnA	PCR & Seq. For.	TTCATGGATGGCAACCTATTG	50		477	[28]
	PCR & Seq. Rev.	GCTTTGGCATAAAAGTTGCAG				
gltA	PCR & Seq. For.	GATGTAGTGCATCTTTTACTC	50		402	[28]
	PCR & Seq. Rev.	AAGCGCTCCAATACCTGCTG				
glyA	PCR & Seq. For.	TCAAGGCGTTTATGCTGCAC	50		507	[28]
	PCR & Seq. Rev.	CCATCACTTACAAGCTTATAC				
pgm	PCR & Seq. For.	TTATAAGGTAGCTCCGACTG	50		498	[28]
	PCR & Seq. Rev.	GTTCCGAATAGCGAAATAACAC				
tkt	PCR & Seq. For.	AGGCTTGTGTTTTCAGGCGG	50		459	[28]
	PCR & Seq. Rev.	TGACTTCCTTCAAGCTCTCC				
uncA	PCR & Seq. For.	AAGCACAGTGGCTCAAGTTG	50		489	[28]
	PCR & Seq. Rev.	CTACTTGCCTCATCCAATCAC				

[B]http://pubmlst.org/campylobacter/mlst-info/cjejuni-info.shtml

Locus	Primer Type	Primer Sequence	Annealing Temp. °C	Amplicon size*	Locus size	Reference
Escherichia coli[C]						
adk	PCR & Seq. For.	ATTCTGCTTGGCGCTCCGGG	54		536	[38]
	PCR & Seq. Rev.	CCGTCAACTTTCGCGTATTT				
fumC	PCR & Seq. For.	TCACAGGTCGCCAGCGCTTC	54		469	[38]
	PCR & Seq. Rev.	GTACGCAGGCGAAAAAGATTC				
gyrB	PCR & Seq. For.	TCGGCGACACGGATGACGGC	60		460	[38]
	PCR & Seq. Rev.	ATCAGGGCCTTCACGGCGCATC				
icd	PCR & Seq. For.	ATGGAAAGTAAAGTAGTTGTTCCGGCACA	54		518	[38]
	PCR & Seq. Rev.	GGACGCAGCAGGATCTGTT				
mdh	PCR & Seq. For.	ATGAAAGTCGCAGTCCTCGGCGCTGCTGGCGG	60		452	[38]
	PCR & Seq. Rev.	TTAACGAACTCCTGCCCAGAGCGATATCTTTCTT				
purA	PCR & Seq. For.	CGCGCTGATGAAAGAGATGA	54		478	[38]
	PCR & Seq. Rev.	CATACGGTAAGCCACGCAGA				
recA	PCR & Seq. For.	CGCATTCGCTTTACCCTGACC	58		510	[38]

Locus	Primer Type	Primer Sequence	Annealing Temp. °C	Amplicon size*	Locus size	Reference
	PCR & Seq. Rev.	TCTGATCAGCTTCTCTTTT				

[C] http://mlst.ucc.ie/mlst/dbs/Ecoli

Salmonella enterica[D]

Locus	Primer Type	Primer Sequence	Annealing Temp. °C	Amplicon size*	Locus size	Reference
thrA	PCR Forward	GTCACGGTGATCGATCCGGT	55	852	501	[31]
	PCR Reverse	CACGATATTGATATTAGCCCG				
	Seq. Forward	ATCCCGGCCGATCACATGAT				
	Seq. Reverse	CTCCAGCAGCCCCTCTTTCAG				
purE	PCR Forward	ATGTCTTCCCGCAATAATCC	55	510	399	[31]
	PCR Reverse	TCATAGCGTCCCCGCGGATC				
	Seq. Forward	CGCATTATTCCGGCGCGTGT				
	Seq. Reverse	CGCGGATCGGGATTTTCCAG				
sucA	PCR Forward	AGCACGGAAGAGAAAGCGTG	55	643	501	[31]
	PCR Reverse	GGTTGTTGATAACGATACGTAC				
	Seq. Forward	AGCACGGAAGAGAAAGCGTG				
	Seq. Reverse	GGTTGTTGATAACGATACGTAC				
hisD	PCR Forward	GAAACGTTCATTCCGCGCAGAC	55	894	501	[31]
	PCR Reverse	CTGAACGGTCATCCGTTTCTG				
	Seq. Forward	GTCGGTCTGTATATTCCCGG				
	Seq. Reverse	GGTAATCGCATCCACCAAATC				
aroC	PCR Forward	CCTGGCACCTCGGCTATAC	55	826	501	[31]
	PCR Reverse	CCACACACGATCGTGGCG				
	Seq. Forward	GGCACCAGTATTGGCCTGCT				
	Seq. Reverse	CATATGCCACAAATGTGTTG				
hemD	PCR Forward	GAAGCGTTAGTGAGCCGTCTGCG	55	666	432	[31]
	PCR Reverse	ATCAGCGACCTTAATATCTTGCCA				
	Seq. Forward	GTGGCCTGGAGTTTTCCACT				
	Seq. Reverse	GACCAATAGCCGACAGCGTAG				
dnaN	PCR Forward	ATGAAATTTACCGTTGAACGTGA	55	833	501	[31]
	PCR Reverse	AATTTCTCATTCGAGAGGATTGC				
	Seq. Forward	CCGATTCTCGGTAACCTGCT				
	Seq. Reverse	CCATCCACCAGCTTCGAGGT				

[D] http://mlst.ucc.ie/mlst/dbs/Senterica

*When PCR and Sequencing primers are different

Listeria monocytogenes[E]

Table 2. (Continued)

Locus	Primer Type	Primer Sequence	Annealing Temp. °C	Amplicon size*	Locus size	Reference
abcZ	PCR Forward[F]	**GTTTTCCCAGTCACGACGTTGTA**TCGCT GCTGCCACTTTATCCA	52		537	[44]
	PCR Reverse	**TTGTGAGCGGATAACAATTTCT**CAAGG TCGCCGTTTAGAG				
bglA	PCR Forward	**GTTTTCCCAGTCACGACGTTGTA**GCCG ACTTTTTATGGGGTGGAG	45		399	[44]
	PCR Reverse	**TTGTGAGCGGATAACAATTTCC**GATTA AATACGGTGCGGACATA				
cat	PCR Forward	**GTTTTCCCAGTCACGACGTTGTA**ATTG GCGCATTTTGATAGAGA	52		486	[44]
	PCR Reverse	**TTGTGAGCGGATAACAATTTCA**GATTG ACGATTCCTGCTTTTG				
dapE	PCR Forward	**GTTTTCCCAGTCACGACGTTGTA**CGAC TAATGGGCATGAAGAACAAG	52		462	[44]
	PCR Reverse	**TTGTGAGCGGATAACAATTTCA**TCGAA CTATGGGCATTTTTACC				
dat	PCR Forward	**GTTTTCCCAGTCACGACGTTGTA**GAAA GAGAAGATGCCACAGTTGA	52		471	[44]
	PCR Reverse	**TTGTGAGCGGATAACAATTTCT**GCGTCC ATAATACCACCATCTTT				
ldh	PCR Forward	**GTTTTCCCAGTCACGACGTTGTA**GTAT GATTGACATAGATAAAGA	52		453	[72]
	PCR Reverse	**TTGTGAGCGGATAACAATTTCT**ATAAA TGTCGTTCATACCAT				
lhkA	PCR Forward	**GTTTTCCCAGTCACGACGTTGTA**AGAA TGCCAACGACGAAACC	52		480	[44]
	PCR Reverse	**TTGTGAGCGGATAACAATTTCT**GGGAA ACATCAGCAATAAAC				
Sequencing	Seq. Forward	GTTTTCCCAGTCACGACGTTGTA				[44]
	Seq. Reverse	TGTGAGCGGATAACAATTTC				

[E] http://www.pasteur.fr/recherche/genopole/PF8/mlst/Lmono.html

[F] each of the primer pairs incorporates a universal recognition site (in bold) for the sequencing primers to bind.

Locus	Primer Type	Primer Sequence	Annealing Temp. °C	Amplicon size*	Locus size	Reference
Vibrio parahaemolyticus[G]						
recA	PCR Forward[H]	**TGTAAAACGACGGCCAGT**GAAACCATT TCAACGGGTTC	58		773	[47]
	PCR Reverse	**CAGGAAACAGCTATGACC**CCATTGTAG CTGTACCAAGCACCC			629	[47]
gyrB	PCR Forward	**TGTAAAACGACGGCCAGT**GAAGGBGGT ATTCAAGC	58			
	PCR Reverse	**CAGGAAACAGCTATGACC**GAGTCACCC TCCACWATGTA			596	[47]
dnaE	PCR Forward	**TGTAAAACGACGGCCAGT**CGRATMACC GCTTTCGCCG	58			
	PCR Reverse	**CAGGAAACAGCTATGACC**GAKATGTGT GAGCTGTTTGC			497	[47]
dtdS	PCR Forward	**TGTAAAACGACGGCCAGT**TGGCCATAA CGACATTCTGA	58			
	PCR Reverse	**CAGGAAACAGCTATGACC**GAGCACCAA CGTGTTTAGC			470	[47]
pntA	PCR Forward	**TGTAAAACGACGGCCAGT**ACGGCTACG CAAAGAAATG	58			
	PCR Reverse	**CAGGAAACAGCTATGACC**TTGAGGCTG AGCCGATACTT			533	[47]
pyrC	PCR Forward	**TGTAAAACGACGGCCAGT**AGCAACCGG TAAAATTGTCG	58			
	PCR Reverse	**CAGGAAACAGCTATGACC**CAGTGTAAG AACCGGCACAA			463	[47]
tnaA	PCR Forward	**TGTAAAACGACGGCCAGT**TGTACGAAA TTGCCACCAAA	58			
	PCR Reverse	**CAGGAAACAGCTATGACC**AATATTTTCG CCGCATCAAC				[47]
M13 Sequencing	Seq. Forward	GTAAAACGACGGCCAGT				
	Seq. Reverse	CAGGAAACAGCTATGACC				

[G] http://pubmlst.org/vparahaemolyticus/

[H] each of the primer pairs incorporates a universal recognition site (in bold) for M13 sequencing primers to bind.

Basic Methodology for MLST

MLST has been used for the subtyping of bacterial foodborne pathogens including *Salmonella, Campylobacter, Escherichia coli, Listeria,* and *Vibrio* species. These pathogens are among the most common sources of food contamination, leading to foodborne infection. There are MLST schemes that have been prepared to study these foodborne pathogens using housekeeping genes (Table 2). For these pathogens, MLST is a useful sequence-based molecular technique to study pathogen evolution and in many cases to survey disease epidemiology [13].

The basic protocol for MLST requires a bacterial culture from which genomic DNA is extracted. The DNA is then amplified by polymerase chain reaction (PCR) using primers specific for multiple housekeeping genes. The reaction products are sequenced and the resultant DNA sequences are compared to others using the MLST database for the specific organism. If the ST has previously been detected, its identity is provided to the user or a new ST is defined in the database if not previously detected [14].

GENERAL MLST PROTOCOL

This section provides detailed descriptions of the steps to carry out a MLST. This protocol has been adapted from previous studies on foodborne pathogens and is primarily focused on *Campylobacter, E. coli, Listeria, Vibrio* and *Salmonella*. A flow diagram of the steps involved in the MLST procedure is shown in Figure 2.

Culturing and DNA Extraction

For MLST, it is important to start with a pure culture of the organism to be studied, which helps ensure that the final results are not skewed due to potential contamination. The organism is grown on specific growth media and incubated at a temperature and conditions specific for optimum growth (for example overnight incubation at 37°C in ambient air for *E. coli* and *Salmonella,* or at 42°C in 5% O_2 and 10% CO_2 for *Campylobacter* spp.). After incubation, DNA is extracted from the samples using a commercially available DNA extraction kit or through manual methods. The two most common types of manual DNA extraction methods used for bacteria are the alkaline lysis method and the boiling method [15, 16].

For the alkaline extraction method, 1 ml of the growth culture is transferred to a 1.5 ml microcentrifuge tube. The cell suspension is centrifuged for 10 min at 14,000 X *g*. The supernatant is discarded and the pellet is resuspended in 50 µl of 0.05 N NaOH. The tube is then centrifuged at 4°C for 5 min at 14,000 X *g*. The supernatant is carefully transferred to a new tube and supplemented with 8 µl of 1 M Tris-HCl buffer (pH 7.00) and centrifuged at 4°C for 2 min at 14,000 X *g*. DNase-RNase-free distilled water is added to achieve a final volume of 200 µl and the extracted DNA can be stored at -20°C until further use [16].

In the boiling method of DNA extraction, a colony is suspended in 40 µl of single cell lysis buffer (SCLB). The SCLB contains 1.0 ml of TE buffer (10 mM Tris-Cl, 1 mM EDTA, pH 8.0) and 10 µl of 5mg/ml proteinase K. The cells are lysed by heating at 80°C for 10 min, followed by cooling at 55°C for 10 min in a thermal cycler. The suspension is then diluted 1:2 by adding sterile water and centrifuged at 4500 X *g* for 30 sec to pellet the cellular debris. The supernatant containing the DNA is collected and ready for PCR or can be stored at -20°C until use [15].

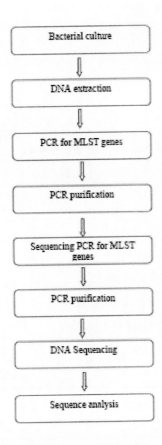

Figure 2. Flow diagram of the steps involved in the MLST procedure.

Another boiling method is the one described by de Medici et al. [16]. One ml of culture is transferred to a 1.5 ml microcentrifuge tube and centrifuged at 14,000 X *g* for 10 min. The supernatant is removed and the pellet resuspended in 300 µl of DNase-RNase-free distilled water by vortexing. The suspension is centrifuged again at 14,000 X *g* for 5 min and the supernatant discarded. The pellet is resuspended in 200 µl of DNase-RNase-free distilled water by vortexing [16]. Alternatively, 4-5 colonies of bacteria can be isolated from a culture plate and suspended in 200 µl of sterile water [5]. In either scenario, the tube is then incubated for 10-15 min at 100°C followed by immediate chilling on ice. The tube is centrifuged for 5 min at 14,000 X *g* at 4°C and the supernatant is carefully removed to a new tube to serve as the DNA template [16].

An alternative method for DNA extraction is the phenol-chloroform method. A 1 ml aliquot of a fresh bacterial culture is centrifuged and the pellet is washed in 1 ml of 0.5 M NaCl, and resuspended in 0.5 ml of TE buffer (10 mM Tris-HCl (pH 8.0), 1 mM EDTA). Fifty µg of proteinase K and Sarkosyl up to 1% are added and the cell suspension is incubated at 37°C for 3 h to overnight. The lysate is then extracted with an equal volume of phenol-chloroform (1:1); washed two times with 1.5 volumes of chloroform and precipitated with ethanol. The precipitates are dissolved in 150 µl of TE and the DNA can be used as PCR template [17].

DNA can also be extracted from previously run gels by freeze-thaw methods. Gel bands are cut from agarose gels or agarose pulsed field gel electrophoresis (PFGE) plugs are suspended in TE buffer and subjected to two cycles of freezing at -70°C and followed by thawing at 55°C. The samples are centrifuged at 5,000 X g for 10 min and the supernatants collected. The supernatant contains the pure DNA from the gels and can be used for PCR reactions [4].

PCR

For MLST, a standard PCR master mix is prepared by mixing the reagents shown below (the volumes can be adjusted for the overall size of the reaction or varied if a pre-mixed master mix is used):

MLST PCR	µl per rxn.
10X Buffer	5
MgCl$_2$ (25 mM)	3
dNTPs (10 mM each)	5
Forward Primer (10 pmol/µl)	5
Reverse Primer (10 pmol/µl)	5
Taq (5U/µl)	0.2
H$_2$O	26.8-X
Total	40
Template	X
Total per tube	50

In preparing the reactions, an adequate template concentration is 50 µg/ml. At this concentration, X will be 10 µl. If the template concentration is varied, then the amount of template added will need to be adjusted accordingly and the amount of water added to the master mix will need to be varied as well. Once the master mix is prepared, it is dispensed into PCR tubes/trays along with the corresponding templates and placed into the thermal cycler for amplification. A representative amplification protocol is as follows: 94°C for 10 min, followed by 35 cycles of 94°C for 1 min, X°C for 1 min, and 72°C for 1 min, and following the cycling the reactions are held at 72°C for 5 min followed by storage at 4°C. The annealing temperature (X) will vary depending on the primers used, Table 2 contains the most commonly used primers pairs for MLST schemes along with the recommended annealing temperatures.

Table 3. Genes used in SNP schemes

Organism	Genes	References
Campylobacter jejuni	*aspA, glyA, glnA,gltA, uncA, pgm, tkt*	[63]
Listeria monocytogenes	*inlB, inlA*	[61, 62, 71]
Salmonella	*tlr4, cd28, md-2, litaf, mif*	[72]

DNA Purification

Following the PCR reaction, the PCR products are typically separated by agarose gel electrophoresis to determine whether high quality amplification of the proper sized products occurred. Following confirmation of PCR amplification, the amplified PCR products are purified using manual methods or commercially available PCR purification kits that rely on gel filtration, spin columns or membrane filtration plates (e.g. MultiScreen PCR plates, Millipore, Billerica, MA). Most of commercial methods are convenient and efficiently purify the PCR product. The cleanup step is important to remove the bi-products of the PCR reaction (unused primers, dNTPs, non-amplified DNA, etc.) that may interfere with the dye termination labeling reactions. In addition to the commercial kits, other methods for purifying PCR products are electroelution, exonuclease I Shrimp Alkaline Phosphatase (exo-SAP) treatment and manual gel purification [4, 18]. Exo-SAP is a commercially available product for which the exonuclease cleaves the residual primers and the shrimp alkaline phosphatase removes the dNTPs from the reaction mixture. For PCR cleanup, the exo-SAP is added to the PCR products and incubated at 37°C for 30 min followed by 95°C for 5 min in a thermal cycler and the purified products can be stored at -20°C prior to sequencing (http://www.nucleics.com/DNA_sequencing_support/exonucleaseI-SAP-PCR-protocol.html).

Following clean up, the DNA concentrations of the PCR products are determined spectrophotometrically at 260nm wavelength. Alternatively, the concentration can be estimated by comparing the band intensity on agarose gels to samples with known DNA concentrations. This comparative method is typically accurate enough for successful sequencing. For cycle sequencing of bacterial genomic DNA with the BigDye Terminator sequencing chemistry (Applied Biosystems, Foster City, CA), the manufacturer recommends between 2-3 µg of template DNA/reaction. For illustrative purposes the following sequencing description is based on the methods for an ABI sequencer using the BigDye Terminator chemistry. If you are using another sequencing platform, such as a Beckman-Coulter (Brea CA) or LI-COR (Lincoln, NE) instrument, please refer to the manufacturer's instructions.

DNA Sequencing of PCR Product

For each sequencing reaction, whether in a 96-well format or individual PCR tube, the following are combined (the volumes can be adjusted proportionally if smaller volume reactions are utilized):

Component	µl per rxn.
Big Dye Terminator Ready Reaction	8.0
Template (3-10 ng of clean PCR product)	X
Sequencing Primer (to 3.2 pmol)	0.32
Sterile ddH$_2$O	11.68-X
Total per tube	20.0

For MLST, it is important that PCR products are sequenced in both directions by setting up reactions for both the forward and reverse sequencing primers (see Table 2). The reactions are mixed, placed into a thermal cycler and labeled with the following protocol: 25 cycles of 96°C for 10 sec, 50°C for 5 sec, and 60°C for 4 min followed by a 4°C hold. Following the labeling reaction the labeled products are subjected to either ethanol precipitation or spin column treatment to remove unbound dye terminator.

To precipitate the DNA, an equal volume of 4 M ammonium acetate (pH 4.8) is added to DNA and the mixture is vortexed briefly. Two volumes of 100% ice-cold ethanol are added and mixed by vortexing and then placed on crushed dry ice for at least 5 min (or at -70°C for 15 min or -20°C for 30 min). The mixture is microcentrifuged for 5 min at maximum speed and the supernatant discarded. The pellet is redissolved in 100 µl TE buffer (pH 8.0) and the steps are repeated starting with the addition of 4 M ammonium acetate. After that, 1 ml of 70% ethanol is added and the tube mixed by inverting several times then microcentrifuged again. The pellet is dried in a desiccator or evaporator and dissolved in appropriate volume of water or TE buffer [15, 18]. The precipitated DNA is then suspended in 20 µl of HI DI formamide (Applied Biosystems; note if smaller reaction volumes were used in the labeling reaction adjust the formamide volume accordingly) and the DNA samples denatured for 2 min at 96°C followed by snap cooling for 2 min on ice. The samples are then placed in the DNA sequencer and the separation and detection of the labeled fragments was carried out as recommended by the manufacturer for the specific instrument.

Data Analysis and ST Assignments

To ensure quality data, sequence reads originating from each primer should be aligned to confirm that there is no ambiguity in results that would lead to an erroneous allele type being assigned. For traditional analysis, the sequence is uploaded into its respective database (Table 1) and compared to other previously sequenced alleles. If the allele was previously represented in the database, the corresponding allele type (number) is assigned to the strain. If the allele is novel to the database, it is assigned a new allele number. The sequences for each of the genes sequenced are uploaded and a sequence type is assigned based on the allele profile (Figure 1). The sequence types for each of the isolates can be compared to one another for phenetic analysis.

Some of the more common methods used for analysis of sequence typing data are the based upon related sequence type (BURST) methods and the related eBURST program [19, 20]. These methods, in part, rely on the assumption that most genetic diversity detected is based on recombination events and as such, each set of genetic differences among alleles is weighted equally, regardless if there were multiple base changes in the locus or a single base pair change [3]. With the BURST program, the MSLT data sets are divided into distinct groups based upon the likelihood that they arise from a common ancestor [19]. These groups with common ancestry are referred to as clonal complexes. The eBURST program (http://eburst.mlst.net) works to separate the isolates broadly into the clonal complexes (CC) and then within each group separates strains in the most likely pattern of evolution from the predicted founder ST [20]. Figure 3 displays an eBURST diagram generated from the analysis of identified alleles of MLST data presented by Foley et al. [5]. In the center of Figure 3 is ST 4, which was identified as the founder for the group of strains in the CC and radiating from this founder are the other ST in a pattern that they were predicted to descend from the founder. Sequence types 1, 6 and 17 form secondary hubs off of the founder from which further differentiation occurs.

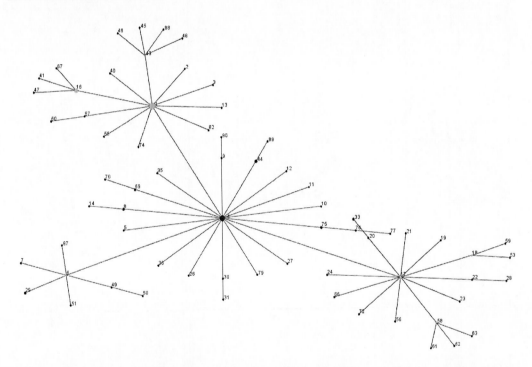

Figure 3. eBURST diagram of the results of MLST of 128 isolates from *S. enterica* serovar Typhimurium isolates [5]. The numbered STs in the figure form a single clonal complex, with ST4 determined to be the founding ST of the complex. The STs radiate from the founder based on the cumulative differences in the alleles from the founder.

Another way to analyze MLST data, which does not utilize the assumption that recombination is the primary means of sequence differentiation in each of the loci, is the phylogenetic analysis of the raw sequence data for each locus or based on a composite of all loci. Typically this analysis can be done using maximum likelihood or parsimony analyses (described in Chapter 14), the unweighted pair-group means with arithmetic averages (UPGMA; see Chapter 14) analysis of sequence similarities (Figure 4) or through the generation of a tree structure with minimum spanning tree analyses (Figure 5).

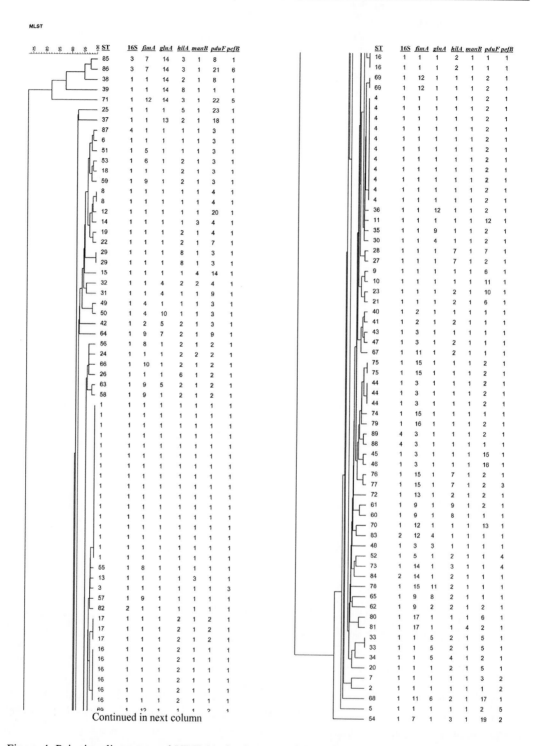

Figure 4. Pairwise alignment and UPGMA dendrogram of the results of MLST of 128 isolates from *S. enterica* serovar Typhimurium isolates [5]. The similarities are calculated based on the differences in the individual nucleotides in the sequence data rather than the allele types. The column to the right of the dendrogram lists the ST and the next seven column provide the numbered allele types for each of the loci.

The choice of whether to use a method such BURST analysis or minimum spanning tree analysis is somewhat dependant on the plasticity of the gene sequences being analyzed, since the way sequence variation is handled in the calculations is different. If the organisms being typed are likely to undergo recombination, then each genetic event will typically lead to multiple base changes. Thus the BURST methods using the allele types are likely to provide a more representative view of the phylogenetic relationship among strains [3]. On the other hand, in strains less susceptible to recombination the presence of multiple bases changes likely represents multiple genetic events and methods such as the minimum spanning tree will likely be more representative.

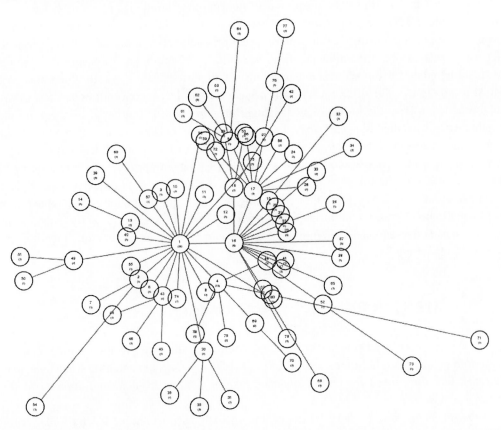

Figure 5. Minimum spanning tree of the results of MLST of 128 isolates from *S. enterica* serovar Typhimurium isolates [5]. The similarities are calculated based on the differences in the individual nucleotides in the sequence data rather than the allele types. In the spanning tree the distances of the branches are associated with the differences in the sequences among the STs.

Troubleshooting

Due to the number of steps involved in the MLST process and the different reagents used, the results may not always be optimum. To ensure best results, it is required that you begin with a fresh pure culture because older cultures may contain a high percentage of dead cells that may reduce the efficiency of the PCR reactions. Also, ensuring that the chemicals and reagents used are properly stored and used will reduce problems that may lead to PCR and/or sequencing failure. During DNA extraction, care is required to avoid contamination. In some cases contamination will lead to the presence of overlapping peaks in the sequencing results, indicating that more than one template is present. Also if excessive cell debris is present in the tubes after DNA extraction, it could cause problems of inefficiency during the PCR reactions which, if not enough PCR product were generated would lead to problems in the sequencing steps.

Additional factors that need to be considered are whether the PCR primers are efficiently designed and the PCR protocol is optimized for amplification. If there is a problem with either of these factors, the PCR reaction will not amplify the alleles efficiently, leading to failure of the MLST results. After PCR, it may be helpful to run the products on an electrophoresis gel to ensure that the correct sized products were amplified. Alternatively, the electrophoresis can be done after purification of the PCR amplicons to ensure that there is adequate template for the sequencing reactions. PCR purification is usually done using kits which are optimized for different types of organisms and DNA concentrations. It is always good practice to keep the kit components stored properly and do not use if they get too old. Expired or mishandled reagents may become denatured or lose their efficiency. During sequencing, care should be taken to avoid contamination of the DNA, which may reduce the quality of the sequencing results. When sending the sequencing products to core sequencing centers, care should be taken to properly transport the DNA and as quickly as possible to avoid denaturation of DNA. Once the sequencing reactions and separations are completed, the reads need to be aligned so the forward and reverse sequences overlap properly. Not entering the right consensus sequence data into databases would give the incorrect allele identities and ultimately the wrong ST.

MLST IN PRACTICE FOR FOODBORNE PATHOGENS

MLST has been used to successfully type multiple pathogens, including most bacterial foodborne pathogens. There are various online MLST schemes available on MLST database websites, including those for *Campylobacter*, *Listeria*, *Vibrio*, *E. coli*, and *Salmonella* (see Tables 1 and 2).

Campylobacter species. MLST has become a widely used technique for molecular typing of *Campylobacter* isolates. The number of manuscripts has grown quite significantly over the recent few years, likely due to *Campylobacter* genome plasticity and potential problems with typeability with pulsed field gel electrophoresis (PFGE) methods for certain strains, in which MLST was effective in typing [21]. Many of the studies that compared MLST to PFGE have found that they have similar capabilities to distinguish among strains [22, 23] or that PFGE is somewhat more discriminatory than MLST [24-26]. As mentioned above one of the potential problems with *Campylobacter* PFGE is typeability, or the ability to return a useable typing result, in some instances. The standard MLST typing methods for *C. jejuni* and *coli* described in the online databases rely on the sequencing of seven common genes in both species, these being *asp*A, *gln*A, *glt*A, *gly*A, *pgm*, *tkt*, and *unc*A [27, 28]. Even though in several studies, PFGE had higher levels of discrimination, MLST has been described as the most appropriate typing method to characterize the population structure of *Campylobacter* species due to the problems with PFGE typeability [29].

Salmonella enterica. There have been multiple approaches that have been applied for MLST for *Salmonella.* Some of the initial studies utilized the sequencing of four different housekeeping genes for *Salmonella* MLST with mixed results. For example, Fakhr et al. [12] found that MLST was less discriminatory than PFGE for separating serovar Typhimurium isolates. Conversely, Kotetishvili et al. [4] reported that MLST was better able to discriminate among serovar Typhimurium isolates than PFGE. Because of the mixed results, other studies increased the number of genes sequenced and in some cases included virulence genes typing scheme [5, 30]. Using this approach, Foley et al. [5] reported that PFGE and MLST provided a comparable number of subtypes for serovar Typhimurium isolates, however the isolates that clustered with each technique were not consistent across platforms. Thus, MLST was able to separate isolates with common PFGE profiles, and PFGE to separate among isolates in the predominant ST [5]. The differences among the MLST results in these studies were likely due, in part, to the selection of loci that were sequenced. To avoid some of these issues, a common method and set of genes were adopted that allow for the comparison of results among labs throughout the world. The genes used were initially described by Kidgell et al. [31] for serovar Typhi isolates and feature *thrA, purE, sucA, hisD, aroC, hemD,* and *dnaN* [31]. A number of researchers have successfully used the approach for typing *Salmonella* of various serovars [32-35].

Escherichia coli. As with *Salmonella,* there were multiple different approaches taken to the development of an optimal MLST method for *Escherichia coli.* Foley et al. [36] developed an approach for *E. coli* O157:H7 with four genes that included *uidA* and the virulence genes *eaeA, hlyA* and *fliC.* MLST was less discriminatory than PFGE or repetitive element PCR. Noller et al. [37] developed a nine gene MLST scheme for *E. coli* O157:H7 and found no diversity using eight of the loci sequenced among isolates that were selected for the study based on having diverse PFGE profiles. Others have had better success for *E. coli* O157:H7 MLST. Researchers that have used the standard *E. coli* MLST scheme (*adk, fumC, gyrB, icd, mdh, purA,* and *recA*) developed by Wirth and colleagues [38] (Table 2) have been able to separate distinct *E. coli* O157:H7 isolates into various sequence types [39, 40]. In addition to *E. coli* O157:H7 isolates, others have used MLST schemes to genotype other enteropathogenic *E. coli* (EPEC) isolates [41, 42].

Other Potential Foodborne Pathogens. While not used as widespread as the methods for *Campylobacter, Salmonella* and *E. coli,* MLST methods have been developed and successfully used to type *Shigella* spp., *Vibrio* spp., and *Listeria* spp. Choi et al. [43] performed MLST with the *E. coli* MLST housekeeping genes *adk, fumC, gyrB, icd, mdh, purA,* and *recA* to genotype 107 *Shigella flexneri* isolates; these were able to be separated into 18 STs. Others have developed and used MLST for *Listeria monocytogenes* subtyping. The current web-based MLST scheme uses the primers and conditions developed by Salcedo *et al.* [44] and focuses on the *abcZ, bglA, cat, dap, dat, ldh,* and *lhkA* genes. The seven gene MLST had similar results to PFGE, in that isolates with similar PFGE profiles were often in common STs [44]. Likewise, others have found that MLST performs well as a *Listeria* subtyping method, on par or more discriminatory than PFGE or amplified fragment length polymorphisms (AFLP) analyses [45, 46]. For *Vibrio parahaemolyticus,* a seven gene approach developed by González-Escalona and colleagues [47] is used by the MLST database and includes the genes *dnaE, gyrB, recA, dtdS, pntA, pyrC* and *tnaA.* In their study of 100 isolates, the MLST methods were able to separate the isolates into 62 distinct STs and three clonal complexes, which were generally associated with the distinct origins of the isolates [47]. *V. vulnificus* MLST utilizes a ten gene MLST scheme targeting the following gene loci *glp, gyrB, mdh, metG, purM, dtdS, lysA, pntA, pyrC,* and *tnaA* [48]. This approach has been used successfully by multiple investigators to define the population structure of *V. vulnificus* [48, 49].

SINGLE NUCLEOTIDE POLYMORPHISM (SNP) ANALYSIS

Background

Single nucleotide polymorphism (SNP) analysis has been most widely used in eukaryotic genotyping, especially in human medicine where specific polymorphisms in the DNA sequence can be associated with certain disease conditions or different responses to treatments [50]. In recent years, SNP typing has become more widespread for the characterization of bacterial strains [51, 52]. SNP analysis is a sequence-based method of subtyping that detects single nucleotide polymorphisms in the bacterial DNA. A SNP is a single change in the nucleotide sequence when compared to a corresponding reference sequence that occurs due to single mutation, recombination events, or horizontal gene transfer [53]. These nucleotide changes can either lead to a change in the amino acid that is encoded (a non-synonymous mutation) or not (synonymous mutation) based on the location of the nucleotide change. Because many SNPs, especially those that are synonymous mutations persist in the genome, they are useful to study the evolutionary history of organisms [54].

Basic Approaches to SNP Analysis

There are multiple approaches to select loci for inclusion in an SNP genotyping protocol including using software to predict likely polymorphic loci or scanning the literature for genes that are known to be polymorphic, such as some of those associated with antimicrobial resistance [55, 56]. Some investigators have utilized microarray approaches to identify multiple potential SNPs simultaneously [52]. These approaches rely on genome sequencing data to generate comprehensive microarrays containing probes that identify each of the nucleotides in potential SNP loci. If a SNP occurs at a particular nucleotide position in a specific locus, the binding efficiency to the probe corresponding to loci will be reduced leading to altered signal strength that can be detected [52]. Once the polymorphic loci are identified by microarray, more targeted and cost effective approaches can be developed to detect the SNPs in specific loci. Once the genes are selected, PCR primers are generated to amplify and subsequently sequence the gene. The gene sequence is then compared against others to help give a description of the phylogenetic makeup of the organism. The detection of individual SNPs offers a potentially easier and cheaper option to MLST, although it does not have the resolution or the power to identify new allele types [53]. SNP analyses have been most widely applied to the study of *Campylobacter, Listeria* and *Salmonella* [53].

Scientists have used a variety of approaches for the detection of SNPs in different specific locations within a DNA sequence. The most direct way is to amplify and sequence the locus as done for the MLST alleles described above [57]. Alternatively different pyrosequencing approaches have been developed in which short DNA fragments that include the SNP locus are tagged and sequenced to determine whether there are SNPs in the locus [58]. Additionally other approaches that do rely on direct DNA sequences have been successfully applied to SNP detection at a specific locus in a target. These methods are often more rapid and less expensive and as such have been widely adopted. One such approach is the use of mass spectrometry (MS) to detect differences in the mass of a specific locus; if there are nucleotide substitutions, then the mass of the fragment is altered and the differences detected by MS [59]. The use of realtime PCR has also been used for SNP detection. Typically hybridization probes that span the sequence of interest are designed to be a perfect match to a reference sequence, when a nucleotide substitution(s) occurs in the target, the binding efficiency of the probe is reduced. As such, the probe melts from the template at a lower temperature, which is as observed as a shift in the melt curve profile for the reaction [60]. Other approaches, including microarrays, restriction fragment polymorphisms analysis, flow cytometry and other methods that can detect alterations in the nucleotide sequences at specific locations have been used for SNP detection [50].

Limitations and Troubleshooting

Unlike MLST where multiple nucleotides within a particular loci are examined and potentially used for genotyping, SNP analyses typically identify differences at a specific nucleotide position within a particular locus. While this approach potentially increases the ability for high-throughput analysis methods, it may also limit the number of potential nucleotides/target examined in a particular genotyping event. If direct sequencing is used to identify the SNPs, many of the same pitfalls and limitations described for MLST also apply to SNP identification. In general, the troubleshooting for different procedural problems are SNP-detection-platform dependant and range from trouble with sample preparation to PCR inefficiency to problems with the SNP detection schemes. Additionally for source tracking applications, problems can arise when mutations occur in a target locus as a pathogen moves along the production-processing-consumption continuum. This phenomenon would lead to errors in the classification of isolate as not being from a common source even if they are. Also, if genetic differences that distinguish strains are outside of the regions examined by SNP typing, strains may considered clonal or from a common source, even if they are unrelated. This last pitfall is a common challenge for most typing methods.

SNP IN PRACTICE FOR FOODBORNE PATHOGENS

Presently, SNP typing of bacterial foodborne pathogens has been somewhat limited; however, methods have been successfully adapted for use with *Listeria monocytogenes* [61, 62]. Additionally some studies have looked at using SNP typing for *Campylobacter* as well [63, 64]. The approach taken by Price et al. [64] for *Campylobacter* isolates was to explore specific SNP loci with in the genes used in the standard MLST scheme (*asp*A, *gln*A, *glt*A, *gly*A, *pgm*, *tkt*, and *unc*A). The investigators found that when the SNP analysis was combined with sequence analysis of the short variable regions of *flaA*, the discriminatory power was similar to the full MLST analysis of the isolates [64]. *Salmonella* SNP typing has focused primarily on the analysis of differences in genes associated with the flagellar antigens [57] or antimicrobial resistance [55, 56]. With more genomes being sequenced and published for different organisms, the use of SNP for typing foodborne pathogens will likely increase. For example, Zhang et al. [52] explored sequence diversity in *E. coli* O157:H7, trying to determine the different polymorphisms in 523 chromosomal genes. From this analysis, they discovered 906 different SNPs in the genes, which could provide a number of future targets to evaluate for use in high-throughput SNP typing schemes for *E. coli* O157:H7. One of the important limitations to the wide application of SNP typing is the determination of whether SNPs detected in the bacterial genome are phylogenetically relevant and thus have utility in a subtyping scheme. These types of analyses should results in more publications on what genes work best with the organisms of interest hence making it easier for future scientists to work with this set of methods for typing organisms.

CONCLUSIONS AND FUTURE DIRECTIONS

This chapter has examined MLST and SNP typing in some detail. One sequencing approach not covered in great detail is the use of whole genome sequencing (WGS) for typing foodborne pathogens. The discussion of WGS for subtyping is covered in Chapters 2 and 16 and thus was not given extensive coverage here. Additionally, there have been few studies, to date, that have evaluated WGS for subtyping. In one study, Lienau et al. [65] used WGS to genotype *S. enterica* serovar Montevideo isolates potentially associated with a foodborne disease outbreak in the United States.

MLST has become a very useful sequencing-based technique that has been found to have good utility for genotyping foodborne pathogens. A number of schemes have been developed and have corresponding databases that allow for the efficient genotyping of foodborne pathogens such as *Campylobacter, Salmonella, E. coli, Vibrio* and *Listeria* (Tables 1 and 2). As with most typing methods, different MLST approaches work better for some organisms than others, thus the optimization and refinement of methods has helped to make MLST more widely available to scientists. As the methods continue to improve, there will likely be better MLST schemes to characterize the assortment of organisms that can potentially contaminate food. PFGE currently wears the banner of "gold standard" for many bacterial foodborne pathogens, however for some foodborne pathogens MLST has the ability to become the new standard subtyping technique. Some studies have found that MLST has better reproducibility than PFGE [21] and also is much more time efficient and does not require a great deal of specialized instrumentation in house. While there have been conflicting studies about the power of MLST compared to PFGE for certain organisms [4, 61], the simple procedure, high resolution power and reproducibility and ease of analysis of MLST make it a very powerful tool for understanding the diversity of bacterial foodborne pathogens.

SNP typing is a useful set of techniques that can be used in place of, or alongside, other more laborious and expensive typing methods. SNP analyses are helpful genotyping tools because with their many detection platforms, they are able to provide valuable information that can be used for comparisons among bacterial strains in a short period of time and with a minimal amount of labor. SNP can be used to differentiate organisms based on their polymorphic sites and since only one or few sites are usually studied, this can make it a simpler and cost effective approach. A drawback of SNP is that the full genome of the organism needs to have been sequenced and published for the polymorphisms to be identified and mapped [53]. As with the growth in MLST, there is a likelihood of the growth of SNP typing as well, especially with the increasing amount of microbial genomics data and better software to identify polymorphic sites that are genotypically important [66]. Additionally there is a large amount of flexibility in the ways in which SNPs can be detected and analyzed in a rapid fashion. Sequence typing, whether with MLST, SNP analyses or WGS, is likely to have a prominent presence in the toolbox of molecular epidemiologists to help in the search for the sources of bacterial foodborne pathogens.

DISCLAIMER

The use of trade names is for identification purposes only, and does not imply endorsement by the U.S. Food and Drug Administration or the U.S. Department of Health and Human Services. The views presented in this manuscript do not necessarily reflect those of the FDA.

REFERENCES

[1]   Maiden MC, Bygraves JA, Feil E, Morelli G, Russell JE, Urwin R, et al. Multilocus sequence typing: a portable approach to the identification of clones within populations of pathogenic microorganisms. *Proc Natl Acad Sci USA*. 1998;95(6):3140-5.

[2]   Spratt BG. Multilocus sequence typing: molecular typing of bacterial pathogens in an era of rapid DNA sequencing and the internet. *Curr Opin Microbiol*. 1999;2(3):312-6.

[3]   Maiden MC. Multilocus sequence typing of bacteria. *Annu Rev Microbiol*. 2006;60:561-88.

[4]   Kotetishvili M, Stine OC, Kreger A, Morris JG, Jr., Sulakvelidze A. Multilocus sequence typing for characterization of clinical and environmental *Salmonella* strains. *J Clin Microbiol*. 2002;40(5):1626-35.

[5]   Foley SL, White DG, McDermott PF, Walker RD, Rhodes B, Fedorka-Cray PJ, et al. Comparison of subtyping methods for differentiating *Salmonella enterica* serovar Typhimurium isolates obtained from food animal sources. *J Clin Microbiol*. 2006;44(10):3569-77.

[6]   Chen Y, Zhang W, Knabel SJ. Multi-virulence-locus sequence typing identifies single nucleotide polymorphisms which differentiate epidemic clones and outbreak strains of *Listeria monocytogenes*. *J Clin Microbiol*. 2007;45(3):845-56.

[7]   Zhang W, Jayarao BM, Knabel SJ. Multi-virulence-locus sequence typing of *Listeria monocytogenes*. *Appl Environ Microbiol*. 2004;70(2):913-20.

[8]   Chen Y, Zhang W, Knabel SJ. Multi-virulence-locus sequence typing clarifies epidemiology of recent listeriosis outbreaks in the United States. *J Clin Microbiol.* 2005;43(10):5291-4.

[9]   Nemoy LL, Kotetishvili M, Tigno J, Keefer-Norris A, Harris AD, Perencevich EN, et al. Multilocus sequence typing versus pulsed-field gel electrophoresis for characterization of extended-spectrum beta-lactamase-producing *Escherichia coli* isolates. J *Clin Microbiol.* 2005;43(4):1776-81.

[10]   Trobos M, Christensen H, Sunde M, Nordentoft S, Agerso Y, Simonsen GS, et al. Characterization of sulphonamide-resistant *Escherichia coli* using comparison of sul2 gene sequences and multilocus sequence typing. *Microbiology.* 2009;155(Pt 3):831-6.

[11]   Enright MC, Spratt BG. Multilocus sequence typing. *Trends Microbiol.* 1999;7(12):482-7.

[12]   Fakhr MK, Nolan LK, Logue CM. Multilocus sequence typing lacks the discriminatory ability of pulsed-field gel electrophoresis for typing *Salmonella enterica* serovar Typhimurium. *J Clin Microbiol.* 2005;43(5):2215-9.

[13]   Urwin R, Maiden MC. Multi-locus sequence typing: a tool for global epidemiology. *Trends Microbiol.* 2003;11(10):479-87.

[14]   Manning G, Dowson CG, Bagnall MC, Ahmed IH, West M, Newell DG. Multilocus sequence typing for comparison of veterinary and human isolates of *Campylobacter jejuni. Appl Environ Microbiol.* 2003;69(11):6370-9.

[15]   Marmur J. A procedure for the isolation of deoxyribonucleic acid from microorganisms *J Mol Biol.* 1961;3:208-18.

[16]   De Medici D, Croci L, Delibato E, Di Pasquale S, Filetici E, Toti L. Evaluation of DNA extraction methods for use in combination with SYBR green I real-time PCR to detect *Salmonella enterica* serotype Enteritidis in poultry. *Appl Environ Microbiol.* 2003;69(6):3456-61.

[17]   Kinscherf TG, Coleman RH, Barta TM, Willis DK. Cloning and expression of the tabtoxin biosynthetic region from *Pseudomonas syringae. J Bacteriol.* 1991;173(13):4124-32.

[18]   Ausubel FM, Brent R, Kingston RE, Moore DD, Seidman JG, Smith JA, et al. Short Protocols in Molelcular Biology: A Compendium of Methods from Current Protocols in *Molecular Biology.* 5 ed. New York: John Wiley and Sons; 2002.

[19]   Spratt BG, Hanage WP, Li B, Aanensen DM, Feil EJ. Displaying the relatedness among isolates of bacterial species -- the eBURST approach. *FEMS Microbiol Lett.* 2004;241(2):129-34.

[20]   Feil EJ, Li BC, Aanensen DM, Hanage WP, Spratt BG. eBURST: inferring patterns of evolutionary descent among clusters of related bacterial genotypes from multilocus sequence typing data. *J Bacteriol.* 2004;186(5):1518-30.

[21]   National Advisory Committee on Microbiological Criteria for Foods. Analytical utility of Campylobacter methodologies. *J Food Prot.* 2007;70(1):241-50.

[22]   Parsons BN, Cody AJ, Porter CJ, Stavisky JH, Smith JL, Williams NJ, et al. Typing of *Campylobacter jejuni* isolates from dogs by use of multilocus sequence typing and pulsed-field gel electrophoresis. *J Clin Microbiol.* 2009;47(11):3466-71.

[23]   Cornelius AJ, Gilpin B, Carter P, Nicol C, On SL. Comparison of PCR binary typing (P-BIT), a new approach to epidemiological subtyping of *Campylobacter jejuni,* with

serotyping, pulsed-field gel electrophoresis, and multilocus sequence typing methods. *Appl Environ Microbiol.* 2010;76(5):1533-44.

[24] Oporto B, Juste RA, Lopez-Portoles JA, Hurtado A. Genetic Diversity among *Campylobacter jejuni* Isolates from Healthy Livestock and Their Links to Human Isolates in Spain. *Zoonoses Public Health.* 2010 Oct 7.

[25] Sails AD, Swaminathan B, Fields PI. Utility of multilocus sequence typing as an epidemiological tool for investigation of outbreaks of gastroenteritis caused by *Campylobacter jejuni. J Clin Microbiol.* 2003;41(10):4733-9.

[26] Behringer M, Miller WG, Oyarzabal OA. Typing of *Campylobacter jejuni* and *Campylobacter coli* isolated from live broilers and retail broiler meat by *flaA*-RFLP, MLST, PFGE and REP-PCR. *J Microbiol Methods.* 2011;84(2):194-201.

[27] Dingle KE, Colles FM, Wareing DR, Ure R, Fox AJ, Bolton FE, et al. Multilocus sequence typing system for *Campylobacter jejuni. J Clin Microbiol.* 2001;39(1):14-23.

[28] Dingle KE, Colles FM, Falush D, Maiden MC. Sequence typing and comparison of population biology of *Campylobacter coli* and *Campylobacter jejuni. J Clin Microbiol.* 2005;43(1):340-7.

[29] Levesque S, Frost E, Arbeit RD, Michaud S. Multilocus sequence typing of *Campylobacter jejuni* isolates from humans, chickens, raw milk, and environmental water in Quebec, Canada. *J Clin Microbiol.* 2008;46(10):3404-11.

[30] Sukhnanand S, Alcaine S, Warnick LD, Su WL, Hof J, Craver MP, et al. DNA sequence-based subtyping and evolutionary analysis of selected *Salmonella enterica* serotypes. *J Clin Microbiol.* 2005;43(8):3688-98.

[31] Kidgell C, Reichard U, Wain J, Linz B, Torpdahl M, Dougan G, et al. *Salmonella typhi,* the causative agent of typhoid fever, is approximately 50,000 years old. *Infect Genet Evol.* 2002;2(1):39-45.

[32] Harbottle H, White DG, McDermott PF, Walker RD, Zhao S. Comparison of multilocus sequence typing, pulsed-field gel electrophoresis, and antimicrobial susceptibility typing for characterization of *Salmonella enterica* serotype Newport isolates. *J Clin Microbiol.* 2006;44(7):2449-57.

[33] Liu WB, Liu B, Zhu XN, Yu SJ, Shi XM. Diversity of *Salmonella* isolates using serotyping and multilocus sequence typing. *Food Microbiol.* 2011;28(6):1182-9.

[34] Sangal V, Harbottle H, Mazzoni CJ, Helmuth R, Guerra B, Didelot X, et al. Evolution and population structure of *Salmonella enterica* serovar Newport. *J Bacteriol.* 2010;192(24):6465-76.

[35] Ikumapayi UN, Antonio M, Sonne-Hansen J, Biney E, Enwere G, Okoko B, et al. Molecular epidemiology of community-acquired invasive non-typhoidal *Salmonella* among children aged 2-29 months in rural Gambia and discovery of a new serovar, *Salmonella enterica* Dingiri. *J Med Microbiol.* 2007;56(Pt 11):1479-84.

[36] Foley SL, Simjee S, Meng J, White DG, McDermott PF, Zhao S. Evaluation of molecular typing methods for *Escherichia coli* O157:H7 isolates from cattle, food, and humans. *J Food Prot.* 2004;67(4):651-7.

[37] Noller AC, McEllistrem MC, Stine OC, Morris JG, Jr., Boxrud DJ, Dixon B, et al. Multilocus sequence typing reveals a lack of diversity among *Escherichia coli* O157:H7 isolates that are distinct by pulsed-field gel electrophoresis. *J Clin Microbiol.* 2003;41(2):675-9.

[38] Wirth T, Falush D, Lan R, Colles F, Mensa P, Wieler LH, et al. Sex and virulence in *Escherichia coli*: an evolutionary perspective. *Mol Microbiol.* 2006;60(5):1136-51.

[39] Kappeli U, Hachler H, Giezendanner N, Beutin L, Stephan R. Human infections with non-O157 Shiga toxin-producing *Escherichia coli*, Switzerland, 2000-2009. *Emerg Infect Dis.* 2011;17(2):180-5.

[40] Ji XW, Liao YL, Zhu YF, Wang HG, Gu L, Gu J, et al. Multilocus sequence typing and virulence factors analysis of *Escherichia coli* O157 strains in China. *J Microbiol.;* 48(6):849-55.

[41] Lacher DW, Steinsland H, Blank TE, Donnenberg MS, Whittam TS. Molecular evolution of typical enteropathogenic *Escherichia coli*: clonal analysis by multilocus sequence typing and virulence gene allelic profiling. *J Bacteriol.* 2007;189(2):342-50.

[42] Clermont O, Olier M, Hoede C, Diancourt L, Brisse S, Keroudean M, et al. Animal and human pathogenic *Escherichia coli* strains share common genetic backgrounds. *Infect Genet Evol.* 2011;11(3):654-62.

[43] Choi SY, Jeon YS, Lee JH, Choi B, Moon SH, von Seidlein L, et al. Multilocus sequence typing analysis of *Shigella flexneri* isolates collected in Asian countries. *J Med Microbiol.* 2007;56(Pt 11):1460-6.

[44] Salcedo C, Arreaza L, Alcala B, de la Fuente L, Vazquez JA. Development of a multilocus sequence typing method for analysis of *Listeria monocytogenes* clones. *J Clin Microbiol.* 2003;41(2):757-62.

[45] Revazishvili T, Kotetishvili M, Stine OC, Kreger AS, Morris JG, Jr., Sulakvelidze A. Comparative analysis of multilocus sequence typing and pulsed-field gel electrophoresis for characterizing *Listeria monocytogenes* strains isolated from environmental and clinical sources. *J Clin Microbiol.* 2004;42(1):276-85.

[46] Parisi A, Latorre L, Normanno G, Miccolupo A, Fraccalvieri R, Lorusso V, et al. Amplified Fragment Length Polymorphism and Multi-Locus Sequence Typing for high-resolution genotyping of *Listeria monocytogenes* from foods and the environment. *Food Microbiol.* 2010;27(1):101-8.

[47] Gonzalez-Escalona N, Martinez-Urtaza J, Romero J, Espejo RT, Jaykus LA, DePaola A. Determination of molecular phylogenetics of *Vibrio parahaemolyticus* strains by multilocus sequence typing. *J Bacteriol.* 2008;190(8):2831-40.

[48] Bisharat N, Cohen DI, Maiden MC, Crook DW, Peto T, Harding RM. The evolution of genetic structure in the marine pathogen, *Vibrio vulnificus*. *Infect Genet Evol.* 2007;7(6):685-93.

[49] Gonzalez-Escalona N, Whitney B, Jaykus LA, DePaola A. Comparison of direct genome restriction enzyme analysis and pulsed-field gel electrophoresis for typing of *Vibrio vulnificus* and their correspondence with multilocus sequence typing data. Appl Environ Microbiol. 2007;73(22):7494-500.

[50] Weiner MP, Hudson TJ. Introduction to SNPs: discovery of markers for disease. *Biotechniques.* 2002;Suppl:4-3.

[51] Cebula TA, Jackson SA, Brown EW, Goswami B, LeClerc JE. Chips and SNPs, bugs and thugs: a molecular sleuthing perspective. *J Food Prot.* 2005;68(6):1271-84.

[52] Zhang W, Qi W, Albert TJ, Motiwala AS, Alland D, Hyytia-Trees EK, et al. Probing genomic diversity and evolution of *Escherichia coli* O157 by single nucleotide polymorphisms. *Genome Res.* 2006;16(6):757-67.

[53] Hyytia-Trees EK, Cooper K, Ribot EM, Gerner-Smidt P. Recent developments and future prospects in subtyping of foodborne bacterial pathogens. *Future Microbiol.* 2007;2:175-85.

[54] Foley SL, Lynne AM, Nayak R. Molecular typing methodologies for microbial source tracking and epidemiological investigations of Gram-negative bacterial foodborne pathogens. *Infect Genet Evol.* 2009;9(4):430-40.

[55] Esaki H, Noda K, Otsuki N, Kojima A, Asai T, Tamura Y, et al. Rapid detection of quinolone-resistant *Salmonella* by real time SNP genotyping. *J Microbiol Methods.* 2004;58(1):131-4.

[56] Levy DD, Sharma B, Cebula TA. Single-nucleotide polymorphism mutation spectra and resistance to quinolones in *Salmonella enterica* serovar Enteritidis with a mutator phenotype. *Antimicrob Agents Chemother.* 2004;48(7):2355-63.

[57] Mortimer CK, Peters TM, Gharbia SE, Logan JM, Arnold C. Towards the development of a DNA-sequence based approach to serotyping of *Salmonella enterica.* *BMC Microbiol.* 2004;4:31.

[58] Roos A, Dieltjes P, Vossen RH, Daha MR, de Knijff P. Detection of three single nucleotide polymorphisms in the gene encoding mannose-binding lectin in a single pyrosequencing reaction. *J Immunol Methods.* 2006;309(1-2):108-14.

[59] Lechner D, Lathrop GM, Gut IG. Large-scale genotyping by mass spectrometry: experience, advances and obstacles. *Curr Opin Chem Biol.* 2002;6(1):31-8.

[60] Tyagi S, Bratu DP, Kramer FR. Multicolor molecular beacons for allele discrimination. *Nat Biotechnol.* 1998;16(1):49-53.

[61] Ducey TF, Page B, Usgaard T, Borucki MK, Pupedis K, Ward TJ. A single-nucleotide-polymorphism-based multilocus genotyping assay for subtyping lineage I isolates of *Listeria monocytogenes.* *Appl Environ Microbiol.* 2007;73(1):133-47.

[62] Unnerstad H, Ericsson H, Alderborn A, Tham W, Danielsson-Tham ML, Mattsson JG. Pyrosequencing as a method for grouping of *Listeria monocytogenes* strains on the basis of single-nucleotide polymorphisms in the *inlB* gene. *Appl Environ Microbiol.* 2001;67(11):5339-42.

[63] Merchant-Patel S, Blackall PJ, Templeton J, Price EP, Miflin JK, Huygens F, et al. Characterisation of chicken *Campylobacter jejuni* isolates using resolution optimised single nucleotide polymorphisms and binary gene markers. *Int J Food Microbiol.* 2008;128(2):304-8.

[64] Price EP, Thiruvenkataswamy V, Mickan L, Unicomb L, Rios RE, Huygens F, et al. Genotyping of *Campylobacter jejuni* using seven single-nucleotide polymorphisms in combination with *flaA* short variable region sequencing. *J Med Microbiol.* 2006;55(Pt 8):1061-70.

[65] Lienau EK, Strain E, Wang C, Zheng J, Ottesen AR, Keys CE, et al. Identification of a salmonellosis outbreak by means of molecular sequencing. *N Engl J Med.* 2011;364(10):981-2.

[66] Sullivan CB, Diggle MA, Clarke SC. Multilocus sequence typing: Data analysis in clinical microbiology and public health. *Mol Biotechnol.* 2005;29(3):245-54.

[67] Miller WG, On SL, Wang G, Fontanoz S, Lastovica AJ, Mandrell RE. Extended multilocus sequence typing system for *Campylobacter coli, C. lari, C. upsaliensis,* and *C. helveticus.* *J Clin Microbiol.* 2005;43(5):2315-29.

[68] Thakur S, Morrow WE, Funk JA, Bahnson PB, Gebreyes WA. Molecular epidemiologic investigation of *Campylobacter coli* in swine production systems, using multilocus sequence typing. *Appl Environ Microbiol.* 2006;72(8):5666-9.

[69] Adiri RS, Gophna U, Ron EZ. Multilocus sequence typing (MLST) of *Escherichia coli* O78 strains. *FEMS Microbiol Lett.* 2003;222(2):199-203.

[70] Rudi K, Holck AL. Real-time closed tube single nucleotide polymorphism (SNP) quantification in pooled samples by quencher extension (QEXT). *Nucleic Acids Res.* 2003;31(19):e117.

[71] Malek M, Hasenstein JR, Lamont SJ. Analysis of chicken TLR4, CD28, MIF, MD-2, and LITAF genes in a *Salmonella enteritidis* resource population. *Poult Sci.* 2004;83(4):544-9.

[72] Ragon M, Wirth T, Hollandt F, Lavenir R, Lecuit M, Le Monnier A, et al. A new perspective on *Listeria monocytogenes* evolution. *PLoS Pathog.* 2008;4(9):e1000146.

In: Molecular Typing Methods for TFM
Editors: S. Foley, R. Nayak, T. Johnson et al.

ISBN: 978-1-62100-643-5
© 2012 Nova Science Publishers, Inc.

Chapter 10

TANDEM REPEAT-BASED TYPING METHODS

Kristin Pederson Gulrud

Department of Biological Sciences
St. Cloud State University
St. Cloud, MN, US

ABSTRACT

DNA sequencing has revealed the presence of tandem repeat regions in both eukaryotic and prokaryotic genomes. Although the sequences flanking these regions are conserved, the number of repeats (copy number) at each region varies between individual chromosomes, which have given rise to the term, variable number tandem repeat regions or VNTRs. Differences in the repeat number at multiple VNTRs (Multilocus Variable-repeat Analysis or MLVA) provide the basis for a genetic fingerprinting method that can distinguish between individuals or individual bacteria. MLVA genetic fingerprinting on microbes has been utilized successfully for a variety of uses including forensic analysis of bioterrorism events and foodborne disease surveillance.

INTRODUCTION

Tandem repeat regions were first discovered in the human genome in 1980 [1]. These loci consist of identical DNA sequences of 1 base pair to 100+ base pairs that are located next to each other (in tandem) and repeated numerous times. In 1985, Jeffreys et. al. [2] discovered that the number of repeats at each of these regions often varied between different genomes and subsequently named them Variable Number of Tandem Repeats or VNTRs. The number of repeats at each VNTR changed due to replication or recombination errors and this difference allowed for differentiation of individuals on the basis of the number of repeats (copy number) [2, 3].

A difference in the copy number of VNTRs has been successfully utilized as a "genetic fingerprinting" tool that can identify specific individuals and also predict the relatedness of two DNA samples. VNTR analysis is utilized world-wide for forensic testing, paternity testing, analysis of genetic disorders, and population studies [4].

VNTRs are not exclusive to humans. Several different families of tandem repeat regions have been identified in numerous prokaryotic and eukaryotic genomes including bacteria, fungi, parasites, and viruses [5-7]. Minisatellites consist of repeats that are 6 base pairs to 100 base pairs in length. Microsatellites which have also been termed short tandem repeats (STRs) and simple sequence repeats (SSRs) consist of repeat regions of 1-5 base pairs in length that are repeated a varying number of times. Some SSRs exist outside coding regions while other tandem repeats are found within genes and can affect gene function [8]. The rate of change in the number of repeats due to strand slippage can sometimes be as high as 1 per 1000 replications making SSRs a good marker for epidemiological typing [8].

In order to be a useful method, any subtyping scheme must be able to discriminate between isolates of the same species [9]. Amplification of a VNTR by polymerase chain reaction (PCR) and the subsequent sizing of each amplified piece, allows for the determination of the repeat copy number which is individual to each bacterium, even within a species [8, 9]. This gives phenotypically identical bacteria a specific genetic "fingerprint" and allows for their differentiation. This information can be utilized in a variety of methods to identify individual bacteria. When multiple microbial VNTRs are assessed for differences in copy number, the fingerprinting technique is termed Multiple Variable-Number Tandem Repeat Analysis or MLVA [7, 10].

Microbial MLVA subtyping schemes were initially developed for tracking clinical isolates of clonal organisms that were not well discriminated by standard molecular subtyping methods. This included analysis of strains of *Hemophillus influenza* and *Mycobacterium tuberculosis* and the potential bioterrorism pathogens *Bacillus anthracis* and *Yersinia pestis* [10-15]. Whole genome sequencing of numerous bacteria has also greatly advanced the utilization of MLVA as a fingerprinting technique by providing for faster identification of the tandem repeat regions [16].

Since its development, MLVA subtyping has ushered in a new era of genetic fingerprinting, especially for those microbes that have clinical significance [6, 7]. Uses for MLVA have included tracking of outbreaks and foodborne disease surveillance, forensic analysis of bioterrorism weapons, phylogenetic analysis, discovery of *Escherichia coli* cattle dissemination routes, and the ability to identify cross-contamination in the clinical laboratory [6, 7, 17-20].

Worldwide estimates in 2005 attributed millions of cases and at least 1 million deaths to diarrhea caused by foodborne microbes. In the United States, statistics are estimated at an annual burden of foodborne illness of 76 million cases, 325,000 hospitalizations, and 5,200 cases each year [21]. Furthermore, the economic costs of recalled food, loss-of-work, medical care, and hospitalizations of all of these cases of illness are staggering [21].

A critical component of food safety measures are government-funded surveillance systems that exist to identify emerging outbreaks as quickly as possible to prevent future disease. By matching epidemiological information with microbial typing, sources of contaminated food can be identified and eliminated [22-25]. One highlight of these surveillance systems is PulseNet, the United States national molecular subtyping network, which since 1996 has utilized molecular fingerprinting to identify numerous outbreaks and prevent thousands of cases of foodborne illliness [22, 23]. Molecular typing has been so successful that PulseNet has branched out internationally into several PulseNet International organizations in Africa, Asia-Pacific, Canada, Europe, Latin America & Caribbean and the Middle East, where numerous health departments utilize genetic fingerprinting to solve multinational outbreaks [22, 24, 26].

Table 1. Pathogens for which a VNTR subtyping scheme for analysis of foodborne disease is published

Foodborne pathogen	Selected Citations
Bacillus anthracis	[10, 11, 13]
Bacillus cereus	[44, 47]
Brucella sp.	[53]
Clostridium botulinum	[54]
Clostridium perfringens	[50]
Escherichia coli O26	[49, 55]
Escherichia coli O11	[49]
Escherichia coli O55:H7	[48]
Escherichia coli O103:H25	[56]
Escherichia coli O157:H7	[27, 31, 35, 48]
Listeria monocytogenes	[34, 35, 57]
Salmonella enterica serovar Enteritidis	[29]
Salmonella enterica serovar Infantis	[58]
Salmonella enterica serovar Newport	[59]
Salmonella *enterica* serovar Paratyphi	[60]
Salmonella enterica serovar Typhi	[40, 60]
Salmonella enterica serovar Typhimurium	[32, 33, 61]
Salmonella enterica sp.	[50]
Shigella sonnei	[14]
Shigella sp.	[62]
Vibrio cholerae	[63]
Vibrio parahaemolyticus	[64]
Vibrio vulnificus	[51]
Yersinia enterocolitica	[65, 66]

Historically, PulseNet has utilized what has been the gold standard for molecular typing of foodborne pathogens, the technique of pulsed-field gel electrophoresis or PFGE. In PFGE, the bacterial genome is cleaved by a restriction enzyme and the resulting fragments are separated by size, which creates a specific pattern for each isolate (see Chapter 7 for more details). However, even though the use of PFGE has been very successful, there are some drawbacks to this genetic fingerprinting technique. PFGE is labor-intensive and the resulting data lacks portability [27, 28]. Finally, for some clonal pathogens, such as *Salmonella enterica* serovar Enteritidis, PFGE does not always discriminate well between isolates [28, 29].

In 2001, PulseNet sought to augment their molecular fingerprinting gold standard of PFGE by developing MLVA subtyping schemes for *E. coli* O157:H7, *Salmonella enterica* serovar Enteritidis, *S. enterica* serovar Typhimurium, and *Listeria monocytogenes* [27-30]. Concurrently, numerous researchers worldwide, most notably Lindstedt, et. al. also developed

MLVA subtyping schemes for these foodborne pathogens and many others (Table 1) [6, 31-35].

Several of these second generation subtyping methods have been standardized and validated and are currently being utilized in conjunction with PFGE to solve disease outbreaks worldwide [28, 36, 37]. MLVA protocols for *E. coli* O157:H7, *S. enterica* serotype Enteriditis and *S. enterica* serotype Typhimurium are freely available on the PulseNet International website (http://pulsenetinternational.org/protocols/mlva.asp).

In addition, the application of VNTR genetic fingerprinting to microbial identification has proven so useful that several public websites exist to provide VNTR tools, sequences, and databases. Some examples of these websites are the Genomes, Polymorphism and Minisatellites website (http://minisatellites.u-psud.fr/), MLVAbank (http://minisatellites.u-psud.fr/MLVAnet), the MIRU-VNTRplus website (http://www.miru-vntrplus.org/MIRU), the Multiple-Locus Variable number tandem repeat Analysis home page (http://www.mlva.net/), and MLVA-NET (http://www.pasteur.fr/mlva), and numerous other websites as well [6, 14, 16, 38, 39].

This chapter will describe the process of MLVA in detail and provide a generalized protocol for performing MLVA. At the end of the chapter the utility of MLVA for foodborne disease surveillance will be discussed.

Background

Tandem repeat-based typing methods rely on the technique of PCR to amplify genetic loci that show differences or polymorphisms. This is different from genetic fingerprinting methods like PFGE which separates genome-restricted fragments by size, to form complicated patterns which are compared between isolates. In Variable-Number Tandem-repeat analysis each repeat region is amplified by PCR and then sized by agarose gel electrophoresis, capillary electrophoresis, microarrays or other methods [7]. When a repeat region is present, it is amplified during the PCR reaction; however, if the repeat region is not present or if there are point mutations which prevent PCR, then no amplification is observed.

The presence of each repeat region is specific to a bacterial species and the number of repeats at each region can be discriminatory for isolates within a species [7]. The larger the amplified fragment, the more repeats are present in that region. Discriminatory power at one locus can be further enhanced by sequencing the entire region and cataloguing any point mutations within individual repeats [7]. Furthermore, the greater the number of analyzed VNTRs the greater the potential discrimination, so the examination of several VNTRs in Multiple-Locus VNTR analysis or MLVA has evolved.

Introduction into the VNTR/MLVA Methodology

Although VNTR methods that utilize direct specimens such as food or blood are being investigated, most procedures start with a bacterial isolate that is grown up in pure culture on a rich media such as Trypticase Soy agar or Trypticase Soy agar plus 5% sheep blood. The genomic DNA from each isolate is then purified (Figure 1). The VNTR regions of interest in each genome are then amplified (copied) by PCR.

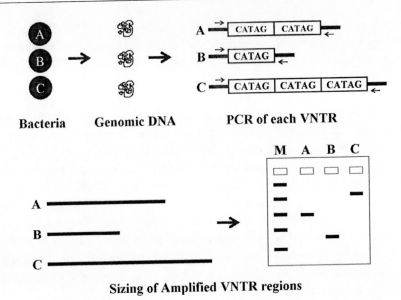

Sizing of Amplified VNTR regions

Figure 1. Diagram of VNTR Analysis of three isolates of the same bacterial genus and species. M=size standards.

PCR is a widely utilized method that allows the user to reproduce sections of DNA. By utilizing an enzyme (polymerase) that copies DNA and small DNA primers that mark the start and end of where the copy should be made, each VNTR region can be amplified by PCR. VNTR regions in the bacterial genome of interest are first identified by tandem-repeat region software. Then, primers to the flanking regions outside of the variable repeats are designed. Because the DNA sequences surrounding these repeat regions are usually conserved, one set of primers will generally amplify the same repeat region in a wide number of strains (Figure 1). The repeat regions can then be sized by agarose gel or capillary electrophoresis. The differences in the size of the amplified piece can be directly correlated to different numbers of repeats (Figure 1).

Agarose gel electrophoresis is a simple, inexpensive, and widely-available technique that is practiced worldwide [9, 40]. Following each PCR reaction the amplified VNTR regions are placed in an agarose gel and the gel is then exposed to an electrical current (electrophoresis) and the negatively charged DNA will migrate toward the positive electrode. The smaller the fragment, the faster it migrates through the pores in the gel matrix and the farther it travels down the length of the gel. By running marker lanes with known DNA standards such as a 100 base pair ladder, each of the VNTRs can be compared to the DNA standards and sized. The type of agarose and concentration can be adjusted to fit the size range of the DNA fragments being evaluated. Agarose gel electrophoresis is simple compared to other VNTR sizing methods, and it is much less expensive and easier to use. Many laboratories will already have the equipment and reagents available for this method. Several successful protocols in the literature including one for *S. enterica* serovar Typhi only utilize agarose gel electrophoresis [40].

Capillary electrophoresis is an alternative method to size the VNTR DNA. In this method, the VNTR PCR products are fluorescently tagged and then separated through polyacryamide gel in tiny capillaries on an automated sequencer. This technique costs more and requires the use of a sequencer. However, the size resolution of capillary electrophoresis is higher than agarose gel electrophoresis, and the technique is much easier to automate. Also, software programs exist that will assign a score to each fragment as it is being sized which shortens the time of the subtyping and eliminates the analysis step after agarose gel electrophoresis.

The greater the number of VNTR sizes, the greater the variability of that VNTR. Generally, the more variable the VNTR, the more useful it is in differentiating individual bacteria from each other. An example of a polymorphic locus (VNTR 1) with high variability and a monomorphic locus with little variability (VNTR 2) are shown in Figure 2. Agarose gel electrophoresis of the VNTR 1 locus from nine different isolates is illustrated in the left side of the figure. Between nine isolates, there are four different VNTR sizes and one isolate in which there was no amplification. In the right side of the figure, all of the VNTR 2 loci are the same size, providing little discrimination between the isolates. Various VNTR loci can be quantitated for diversity by utilizing numerical formulas such as Nei's or Simpson's Diversity Index [41, 42]. Greater levels of differentiation are also possible as the number of VNTRs that are examined are increased.

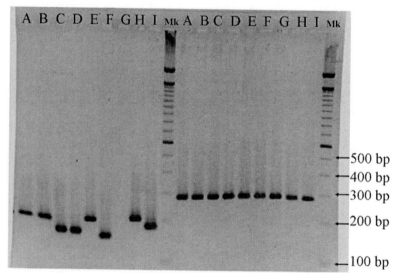

VNTR 1 - Polymorphic   VNTR 2 - Monomorphic

Figure 2. Agarose gel electrophoresis of the PCR-amplified VNTR locus from eight bacterial isolates (A, B, C, D, E, F, G, H, and I). (Left) VNTR 1 is an example of a polymorphic locus. (Right) VNTR 2 is an example of a monomorphic locus. Mk = size standards.

After sizing of the VNTR loci, each isolate to be subtyped is then assigned a score (Table 2). Isolates with the same size VNTR (allele) are given the same numerical score, while each different size (allele) is given a new score. The scores for each VNTR are assigned and then strung together with a dash separating each loci score (Table 2). With more than one VNTR analyzed, each string of scores can be assigned by a key to a final MLVA score.

One of the greatest advantages of MLVA subtyping is the portability of the data. A numerical score can easily be shared verbally, by phone, or over the internet without any specialized equipment. In addition, as a PCR-based method, MLVA is generally faster than the gold subtyping standard of PFGE and cheaper and less labor intensive than other subtyping methods that utilize sequencing such as multilocus sequence typing (MLST; discussed in Chapter 9).

Table 2. VNTR scoring of the two VNTR loci depicted in Figure 2

Isolate	VNTR 1 Size (bp)	VNTR 1 Score	VNTR 2 Size (bp)	VNTR 2 Score	Combined VNTRs	MLVA Score
A	200	4	290	1	4-1	5
B	200	4	290	1	4-1	5
C	170	2	290	1	2-1	3
D	170	2	290	1	2-1	3
E	200	4	290	1	4-1	5
F	160	1	290	1	1-1	2
G	0	0	290	1	0-1	1
H	200	4	290	1	4-1	5
I	180	3	290	1	3-1	4

GENERALIZED VNTR PROCEDURE

A detailed procedure for the performance of VNTR is outlined in this section. This generalized procedure is a compilation of multiple protocols and can potentially be applied to a variety of organisms, with the caveat that each PCR must have primers and reaction conditions that are species specific. The primers and PCR conditions listed here are for *Bacillus cereus* and are a compilation of previously published protocols that is currently being utilized in our laboratory (Gucinski and Gulrud, unpublished data).

Determination of Tandem Repeat Loci

The first step in performing VNTR is to decide which repeat regions should be utilized in the subtyping method. Numerous published VNTR schemes exist in the literature and an investigator may choose to employ one of these. Alternatively, one can analyze any available chromosomal sequences or genomes with computer software that will identify the tandem repeat regions.

One highly useful program is the freely available program Tandem Repeats Finder [5], found at the following website: (http://tandem.bu.edu/trf/trf.html). However, several other programs are also available for use [38, 39, 43]. As mentioned earlier, several useful websites such as the Genomes, Polymorphism and Minisatellites website (http://minisatellites.u-psud.fr/), exist where genomes can be queried for tandem repeat regions from hundreds of genomes [16, 32, 39]. Multiple sequences can also be compared for the presence of different VNTRs and the website also provides links to previously published tandem repeats.

In order to design a MLVA subtyping scheme, a set of VNTR loci must be chosen for the bacteria of interest. Several factors may influence the decision of which tandem-repeat loci to employ. First, the user will have to decide how many VNTRs to utilize. An important consideration is that the more clonal a bacteria population is and the harder it is to discriminate between isolates, thus more loci may be needed for efficient subyping. Many current MLVA schemes have been reduced to 5-10 loci to reduce subytping time and effort. However, a protocol may not achieve good discrimination with only five loci, and it may be necessary to employ more.

One factor that can strongly influence the choice of which particular loci to utilize is how a user wishes to measure the genetic polymorphisms present in the different VNTRs. Depending on the desired method of size analysis, a particular type of VNTR may be desired. For example, loci with smaller repeats such as STRs and SSRs (1-5 base pairs) tend to have the greatest rate of size variability due to strand slippage [8]. However, separation of amplified tandem repeat regions that vary by only a few bases is difficult to resolve by agarose gel electrophoresis. In contrast, analysis with capillary electrophoresis can generally discriminate fragments that differ in size by only 1 base pair [9]. Thus, while the larger tandem repeats tend to vary less in copy number, they can be easily sized by an agarose gel [40]. Larger tandem repeats also often contain single nucleotide polymorphisms (SNPs) [8]. If capillary electrophoresis will be used to not only measure the size of each VNTR but also its DNA sequence, one can decide to include several large tandem repeat regions and also identify SNPs in the fragments. The use of SNPs for microbial subtyping is described in greater detail in Chapter 9.

Design of Primers for the Amplification of Each VNTR

Tandem repeat software provides the location of each tandem repeat region as well as the sequence and repeat copy number for the sequence analyzed. It also provides the conserved sequences flanking each repeat region. For each VNTR to be examined, design primers in the conserved areas that mark where the polymerase chain amplification (PCR) of each tandem repeat locus should start (forward primer) and end (reverse primer). Because the DNA sequences surrounding these repeat regions are homologous, one set of locus-specific primers will generally amplify the same repeat region in a significant number of isolates.

Numerous primer software programs exist that can analyze a sequence, or the primers may be designed manually. One free program that is available for download is Primer 3 at the website (http://primer3.sourceforge.net/). Follow general PCR guidelines in the design of the primers, making sure that the primers do not contain multiple G's on their 3' end or that the two primers are not significantly homologous to each other. By counting 2 for each A and T in the primer sequence and 3 for each C and G, the individual annealing temperature of each primer can be calculated. It is desirable to keep each forward and reverse primer as close in annealing temperature as possible. If the desired goal is to amplify multiple VNTRs in a multiplex PCR, then the annealing temperature of all of the primers should be as close as possible. An investigator may also utilize primer sequences from published MLVA schemes or those available at the numerous MLVA resource websites. Primers may be ordered from any source, such as Integrated DNA Technologies (IDT, Coralville, IA).

Growth of Cells and Preparation of Genomic Template

Although protocols that assay VNTRs directly from clinical specimens are being investigated, the vast majority of methods start with a pure culture of each isolate. Each organism(s) to be typed is streaked for isolation on a rich media such as Tryptic Soy Broth Agar (TSB) or TSB + 5% sheep blood. Two to three colonies of the isolate are recovered with a sterile loop which can be added directly to the PCR mixture [15]. If desired, the sample being analyzed can be stored for future use by utilizing one of the following methods. The genomic DNA can be purified from two to three colonies of each isolate utilizing any standard protocol and stored in aliquots at -20°C. Alternatively, colonies may be evenly resuspended in 100 μl of sterile molecular grade water in a 0.5 ml tube, and then heated at 100°C for 10 minutes. The tubes are then cooled and centrifuged for 10 minutes at 10,000 rpm (PulseNet protocols, 24). The supernatant (DNA template) can be stored for numerous years at -20°C or -80°C.

Polymerase Chain Reaction (PCR)

The specific protocol listed is an adaptation of the protocols by Andersen et. al., [11] and Valjevac et. al. [1]. If the anticipated sizes of a set of VNTRs are not expected to overlap, multiple VNTRs can be amplified together in the same multiplex PCR as illustrated below.

Any PCR reaction must contain dNTPs of all four bases, DNA polymerase, and some type of PCR amplification buffer (with $MgCl_2$). A widely used option for microsatellite amplification is the Multiplex kit from Qiagen (Basel, Switzerland) which comes with 10X reaction buffer and contains the above ingredients in one master mix. The primers utilized in each reaction were EWA1, (5'-TATCCTTGGTATTGCTG-3'), EWA2, (5'-ATGGTTCCGC CTTATCG-3') for the *vrr*A VNTR [11] and Bcms 19 F, (5'-GGAATAGAAGATGAAGAA GAAGTTACG-3') and Bcms 19 R, (5'-TTTCG(S)TTTTATTGGTGGTTG) for the Bcms 19 locus [44].

For each isolate, a 20 μl PCR reaction is added to a sterile 0.2 mL PCR tube. Each PCR reaction should consist of a final concentration of 0.2 μM of each flanking primer, 1X Qiagen Master Mix (final concentration of 3mM $MgCl_2$), 100 ng of template DNA, and sterile molecular-grade water to a final volume of 20 μl. If the VNTR to be amplified is very GC-rich, also add 1 μl of the Q solution that comes with the kit. It is also important to prepare a positive control tube with genomic DNA containing a VNTR that is present and should be amplified, such as from one of the many sequenced strains that are available. Also, prepare a negative control tube that only contains sterile molecular-grade water as a template. Make one master mix of all of the reagents except template and aliquot this into each PCR tube before adding the template DNA. Place the PCR tubes in any standard thermocycler and run the following cycling conditions: 96°C for 15 minutes, 30 cycles of (96°C 1 minute, 56°C, 90 seconds, 72°C, 1 minute), 72°C for 5 minutes, 4°C indefinitely.

If the VNTR amplicons are to be sized by capillary electrophoresis, then the PCR reaction has some differences. First, the forward primers will need to be tagged at the 5' end with a fluorescent dye. Examples of these dyes are the WellRED dyes from Beckman Coulter (Brea, CA), such as D2 (black), D3 (green), or D4 (blue), however many other dyes are available. Dye-tagged primers may be ordered from a variety of sources including Proligo and IDT. The amount of primers utilized in the PCR reaction is also increased to 10 uM for each flanking primer.

SIZE ANALYSIS OF VNTR REGIONS

Agarose Gel Electrophoresis

Depending on the size of the VNTR to be analyzed and the number of isolates to be compared, the overall size of each gel that is utilized may vary. Prepare the casting apparatus by sealing off the ends of the gel, usually with rubber gaskets. Add the desired comb to the wells and prepare the agarose gel. For most VNTRs a 2.0% gel will separate the different sized PCR amplicons well. However, a different concentration of agarose may be utilized. Add the desired amount of molecular-grade agarose, such as OmniPur® (EMD Chemicals), to the correct volume of 0.5X TBE buffer (0.89M boric acid, 20mM EDTA, pH 8.0) needed for the individual casting stand or gel apparatus. Heat the mixture on a hot plate or in a microwave until the agarose is dissolved. Use a larger container than the volume of gel mixture as the gel tends to easily boil over when it is heated. Add the desired amount of 10 mg/mL ethidium bromide to a final concentration of 0.25 µg/mL, let the gel cool and pour the molten agarose into the gel apparatus when the temperature is between 60°C and 65°C. Allow the gel to further cool at room temperature until it is hardened, usually at least 30 minutes.

The hardened gel is placed in the voltage apparatus and covered with 0.5X TBE. The comb is removed, taking care not to break the bottoms of the wells. Ten µl of each PCR reaction is added to a new 0.2 mL tube with 2 µl tracking dye (40% sucrose, 0.25% bromothymol blue). The tracking dye contains sucrose to weight the DNA and allows monitoring of the progress of DNA migration. Each sample is then loaded with a micropipette into one well on the gel. 100 bp DNA size standards (Quanti-Marker 100 bp, GENE Mate) are added to the outside gel lanes and in gel lanes between every eight PCR samples.

Run the gel at 80V for four hours or until the DNA has traveled down the desired length of gel. VNTRs with smaller repeats may need a longer run time to be separated than VNTRs with larger repeats. The gel is then illuminated with any standard UV illumination source to visualize the ethidium bromide and photographed. Wear gloves to avoid contact with the ethidium bromide, and UV protective goggles to protect your eyes.

Capillary Electrophoresis

A more sophisticated method involves the analysis of tandem-repeat regions with capillary electrophoresis. For this method, each VNTR amplicon is tagged with a fluorescent dye that is attached to the 5' end of the forward primer. Multiple systems are available for the performance of capillary electrophoresis, including the CEQ 8000 from Beckman Coulter, Inc. and the ABI310 from Applied Biosystems (Life Technololgies Corporation, Carlsbad, CA). By utilizing different dyes on fragments with overlapping size ranges, multiple fragments can be sized simultaneously.

An example of a generalized protocol for capilliary electrophoresis sizing of PCR products is as follows: One μl of each PCR reaction is put into one well of a 96 well sample plate (Beckman Coulter). Size standard markers of 60-600 bp (0.5 μl) (Beckman Coulter) and 38.5 μl of formamide (Beckman sample loading solution) are added to each well for a final volume of 40 μl. Then each well is covered with a drop of mineral oil. The plate is then analyzed on the CEQ 8000 utilizing standard analysis conditions of: capillary temperature of 35°C, denaturation temperature of 90°C for a duration of 120 seconds, injection voltage of 2.0kV for a duration of 30 seconds, and separation voltage of 7.5 kV for a duration of 45 minutes.

Assignment of VNTR Scores

The agarose gel photograph may be analyzed manually for size differences or analyzed with a software program such as BioNumerics (Applied Maths, Sint-Martens-Latem, Belgium). Each VNTR size is assigned a numerical score (Table 2). Isolates with the same size VNTR (allele) are given the same numerical score, while each different size (allele) is given a new score. Multiple VNTR alleles are listed in the desired order with a dash separating each locus score (Table 2). With more than one VNTR analyzed, each string of scores can be assigned by a key to a final MLVA score. Allele designations for each isolate may also be imported into BioNumerics. In BioNumerics, the relatedness of each isolate can be analyzed by constructing a dendrogram using the Dice coefficient of similarity and the unweighted pair-group means with arithmetic averages method for cluster analysis. The methods for analysis of molecular typing data is described in chapter 14.

Screening of the Genetic Polymorphisms (Diversity Level) of Each VNTR

Once a successful PCR amplification protocol has been produced, the chosen VNTRs need to be analyzed for diversity within a group of known isolates. Previous studies have demonstrated that it is not always possible to predict the level of diversity that a VNTR will possess [9]. Some tandem repeat regions will have high levels of polymorphic diversity, while others will have low diversity as shown in Figure 2. VNTRs that show a high level of diversity on one set of geographically related isolates may lack diversity on a set of isolates from a different geographical region. It is best to utilize a set of isolates for screening that is as diverse as possible by genetic diversity, source and geographical location. At the end of screening, a set of VNTR loci with the desired levels of diversity can be chosen for a final genotyping method.

Troubleshooting

The most likely problem to be encountered during MLVA analysis is lack of amplification during PCR. All reagents and primers used should be stored in small aliquots as multiple freeze-thaw cycles may negatively affect amplification. Repeating the PCR with new reagents will often fix the problem. Sometimes a tandem repeat region does not amplify in a particular isolate, presumably due to mutation or loss of one or both of the primer annealing sites. This is called a null allele and scored as a zero. True null alleles can be confirmed by sequencing the region. Care should be taken to adhere to the protocol specifications to maximize reproducibility.

If a PCR shows more than one predominant VNTR band, it should be repeated with new reagents and new template DNA to rule out contamination. If the problem persists, the PCR primers may have to be redesigned, or the VNTR region may have to be sequenced to determine the correct size. The size of an amplified VNTR region may be slightly different from one PCR reaction to the next [27, 36]. For most VNTRs a size range differing by 1-2 base pairs is utilized for each allele.

MLVA IN PRACTICE FOR FOODBORNE PATHOGENS

VNTR/MLVA subtyping schemes have been developed for a significant number of clinical pathogens [40, 45]. This molecular subtyping method has proven to be an effective way to genetically fingerprint and identify microbes and useful for microbial tracking for a variety of purposes. In particular, VNTR and MLVA subtyping assays have been shown to be valuable during disease outbreaks [9]. The advantages of this technique are significant levels of discriminatory power for most pathogens, speed, ease of use, potential for automation and data portability [28, 36].

Genetic fingerprinting by MLVA has become an important tool for tracking foodborne pathogens and has been developed as an extremely useful surveillance tool by numerous surveillance systems [15, 18, 36]. Some species of bacteria are more amenable to MLVA analysis, depending on the number and type of tandem repeats and amount of clonality found in each genome [46]. Sometimes, a particularly useful VNTR locus from one bacterium can also be utilized in closely related bacteria, such as between *Shigella* spp. and *E. coli* [38].

In order for a molecular subytping method to be useful, it must have sufficient discriminatory power to differentiate individual isolates from one another [27, 45]. One of the greatest strengths of MLVA subtyping has been its high levels of discriminatory power for certain organisms. MLVA has proven to be particularly useful with bacteria with a high degree of clonality that are not well separated by PFGE such as *E. coli* O157:H7, *S. enterica* serovar Enteritidis and *Shigella sonnei* [6, 29, 31, 47].

No genetic fingerprinting method can stand alone. Any subtyping method must be paired with epidemiological information to be considered useful for microbial epidemiology. Studies of MLVA subtyping have shown that MLVA has good epidemiological concordance and a high ability to differentiate outbreak isolates from non-outbreak related isolates or sporadic cases [6, 29, 32, 37].

Currently MLVA subtyping is being utilized for a wide number of different foodborne pathogens of the Enterobacteriaceae such as *E. coli*, *S. enterica* serovars, *Shigella* spp., and *Yersinia enterocolitica* [6, 7, 28, 46]. In particular, MLVA has been an extremely useful subtyping method for *E. coli* and *Salmonella* [6, 7]. Numerous subtyping methods have been developed for several serotypes of *E. coli* and various serovars of *S. enterica* (Table 1). The first *E. coli* MLVA subtyping methods were developed for serotype O157:H7 and MLVA has proven to be an effective, fast, highly discriminatory subtyping method for this organism [30, 35, 47]. However, not all serotypes of *E. coli* can be typed by this method. Other serotype-specific MLVA schemes have developed for those additional serogroups such as O26, O55, and O111 [48, 49].

Members of the *Salmonella enterica* spp. group cause significant numbers of foodborne infections each year with the largest numbers of infections often caused by *S.* Enteritidis and *S.* Typhimurium [29, 32, 46]. In 2003, the first *Salmonella* MLVA subtyping scheme was published for the clonal definitive-type 104 (DT104) group of *S.* Typhimurium, which at the time was not well differentiated by available subtyping methods [32]. In this study, MLVA provided much higher discrimination between members of this group than PFGE, amplified fragment length polymorphism analysis (AFLP), integron-cassette profile analysis and multiple PCRs of individual genes [32]. Further studies have focused on adapting this MLVA technique to capillary electrophoresis for a faster output and increased throughput through automation, and refining the choice of loci for *S.* Typhimurium [33]. A two-year real-time surveillance study of *S.* Typhimurium infections demonstrated that MLVA subtyping was better than PFGE for investigating outbreaks and routine surveillance [37].

Like the different serotypes of *E. coli*, MLVA subtyping for *S.* Typhimurium can not always be utilized for other serovars of *S. enterica*. Several subtyping methods have been published for *S. enterica* serovar Enteritidis. In 2007, Boxrud et al. [29] demonstrated that MLVA subtyping had increased discriminatory power over other subtyping methods like PFGE and phage typing, but was also reproducible, and demonstrated good epidemiological concordance. Subsequent studies have focused on the development of MLVA for other *Salmonella* serovars and even a MLVA subtyping scheme that can subtype multiple serovars at once (Table 1). MLVA has even been utilized to detect cross-contamination of *Salmonella* in the clinical laboratory [17].

MLVA has performed so well for *E. coli* and *S. enterica* serovars that numerous foodborne disease surveillance systems such as Enter-net, PulseNet, and Salm-gene are utilizing MLVA to identify and track outbreaks of these foodborne pathogens [26-28, 37]. However, in order to be utilized as a worldwide subtyping method, various MLVA protocols need to be standardizd and validated between countries [26-28]. In addition, a common nomenclature system for the naming of alleles needs to be adopted [7, 26, 27]. The establishment of a multi-national database of MLVA subtypes would also contribute to foodborne disease surveillance and greatly facilitate the exchange of international MLVA data [27].

One concern with MLVA is that the rate of copy number change will be so high that VNTR profiles may change during an epidemiological investigation or during an outbreak. Boxrud et al. [29] showed that the MLVA profiles of *S.* Enteritidis remained stable through multiple in vitro passages and multiple freeze-thaw cycles. However, 2 of 12 sequential isolates recovered from one patient had a MLVA pattern differing at one VNTR locus. This indicated that there may be a greater rate of change *in vivo*, and that MLVA patterns that differed slightly at one or two loci could appear during an outbreak.

In addition, MLVA has also proven useful for Gram positive foodborne pathogens such as *Brucella* spp., *Clostridium* spp. *Listeria monocytogenes*, *Vibrio* spp. and *Bacillus cereus* (Table 1). MLVA has been developed for *Clostridium perfringens* and had significant discriminatory power and reproducibility among 112 isolates, making it a cost-effective and efficient molecular fingerprinting tool for *C. perfringens* [50]. Analysis of *Vibrio vulnificus* by MLVA provided high levels of discrimination even among the clonal highly virulent biotype 3 group that is not always differentiated well by other subtyping methods [51].

Genetic fingerprinting by MLVA has the advantage of being much faster than many of the current subtyping methods. By adapting the protocol to capillary electrophoresis, MLVA analysis can be completed in a few hours. Heck et al. [52] maintain that MLVA is as discriminatory as phage typing and PFGE for identifying outbreaks of *S.* Typhimurium, but also has the added advantage of being a faster method. This PCR-based protocol is also less labor-intensive and is amenable to automation. By using multiple dyes and multiplexing PCR reactions, and pooling the analysis of MLVA fragments, several MLVA loci can be screened simultaneously.

There also are some drawbacks to MLVA. Capillary electrophoresis can be costly and require a significant monetary investment to implement [7, 9]. The development of new, less expensive sizing methods may help to address the cost issue [7]. Depending on the analysis method utilized, different VNTRs may show differences in fragment sizing [27, 36]. Also, highly variable VNTR loci may change at a rate too high for effective use during an outbreak [27]. Finally, it has been necessary to develop species-specific and even serovar-specific MLVA protocols, rather than relying on one standard protocol [7, 9, 27].

CONCLUSION

To date, variable-number of tandem-repeat regions have been identified in every microbial genome that has been examined. Because of their ubiquitous presence and the polymorphisms in repeat copy number between individual genomes, these loci represent a valuable opportunity for the identification and characterization of bacterial pathogens.

This subtyping technique is rapid, amenable to automation, and has demonstrated similar or increased discriminatory power and epidemiological concordance than many standard subtyping methods [6, 7, 9]. MLVA is already being utilized in conjunction with PFGE to solve outbreaks of foodborne disease and may eventually replace PFGE in the future [28]. It remains to be seen if the second generation subtyping of MLVA is fully adopted in the future, or if an even better, faster, and cheaper method than MLVA is developed.

REFERENCES

[1]   Wyman, A.R. and R. White. A highly polymorphic locus in human DNA. *Proc Natl Acad Sci USA.* 1980;77:6754-6758.

[2]   Jeffreys, A.J. V. Wilson, and S.L. Thein. Individual-specific 'fingerprints' of human *DNA. Nature.* 1985;316:76-70.

[3]   Bois, P. and A. J. Jeffreys. Minisatellite instability and germline mutation. *Cell Mol Life Sci.* 1999;55:1636-1648.

[4]   Decorte, R. Genetic identification in the 21st century – Current status and future developments. *Forensic Sci Int.* 2010;201(1-3):160-4.

[5]   Benson, G. Tandem repeats finder: a program to analyze DNA sequences. *Nucleic Acids Res.* 1999;27:573-580.

[6]   Lindstedt. B-A. Multiple-locus variable number tandem repeats analysis for genetic fingerprinting of pathogenic bacteria. *Electrophoresis*. 2005;26:2567-2582.

[7]   van Belkum, A. Tracing isolates of bacterial species by multilocus variable number of tandem repeat analysis (MLVA). *FEMS Immunol Med Microbiol*. 2007;49:22-27.

[8]   van Belkum, A. Short sequence repeats in microbial pathogenesis and evolution. *Cell Mol Life Sci*. 1999;56:729-734.

[9]   Yazdankhah, S. P. and B.-A. Lindstedt. Variable number tandem repeat typing of bacteria. *Methods Mol Biol*. 2007;396:395-405.

[10] Keim, P., L.B. Price, A.M. Klevyska, K.L. Smith, J.M. Schupp, R. Okinaka, P.J. Jackson, and M.E. Hugh-Jones. Multiple-locus variable-number tandem repeat analysis reveals genetic relationships within *Bacillus anthracis*. *J Bacteriol*. 2000;182:2928-2936.

[11] Andersen, G.L., J.M. Simchock, and K.H. Wilson. Identification of a region of genetic variability among *Bacillus anthracis* and related species. *J. Bacteriol*. 1996;178:377-384.

[12] Frothingham, R. and W. A. Meeker-O'Connell. Genetic diversity in the *Mycobacterium tuberculosis* complex based on variable numbers of tandem DNA repeats. *Microbiology*. 1998;144:1189-1196.

[13] Klevytska, A. M., L. B, Price, J. M. Schupp, P.L. Worsham, J. Wong, and P. Keim. Identification and characterization of variable-number tandem repeats in the *Yersinia pestis* genome. *J Clin Microbiol*. 2001;39:3179-3185.

[14] LeFlèche, P., Y. Hauck, L. Onteniente, A. Prieur, F. Denoeud, V. Ramisse, P. Sylvestre, G. Benson, F. Ramisse, and G. Vergnaud. A tandem repeats database for bacterial genomes: application to the genotyping of *Yersinia pestis* and *Bacillus anthracis*. *BMC Microbiol*. 2001;1:2.

[15] vanBelkum, A., W.J.G. Melchers, C. Ijsseldijk, L. Nohlmans, H. Verbrugh, and J.F.G. Meis. Outbreak of Amoxicillin-resistant *Haemophilus influenza* Type b: variable number of tandem repeats as novel molecular markers. *J Clin Microbiol*. 1997;35:1517-1520.

[16] Denoeud, F., and G. Vergnaud. Identification of polymorphic tandem repeats by direct comparison of genome sequence from different bacterial strains: a web-based resource. *BMC Informatics*. 2004;5:4.

[17] De Lappe, N. J. O Connor, G. Doran, G. Devane, and M. Cormican. Role of subtyping in detecting *Salmonella* cross contamination in the laboratory. *BMC Microbiol*. 2009;9:155.

[18] Hoffmaster, A.R., C. C. Fitzgerald, E. Ribot, L.W. Mayer, T. Popovic. Molecular subtyping of *Bacillus anthracis* and the 2001 bioterrorism-associated anthrax outbreak, United States. *Emerging Infect Dis*. 2002;8:1111-1116.

[19] Martin, A., M. Herranz, M. MartinezLirola, R. F. Fernández, INDAL-TB group, E. Bouza, and D. Garcia de Viedma. Optimized molecular resolution of cross-contamination alerts in clinical mycobacteriology laboratories. *BMC Microbiol*. 2008;8:30.

[20] Murphy, M., D. Minihan, J. F. Buckley, M. O'Mahony, P. White, and S. Fanning. Multiple-locus variable number of tandem repeat analysis (MLVA) of Irish verocytotoxigenic *Escherichia coli* O157 from feedlot cattle: uncovering strain dissemination routes. *BMC Vet Res*. 2008;4:2.

[21] Buzby, J.C., and T. Roberts. The economics of enteric infections: human foodborne disease costs. *Gastroenterology.* 2009;136(6):1851-1862.

[22] Gerner-Smidt, P., K. Hise, J. Kincaid, S. Hunter, S. Rolando, E Hyytiä-Trees, E.M. Ribot, B. Swaminathan, and the PulseNet Taskforce. PulseNet USA: a five-year update. *Foodborne Pathog Dis.,* 2006;3(1):9-19.

[23] Swaminathan, B., T.J. Barrett, S.B. Hunter, R.V. Tauxe, and the CDC PulseNet TaskForce. PulseNet: The molecular subtyping network for foodborne bacterial disease. *Emerging Infect Dis.* 2001;7:382-389.

[24] Swaminathan, B., P. Gerner-Smidt, L. K. Ng, S. Lukinmaa, K. M. Kam, S. Rolando, E. P. Gutierrez, and N. Binsztein. Building PulseNet International:an interconnected system of laboratory networks to facilitate timely public health recognition and response to foodborne disease outbreaks and emerging foodborne diseases. *Foodborne Pathog. Dis.* 2006;3:36–50.

[25] Tauxe, R.V., M.P. Doyle, T. Kuchenmuller, J. Schlundt, and C.E. Stein. Evolving public health approaches to the global challenge of foodborne infections. *Int J Food Microbiol.* 2010;139(Suppl 1): S16-28.

[26] Ammon, A. and R.V. Tauxe. Investigation of multi-national foodborne outbreaks in Europe: some challenges remain. *Epidemiol Infect.* 2007;135:887-889.

[27] Hyytiä-Trees E, Smole SC, Fields PA, Swaminathan B, Ribot EM. Second generation subtyping: a proposed PulseNet protocol for multiple-locus variable-number tandem repeat analysis of Shiga toxin-producing *Escherichia coli* O157 (STEC O157). *Foodborne Pathog Dis.* 2006;3:118--31.

[28] Hyytiä-Trees E. K., K. Cooper, E. M. Ribot, P. Gerner-Smidt. Recent developments and future prospects in subtyping of bacterial pathogens. *Future Microbiol.* 2007;2:175-185.

[29] Boxrud, D., K. Pederson-Gulrud, J. Wotton, C. Medus, E. Lyskowicz, J. Besser, and J.M. Bartkus. Comparison of multiple-locus variable-number tandem repeat analysis, pulsed-field gel electrophoresis, and phage typing for subtype analysis of *Salmonella enterica* serotype Enteritidis. *J Clin Microbiol.* 2007;45:536-543.

[30] Sperry, K.E. V., S. Kathariou, J. S. Edwards, and L.A. Wolf. Multiple-locus variable-number tandem-repeat analysis as a tool for subtyping *Listeria monocytogenes* strains. *J Clin Microbiol.* 2008;46:1435-1450.

[31] Lindstedt, B.-A., E. Heir, E. Gjernes, T. Vardund, and G. Kapperud. DNA fingerprinting of Shiga-toxin producing *Escherichia coli* O157 based on Multiple-Locus Variable-Number Tandem-Repeats Analysis (MLVA). *Annals of Clin Microbiol Antimicrob.* 2003;2:12.

[32] Lindstedt, B-A., E. Heir, E. Gjernes, and G. Kapperud. DNA fingerprinting of *Salmonella enterica* subsp. *enterica* serovar Typhimurium with emphasis on phage type DT104 based on variable number of tandem repeat loci. *J Clin Microbiol.* 2003;41:1469-1479.

[33] Lindstedt, B-A.,T. Vardund, L. Aas, and G. Kapperud. Multiple-locus variable-number tandem repeats analysis of *Salmonella enterica* subsp. *enterica* serovar Typhimurium using PCR multiplexing and multicolor capillary electrophoresis. *J Microbiol Methods.* 2004;59:163-172.

[34] Lindstedt, B.-A., W. Tham, M. L. Danielsson-Tham, T. Vardund, S. Helmersson, and G. Kapperud. Multiple-locus variable-number tandem-repeats analysis of *Listeria*

monocytogenes using multicolor capillary electrophoresis and comparison with pulsed-field gel electrophoresis typing. *J Microbiol Methods.* 2008;72:141-148.

[35]   Noller, A.C., M.C. McEllistrem, A. G. F Pacheco. Multilocus variable-number tandem repeat analysis distinguishes outbreak and sporadic *Escherichia coli* O157:H7 isolates. *J Clin Microbiol.* 2003;41:5389-5397.

[36]   Hyytiä-Trees E., P. Lafon, P. Vauterin, and E.M. Ribot. Multilaboratory validation study of standardized multiple-locus variable-number tandem repeat analysis protocol for Shiga toxin-producing *Escherichia coli* O157: A novel approach to normalize fragment size data between capillary electrophoresis platforms. *Foodborne Pathog Dis.* 2010;7:129-136.

[37]   Torpdahl, M. G. Sørensen, B.-A. Lindquist, and E.M. Nielsen. Tandem Repeat Analysis for Surveillance of Human *Salmonella* Typhimurium Infections. *Emerging Infect Dis.* 2007;13:388-395.

[38]   Grissa, I., P. Bouchon, C. Pourcel, and G. Vergnaud. On-line resources for bacterial micro-evolution studies using MLVA or CRISPR typing. *Biochimie.* 2008;90:660-668.

[39]   Guigon, G., J. Cheval, R. Cahuzac, and S. Brisse. MLVA-NET – A standardized web database for bacterial genotyping and surveillance. *Eurosurveillance.* 2008;13:1-3.

[40]   Liu, Y., M.-A., Lee, E.-E Ooi, Y. Mavis, A.-L. Tan, and H.-H. Quek. Molecular typing of *Salmonella enteric* serovar Typhi isolates from various countries in Asia by a multiplex PCR assay on variable-number tandem repeats. *J Clin Microbiol.* 2003,41:4388-4394.

[41]   Hunter, P. R., and M. A. Gaston. Numerical index of the discriminatory ability of typing systems: an application of Simpson's index of diversity. *J Clin Microbiol.* 1988;26:2465–2466.

[42]   Nei, M. Analysis of gene diversity in subdivided populations. *Proc Natl Acad Sci USA.* 1973;70: 3321-3323.

[43]   O'Dushlaine, C.T. and D.C. Shields. Tools for the identification of variable and potentially variable tandem repeats. *BMC Genomics.* 2006;7:290.

[44]   Valjevac, S., V. Hilaire, O. Lisanti, F. Ramisse, E. Hernandez, J.-D. Cavallo, C. Poucel, and G. Vergnaud. Comparison of minisatellite polymorphisms in the *Bacillus cereus* complex: a simple assay for large-scale screening and identification of strains most closely related to *Bacillus anthracis. Appl Environ Microbiol.* 2005;71: 6613–6623

[45]   van Belkum, A., P. T. Tassios, L. Dijkshoorn, S. Haeggman, B. Cookson, N. K. Fry, V. Fussing, J. Green, E. Feil, P. Gerner-Smidt, S. Brisse, and M. Struelens. Guidelines for the validation and application of typing methods for use in bacterial epidemiology. *Clin Microbiol Infect.* 2007;13(Suppl 3):1-46.

[46]   Foley, S. L., S. Zhao, and R. D. Walker. Comparison of molecular typing methods for the differentiation of *Salmonella* foodborne pathogens. *Foodborne Pathog Dis.* 2007;4:253-76.

[47]   Liang, S.-Y., H. Watanabe, J. Terajima, C.-C. Lin, J.-C. Liao, S. K. Tung, C.-S. Chiou. Multilocus variable-number tandem-repeat analysis for molecular typing of *Shigella sonnei. J Clin Microbiol.* 2007;45:3574-3580.

[48]   Keys, C., S. Kemper, and P. Keim. Highly diverse variable number tandem repeat loci in the *E. coli* O157:H7 and O55:H7 genomes for high-resolution molecular typing. *J Appl Microbiol.* 2005;98:928-940.

[49] Izumiya, H. Y. Pei, J. Terajima, M. Ohnishi, T. Hayashi, S. Iyoda, and H. Watanabe. New system for multilocus variable-number tandem-repeat analysis of the enterohemorrhagic *Escherichia coli* strains belonging to three major serogroups: O157, O26, and O111. *Microbiol Immunol.* 2010;54:569-577.

[50] Sawires, Y.S. and J. G. Songer. Multiple-locus variable-number tandem repeat analysis for strain typing of *Clostridium perfringens. Anaerobe.* 2005;11:262-272.

[51] Broza, Y. Y., Danin-Poleg, L. Lerner, M. Broza, and Y. Kashi. *Vibrio vulnificus* typing based on simple sequence repeats insights into the Biotype 3 group. *J Clin Microbiol.* 2007;45: 2951-2959.

[52] Heck, M. Multilocus variable number of tandem repeats analysis (MLVA) – A reliable tool for rapid investigation of *Salmonella* Typhimurium outbreaks. *Eurosurveillance.* 2009;14:1.

[53] Bricker, B., D.R. Ewalt, and S.M. Halling. *Brucella* 'HOOF-Prints': strain typing by multi-locus analysis of variable number tandem repeats (VNTRs). *BMC Microbiology.* 2003;3:15.

[54] Macdonald, T.E., and C. H. Helma, L. O. Ticknor, P. J. Jackson, R. T. Okinaka, L. A. Smith, and K. K. Hill. Differentiation of *Clostridium botulinum* serotype A strains by multiple-locus variable-number tandem repeat analysis. *Appl Env Microbiol.* 2008;74:875-882.

[55] Miko, A., B. A. Lindstedt, L. T. Brandal, I. Lobersli, and L. Beutin. Evaluation of multiple-locus variable number of tandem repeats analysis (MLVA) as a method for identification of clonal groups among enteropathogenic, enterohaemorrhagic and avirulent *Escherichia coli* O26 strains. *FEMS Microbiol Lett.* 2010;303:137-146.

[56] Schimmer, B., K. Nygard, H.-M. Eriksen, J. Lassen, B.-A. Lindstedt, L. T. Brandal, G. Kapperud, and P. Aavitsland. Outbreak of haemolytic uraemic syndrome in Norway caused by stx2-positive *Escherichia coli* O103:H25 traced to cured mutton sausages. *BMC Infectious Dis.* 2008;8:41.

[57] Miya, S., B. Kimura, H. Takahashi, T. Ishikawa, T. Suda, C. Takakura, T. Fujii, and M. Wiedmann. Development of a multilocus variable-number of tandem repeat typing method for *Listeria moncytogenes* serotype 4b strains. *Int J Food Microbiol.* 2008;124:239-249.

[58] Ross, I.L., and M. W. Heuzenroeder. A comparison of three molecular typing methods for the discrimination of *Salmonella enterica* serovar Infantis. *FEMS Immunol Med Microbiol.* 2008;53:375-384.

[59] Witonski, D., R. Stefanova, A. Ranganathan, G. E. Schultze, K. D. Eisenach, and M.D. Cave. Variable-number tandem repeats that are useful in genotyping isolates of *Salmonella enterica* subsp. enterica serovars Typhimurium and Newport. *J Clin Microbiol.* 2008;44:3849-3854.

[60] Ramisse, V., P. Houssu, E. Hernandez, F. Denoeud, V. Hilaire, O. Lisanti, F. Ramisse, J. D. Cavallo, and G. Vergnaud. Variable number of tandem repeats in *Salmonella enterica* subsp. enterica for typing purposes. *J Clin Microbiol.* 2004;42:5722-5730.

[61] Pederson-Gulrud, K.J., D. Boxrud, S. Vetter, J. Besser, and J. Bartkus, Molecular subtyping of *Salmonella* Typhimurium by Multi-Locus VNTR Analysis (MLVA), abstr. C-407, p 193. In Abstracts of the 101st General meeting of the American Society for Microbiology, Washington D.C. 2003.

[62] Gorgé, O., S. Lopez, V. Hilaire, O. Lisanti, V. Ramisse, and G. Vergnaud. Selection and validation of a multilocus variable-number tandem-repeat analysis panel for typing *Shigella* spp. *J Clin Microbiol.* 2008;46:1026-1035.

[63] Danin-Poleg, Y., L. A. Cohen, H. Ganez, Y. Y. Broza, H. Goldshmidt, E. Malul, L. Valinsky, L. Lerner, M. Broza, and Y. Kashi. *Vibrio cholerae* strain typing and phylogeny study based on simple sequence repeats. *J Clin Microbiol.* 2007;45:736-746.

[64] Kimura, B., Y. Sekine, H. Takahashi, Y. Tanaka, H. Obata, A. Kai, S. Morozumi, and T. Fujii. Multiple-locus variable-number of tandem repeats analysis distinguishes *Vibrio parahaemolyticus* pandemic O3:K6 strains. J Microbiol Methods 2008;72:313–320.

[65] de Benito, I., M.E. Cano, J. Aguero, J. M. G. Lobo. A polymorphic tandem repeat potentially useful for typing in the chromosome of *Yersinia enterocolitica*. *Microbiology.* 2004;150:199-204.

[66] Gierczyński, R., A. Golubov, H. Neubauer, J. N. Pham, and A. Rakin. Development of multiple-locus variable-number tandem-repeat analysis for *Yersinia enterocolitica* subsp. paleartica and its application to bioserogroup 4/O3 subtyping. *J Clin Microbiol.* 2007;45:2508-2515.

In: Molecular Typing Methods for TFM
Editors: S. Foley, R. Nayak, T. Johnson et al.

ISBN: 978-1-62100-643-5
© 2012 Nova Science Publishers, Inc.

Chapter 11

PCR-BASED MOLECULAR TYPING METHODS FOR TRACKING FOODBORNE MICROORGANISMS

Jing Han[1], Yang Wang[2], Zhangqi Shen[3], Bing Wang[3], Hailin Tang[4], Joseph Meehan[4], Congming Wu[2] and Jianzhong Shen[2]

[1] Division of Microbiology
National Center for Toxicological Research
US Food and Drug Administration
Jefferson, AR, US

[2] Department of Pharmacology and Toxicology
College of Veterinary Medicine
China Agricultural University
Beijing, Peoples Republic of China

[3] Department of Veterinary Microbiology and Preventative Medicine
College of Veterinary Medicine
Iowa State University
Ames, IA, US

[4] Z-Tech Corporation
An ICF International Company at the National
Center for Toxicological Research
US Food and Drug Administration
Jefferson, AR, US

ABSTRACT

Foodborne pathogens are responsible for a number of illnesses and deaths each year. Understanding how these microorganisms disseminate through the food chain is an important step in developing pathogen control strategies. PCR genotyping can be used to differentiate strains of similar bacteria based on the possession of virulence and antimicrobial genes. This can aid researchers in investigating population dynamics of clinical isolates and tracking multidrug isolates through the environment. This chapter introduces PCR genotyping, provides a general PCR protocol and discusses the use of PCR genotyping in food-borne pathogen research.

INTRODUCTION

Bacterial foodborne diseases present a growing health problem worldwide. In the United States, for example, it is estimated that there are about 3.6 million infections caused by bacterial foodborne pathogens every year [1]. These illnesses lead to approximately 35,816 hospitalizations and 865 deaths [1]. The significant impact of bacterial foodborne pathogens on public health makes the ability to determine the primary sources of bacterial contamination of foods very important. Typing methods that can discriminate outbreak strains from common serotypes are usually used for source tracking of bacterial contamination in the food.

Traditionally, phenotyping methods, including colony morphology, biochemical tests, serotyping, and antimicrobial susceptibility were used in the epidemiological studies of bacterial infections. However, these methods are not powerful enough for discriminating between closely related strains [2]. Over the last three decades, multiple molecular-based typing methods have been developed and used in epidemiological surveillance of bacterial infections, source tracking of bacterial contamination during foodborne illness outbreaks, and bacterial transmission in food production and processing systems. Pulsed-field gel electrophoresis (PFGE) has been one of the most common molecular typing techniques that has been widely used for genotyping bacterial foodborne pathogens and has been considered as a gold standard typing method due to its high reproducibility and discriminatory power to distinguish between non-clonal isolates. However, the process to carry out PFGE is labor-intensive and time-consuming, often taking 2 to 4 days to complete the procedure. Because strain identification and characterization are important in the epidemiological investigation, rapid discriminatory methods for molecular typing are desirable to manage or prevent foodborne disease outbreaks. Several efforts have been made to develop laboratory-based molecular typing methods that rapidly identify and classify bacterial species and strains. One class of attractive typing methods developed during the past few decades are the polymerase chain reaction (PCR)-based molecular tying methods. Compared to other molecular typing techniques, PCR-based methods are easier, faster, less expensive, and require minimal amounts of genomic DNA. In addition, the techniques can be performed with equipment available in many clinical laboratories.

In this chapter, the most commonly used PCR-based typing methods are explored in detail. These include repetitive element PCR (rep-PCR), amplified fragment length polymorphisms (AFLP) analysis, infrequent-restriction-site PCR (IRS-PCR), restriction fragment length polymorphism PCR (PCR-RFLP), and random amplified polymorphic DNA PCR (RAPD-PCR). For each of the methods reviewed, there will be an overview and description of the typing technique along with a discussion of its strengths and weaknesses and its application for subtyping of bacterial foodborne pathogens.

REPETITIVE ELEMENT PCR (REP-PCR)

Most bacteria contain a number of short repetitive DNA elements more or less randomly distributed throughout their genomes and the locations of these repetitive sequences may vary in different species/strains [3]. Based on these characteristics elements, rep-PCR typing methods were developed [4, 5]. When the location of two repetitive elements are close enough, PCR primers specific for these elements amplify the intervening regions of DNA and generate multiple amplicons with different sizes [5]. The amplicons are then separated by electrophoresis and the subsequent species (sometimes strain)-specific banding patterns are analyzed using commercially available software programs [6].

There are three families of dispersed repetitive sequences present in the bacterial genomes of many foodborne pathogens: enterobacterial repetitive intergenic consensus (ERIC) sequences, repetitive extragenic palindromic (REP) sequences and BOX A1R elements. ERIC sequences, which were found in *Escherichia coli*, *Salmonella enterica* and other Enterobacteriaceae, are highly conserved 124 to 127-bp motifs located in the intergenic regions [5, 7, 8]. REP elements are approximately 38-bp short sequences and contain conserved regions of palindromic DNA which serve as good targets for PCR primers [4, 9]. BOX element sequences are 154-bp long mosaic repetitive sequences located within intergenic regions. Due to dyad symmetry in these BOX repeats, a single PCR primer can be used to distinguish bacterial species [10].

Traditionally rep-PCR includes four steps: (1) template preparation; (2) rep-PCR amplification; (3) fragments detection; and (4) data analysis. Techniques for the isolation of genomic DNA (such as the boiling method, phenol-chloroform extraction method and commercial genomic extraction kits) are widely available and can be easily adapted for any foodborne microorganisms of choice. The most convenient way to prepare the PCR templates is by suspending bacterial cells in water or buffer and then boiling for approximately 10 minutes. This process lyses the cells and releases the DNA template. However, to get the most reliable and reproducible result, the use of a standardized amount of purified genomic DNA as template is often encouraged in rep-PCR. A number of representative primers used for rep-PCR of foodborne pathogens are listed in Table 1. The PCR reaction conditions vary with different bacterial species. Usually, the PCR performed with REP-primers is initiated by incubating the reaction mixture at 95°C for 2 minutes, followed by 35 cycles consisting of 90°C for 30 seconds, annealing for 1 minute (variable temperature), and extension at 65°C for 8 minutes. The reaction is terminated with a final 16 minute extension step at 65°C. PCR with ERIC-primers is typically performed with one initial cycle at 94°C for 4 minutes, 35 cycles of denaturation at 94°C for 1 minute, annealing at 52°C for 1 minute, and extension at 65°C for 8 minutes, followed by a single final extension step at 65°C for 15 minutes. For PCR with the BOX A1R primer, the reaction is initiated by incubating the reaction mixture at 95°C for 2 minutes, followed by 30 cycles consisting of 94°C for 3 seconds, 92°C for 30 seconds, 50°C for 1 minute, and 65°C for 8 minutes. After cycling, the reaction is terminated with a final extension step at 65°C for 8 minutes.

Table 1. Common used primers for Rep-PCR

PCR type	Primers	References
REP-PCR	REP-1 (5'-IIIGCGCCGICATCAGGC-3')	[5]
	REP-2 (5'- ACGTCTTATCAGGCCTAC -3')	
ERIC-PCR	ERIC-1 (5'-ATGTAAGCTCCTGGGGATTCAC-3')	[5]
	ERIC-2 (5'-AAGTAAGTGACTGGGGTGAGCG- 3')	
BOXAIR-PCR	5'- CTACGGCAAGGCGACGCTGACG -3'.	[133]

In each of the rep-PCR procedures, the amplicons generated are separated by electrophoresis. The images are visualized and captured using a high resolution digital charge-coupled device camera. The patterns can be analyzed using commercial software package, such as BioNumerics (Applied Maths, Sint-Martens-Latem, Belgium). To compare relatedness among isolates a dendrogram can be constructed using hierarchical cluster analysis methods such as the unweighted pair group method with arithmetic averages (UPGMA) analysis and Pearson product–moment correlation coefficient (see Chapter 14). Isolates with similar patterns (i.e. those typically more closely related) will cluster together. The identification of common profiles among isolates along the food production continuum can provide insights into whether a particular product/location is likely the source of bacterial contamination.

Overall, rep-PCR is a simple and rapid method for pathogen characterization. The results can be obtained in a relatively short amount of time (hours versus days for some other methods) with relatively high discrimination [11, 12]. However, rep-PCR has some weaknesses. In some instances, the methods have relatively low reproducibility. Like other PCR-based typing methods, variations in PCR reaction conditions (PCR templates and reagents) and the methods used to separate the amplicons will greatly impact the reproducibility [12, 13]. Additionally, rep-PCR methods may not be suitable for strains without an adequate number of repetitive sequences, because for the typing to work efficiently there needs to be ample repetitive elements to generate sufficient amplicons for discrimination [12]. In addition, these methods are not able to distinguish strains with genomic differences located outside of the amplified regions. Therefore, for some strains multiple primers may be required to increase the discrimination [14].

Several modifications have been investigated to increase the accuracy, discrimination and reproducibility of rep-PCR. These methods can be adapted to run using an automated DNA sequencer, which can improve the separation profiles and increase the reproducibility of the results [15]. Additionally, a horizontal, fluorophore enhanced rep-PCR (HFERP) technique has been developed that uses conventional horizontal agarose gel electrophoresis separation following amplification of the PCR product with fluorescently labeled primers. With the HFERP technique, the fluorescent amplicons are separated along with internal size standards labeled with a separate fluorophore. This approach provides for an in-lane standard for each reaction mixture, which increases the resolution and aids in cross sample normalization thereby improving the accuracy of the technique over standard gel electrophoresis [16]. Also, a commercial automated rep-PCR kit, known as the DiversiLab system (bioMérieux, North Carolina, USA), has recently been made available to provide a reliable PCR-based typing system for clinical laboratories. The steps of DiversiLab system are similar to manual rep-PCR and the similarities and differences between these two methods were well summarized by Healy et al. [17]. The DiversiLab software package allows database building, interlaboratory comparisons, and data retrieval.

REP-PCR has been widely used for typing a number of foodborne bacterial strains, including *E. coli* [18, 19], *Salmonella* [20-22], *Listeria monocytogenes* [23], *Campylobacter* [24], *Staphylococcus aureus* [25, 26], *Vibrio* [27], *Bacillus cereus* [28], *Clostridium* [29], *Shigella* [30], and *Yersinia enterocolitica* [31]. Hahm et al. [19] used rep-PCR (REP-PCR and Box A1R PCR) along with four other DNA fingerprinting methods to characterize 54 *E.coli* isolates from food, animal feces, and clinical samples. Compared to the other methods used in this study, rep-PCR analysis using either primer set tested was the easiest and quickest method that could be performed for the discrimination of *E. coli* O157:H7 and strains from other serotypes [19]. Compared to the RAPD-PCR typing method, rep-PCR showed greater discriminatory power in differentiating closely related strains of *Salmonella* and produced more complex banding patterns [32]. Johnson et al. [21] used rep-PCR to type the isolates from a hospital cafeteria-associated outbreak of gastroenteritis due to *Salmonella* Infantis and found that rep-PCR was able to reproducibly resolve isolates to the serotype level with ERIC-PCR, BOXA1R-PCR and a composite of both methods. Additionally, these methods aided in typing certain strains that had ambiguous, incomplete, or incorrect serotypes. Overall, the methods were limited at discriminating isolates at the subserotype level and thus are unlikely to supersede PFGE for genotyping *Salmonella* [21]. Recently, Ben-Darif *et al.* [33] showed that DiversiLab rep-PCR system had greater discriminatory power than MLST typing for *Salmonella* indicating that DiversiLab rep-PCR system may provide a rapid (less than 4 hours) and standardized method for subtyping isolates of *S. enterica*. Compared to the application of rep-PCR in the molecular typing of *Salmonella*, few studies have used rep-PCR for typing *Campylobacter* strains to date. Hiett et al. [34] compared rep-PCR typing technique with the established genotyping method of *flaA* short variable region (SVR) DNA sequence analysis for the differentiation of *Campylobacter* spp. The results from this study showed that rep-PCR was able to generate highly reproducible and informative fingerprints for all *Campylobacter* isolates examined in this study and segregate these isolates into similar groups to that of *flaA* SVR analysis. These findings indicated that rep-PCR analysis may be a useful and effective tool for accurate differentiation and epidemiological analyses of *Campylobacter* spp.. A study by Wilson et al. showed that rep-PCR, including REP-PCR, ERIC-PCR and BOX-PCR, has greater discriminatory power than PFGE and MLST when these methods were evaluated as typing methods for *C. jejuni* isolates [35]. A recent study by Behringer et al. showed that rep-PCR was better for the typing of *C. jejuni* than *C. coli*, and demonstrated a lower discriminatory power for *C. coli* isolates compared to PFGE and MLST [13]. Rep-PCR can also be used to identify *Listeria* species and to distinguish serotypes of *L. monocytogenes* [23, 36]. Chou and Wang used PFGE and REP-PCR to investigate the genetic relationship between *L. monocytogenes* isolates from catfish, non-catfish seafood and humans [37]. Results from their study suggested that the Rep-PCR possesses a similar discriminatory power as the PFGE, therefore it represents a rapid and less expensive alternative method for subtyping *L. monocytogenes*.

AMPLIFIED FRAGMENT LENGTH POLYMORPHISMS (AFLP)

AFLP was first described in the early 1990's by Vos et al [38]. The technique combines the beneficial traits of restriction digestion analysis and PCR amplification to detect polymorphisms in different genomic regions for determining the relatedness of bacterial strains. Because this technique relies not only on PCR, but also restriction digestion, information on AFLP is also discussed in chapter 8, which focuses on restriction digestion based methods.

There are five main steps: (1) genomic DNA isolation; (2) restriction digestion of purified DNA; (3) adapter ligation; (4) selective amplification; and (5) gel electrophoresis and pattern analysis. AFLP analysis starts with isolation and purification of genomic DNA from bacteria isolates. The purified genomic DNA is then digested with one or more restriction enzymes. The variability in restriction enzyme recognition sites within the bacterial genome determines the discriminatory power of AFLP. Methods using one or two restriction endonucleases have been widely described for foodborne microorganisms (Table 2) [39]. When two enzymes are used in concert, one of the enzymes is typically using a rare cutting enzyme (such as *Eco*RI, 5′-G$^{\blacktriangledown}$AATT$_{\blacktriangle}$C-3′, *Pst*I, 5′-C$_{\blacktriangle}$TGCA$^{\blacktriangledown}$G-3′, where $^{\blacktriangledown}$ is the cut position within the top strand and $_{\blacktriangle}$ in the bottom stand of the recognition site) and the other as a frequent cutting enzyme (for example *Mse*I, 5′-T$^{\blacktriangledown}$TA$_{\blacktriangle}$A-3′). The enzyme *Hind*III (5′-A$^{\blacktriangledown}$AGCT$_{\blacktriangle}$T-3′) has shown to generate adequate number of suitably sized restriction fragments in bacteria with genomic DNA of G+C ratio 40-50 % [40]. The *Hind*III single-enzyme-AFLP is considered to be an efficient, rapid, and easily performed method [41]. Following enzyme digestion, short double-stranded adapter sequences, with 5′ overhangs that are complementary to the 5′ overhangs generated by restriction digestion are generated. These short adapters are ligated to the free ends of the restriction fragments to generate unique DNA templates for PCR amplification. All adaptors contain their specific DNA sequences which are typically between 18 and 22 base pairs in length upstream of their 5′ overhangs. In designing the adapters, the first double stranded base pair and last base of the restriction enzyme is altered to remove the original restriction site to avoid subsequent re-ligation of the restriction fragments. For example, the *Eco*RI adaptor contains a 3′-G, rather than containing a 3′-C after the 5′-AATT-3′ overhang, which destroys the *Eco*RI recognition site once ligated [42]. Similar approaches are also applied when adapters are designed for the *Mse*I and *Hind*III restriction fragments.

Generally, the AFLP PCR primers have two components: a core sequence that anneals with part of the adaptor and a restriction enzyme-specific sequence that anneals with the altered restriction enzyme recognition site sequence [38]. To reduce the number of fragments amplified to a manageable number, a selective nucleotide extension is added to the 3′ end of the primers, which interacts with unknown nucleotides just inside the adapter fragment [38, 43]. The PCR amplification is carried out under highly stringent conditions, so that the amplification can occur only if the primers and their selective nucleotide extension are complementary to bases in the target sequences. Variation in the number of selective bases (one nucleotide commonly) affects the resulting complexity of the patterns produced. In other words, the number of amplicons is reduced by about a factor of four for each additional nucleotide added [39, 43]. Examples of different enzyme-AFLP primers with one selective nucleotide are showed in Table 2. When two enzymes (e.g. *Eco*RI and *Mse*I) are used in concert, two different AFLP primers are used, one complementary to the *EcoRI* terminus and the other complementary to the *MseI* terminus, to selectively amplify a smaller number of genomic DNA fragments. The PCR reactions can simultaneously amplify a wide range of DNA fragment sizes based on the length of the original *EcoRI-MseI* or *Hind*III DNA fragments ligated to the respective adaptors.

High-resolution electrophoresis is commonly used to separate the DNA fragments based on their size to determine the genotypes of foodborne microorganisms. Following electrophoresis, the DNA banding patterns are analyzed to determine the DNA fingerprint associated with a given sample. Depending on the complexity of the banding patterns, band sizes can be determined manually or by automated approaches. For the molecular typing of foodborne pathogens, the reaction products are often separated using a DNA sequencing system and the raw data are collected with fragment analysis software such as GeneScan (PE Applied Biosystem, Boston, MA), and profiles are subsequently analyzed by BioNumerics or other similar commercial software [44, 45]. To facilitate higher throughput analysis, one of the two PCR primers can be fluorescently labeled (usually the rare cutter enzyme primer, e.g. *EcoRI*), which leads to the production of labeled PCR products that allows the separation and detection of the fragments with an automated DNA sequencer [46]. An additional benefit of this approach is that an internal size standard can be included with each sample, which allows increased accuracy in comparing elution profiles of strains and making phylogenetic comparisons [43].

One of the advantages of AFLP analysis is the ability to use a universal protocol in combination with different restriction endonucleases to simultaneously amplify multiple genomic DNA fragments with high discrimination, reliability, specificity and reproducibility [14, 47]. A basic protocol is described in Chapter 8 that can be adapted to different foodborne pathogens using the enzymes, adapters and primers described in Table 2 of this chapter. Additionally, since the PCR primers are directed at the adaptors, no prior knowledge of the organism's DNA sequence is required for amplification. The fragments generated usually represent a wide range of different locations throughout the bacterial genome, providing a relatively good coverage of the genome to identify differences [14]. In addition, the use of an automated DNA sequencer allows a large number of isolates to be screened fairly rapidly, which makes AFLP an attractive typing technique [14, 48]. However, the AFLP also has some limitations. First, the PCR products of AFLP are better processed with an automated DNA sequencer for high throughput analysis, which means the laboratories without access to a sequencer would have a more difficult time to carry out AFLP efficiently [43, 46]. Second, the reproducibility of AFLP analysis is platform dependent, which could potentially limits some inter-laboratory data comparison when the PCR products are separated on different sequencing platforms [49]. Additionally, to detect differences among strains, only those strains with sequence variability in the restriction sites or within the regions of DNA amplified from the adaptors can generate PCR products with distinct sizes needed, to differentiate the strains [47].

Table 2. Restriction enzymes, adaptors and primers used in AFLP analysis for tracking foodborne microorganisms

Foodborne Bacteria	Restriction Enzymes	Adapters	Primers (5'→3')[A]	References
E. coli	*EcoR* I/*Mse* I	*EcoR* I 5'-CTCGTAGACTGCGTACC CTGACGCATGGTTAA-5' *Mse* I 5'-GACGATGAGTCCTGAG TACTCAGGACTCAT-5'	*EcoR* I GACTGCGTACCAATTCN[B] *Mse* I GATGAGTCCTGAGTAA	[42]
	Pst I/*Mse* I	*Pst* I 5'-CTCGTAGACTGCGTACATGCA' CATC T G ACGCATGT-5' *Mse* I 5'-GACGATGAGTCCTGAG TACTCAGGACTCAT-5'	*Pst* I GACTGCGTACATGCAN *Mse* I GATGAGTCCTGAGTAA	
Salmonella	*EcoR* I/*Mse* I	*EcoR* I 5'-CTCGTAGACTGCGTACC CATCTGACGCATGGTTAA-5' *Mse* I 5'-GACGATGAGTCCTGAG TACTCAGGACTCAT-5'	*EcoR* I GACTGCGTACCAATTC *Mse* I GATGAGTCCTGAGTAAC	[38, 50]
Shigella	*EcoR* I/ *Mse* I	Adapters from Microbial Fingerprinting Kit (Applied Biosystems, Foster City, CA)	From Microbial Fingerprinting Kit (Applied Biosystems, Foster City, CA)	[55]
Yersinia	*Bam* HI/ *Bsp* DI	*BamH* I 5'-GATCGACAGTGTACTCTAGTC *BspD* I CTGTCACATGAGATCAGGC-5'	*BamH* I GAGTACACTGTCGATCC *BspD* I GTGTACTCTAGTCCGAT	[56]
Campylobacter	*Hind* III/ *Hha* I	Adapters from Microbial Fingerprinting Kit (Applied Biosystems, Foster City, CA)	*Hind* III GACTGCGTACCAGCTTA *Hha* I GATGAGTCCTGATCGCA	[54]
	Hind III	*Hind* III 5'-AGCTCTGTCGCATACCGTGAG GACAGCGTATGGCA-5'	*Hind* III GGTATGGCGACAGAGCTTG	[53]
Bacillus cereus	*Hind* III	*Hind* III 5'-AGCTCTGTCGCATACCGTGAG GACAGCGTATGGCA-5'	*Hind* III GGTATGGCGACAGAGCTTN	[57]

[A] The nucleotide in box represents the component of selective extension (EXT)
[B] N can be any of four nucleotides.

AFLP can be useful in assessing genetic variation within a bacterial species or among closely related bacterial species [43]. AFLP has been successfully used to subtype *E. coli* O157:H7 and *Salmonella* and showed similar discriminatory ability as PFGE [42, 46, 50, 51]. Duim et al. successfully used AFLP for the typing of epidemiologically related and unrelated *C. jejuni* strains [52]. Gonzalez et al. found AFLP was able to differentiate minimal variations in genomes of *Campylobacter* and *Arcobacter* isolated from chicken and water, which makes AFLP a valuable tool for the identification of these isolates [53]. Overall, AFLP has been shown to be a reliable method that allows the identification of *Campylobacter* strains at the species and subspecies levels and a suitable tool for the determination of strain relationships at the taxonomic and epidemiological levels [41, 52-54]. Sirisriro et al. [55] used AFLP to determine the genetic relatedness of 230 isolates of *Shigella flexneri* and *S. sonnei* strains. The results from their study showed that AFLP was capable of grouping *S. flexneri* and *S. sonnei* strains into separate clusters according to their serotypes, and identify isolates untypeable by other methods. These findings indicate that AFLP can be used for genetic fingerprinting of *Shigella* strains and aid in the identification of variant untypeable isolates, as well as serve as a useful epidemiological tool to evaluate the circulation and distribution of *Shigella* in different settings [55]. The value of AFLP for distinguishing between strains of *Yersinia* has been demonstrated when it was used to investigate 70 *Y. enterocolitica* strains isolated from humans, pigs, sheep, and cattle in the United Kingdom [56]. AFLP analysis not only divided the isolates into distinct clusters according to their biotype, but also allowed for the differentiation of strains within the serotype-related subclusters. The ability of AFLP to differentiate *Y. enterocolitica* augmented data obtained by serotyping and biotyping, thereby demonstrating the high discriminatory power of this technique for *Y. enterocolitica*. When applied to the characterization of *Bacillus cereus*, AFLP was also found to be highly reproducible and be able to discriminate three subtypes within serotype H1 [5]).

INFREQUENT-RESTRICTION-SITE PCR (IRS-PCR)

Infrequent-Restriction-Site PCR (IRS-PCR) is a DNA fingerprinting technique based on selective amplification of DNA sequences located between a restriction site for a frequent cutting enzyme and a restriction site for an infrequently cutting enzyme. It is similar to AFLP in that the method utilizes a combination of restriction digest analysis and PCR amplification. Unlike AFLP, IRS-PCR uses two sets of adapters [14, 58].

The procedure of IRS-PCR contains five main steps: (1) genomic DNA isolation; (2) restriction digestions of purified DNA; (3) adapter ligation; (4) selective amplification; and (5) gel electrophoresis and pattern analysis. To carry out IRS-PCR, purified bacterial genomic DNA is digested with a combination of an infrequent and a frequent cutting restriction enzyme to generate a large number of fragments with cohesive ends [14, 58]. Following the digestion, two sets of double-stranded adapters containing sequences complementary to the cohesive ends of the restriction fragments are ligated to the corresponding free ends of the restriction fragments. Each double stranded adaptor consists of a long oligonucleotide (approximately 20 base pairs) and a shorter oligonucleotide (7 base pairs) that is complementary to a portion of the long oligonucleotide [59]. The inclusion of the short oligonucleotide allows efficient ligation of the adaptors to the restriction fragments at low temperatures (usually at 16°C) [58, 60].

After ligation, the selective amplification is carried out by PCR using the restriction fragments ligated to adapters as template. The primers used in the selective amplification are special, in that one of the primers (termed FC) is identical to the long oligonucleotide adapter ligated to the restriction site of the frequent cutter. The short adapter oligonucleotides are not ligated to the restriction fragments due to lack of phosphorylation and dissociates from the rest of the strand as temperatures increases during denaturation and frees the annealing site for primer binding during the first round of PCR amplification [58]. The other primer (termed IC) is designed complementary to the adapter at the restriction site of an infrequent cutter, and it anneals to the long oligonucleotide of this adaptor and primes the extension of the initial daughter strand that extends the sequence until the strand reaches the other end of this restriction fragment. If the terminal end of this restriction fragment is the restriction site of a frequent cutter, the extension generates the binding site for the FC primer in the daughter strand. This binding facilitates the specific amplification of the intervening sequence between the infrequent and frequent restriction sites during the subsequent rounds of amplification [14, 58]. Since the elongation from the infrequent restriction site is required for the primer binding at the frequent restriction site, fragments generated by restriction with the frequent cutter on both sites (which constitute the majority of fragments generated) are not amplified [58, 61]. Likewise the fragments with the infrequent cutter's restriction site on both sites do not amplify, thus only the fragments generated by cutting with both enzymes are amplified and analyzed [61].

After PCR amplification, the PCR products are separated and visualized by gel electrophoresis. The band patterns are compared to assess genetic relatedness of bacterial strains. Like with AFLP, the primers used in IRS-PCR can be labeled with fluorescent dye to generate DNA fragment patterns that are highly resolved and accurately sized with internally labeled DNA fragment size standards [61]. The amplification scheme of IRS-PCR greatly reduces the number of amplicons generated and makes the analysis simpler [59, 60]. An additional 3' nucleotide can be added to the primer complementary to the adapter at the infrequent cutter's restriction site to increase the selectivity and specificity and to facilitate the production of four sets of electrophoretic patterns [58]. In addition, a set of different patterns can be adjusted by use of different enzymes. Like other DNA restriction based methods, some enzymes may provide more or less discriminating patterns. An appropriate set of enzymes can be selected based on known characteristics of the bacterial genome to provide more discriminating patterns [58].

IRS-PCR has several advantages over other PCR-related genotyping methods. First, only limited information about the target DNA is needed for designing the primers used in the PCR reactions, because the primers are specific to the ligated adapter sequences [58]. Second, there is little concern for the integrity of genomic DNA template due to the small size of the target fragments (usually less than 2 kb); therefore, genomic DNA can be extracted from the organisms in a variety of ways [58, 61]. Several studies have shown that similar results were observed when using purified DNA or crude bacterial lysate as templates [62, 63]. In addition, the small-molecular sizes of fragments amplified by IRS-PCR facilitates the separation by conventional agarose gel electrophoresis within short time [58, 60]. Third, the technique used in IRS-PCR is highly adaptable. Identical digestion enzymes, adaptors, primers, and PCR conditions can be used for several bacterial species with acceptable reproducibility [59, 61, 64]. Forth, IRS-PCR has a high level of reproducibility compared to other PCR-based molecular typing methods [59, 62, 63, 65]. The only drawback of IRS-PCR is that if the genetic differences are not within the amplified DNA restriction fragments or the differences are not significant enough to generate variably sized amplicons, then this method might lack the ability to identify distinct strains [14].

Since it was developed by Mazurek et al. [58], IRS-PCR has been shown to be a potentially powerful epidemiologic tool for the molecular characterization of several bacterial species [59-63, 65-70]. However, this technique has only been used in a few foodborne pathogens so far [59, 63, 65]. Garaizar et al. [59] explored the possibilities of establishing a library-based computerized typing system for *Salmonella* serovar Enteritidis on the basis of PFGE and PCR-based fingerprinting techniques including IRS-PCR. A collection of nine strains belonging to different *Salmonella* serovars and two combinations of restriction enzymes (*Xba*I-*Hha*I and *Xba*I-*Taq*I) were used to optimize the IRS-PCR method. More bands [7-16] were obtained with the enzyme combination of *Xba*I and *Hha*I than obtained with the enzyme combination of *Xba*I and *Taq*I [3-8]. Then a total of 36 strains of *Salmonella* serovar Enteritidis were analyzed by IRS-PCR with the restriction enzymes combination of *Xba*I and *Hha*I. They found that the typeability IRS-PCR reached 100%. However, the discrimination between strains within serovar Enteritidis with these enzymes yielded relatively low values (DI = 0.52). Franciosa et al [63] used IRS-PCR along with PCR-ribotyping and arbitrarily primed PCR (AP-PCR) to characterize 29 unrelated *L. monocytogenes* isolates of food origin and 32 *L. monocytogenes* outbreak strains from human cases to compare the relatedness of isolates from different types of foods and human cases in outbreaks. When PCR-ribotyping, AP-PCR and IRS-PCR were all used to evaluate the *L. monocytogenes* food isolates, IRS-PCR technique showed highest discriminatory ability (DI = 0.919) followed by PCR-ribotyping (DI = 0.714) and AP-PCR (DI = 0.690). IRS-PCR was also more capable of distinguishing strains from the invasive listeriosis outbreak than PCR-ribotyping and AP-PCR. When the related strains were compared to unrelated ones, only IRS-PCR succeeded in clearly discriminating the strains related to noninvasive listeriosis from all of the other strains included in the study.

Overall, IRS-PCR is a rapid, versatile and reproducible method that can be easily established in a general molecular laboratory for a wide array of organisms [58, 62]. The results obtained by IRS-PCR are concordant with the results observed from the PFGE typing method [62, 66]. However, IRS-PCR is much simper and less time-consuming compared to PFGE. All these advantages of IRS-PCR indicate that it may serve as an efficient alternative epidemiologic tool to PFGE in epidemiological investigations of bacterial foodborne pathogens

RESTRICTION FRAGMENT LENGTH POLYMORPHISM-PCR (RFLP-PCR)

Restriction Fragment Length Polymorphism (RFLP) refers to differences between two or more samples of DNA following digestion by restriction enzymes and subsequent comparison of the resultant following separation (see chapter 8). However, the DNA fingerprints are typically difficult to interpret when a frequent cutting restriction enzyme is used. Normally, the fragments of at least 100 bases should be used in the comparison between the bacterial isolates [71]. Therefore, a variation of the traditional RFLP method, RFLP-PCR, was developed to overcome the shortcomings of RFLP analysis for subtyping of foodborne microorganisms. In RFLP-PCR, the specific DNA sequences of interest are amplified and the PCR amplified products are digested to generate a DNA banding pattern [72].

To carry out the RFLP-PCR, four steps are needed: (1) genomic DNA isolation; (2) PCR amplification of specific sequences in the bacteria; (3) restriction digestion of amplicons; and (4) DNA banding pattern analysis. Genomic DNA can be isolated from the bacteria using any of the methods available (boiling method, phenol-chloroform extraction method, commercial genomic extraction kit, etc.). After DNA isolation, the PCR is performed using primers for specific sequences of interest. In order to acquire adequate discrimination, the primers are usually designed to anneal to conserved regions of DNA that flank more variable sequences, which allows for differences in the digestion of the amplicons [73]. Different genes and fragments are typically selected in different bacteria for RFLP-PCR. In *Campylobacter*, the *flaA* gene, which contains both highly conserved and variable regions, is the most common DNA sequence used in RFLP-PCR for subtyping of *Campylobacter* [72, 74-76]. Alternatively, a *Campylobacter* species identification scheme using the 23S rRNA gene (23S PCR-RFLP) has been described and shown to be able to identify these species [41, 77]. The phase 1 (*fliC*) and phase 2 (*fljB*) *Salmonella* flagella genes have been analyzed by RFLP-PCR to aid in the identification of different *Salmonella* serotypes [78]. Additionally, genes encoding two specific proteins in *Staphylococcus aureus*, coagulase (*coa*) and the X region of the protein A gene (*spa*), both contain highly polymorphic repeat units and have been used in RFLP-PCR for the molecular epidemiological analyses of *S. aureus* [79, 80].

Following PCR amplification, the DNA fragments are digested with restriction enzymes to generate a DNA banding profile. Typically, one to two restriction enzymes are used in the RFLP analysis. Because the amplicons contain variable sequences, different fingerprint patterns from bacteria of different subtypes will be displayed following separation on an agarose gel. The pattern analysis can be performed manually by observing the bands on the agarose gel. Alternatively, computer-assisted analysis using BioNumerics, GelCompar (Applied Maths) or Taxotron package (Taxolab software; Institut Pasteur) can be performed to identify the RFLP-PCR profiles [75, 81].

Like other PCR-based typing methods, the RFLP-PCR is a simple and rapid method. The limited number of restriction fragments resulting from restriction enzyme digestion of the PCR amplicons can be separated by conventional agarose gel electrophoresis within short time. However, RFLP-PCR is usually less discriminatory compared to other typing methods since only one single locus is amplified and analyzed [75].

PCR-RFLP has been frequently used for typing a variety of foodborne microorganisms. Several studies used *flaA* gene as the target sequence of RFLP-PCR for *Campylobacter* subtyping [72, 74-76]. In a study by Nielsen et al. [75], RFLP of the flagellin gene (*fla*-RFLP), along with Penner heat-stable serotyping, automated ribotyping (RiboPrinting), random amplified polymorphic DNA typing (RAPD), pulsed-field gel electrophoresis (PFGE), and denaturing gradient gel electrophoresis of *flaA* (*fla*-DGGE), were used to subtype *C. jejuni* isolates from humans, poultry, and cattle. The data from their study showed that *fla*-RFLP was able to type all the isolates in that study and the discriminatory ability of *fla*-RFLP was better than ribotyping and serotyping, but less than PFGE and RAPD [75]. Nayak et al. [72], evaluated the genetic diversity of multidrug resistant *C. jejuni* and *C. coli* isolated from 18 turkey houses by using the *flaA*-RFLP and found that the *flaA*-RFLP had similar discriminatory ability as PFGE, while it was more suitable in discriminating *C. coli* than PFGE. Overall, *flaA*-RFLP method worked well in subtyping *Campylobacter* isolates and was more discriminatory, faster and more cost effective than phenotypic tests. Another PCR-RFLP, 23S PCR-RFLP, was developed to identify and analyze *Campylobacter* species and showed to be a reliable typing method for *Campylobacter* isolates [41, 77]. When combined with single-enzyme AFLP method, 23S PCR-RFLP can be used to determine taxonomic and epidemiological relationships among thermophilic *Campylobacter* isolates [41].

Several studies reported the successful application of *fliC* and *fljB* in the RFLP-PCR to distinguish *Salmonella* serovars [78, 82, 83]. Hong et al. [83], applied restriction fragment patterns of *fliC* and *fljB* (the amplicons were digested with *Sau3A* and *HhaI*) for serotyping of 112 *Salmonella* isolates obtained from poultry and poultry production environment. The results from their study showed that 90% of the *Salmonella* serotypes could be identified by this double restriction enzyme RFLP analysis of *fliC* and *fljB* genes and there was a high concordance between the RFLP-PCR flagellar typing scheme and conventional serotyping. Kwon et al. [78] demonstrated that *fliC* RFLP-PCR using *Hinp*1I enzyme can be successfully applied to differentiate *Salmonella* biotype Gallinarum from biotype Pullorum. Recently, Paiva et al. [82] demonstrated that enzymatic restriction of the amplified *fliC* gene using *Hinp*1I enzyme can differentiate *S.* Gallinarum and *S.* Pullorum isolates in Brazil. However, others have found that RFLP-PCR analysis of the *fliC* gene alone was not able to distinguish between *Salmonella* serovars [81].

Additionally, Chiou et al. [79] used PFGE and coagulase gene restriction profile (CRP) to analyze 71 *S. aureus* isolates recovered from nine foodborne disease outbreaks in central Taiwan between 1995 and 1997. Results from their study showed that CRP analysis exhibits the same discriminatory power as PFGE for *Staphylococcal* enterotoxins A-E -producing (SEA-E) isolates, but it is much less discriminatory than PFGE in the case of non-SEA-E-producing isolates. However, compared to PFGE, CRP analysis is fast, easy to perform and has high levels of specimen typeability and reproducibility. Recently, a study by Soltan-Dallal et al. [80] used PCR-RFLP that targets the X region of the protein A gene (*spa*) (*spa*-RFLP) to type 93 *S. aureus* isolated from food samples and showed that *spa*-RFLP was an optimal method for epidemiological investigations of *S. aureus*.

RANDOM AMPLIFICATION OF POLYMORPHIC DNA PCR (RAPD-PCR)

RAPD-PCR is a PCR-based method that relies on the amplifications of random segments to reveal polymorphisms throughout the bacterial genome [12]. Unlike traditional PCR, which requires sequence information from the relevant genes, the primers for RAPD-PCR have arbitrary DNA sequences and the specific DNA sequence information of the target to be amplified is unknown [84].

In RAPD-PCR, a single primer with an arbitrarily sequence is able to anneal and prime at multiple locations randomly distributed throughout the genome. Amplification occurs under low stringency conditions to produce a spectrum of amplified products characteristic of the template DNA. Only four major steps are needed in RAPD-PCR: (1) primers design; (2) DNA template preparation; (3) PCR amplification; and (4) gel electrophoresis and pattern analysis. Template DNA is extracted from bacteria using by boiling, kit or other method and the PCR reactions are carried out under low stringency conditions (low annealing temperature), which allows primers to anneal without a perfect match [12, 43]. The primers used for RAPD-PCR are typically 6-10 base pairs in length [84]. These short primers are able to anneal to many sites throughout the target DNA, generating genomic fingerprints [85]. When two primers anneal to the template DNA within a reasonable distance from one another (usually within 1-2 kb) in the proper orientation, the intervening portion is amplified [14, 85]. Bacterial genomic DNA with different sequences will have primers annealing in different places, thereby producing different band patterns [85]. After the PCR reactions are completed, the amplification products containing variably sized amplicons are resolved by agarose gel electrophoresis and the subsequent band patterns are compared to assess genetic relatedness of bacterial strains [43, 84, 86].

As PCR-based genotyping methods, RAPD-PCR is fast, sensitive, and inexpensive. Unlike some other PCR-based typing methods, the specific DNA sequence information of the target being amplified is not required for RAPD-PCR since the primers use arbitrary DNA sequences. However, since PCR is carried out initially under low stringency conditions, minor differences in the PCR amplification (e.g. annealing temperatures, $MgCl_2$ concentration, *Taq* polymerase concentration, DNA template concentration, thermal cyclers) can noticeably alter the banding patterns obtained [43, 87]. Thus, the reproducibility of this method remains a challenge, which makes interpretation and comparison of DNA patterns difficult [87]. Therefore, a series of challenging steps of primer identification and appropriate concentrations of the primers, DNA template, Mg^{2+} ion are required for consistent fingerprint patterns and high discriminatory power when using this method [88, 89].

RAPD-PCR has been used for characterizing of many foodborne pathogens from various sources. RAPD-PCR has been employed to compare the genotypes of *C. jejuni* and *C. coli* isolates of both animal and human origin, which indicated the high discriminatory power of RAPD-PCR [90-93]. RAPD-PCR was successfully applied for source tracking *Campylobacter* outbreaks from contaminated food products [75, 94]. RAPD-PCR also demonstrated its usefulness in delineating horizontal transmission of *Campylobacter* in poultry production and processing plants [95-98]. This method was reproducibly able to recognize the same strain analyzed over time [91, 99] and had similar discriminatory ability to PFGE, but higher than PCR-RFLP, to identify variability among *Campylobacter* strains [75, 100, 101]. Therefore, this method can be used as a tool to study the epidemiology of *Campylobacter* spp. infection.

RAPD-PCR was used to characterize *Salmonella* isolates from human, food sources and environments [102-106]. RAPD-PCR successfully separated clusters from human and non-human *Salmonella* isolates [103] and showed evidence of *Salmonella* transmission from animals to humans [104]. RAPD-PCR has very often been used to identify subgroups of *Salmonella* isolates within a specific serotype [88, 89, 104, 106-109], but in general appears to be less discriminatory compared to ribotyping and PFGE [107, 108, 110, 111]. In another study, RAPD-PCR was useful to identify unique and common subtypes of *Salmonella* with a specific source and location [105].

RAPD-PCR has been used to type *L. monocytogenes* isolates from clinical, food products, food processing environment and veterinary origins and identify sources in food poisoning outbreaks [112-116]. A study by Cao et al. [117] showed that RAPD-PCR analysis was able to indicate the contamination routes of *L. monocytogenes* in seafood processing plants. However, there was lack of solid evidence of the genetic relationship among the isolates of clinical and food source in some studies [118]. RAPD-PCR could differentiate *L. monocytogenes* isolates of the same serotype, *Sau*3A RFLP-PCR (SAU-PCR) type and multilocus enzyme electrophoretic type [113, 119]. In addition, RAPD-PCR was capable of verifying the persistence of closely related *L.monocytogenes* isolates over several months [115, 118].

RAPD-PCR was used to differentiate different types of *E. coli*, such as EHEC, VTEC, STEC and ETEC [120-124] and delineate transmission pathways of *E. coli* from food products and animal origins to humans [125-128]. In addition, RAPD-PCR was able to distinguish *E. coli* isolates from different animal origins [122, 129]. This method also revealed a diverse genetic distribution of the STEC stains from different sources within farms [130]. However, RAPD-PCR might be less discriminatory for differentiating verocytotoxin-producing *E. coli* (VTEC) than PFGE [120, 121].

RAPD-PCR also facilitated the study of the epidemiological investigation of *S. aureus,* such as an indication of outbreak sources [131] and the assessment of spreading of *S. aureus* along the food production lines [132].

CONCLUSIONS

The development of simple, rapid and highly discriminatory typing methods for foodborne pathogens remains an important focus for the source tracking of bacterial contamination during foodborne illness outbreaks. PCR-based molecular typing methods, which have the advantages of being simple, fast and easy to perform, have been rapidly evolving over recent years. Several PCR-based molecular typing methods reviewed in this chapter can rapidly and easily distinguish closely related foodborne bacterial strains, thereby providing useful information in the investigation of foodborne disease outbreaks. However, some of these PCR-based typing techniques have problems with reproducibility. Minor changes in the amplification conditions (e.g., the concentration of PCR templates and reagents) may lead to the variability in the DNA fingerprint pattern generated. In addition, analysis and interpretation of the data may vary among different laboratories. For example, a faint band of PCR amplification products could be explained as a result of insufficient DNA template or an artifact. Therefore, standard guidelines for interpretation of PCR-fingerprints are required.

Since each of the techniques described has strengths and weaknesses, choosing an appropriate typing method is important in determining the sources and relatedness of bacterial isolates during foodborne disease outbreaks. The choice of the most appropriate PCR-based molecular typing method will rely upon the nature of the bacterial species under investigation and the resources available for carrying out the typing. For example, if the foods were contaminated with bacterial strains that lack enough number of adjacent repetitive sequences, rep-PCR will not be able to generate sufficient amplicons for discrimination, thus, it should not be used. With an automated DNA sequencer, AFLP can be used to screen large numbers of isolates in a short amount time. But for the laboratory without an automated DNA sequencer, it is hard to carry out AFLP efficiently. The choice of an appropriate subtyping method also depends on the association between the epidemiological unit of concern and the epidemiological unit of differentiation of which the method is capable. For example, if the objective is to trace back from *Salmonella* contamination at abattoirs to *Salmonella* infection on swine farms using a subtyping method. Since market weight pigs are sent to the abattoir by cohorts, the pigs could be from the same cohorts, or different cohorts within the same farm, or from different farms. Therefore, the epidemiological unit could be either cohorts or farms. If the purpose is to trace back to a specific farm, then the epidemiological unit of concern is on farm level and to pursue this purpose the subtyping method used should be able to differentiate the *Salmonella* population from different farms. If the purpose is to trace back to specific cohorts, then the epidemiological unit of concern is on cohort level and also the subtyping method employed should be able to distinguish the *Salmonella* population from different cohorts within the same farm.

When a large number of bacteria are isolated and rapid results are needed during a foodborne disease outbreak, high throughput PCR-based typing methods work well due to ability to characterize the isolates with relatively high-level of discrimination in a short amount of time. In addition, since different PCR-based methods rely on different conditions to distinguish among isolates, the difference between strains detected by one method may be missed by another technique. Therefore, typing results obtained from one typing method can be used to improve others, and a combination of different typing methods may be required for better discrimination of non-clonal isolates.

ACKNOWLEDGMENTS AND DISCLAIMER

The authors would like to thank Drs. Steven L. Foley and Rajesh Nayak for their reviewing the manuscript. Dr. Jing Han is supported through the Oak Ridge Institute for Science and Education. The views presented in this article do not necessarily reflect those of the U.S. Food and Drug Administration.

REFERENCES

[1] Scallan E, Hoekstra RM, Angulo FJ, Tauxe RV, Widdowson MA, Roy SL, et al. Foodborne illness acquired in the United States-major pathogens. *Emerg Infect Dis.* 2011;17(1):7-15.

[2] Li W, Raoult D, Fournier P-E. Bacterial strain typing in the genomic era. *FEMS Microbiology Reviews.* 2009;33(5):892-916.

[3] Ussery DW, Binnewies TT, Gouveia-Oliveira R, Jarmer H, Hallin PF. Genome update: DNA repeats in bacterial genomes. *Microbiology.* 2004;150(Pt 11):3519-21.

[4] Gilson E, Clement JM, Brutlag D, Hofnung M. A family of dispersed repetitive extragenic palindromic DNA sequences in *E. coli. EMBO J.* 1984;3(6):1417-21.

[5] Versalovic J, Koeuth T, Lupski JR. Distribution of repetitive DNA sequences in eubacteria and application to fingerprinting of bacterial genomes. *Nucleic Acids Res.* 1991;19(24):6823-31.

[6]   Rademaker JL, Hoste B, Louws FJ, Kersters K, Swings J, Vauterin L, et al. Comparison of AFLP and rep-PCR genomic fingerprinting with DNA-DNA homology studies: *Xanthomonas* as a model system. *Int J Syst Evol Microbiol*. 2000;50 Pt 2:665-77.

[7]   Hulton CS, Higgins CF, Sharp PM. ERIC sequences: a novel family of repetitive elements in the genomes of *Escherichia coli, Salmonella typhimurium* and other enterobacteria. *Mol Microbiol*. 1991;5(4):825-34.

[8]   Lupski JR, Weinstock GM. Short, interspersed repetitive DNA sequences in prokaryotic genomes. *J Bacteriol*. 1992;174(14):4525-9.

[9]   Soltysik DA, Bednarek IA, Loch TM, Galka SE, Sypniewski DJ, Machnik GM, et al. Repetitive extragenic palindromic PCR (REP-PCR) as an alternative method for detection of bulking in activated sludge. *Pol J Microbiol*. 2010;59(1):11-20.

[10] Koeuth T, Versalovic J, Lupski JR. Differential subsequence conservation of interspersed repetitive *Streptococcus pneumoniae* BOX elements in diverse bacteria. *Genome Res*. 1995;5(4):408-18.

[11] Appuhamy S, Parton R, Coote JG, Gibbs HA. Genomic fingerprinting of *Haemophilus somnus* by a combination of PCR methods. *J Clin Microbiol*. 1997;35(1):288-91.

[12] Swaminathan B, Barrett TJ. Amplification methods for epidemiologic investigations of infectious diseases. *Journal of Microbiological Methods*. 1995;23(1):129-39.

[13] Behringer M, Miller WG, Oyarzabal OA. Typing of *Campylobacter jejuni* and *Campylobacter coli* isolated from live broilers and retail broiler meat by *flaA*-RFLP, MLST, PFGE and REP-PCR. *J Microbiol Methods*. 2011; 84(2):194-201.

[14] Foley SL, Zhao S, Walker RD. Comparison of molecular typing methods for the differentiation of *Salmonella* foodborne pathogens. *Foodborne Pathog Dis*. 2007;4(3):253-76.

[15] Del Vecchio VG, Petroziello JM, Gress MJ, McCleskey FK, Melcher GP, Crouch HK, et al. Molecular genotyping of methicillin-resistant *Staphylococcus aureus* via fluorophore-enhanced repetitive-sequence PCR. *J Clin Microbiol*. 1995;33(8):2141-4.

[16] Johnson LK, Brown MB, Carruthers EA, Ferguson JA, Dombek PE, Sadowsky MJ. Sample size, library composition, and genotypic diversity among natural populations of *Escherichia coli* from different animals influence accuracy of determining sources of fecal pollution. *Appl Environ Microbiol*. 2004;70(8):4478-85.

[17] Healy M, Huong J, Bittner T, Lising M, Frye S, Raza S, et al. Microbial DNA typing by automated repetitive-sequence-based PCR. *J Clin Microbiol*. 2005;43(1):199-207.

[18] Baldy-Chudzik K, Niedbach J, Stosik M. Application of rep-PCR fingerprinting for genotyping of *Escherichia coli* strains in Wojnowskie Wschodnie and Wojnowskie Zachodnie lake. *Acta Microbiol Pol*. 2001;50(3-4):233-42.

[19] Hahm BK, Maldonado Y, Schreiber E, Bhunia AK, Nakatsu CH. Subtyping of foodborne and environmental isolates of *Escherichia coli* by multiplex-PCR, rep-PCR, PFGE, ribotyping and AFLP. *J Microbiol Methods*. 2003;53(3):387-99.

[20] Beyer W, Mukendi FM, Kimmig P, Bohm R. Suitability of repetitive-DNA-sequence-based PCR fingerprinting for characterizing epidemic isolates of *Salmonella enterica* serovar Saintpaul. *J Clin Microbiol*. 1998;36(6):1549-54.

[21] Johnson JR, Clabots C, Azar M, Boxrud DJ, Besser JM, Thurn JR. Molecular analysis of a hospital cafeteria-associated salmonellosis outbreak using modified repetitive element PCR fingerprinting. *J Clin Microbiol*. 2001;39(10):3452-60.

[22] Foley SL, White DG, McDermott PF, Walker RD, Rhodes B, Fedorka-Cray PJ, et al. Comparison of subtyping methods for differentiating *Salmonella enterica* serovar Typhimurium isolates obtained from food animal sources. *J Clin Microbiol.* 2006;44(10):3569-77.

[23] Jersek B, Gilot P, Gubina M, Klun N, Mehle J, Tcherneva E, et al. Typing of *Listeria monocytogenes* strains by repetitive element sequence-based PCR. *J Clin Microbiol.* 1999;37(1):103-9.

[24] Giesendorf BA, van Belkum A, Koeken A, Stegeman H, Henkens MH, van der Plas J, et al. Development of species-specific DNA probes for *Campylobacter jejuni*, *Campylobacter coli*, and *Campylobacter lari* by polymerase chain reaction fingerprinting. *J Clin Microbiol.* 1993;31(6):1541-6.

[25] Wieser M, Busse HJ. Rapid identification of *Staphylococcus epidermidis*. *Int J Syst Evol Microbiol.* 2000;50 Pt 3:1087-93.

[26] Zhong Z, Chai T, Duan H, Miao Z, Li X, Yao M, et al. REP-PCR tracking of the origin and spread of airborne *Staphylococcus aureus* in and around chicken house. *Indoor Air.* 2009;19(6):511-6.

[27] Shangkuan YH, Lin HC, Wang TM. Diversity of DNA sequences among *Vibrio cholerae* O1 and non-O1 isolates detected by whole-cell repetitive element sequence-based polymerase chain reaction. *J Appl Microbiol.* 1997;82(3):335-44.

[28] Cherif A, Ettoumi B, Raddadi N, Daffonchio D, Boudabous A. Genomic diversity and relationship of *Bacillus thuringiensis* and *Bacillus cereus* by multi-REP-PCR fingerprinting. *Can J Microbiol.* 2007;53(3):343-50.

[29] Pasanen T, Kotila SM, Horsma J, Virolainen A, Jalava J, Ibrahem S, et al. Comparison of repetitive extragenic palindromic sequence-based PCR with PCR ribotyping and pulsed-field gel electrophoresis in studying the clonality of *Clostridium difficile*. *Clin Microbiol Infect.* 2011;17(2):166-75.

[30] Navia MM, Capitano L, Ruiz J, Vargas M, Urassa H, Schellemberg D, et al. Typing and characterization of mechanisms of resistance of *Shigella* spp. isolated from feces of children under 5 years of age from Ifakara, Tanzania. *J Clin Microbiol.* 1999;37(10):3113-7.

[31] Wojciech L, Staroniewicz Z, Jakubczak A, Ugorski M. Typing of *Yersinia enterocolitica* Isolates by ITS profiling, REP- and ERIC-PCR. *J Vet Med B Infect Dis Vet Public Health.* 2004;51(5):238-44.

[32] Albufera U, Bhugaloo-Vial P, Issack MI, Jaufeerally-Fakim Y. Molecular characterization of *Salmonella* isolates by REP-PCR and RAPD analysis. *Infect Genet Evol.* 2009;9(3):322-7.

[33] Ben-Darif E, De Pinna E, Threlfall EJ, Bolton FJ, Upton M, Fox AJ. Comparison of a semi-automated rep-PCR system and multilocus sequence typing for differentiation of *Salmonella enterica* isolates. *J Microbiol Methods.* 2010;81(1):11-6.

[34] Hiett KL, Seal BS, Siragusa GR. Campylobacter spp. subtype analysis using gel-based repetitive extragenic palindromic-PCR discriminates in parallel fashion to *flaA* short variable region DNA sequence analysis. *J Appl Microbiol.* 2006;101(6):1249-58.

[35] Wilson MK, Lane AB, Law BF, Miller WG, Joens LA, Konkel ME, et al. Analysis of the pan genome of *Campylobacter jejuni* isolates recovered from poultry by pulsed-field gel electrophoresis, multilocus sequence typing (MLST), and repetitive sequence

polymerase chain reaction (rep-PCR) reveals different discriminatory capabilities. *Microb Ecol.* 2009;58(4):843-55.

[36]   Jersek B, Tcherneva E, Rijpens N, Herman L. Repetitive element sequence-based PCR for species and strain discrimination in the genus *Listeria*. *Lett Appl Microbiol.* 1996;23(1):55-60.

[37]   Chou CH, Wang C. Genetic relatedness between *Listeria monocytogenes* isolates from seafood and humans using PFGE and REP-PCR. *Int J Food Microbiol.* 2006;110(2):135-48.

[38]   Vos P, Hogers R, Bleeker M, Reijans M, van de Lee T, Hornes M, et al. AFLP: a new technique for DNA fingerprinting. *Nucleic Acids Res.* 1995;23(21):4407-14.

[39]   Savelkoul PH, Aarts HJ, de Haas J, Dijkshoorn L, Duim B, Otsen M, et al. Amplified-fragment length polymorphism analysis: the state of an art. *J Clin Microbiol.* 1999;37(10):3083-91.

[40]   Janssen P, Coopman R, Huys G, Swings J, Bleeker M, Vos P, et al. Evaluation of the DNA fingerprinting method AFLP as an new tool in bacterial taxonomy. *Microbiology.* 1996;142 (Pt 7):1881-93.

[41]   Moreno Y, Ferrus MA, Vanoostende A, Hernandez M, Montes RM, Hernandez J. Comparison of 23S polymerase chain reaction-restriction fragment length polymorphism and amplified fragment length polymorphism techniques as typing systems for thermophilic campylobacters. *FEMS Microbiol Lett.* 2002;211(1):97-103.

[42]   Tsai TY, Luo WC, Wu FT, Pan TM. Molecular subtyping for *Escherichia coli* O157: H7 isolated in Taiwan. *Microbiol Immunol.* 2005;49(7):579-88.

[43]   Foley SL, Lynne AM, Nayak R. Molecular typing methodologies for microbial source tracking and epidemiological investigations of Gram-negative bacterial foodborne pathogens. *Infect Genet Evol.* 2009;9(4):430-40.

[44]   Boghenbor KK, On SL, Kokotovic B, Baumgartner A, Wassenaar TM, Wittwer M, et al. Genotyping of human and porcine *Yersinia enterocolitica, Yersinia intermedia*, and *Yersinia bercovieri* strains from Switzerland by amplified fragment length polymorphism analysis. *Appl Environ Microbiol.* 2006;72(6):4061-6.

[45]   de Boer P, Duim B, Rigter A, van Der Plas J, Jacobs-Reitsma WF, Wagenaar JA. Computer-assisted analysis and epidemiological value of genotyping methods for *Campylobacter jejuni* and *Campylobacter coli*. *J Clin Microbiol.* 2000;38(5):1940-6.

[46]   Tamada Y, Nakaoka Y, Nishimori K, Doi A, Kumaki T, Uemura N, et al. Molecular typing and epidemiological study of *Salmonella enterica* serotype Typhimurium isolates from cattle by fluorescent amplified-fragment length polymorphism fingerprinting and pulsed-field gel electrophoresis. J Clin Microbiol. 2001;39(3):1057-66.

[47]   Mueller UG, Wolfenbarger LL. AFLP genotyping and fingerprinting. *Trends Ecol Evol.* 1999;14(10):389-94.

[48]   Desai M, Threlfall EJ, Stanley J. Fluorescent amplified-fragment length polymorphism subtyping of the *Salmonella enterica* serovar Enteritidis phage type 4 clone complex. *J Clin Microbiol.* 2001;39(1):201-6.

[49]   Fry NK, Afshar B, Visca P, Jonas D, Duncan J, Nebuloso E, et al. Assessment of fluorescent amplified fragment length polymorphism analysis for epidemiological genotyping of *Legionella pneumophila* serogroup 1. *Clin Microbiol Infect.* 2005;11(9):704-12.

[50] Lindstedt BA, Heir E, Vardund T, Kapperud G. Fluorescent amplified-fragment length polymorphism genotyping of *Salmonella enterica* subsp. *enterica* serovars and comparison with pulsed-field gel electrophoresis typing *J Clin Microbiol.* 2000;38(4):1623-7.

[51] Peters TM, Threlfall EJ. Single-enzyme amplified fragment length polymorphism and its applicability for *Salmonella* epidemiology. *Syst Appl Microbiol.* 2001;24(3):400-4.

[52] Duim B, Ang CW, van Belkum A, Rigter A, van Leeuwen NW, Endtz HP, et al. Amplified fragment length polymorphism analysis of *Campylobacter jejuni* strains isolated from chickens and from patients with gastroenteritis or Guillain-Barre or Miller Fisher syndrome. *Appl Environ Microbiol.* 2000;66(9):3917-23.

[53] Gonzalez A, Ferrus MA, Gonzalez R, Hernandez J. Molecular fingerprinting of *Campylobacter* and *Arcobacter* isolated from chicken and water. *Int Microbiol.* 2007;10(2):85-90.

[54] Duim B, Vandamme PA, Rigter A, Laevens S, Dijkstra JR, Wagenaar JA. Differentiation of *Campylobacter* species by AFLP fingerprinting. *Microbiology.* 2001;147(Pt 10):2729-37.

[55] Sirisriro T, Sethabutr O, Mason C, Talukder KA, Venkatesan MM. An AFLP-based database of *Shigella flexneri* and *Shigella sonnei* isolates and its use for the identification of untypeable *Shigella* strains. *J Microbiol Methods.* 2006;67(3):487-95.

[56] Fearnley C, On SL, Kokotovic B, Manning G, Cheasty T, Newell DG. Application of fluorescent amplified fragment length polymorphism for comparison of human and animal isolates of *Yersinia enterocolitica. Appl Environ Microbiol.* 2005;71(9):4960-5.

[57] Ripabelli G, McLauchlin J, Mithani V, Threlfall EJ. Epidemiological typing of *Bacillus cereus* by amplified fragment length polymorphism. *Lett Appl Microbiol.* 2000;30(5):358-63.

[58] Mazurek GH, Reddy V, Marston BJ, Haas WH, Crawford JT. DNA fingerprinting by infrequent-restriction-site amplification. *J Clin Microbiol.* 1996;34(10):2386-90.

[59] Garaizar J, Lopez-Molina N, Laconcha I, Lau Baggesen D, Rementeria A, Vivanco A, et al. Suitability of PCR fingerprinting, infrequent-restriction-site PCR, and pulsed-field gel electrophoresis, combined with computerized gel analysis, in library typing of *Salmonella enterica* serovar Enteritidis. *Appl Environ Microbiol.* 2000;66(12):5273-81.

[60] Riffard S, Lo Presti F, Vandenesch F, Forey F, Reyrolle M, Etienne J. Comparative analysis of infrequent-restriction-site PCR and pulsed-field gel electrophoresis for epidemiological typing of *Legionella pneumophila* serogroup 1 strains. *J Clin Microbiol.* 1998;36(1):161-7.

[61] Handley SA, Regnery RL. Differentiation of pathogenic *Bartonella* species by infrequent restriction site PCR. *J Clin Microbiol.* 2000;38(8):3010-5.

[62] Su LH, Leu HS, Chiu YP, Chia JH, Kuo AJ, Sun CF, et al. Molecular investigation of two clusters ofhospital-acquired bacteraemia caused by multi-resistant *Klebsiella pneumoniae* using pulsed-field gel electrophoresis andinfrequent restriction site PCR. *Journal of Hospital Infection.* 2000;46(2):110-7.

[63] Franciosa G, Tartaro S, Wedell-Neergaard C, Aureli P. Characterization of *Listeria monocytogenes* strains involved in invasive and noninvasive listeriosis outbreaks by PCR-based fingerprinting techniques. *Appl Environ Microbiol.* 2001;67(4):1793-9.

[64] Choi TY, Kang JO. Application of infrequent-restriction-site amplification for genotyping of *Mycobacterium tuberculosis* and non-tuberculous mycobacterium. *J Korean Med Sci*. 2002;17(5):593-8.

[65] Su LH, Chiu CH, Wu TL, Chu C, Chia JH, Kuo AJ, et al. Molecular epidemiology of *Salmonella enterica* serovar Enteritidis isolated in Taiwan. *Microbiol Immunol*. 2002;46(12):833-40.

[66] Su LH, Ou JT, Leu HS, Chiang PC, Chiu YP, Chia JH, et al. Extended epidemic of nosocomial urinary tract infections caused by *Serratia marcescens*. *J Clin Microbiol*. 2003;41(10):4726-32.

[67] Cloeckaert A, Grayon M, Grepinet O, Boumedine KS. Classification of *Brucella* strains isolated from marine mammals by infrequent restriction site-PCR and development of specific PCR identification tests. *Microbes Infect*. 2003;5(7):593-602.

[68] Wu TL, Su LH, Leu HS, Chiu CH, Chiu YP, Chia JH, et al. Molecular epidemiology of nosocomial infection associated with multi-resistant *Acinetobacter baumannii* by infrequent-restriction-site PCR. *Journal of Hospital Infection*. 2002;51(1):27-32.

[69] Su LH, Chia JH, Leu HS, Cheng SW, Kuo AJ, Sun CF, et al. DNA polymorphism of *Mycobacterium abscessus* analyzed by infrequent-restriction-site polymerase chain reaction. *Chang Gung Med J*. 2000;23(8):467-75.

[70] Wu TL, Chia JH, Su LH, Kuo AJ, Chu C, Chiu CH. Dissemination of extended-spectrum beta-lactamase-producing Enterobacteriaceae in pediatric intensive care units. *J Clin Microbiol*. 2003;41(10):4836-8.

[71] Olsen JE, Brown DJ, Skov MN, Christensen JP. Bacterial typing methods suitable for epidemiological analysis. Applications in investigations of salmonellosis among livestock. *Vet Q*. 1993;15(4):125-35.

[72] Nayak R, Stewart T, Nawaz M, Cerniglia C. In vitro antimicrobial susceptibility, genetic diversity and prevalence of UDP-glucose 4-epimerase (*galE*) gene in *Campylobacter coli* and *Campylobacter jejuni* from Turkey production facilities. *Food Microbiol*. 2006;23(4):379-92.

[73] Mohran ZS, Guerry P, Lior H, Murphy JR, el-Gendy AM, Mikhail MM, et al. Restriction fragment length polymorphism of flagellin genes of *Campylobacter jejuni* and/or *C. coli* isolates from Egypt. *J Clin Microbiol*. 1996;34(5):1216-9.

[74] Owen RJ, Leeton S. Restriction fragment length polymorphism analysis of the *flaA* gene of *Campylobacter jejuni* for subtyping human, animal and poultry isolates. *FEMS Microbiol Lett*. 1999;176(2):345-50.

[75] Nielsen EM, Engberg J, Fussing V, Petersen L, Brogren CH, On SL. Evaluation of phenotypic and genotypic methods for subtyping *Campylobacter jejuni* isolates from humans, poultry, and cattle. *J Clin Microbiol*. 2000;38(10):3800-10.

[76] Zorman T, Heyndrickx M, Uzunovic-Kamberovic S, Smole Mozina S. Genotyping of *Campylobacter coli* and *C. jejuni* from retail chicken meat and humans with campylobacteriosis in Slovenia and Bosnia and Herzegovina. *Int J Food Microbiol*. 2006;110(1):24-33.

[77] Hurtado A, Owen RJ. A molecular scheme based on 23S rRNA gene polymorphisms for rapid identification of *Campylobacter* and *Arcobacter* species. *J Clin Microbiol*. 1997;35(9):2401-4.

[78] Kwon HJ, Park KY, Yoo HS, Park JY, Park YH, Kim SJ. Differentiation of *Salmonella enterica* serotype Gallinarum biotype pullorum from biotype gallinarum by analysis of phase 1 flagellin C gene (*fliC*). *J Microbiol Methods.* 2000;40(1):33-8.

[79] Chiou CS, Wei HL, Yang LC. Comparison of pulsed-field gel electrophoresis and coagulase gene restriction profile analysis techniques in the molecular typing of *Staphylococcus aureus*. *J Clin Microbiol.* 2000;38(6):2186-90.

[80] Soltan-Dallal MM, Salehipour Z, Mehrabadi JF. Molecular epidemiology of *Staphylococcus aureus* in food samples based on the protein A gene polymorphic region DNA sequence. *Can J Microbiol.* 2010;56(1):18-21.

[81] Dauga C, Zabrovskaia A, Grimont PA. Restriction fragment length polymorphism analysis of some flagellin genes of *Salmonella enterica*. *J Clin Microbiol.* 1998;36(10):2835-43.

[82] Paiva JB, Cavallini JS, Silva MD, Almeida MA, Ângela HL, Berchieri Junior A. Molecular differentiation of *Salmonella* Gallinarum and *Salmonella* Pullorum by RFLP of *fliC* gene from Brazilian isolates. *Revista Brasileira de Ciência Avícola.* 2009;11:271-5.

[83] Hong Y, Liu T, Hofacre C, Maier M, White DG, Ayers S, et al. A restriction fragment length polymorphism-based polymerase chain reaction as an alternative to serotyping for identifying *Salmonella* serotypes. *Avian Dis.* 2003;47(2):387-95.

[84] Williams JG, Kubelik AR, Livak KJ, Rafalski JA, Tingey SV. DNA polymorphisms amplified by arbitrary primers are useful as genetic markers. *Nucleic Acids Res.* 1990;18(22):6531-5.

[85] Franklin RB, Taylor DR, Mills AL. Characterization of microbial communities using randomly amplified polymorphic DNA (RAPD). *J Microbiol Methods.* 1999;35(3):225-35.

[86] Welsh J, McClelland M. Fingerprinting genomes using PCR with arbitrary primers. *Nucleic Acids Res.* 1990 Dec 25;18(24):7213-8.

[87] Tyler KD, Wang G, Tyler SD, Johnson WM. Factors affecting reliability and reproducibility of amplification-based DNA fingerprinting of representative bacterial pathogens. *J Clin Microbiol.* 1997;35(2):339-46.

[88] Lin AW, Usera MA, Barrett TJ, Goldsby RA. Application of random amplified polymorphic DNA analysis to differentiate strains of *Salmonella enteritidis*. *J Clin Microbiol.* 1996;34(4):870-6.

[89] Lopes VC, Velayudhan BT, Halvorson DA, Lauer DC, Gast RK, Nagaraja KV. Comparison of methods for differentiation of *Salmonella enterica* serovar Enteritidis phage type 4 isolates. *Am J Vet Res.* 2004;65(5):538-43.

[90] Aquino MH, Filgueiras AL, Matos R, Santos KR, Ferreira T, Ferreira MC, et al. Diversity of *Campylobacter jejuni* and *Campylobacter coli* genotypes from human and animal sources from Rio de Janeiro, Brazil. *Res Vet Sci.* 2010;88(2):214-7.

[91] Hilton AC, Mortiboy D, Banks JG, Penn CW. RAPD analysis of environmental, food and clinical isolates of *Campylobacter* spp. *FEMS Immunol Med Microbiol.* 1997;18(2):119-24.

[92] Stern NJ, Bannov VA, Svetoch EA, Mitsevich EV, Mitsevich IP, Volozhantsev NV, et al. Distribution and characterization of *Campylobacter* spp. from Russian poultry. *J Food Prot.* 2004;67(2):239-45.

[93] Lam KM, Yamamoto R, DaMassa AJ. DNA diversity among isolates of *Campylobacter jejuni* detected by PCR-based RAPD fingerprinting. *Vet Microbiol*. 1995;45(2-3):269-74.

[94] Kalman M, Szollosi E, Czermann B, Zimanyi M, Szekeres S. Milkborne *Campylobacter* infection in Hungary. *J Food Prot*. 2000;63(10):1426-9.

[95] Payne RE, Lee MD, Dreesen DW, Barnhart HM. Molecular epidemiology of *Campylobacter jejuni* in broiler flocks using randomly amplified polymorphic DNA-PCR and 23S rRNA-PCR and role of litter in its transmission. *Appl Environ Microbiol*. 1999;65(1):260-3.

[96] Ono K, Yamamoto K. Contamination of meat with *Campylobacter jejuni* in Saitama, Japan. *Int J Food Microbiol*. 1999;47(3):211-9.

[97] Workman SN, Mathison GE, Lavoie MC. An investigation of sources of *Campylobacter* in a poultry production and packing operation in Barbados. *Int J Food Microbiol*. 2008;121(1):106-11.

[98] Zimmer M, Barnhart H, Idris U, Lee MD. Detection of *Campylobacter jejuni* strains in the water lines of a commercial broiler house and their relationship to the strains that colonized the chickens. *Avian Dis*. 2003;47(1):101-7.

[99] Nielsen EM, Engberg J, Fussing V. Genotypic and serotypic stability of *Campylobacter jejuni* strains during in vitro and in vivo passage. *Int J Med Microbiol*. 2001;291(5):379-85.

[100] Oberhelman RA, Gilman RH, Sheen P, Cordova J, Taylor DN, Zimic M, et al. *Campylobacter* transmission in a Peruvian shantytown: a longitudinal study using strain typing of campylobacter isolates from chickens and humans in household clusters. *J Infect Dis*. 2003;187(2):260-9.

[101] Madden RH, Moran L, Scates P. Frequency of occurrence of *Campylobacter* spp. in red meats and poultry in Northern Ireland and their subsequent subtyping using polymerase chain reaction-restriction fragment length polymorphism and the random amplified polymorphic DNA method. *J Appl Microbiol*. 1998;84(5):703-8.

[102] Morshed R, Peighambari SM. Drug resistance, plasmid profile and random amplified polymorphic DNA analysis of Iranian isolates of *Salmonella enteritidis*. *New Microbiol*. 2010;33(1):47-56.

[103] Albufera U, Bhugaloo-Vial P, Issack MI, Jauferally-Fakim Y. Molecular characterization of *Salmonella* isolates by REP-PCR and RAPD analysis. *Infect Genet Evol*. 2009;9(3):322-7.

[104] Betancor L, Schelotto F, Martinez A, Pereira M, Algorta G, Rodriguez MA, et al. Random amplified polymorphic DNA and phenotyping analysis of *Salmonella enterica* serovar enteritidis isolates collected from humans and poultry in Uruguay from 1995 to 2002. *J Clin Microbiol*. 2004;42(3):1155-62.

[105] Moore JE, Murray L, Fanning S, Cormican M, Daly M, Delappe N, et al. Comparison of phenotypic and genotypic characteristics of *Salmonella bredeney* associated with a poultry-related outbreak of gastroenteritis in Northern Ireland. *J Infect*. 2003;47(1):33-9.

[106] Kantama L, Jayanetra P. Salmonella enteritidis outbreak in Thailand: study by random amplified polymorphic DNA (RAPD) analysis. *Southeast Asian J Trop Med Public Health*. 1996;27(1):119-25.

[107] Eriksson J, Lofstrom C, Aspan A, Gunnarsson A, Karlsson I, Borch E, et al. Comparison of genotyping methods by application to *Salmonella livingstone* strains associated with an outbreak of human salmonellosis. *Int J Food Microbiol.* 2005;104(1):93-103.

[108] Lofstrom C, Eriksson J, Aspan A, Haggblom P, Gunnarsson A, Borch E, et al. Improvement and validation of RAPD in combination with PFGE analysis of *Salmonella enterica* ssp. *enterica* serovar Senftenberg strains isolated from feed mills. *Vet Microbiol.* 2006;114(3-4):345-51.

[109] Madadgar O, Tadjbakhsh H, Salehi TZ, Mahzounieh M, Feizabadi MM. Evaluation of random amplified polymorphic DNA analysis and antibiotic susceptibility application in discrimination of *Salmonella* Typhimurium isolates in Iran. *New Microbiol.* 2008;31(2):211-6.

[110] Landers E, Gonzalez-Hevia MA, Mendoza MC. Molecular epidemiology of *Salmonella* serotype Enteritidis. Relationships between food, water and pathogenic strains. *Int J Food Microbiol.* 1998;43(1-2):81-90.

[111] Woo YK, Lee SH. Genetic diversity of multi-resistant *Salmonella enterica* serotype Typhimurium isolates from animals and humans. *J Microbiol.* 2006;44(1):106-12.

[112] Chambel L, Sol M, Fernandes I, Barbosa M, Zilhao I, Barata B, et al. Occurrence and persistence of *Listeria* spp. in the environment of ewe and cow's milk cheese dairies in Portugal unveiled by an integrated analysis of identification, typing and spatial-temporal mapping along production cycle. *Int J Food Microbiol.* 2007;116(1):52-63.

[113] Czajka J, Batt CA. Verification of causal relationships between *Listeria monocytogenes* isolates implicated in food-borne outbreaks of listeriosis by randomly amplified polymorphic DNA patterns. *J Clin Microbiol.* 1994;32(5):1280-7.

[114] Dhanashree B, Otta SK, Karunasagar I. Typing of *Listeria monocytogenes* isolates by random amplification of polymorphic DNA. *Indian J Med Res.* 2003;117:19-24.

[115] Gianfranceschi M, D'Ottavio MC, Gattuso A, Pourshaban M, Bertoletti I, Bignazzi R, et al. Listeriosis associated with gorgonzola (Italian blue-veined cheese). *Foodborne Pathog Dis.* 2006;3(2):190-5.

[116] Mereghetti L, Lanotte P, Savoye-Marczuk V, Marquet-Van Der MN, Audurier A, Quentin R. Combined ribotyping and random multiprimer DNA analysis to probe the population structure of *Listeria monocytogenes*. *Appl Environ Microbiol.* 2002;68(6):2849-57.

[117] Cao J, Clarke M, Witkowsky R, Lu H, Sayedahaman A, Levin RE, et al. Concentrations and tracking of *Listeria monocytogenes* strains in a seafood-processing environment using a most-probable-number enrichment procedure and randomly amplified polymorphic DNA analysis. *J Food Prot.* 2006;69(3):489-94.

[118] Martinez I, Rorvik LM, Brox V, Lassen J, Seppola M, Gram L, et al. Genetic variability among isolates of *Listeria monocytogenes* from food products, clinical samples and processing environments, estimated by RAPD typing. *Int J Food Microbiol.* 2003;84(3):285-97.

[119] Cocolin L, Stella S, Nappi R, Bozzetta E, Cantoni C, Comi G. Analysis of PCR-based methods for characterization of *Listeria monocytogenes* strains isolated from different sources. *Int J Food Microbiol.* 2005;103(2):167-78.

[120] Domingue G, Willshaw GA, Smith HR, Perry N, Radford D, Cheasty T. DNA-based subtyping of verocytotoxin-producing *Escherichia coli* (VTEC) O128ab:H2 strains from human and raw meat sources. *Lett Appl Microbiol.* 2003;37(6):433-7.

[121] Khan A, Das SC, Ramamurthy T, Sikdar A, Khanam J, Yamasaki S, et al. Antibiotic resistance, virulence gene, and molecular profiles of Shiga toxin-producing *Escherichia coli* isolates from diverse sources in Calcutta, India. *J Clin Microbiol.* 2002;40(6):2009-15.

[122] Kim JY, Kim SH, Kwon NH, Bae WK, Lim JY, Koo HC, et al. Isolation and identification of *Escherichia coli* O157:H7 using different detection methods and molecular determination by multiplex PCR and RAPD. *J Vet Sci.* 2005;6(1):7-19.

[123] Ouyang-Latimer J, Ajami NJ, Jiang ZD, Okhuysen PC, Paredes M, Flores J, et al. Biochemical and genetic diversity of enterotoxigenic *Escherichia coli* associated with diarrhea in United States students in Cuernavaca and Guadalajara, Mexico, 2004-2007. *J Infect Dis.* 2010;201(12):1831-8.

[124] Kurazono T, Makino S. Diversity of DNA sequences among enterohemorrhagic *Escherichia coli* O157:H7 detected by PCR-based DNA fingerprinting. *Nippon Rinsho.* 1997;55(3):671-4.

[125] Hannah EL, Johnson JR, Angulo F, Haddadin B, Williamson J, Samore MH. Molecular analysis of antimicrobial-susceptible and -resistant *Escherichia coli* from retail meats and human stool and clinical specimens in a rural community setting. *Foodborne Pathog Dis.* 2009;6(3):285-95.

[126] Johnson JR, Delavari P, O'Bryan TT, Smith KE, Tatini S. Contamination of retail foods, particularly turkey, from community markets (Minnesota, 1999-2000) with antimicrobial-resistant and extraintestinal pathogenic *Escherichia coli*. *Foodborne Pathog Dis.* 2005;2(1):38-49.

[127] Johnson JR, Kuskowski MA, Menard M, Gajewski A, Xercavins M, Garau J. Similarity between human and chicken *Escherichia coli* isolates in relation to ciprofloxacin resistance status. *J Infect Dis.* 2006;194(1):71-8.

[128] Tristao LC, Gonzalez AG, Coutinho CA, Cerqueira AM, Gomes MJ, Irino K, et al. Virulence markers and genetic relationships of Shiga toxin-producing *Escherichia coli* strains from serogroup O111 isolated from cattle. *Vet Microbiol.* 2007;119(2-4):358-65.

[129] Venieri D, Vantarakis A, Komninou G, Papapetropoulou M. Differentiation of faecal *Escherichia coli* from human and animal sources by random amplified polymorphic DNA-PCR (RAPD-PCR). *Water Sci Technol.* 2004;50(1):193-8.

[130] Das SC, Khan A, Panja P, Datta S, Sikdar A, Yamasaki S, et al. Dairy farm investigation on Shiga toxin-producing *Escherichia coli* (STEC) in Kolkata, India with emphasis on molecular characterization. *Epidemiol Infect.* 2005;133(4):617-26.

[131] Colombari V, Mayer MD, Laicini ZM, Mamizuka E, Franco BD, Destro MT, et al. Foodborne outbreak caused by *Staphylococcus aureus*: phenotypic and genotypic characterization of strains of food and human sources. *J Food Prot.* 2007;70(2):489-93.

[132] Esteves A, Patarata L, Aymerich T, Garriga M, Martins C. Multiple correspondence analysis and random amplified polymorphic DNA molecular typing to assess the sources of *Staphylococcus aureus* contamination in alheira production lines. *J Food Prot.* 2007;70(3):685-91.

[133] Dombek PE, Johnson LK, Zimmerley ST, Sadowsky MJ. Use of repetitive DNA sequences and the PCR to differentiate *Escherichia coli* isolates from human and animal sources. *Appl Environ Microbiol.* 2000;66(6):2572-7.

In: Molecular Typing Methods for TFM
Editors: S. Foley, R. Nayak, T. Johnson et al.

ISBN: 978-1-62100-643-5
© 2012 Nova Science Publishers, Inc.

Chapter 12

PCR-BASED GENOTYPING: VIRULENCE AND ANTIMICROBIAL RESISTANCE GENES

Aaron M. Lynne and Brian C. Louden

Department of Biological Sciences
Sam Houston State University
Huntsville, TX, US

ABSTRACT

Bacterial foodborne diseases have become a growing health problem worldwide. Recent report from CDC indicated that bacterial foodborne pathogens contribute to 3.6 millions infection and 861 deaths each year in the United States alone. The ability to identify the primary sources of bacterial contamination from which human infection originated would be of great value in reducing the incidence of foodborne disease and are important to improve public health; therefore, a number of PCR-based genotyping methods have been developed for bacterial source tracking during the last three decades. In this book chapter, we review the current commonly used PCR-based typing methods: Repetitive Element PCR (rep-PCR), Amplified Fragment Length Polymorphisms (AFLP), Infrequent-Restriction-Site PCR (IRS-PCR), Restriction Fragment Length Polymorphism PCR (PCR-RFLP), and Random Amplified Polymorphic DNA PCR (RAPD-PCR). For each of the methods reviewed, an introduction of the method is followed by the description of the procedure, then examples of the applications of the methods in the epidemiological studies are given, and its strengths and weaknesses are discussed.

INTRODUCTION

Microorganisms causing foodborne disease are responsible for a significant number of illnesses and deaths each year. Knowledge of how these pathogens disseminate through the food chain is important in the development of strategies to limit pathogen spread. In order to be able to track these pathogens, it is necessary to identify and determine their source and spread at the different stages of transmission cycle. The ability to characterize the phenotypic and genotypic genetic relatedness of strains and determine the primary sources of contamination provides valuable insights into the epidemiology of the pathogens and provides important tools to improve public health. There are many ways in which foodborne pathogens can be distinguished from one another within their respective species. This chapter will focus on polymerase chain reaction (PCR) based genotyping of virulence and antimicrobial resistance genes.

The genetic composition of microorganisms is highly variable, even within a species, due in part to horizontal gene transfer. Thus, the number of genes present within a particular strain is likely to vary, which can be used to distinguish strains from each other. PCR genotyping takes advantage of these genetic differences to subtype strains. With PCR genotyping, a series of genes (i.e. virulence and antimicrobial resistance) are screened by PCR to detect the presence or absence of that specific gene [1]. Often primer sets are multiplexed in a single reaction to increase throughput and reduce reagent costs, [2] or adapted for the realtime PCR analysis to provide more rapid results [3]. The presence/absence profiles of genes can be combined and analyzed as binary data to carryout phylogenetic analysis. A potentially attractive feature of amplification profiling is that genes of medical importance are often incorporated into the typing scheme, including genes for virulence and antimicrobial resistance [4].

PCR genotyping can be quite useful for scientists investigating foodborne pathogens. Data generated by PCR genotyping can be used to investigate population dynamics of clinical isolates by looking at the spatial and temporal distribution of virulence and resistance genes which can aid in determining the mechanisms and/or method of transmission of those genes. Researchers have used PCR genotyping to characterize isolates in a variety of ways. For example, it can be used to compare isolates from sick vs. healthy animal sources or compare virulence factor possession to outcome of infection [5-7]. PCR genotyping can also be used to track multidrug resistant isolates through the environment where it has been used to suggest transmission of isolates between flocks of production birds and track resistance through the production environment [8, 9]

Microarray technology provides a complementary approach that allows for screening of a large number of gene products simultaneously. Microarrays can be categorized based upon numerous characteristics, such as probe used, the solid-surface support used and the method for target detection [10]. Printed microarrays utilize a glass microscope slide on which the probes are spotted [11]. *In situ* synthesized oligonucleotide microarrays utilizes photochemistry to synthesize oligonucleotides directly on the surface of a quartz wafer [10]. High-density bead microarrays work in a similar manner to printed and *in situ* synthesized except that they use silica beads as substrates [12]. Electronic microarrays use electric fields for active hybridization of nucleic acids. Liquid-bead suspension microarrays utilize beads as the solid support and flow cytometry for target detection. Each of the different microarrays has their own advantages and disadvantages. For a more complete review, see the following reviews [10, 13]. This microarray screening approach has been used in a number of studies to simultaneously detect the presence of multiple virulence and antimicrobial resistance genes in bacterial pathogens [10, 14-19].

GENERALIZED PCR PROCEDURE

This section provides a detailed description of the steps used to carry out PCR genotyping. This generalized protocol has been adapted from many sources [20-27]. While the basic protocol is common for most applications, specific protocols may need to be developed to account for numerous variables, such as pathogen(s) of interest, specific primers used, etc.

Generation of Template DNA

An individual colony of the isolate is inoculated in 1 ml of broth media (i.e. Luria Bertani for *Escherichia coli*) and grown overnight at 37°C with shaking. Cells are pelleted by centrifugation and resuspended in sterile water. Cells are boiled for 10 min to lyse cells then centrifuged to pellet cellular debris. Supernatant containing the crude template DNA can be stored at -20°C for at up to six months or more, without multiple freeze-thaw cycles.

PCR Amplification Conditions

Conditions given here are for a 25µl reaction. Volumes can be scaled up or down based upon need. PCR amplifications can be made by combining 3 µl of DNA template with 2.5 µl of each primer (10 pmol/µl), 2.5 µl 10X Taq PCR buffer (500mM KCl, 15mM MgCl$_2$, 100mM Tris-HCl), 5µl dNTPs (100mM), 2 U of thermostable polymerase and enough water to bring final volume to 25µl. Alternatively, 2X master mixes containing PCR buffer, dNTPs, and polymerase are commercially available, such as PCR MasterMix (Promega, Madison, WI) or *Taq* 2X Master Mix (New England Biolabs, Ipswich, MA). PCR cycling conditions are as follows: one cycle of initial denaturation at 95°C for 5 minutes, followed by 30 cycles of denaturation at 95°C for 1 min, annealing at an optimized temperature for each primer for 1 min, and extension at 72°C, followed by a final extension at 72°C for 7 min. Generally, the annealing temperature is 3-5°C below the T$_m$. However, the annealing temperature should be confirmed practically in a series of test reactions by varying the annealing temperature 2°C in a step-wise manner above and below the calculated T$_m$. The use of a thermocycler with a gradient block can aid this process. PCR products can be stored at 4°C until used.

Gel Electrophoresis

PCR amplicons can be visualized by horizontal gel electrophoresis. A 1.5% agarose gel in 1xX TAE (40 mM Tris-acetate, 1 mM EDTA) is prepared by heating the mixture until dissolved. Due to differences in size of casting trays, volume of solution will vary. Once cooled, the agarose solution is pouring into the casting tray. An appropriate comb is placed to allow formation of wells. Once solidified, the agarose gel is placed into the electorphoresis unit and the comb is removed. The electrophoresis unit is filled with TAE until the gel is covered. PCR sample are mixed with an appropriate DNA loading buffer and loaded into the wells. A DNA size ladder is also loaded into one of the wells which serve as a molecular weight marker. Gels are usually run at 100 V for varying times (1-3 hours), depending on the size of the electrophoresis unit, percentage of agarose, and size of PCR amplicons. Gels need to be stained for imaging of the amplicons. Ethidium bromide is the most commonly used dye, however safer dyes are commercially available (i.e. SYBR Safe, Invitrogen, Carlsbad, CA). Alternatively, the gel electorphoresis process can be streamlined by the use of commercially available pre-cast gels. E-gel 96 (Invitrogen) is a pre-cast, pre-stained gel that can run 96 samples plus molecular weight marker. The layout of the gel is similar to a 96-well plate allowing for easier loading of the gel. E-gel 96 gels are run on a mother base with a run time of 10 minutes, allowing for faster analysis of large number of isolates.

PCR Genotyping in Practice for Foodborne Pathogens

Virulence and Resistance Genes of Salmonella

Salmonella enterica causes a significant number of foodborne infections around the world. In the U.S alone, it is estimated that there 1.4 million cases of salmonellosis with 17,000 hospitalizations and 600 deaths each year [28, 29]. Infections by *Salmonella* can manifest itself in a number of syndromes including gastroenteritis, bacteremia and typhoid fever [30]. Historically, *Salmonella* were separated into species based on serotyping. However, *Salmonella* are classified into one of two species, *S. enterica* and *S. bongori*, with serotyping being used to discriminate strains within a species [31]. Currently, there are over 2,500 identified *Salmonella* serovars with some able to infect a wide ranges of hosts. Broad range serovars such as Typhimurium, Enteritidis and Heidelberg are often the most common serovars that cause human infections [32].

A number of researchers have successfully used PCR amplification to genotype *Salmonella* species based on virulence and antimicrobial resistance gene content [5-9, 20-22, 33-47]. Species of *Salmonella* may possess a variety of virulence factors that can contribute to the success of the pathogenicity of the bacterium [40]. Many of these virulence factors are located on large genomic islands called *Salmonella* pathogenicity island (SPIs) [48]. Some virulence factors not located on SPIs are chromosomally encoded while others reside on large plasmids [49-51]. For a full list of virulence genes and there functions, refer to Table 1.

There are numerous antimicrobial resistance genes that can encode resistance to a variety of antimicrobial agents. Unlike some virulence factors, these genes are often not species-specific and can be found in a variety of genera and species of bacteria. These genes can encode resistance for a number of antimicrobials including, β-lactams, aminoglycosides, tetracycline, trimethoprim, sulfomamides, and chloramphenicol. A summary of common resistance genes used for PCR genotyping is presented in Table 2. While the resistance genes listed in Table 2 are commonly used, it is not a comprehensive list of all gene alleles. For example, there are at least 29 different *tet* genes [52], 16 *dhfr* genes [53], 19 *aph* genes [54], 22 *aac* genes [54], and 75 β-lactamase genes associated with the Enterobacteraceae [5]).

A number of studies have looked at virulence genotyping *Salmonella* isolates from both animal and human clinical isolates. Skyberg et al (2006) genotyped a number of *Salmonella* isolates from healthy and sick chickens and turkeys using multiplex PCR for 17 virulence genes and found that these genes are widely distributed among *Salmonella* isolates form both sick and healthy birds [6]. A study by Nayak et al (2004) examined the molecular diversity of antimicrobial-resistant *Salmonella* isolates from preharvest turkey production sources. The study found that combination of PCR genotyping with PFGE, ribotyping, plasmid patterns and antimicrobial susceptibility patterns can be useful in studying genetic variation of *Salmonella* in turkey populations and delineating transmission pathways [9]. Parvathi et al (2010) compared the virulence genotypes of isolates of *S. enterica* serovar Newport (*S.* Newport) from environmental samples to isolates of *S.* Typhi from clinical samples [40]. The results showed that genes associated with SPI I-VI were detected in close to 100% of all isolates. However virulence genes associated with virulence plasmids were noticeably absent from Newport isolates compared to Typhi [40]. When comparing *S.* Enteritidis isolates causing gastroenteritis or bacteremia, Soto et al (2006) found that all chromosomally encoded virulence genes were found in all isolates while a few isolates (2 causing gastroenteritis, 2 causing bacteremia) were missing plasmid encoded virulence genes [5].

Table 1. Virulence genes used in *Salmonella* PCR genotyping

Gene	Gene function	Reference
sopE	Effector protein	[40]
spiC	Effector protein	[40]
mgtB	Mg^{2+} uptake	[40]
spi4D	Type I secretion system	[40]
spi4R	Type I secretion system	[40]
sopB	Effector protein	[40]
viaB	Vi antigen	[40]
invA	Host recognition/invasion	[87]
orgA	Host recognition/invasion	[88]
prgH	Host recogntion/invasion	[89]
spaN	Entry into nonphagocytic cells	[90]
tolC	Host recognition/invasion	[91]
sipB	Entry into nonphagocytic cells	[90]
sitC	Iron acquisition	[92]
pagC	Survival within macrophages	[93]
msgA	Survival within macrophages	[94]
spiA	Survival within macrophages	[95]
iroN	Iron acquisition	[96]
sopB	Host recognition/invasion	[97]
lpfC	Host recognition/invasion	[98]
cdtB	Host recognition/invasion	[99]
sifA	Filamentous structure formation	[100]
pefA	Host recognition/invasion	[101]
pefC	Plasmid-encoded fimbriae	[40]
spvC	Plasmid-encoded virulence	[40]
spvR	Plasmid-endoded virulence regulator	[40]

Table 2. Antimicrobial resistance genes used in PCR genotyping

Antimicrobial	Resistance gene	Reference*
Aminoglycosides	*aac(3)-Ia*	[56]
	aac(3)-IIa	[56]
	aac(3)-IVa	[56]
	aac(6')	[56]
	aacC2	[56]
	aacC4	[56]
	aadD	[56]
	ant(3")-Ia	[56]
	ant(6)-Ia	[56]
	aph(2")	[56]
	aph(3')-IIa	[56]
	kn	[56]
β-Lactams	*bla*$_{CMY-2}$	[56]
	bla$_{CMY-9}$	[56]
	bla$_{CTX-M1}$	[56]
	bla$_{CTX-M2}$	[56]
	bla$_{CTX-M14}$	[56]
	bla$_{DHA-1}$	[56]
	bla$_{FOX-1}$	[56]
	bla$_{MI1}$	[56]
	bla$_{OXA-1}$	[56]
	bla$_{OXA-2}$	[56]
	bla$_{SHV-1}$	[56]
	bla$_{TEM-1}$	[56]
Chloramphenicol	*cat1*	(56)
	cat2	(56)
	cat3	(56)
	floR	(56)
Sulfomamides	*sulI*	[56]
	sulI	[56]
Tetracycline	*tetA*	[56]
	tetB	[56]
	tetC	[56]
	tetD	[56]
	tetE	[56]
Trimethoprim	*dhfrI*	[56]
	dhfrII	[56]
	dfhrIII	[56]
	dfhrV	[56]
	dhfrVI	[56]
	dhfrVII	[56]
	dhfrVIII	[56]
	dhfrIX	[56]
	dhfrX	[56]
	dhfrXI	[56]

*Genes compiled in the reference manuscript, but originally described elsewhere.

Numerous studies have been conducted looking at the antimicrobial-resistance genotypes of various *Salmonella* serovars [20, 22, 34, 38, 39, 44-46, 56-64]. In all these studies, great genetic diversity was seen among the isolates screened. Often, these genes were correlated with large, transmissible plasmids [20-22, 39, 44, 45, 56, 65]. Recently, Welch et al (2007) published the sequence of a large IncA/C plasmid encoding resistance to a number of antimicrobial agents [65]. This plasmid shared a common backbone with plasmids isolated from the fish pathogen *Yersinia ruckeri* and a multi-drug resistant isolate of *Yersinia pestis*. Of great concern is the presence of the bla_{CMY} gene, which confers resistance to extended cephalosporins. This gene has been indentified in many gram-negative enteric pathogens in numerous countries [45, 66-68]. bla_{CMY} encodes resistance to two cephaloporins (ceftriaxone and ceftiofur) of clinical importance for both human and veterinary medicine. Ceftriazone is the drug of choice for treating severe *Salmonella* infections in children while ceftiofur is approved for systemic use in food animals in the U.S. [69]. This underscores the importance of antimicrobial-resistance genotyping of foodborne pathogens to tract the spread of clinically important resistance genes.

Virulence and Resistance Genes of Escherichia coli

Escherichia coli is responsible for many food and waterborne outbreaks worldwide. *E. coli* O157:H7, an enterhemorrhagic *E. coli* (EHEC) that is of great concern, causes diarrhea, hemorrhagic colitis or hemolytic uremic syndrome. Numerous virulence factors are involved in the pathogenesis of infection and are summarized in Table 3 [70]. These can include the production of shiga toxins and attaching and effacing lesions. Production of shiga toxin can be attributed to one of two classes, Stx1 and Stx2. Stx1 is encoded by *stx1* gene and is highly conserved among shiga toxin producing *E. coli* (STEC) [71]. *stx2* is much less conserved which can be used to distinguish numerous subtypes of Stx2 [71]. A chromosomally encoded region called locus of enterocyte effacement (LEE) is responsible for the attaching and effacing lesions [71]. There are at least 41 genes associated with LEE. An adhesion called intimin, encoded by *eae*, is often found in most human pathogenic STEC [71]. While possession of *stx* and *eae* are typical of *E. coli* O157:H7 strains, the outcomes of infection are broad, which may be due to differences in possession of accessory genes or differential expression of genes [72].

A number of studies have used PCR genotyping to characterize STEC [70, 73-78]. Slanec et al. (2009) characterized a number of STEC from food and drinking water for the possession of virulence factors [70]. They found that these isolates possessed a wide variety of variants of *stx* and other virulence factors indicating the need for molecular analysis to assess the risk of environmental samples for causing human disease. A study by Toth et al (2009) found similar results in isolates derived from healthy cattle originating from Hungary [75]. Islam et al (2008) used PCR genotyping of virulence genes to show that slaughtered animals (buffalo, cows and goats) carried potentially zoonotic STEC [74]. Finally, Loukiadis et al. (2006) used PCR genotyping to detect STEC in wastewater samples from slaughterhouses [78].

Table 3. Virulence genes used in *Escherichia coli* O157:H7 PCR genotyping

Gene	Gene Function	Reference*
stxI	Shiga toxin I	[75]
stxII	Shiga toxin II	[75]
eaeA	Attachment factor intimin	[75]
eaf	EPEC adherence factor	[75]
bfp	Bundle forming pilus	[75]
tir	Translocated intimin receptor	[75]
ehxA	Enterohemolysin	[75]
efaI	*E. coli* factor for adherence	[75]
tccP	Tir-cytoskeleton coupling protein	[75]
ureA	Urease	[75]
terB	Tellurite resistance	[75]
cdt	Cytolethal distending toxin	[75]
fyuA	*Yersinia* siderophore receptor	[75]
sodC	Copper and zinc superoxide dismutase	[75]
espJ	Non-LEE effector gene	[75]
espK	Non-LEE effector gene	[75]
espM1	Non-LEE effector gene	[75]
espM2	Non-LEE effector gene	[75]
espT	Non-LEE effector gene	[75]

* Genes compiled in the reference manuscript, but originally described elsewhere.

Table 4. Virulence genes used in genotyping extra-intestinal *E. coli*

Gene	Gene Function	Reference*
cvaC	Structural gene for Colicin V	[79]
iroN	Catecholate siderophore receptor	[79]
iss	Serum resistance	[79]
iucC	Aerobactin synthesis	[79]
iutA	Aerobactin receptor	[79]
sitA	Iron transport	[79]
traT	Surface exclusion, serum resistance	[79]
tsh	Temperature-sensitive hemagglutinin	[79]
feoB	Iron uptake	[79]
ireA	Siderophore receptor gene	[79]
irp-2	*Yersiniabactin* synthesis	[79]
hlyD	Hemolysin transport	[79]
fliC	Flagellin protein	[79]
papA	Structural subunit of P pilus	[102]
papC	Pilus assembly	[102]
papEF	Minor tip pilins	[102]
pagG	Gal specific pilus tip adhesion molecule	[102]
allele I	J96-associated *papG* variant	[102]
allele II	Pyelonephritis-associated *papG* variant	[102]
allele III	Cystitis-associated *papG* variant	[102]
sfa	S fimbriae	[102]
sfaS	Pilus tip adhesion, S fimbriae	[102]
focG	Pilus tip molecule, F1C	[102]

Gene	Gene Function	Reference*
iha	Novel nonhemagglutinin adhesion	[102]
afa	Central region of DR antigen specific fimbrial adhesion	[102]
gafD	N-acetyl-D-Glucosamine-specific fimbriae adhesion	[102]
bmaE	Blood group M-specific adhesion	[102]
nfaE	Nonfimbrial adhesion I assembly and transport	[102]
fimH	D-mannose-specific adhesion, type 1 fimbriae	[102]
hlyA	α-Hemolysin	[102]
cnfl	Cytotoxic necrotizing factor 1	[102]
cdtB	Cytolethal distending toxin	[102]
kpsMT II	Group II capsular polysaccharide synthesis	[102]
kpsMT K1	Specific for K1 kpsMT	[102]
kpsMT "K5"	Specific for non-K1 and non-K2 group II kpsMT	[102]
kpsMT III	Group III capsular polysaccharide synthesis	[102]
rfc	O4 lipopolysaccharide synthesis	[102]
fyuA	Yersinia siderophore receptor	[102]
ibeA	Invasion of brain endothelium	[102]
ompT	Outer membrane protein T	[102]

*Genes compiled in the reference manuscripts, but originally described elsewhere.

PCR genotyping has also been used to investigate the zoonotic potential among extraintestinal pathogenic *E. coli* (ExPEC) infections [79-81]. Rodriguez-Siek et al (2005) compared *E. coli* isolates from human urinary tract infections with *E.coli* isolates from avian colibacillosis and suggested that avian pathogentic *E. coli* (APEC) may serve as a reservoir of virulence genes for uropathogenic *E. coli* (UPEC) [81]. Johnson et al. (2007) used amplification profiling of virulence genes to genotype *E. coli* isolates from humans and poultry and found that there was genotypic overlap among poultry isolates and antimicrobial resistant isolates recovered from humans [82]. In another study, Johnson et al (2008) compared ExPEC isolates representing APEC, UPEC, and neonatal meningitis *E. coli* [81] and showed that while each subpathotype were genetically distinct according to cluster analysis, a subset of isolates from each subpathotype overlapped in possession of virulence genes. Analysis showed that many of these isolates contained plasmid mediated virulence genes, further strengthening the hypothesis that APEC isolates or their plasmids serve as a reservoirs of virulence genes for ExPEC [81].

Virulence and Resistance Genes of Campylobacter

Campylobacter is recognized as the leading cause of foodborne disease in both the United States and developing countries [28, 83] *Campylobacter* can be found in the feces of poultry and cattle livestock, as well as in wild birds [84, 85]. *Campylobacter* infections occur primarily through consumption of contaminated food, milk and water. *Campylobacter* infection in humans is mainly associated with two species, *Campylobacter jejuni* (*C. jejuni*) and *Campylobacter coli* (*C. coli*) [83]. Recent studies have suggested that great virulence of *Campylobacter* isolates may be associated with increased antibiotic resistant strains [86].

Virulence genes commonly used to characterize *Campylobacter* isolates are summarized in Table 5 [84-88]. Datta et al. showed that in a sample of 231 *Campylobacter* isolates collected chickens, the majority of isolates contained 11 different virulence genes [85]. All isolates were positive for five virulence factors while other virulence factors were detected at high but varying levels. Thakur et al. characterized 360 *Campylobacter* isolates from retail meats and clinical human cases and found that virulence genes were more prevalent in isolates from retail meats then from clinical cases [85].

Table 5. Virulence genes used in PCR genotyping of *Campylobacter species*

Gene	Gene Function	Reference*
cadF	Adhesion Invasion	[85]
flaA	Motility	[85]
dnaJ	Colonization	[85]
pldA	Pathogenesis	[85]
virB11	Plasmid encoded pathogenesis	[85]
racR	Colonization	[85]
cdtA	Damages host enterocytes	[85]
cdtB	Penetration of epithelium	[85]
cdtC	Invasion	[85]
ciaB	Invasion expression	[84]
wlaN	Expression of Gullian-Barre syndrome	[84]

*Genes described elsewhere but compiled here.

CONCLUSIONS AND FUTURE DIRECTIONS

PCR genotyping of virulence and antimicrobial resistance genes is a relatively quick and inexpensive typing method for foodborne pathogens. While not as discriminatory as other typing methods, PCR genotyping can provide researchers with valuable information in regards to virulence potential and antimicrobial resistance profile. With the development of multiplex PCR and microarray technology, data can be generated faster than ever before. For these reasons, it is likely that this method will continue to be utilized by researchers in the foreseeable future.

New technologies will likely push the development of faster and cheaper methods for molecular typing. Currently, next generation DNA sequencers have allowed the sequencing of entire genomes in a fraction of time as classical methods for a fraction of the cost. As these technologies improve, PCR genotyping may become a less prominent means to type bacterial pathogens. However, until these technologies become more cost-effective, PCR genotyping will likely continued to be used.

REFERENCES

[1] Hudson CR, Quist C, Lee MD, Keyes K, Dodson SV, Morales C, et al. Genetic relatedness of *Salmonella* isolates from nondomestic birds in Southeastern United States. *J Clin Microbiol.* 2000;38(5):1860-5.

[2] Hirose K, Itoh K, Nakajima H, Kurazono T, Yamaguchi M, Moriya K, et al. Selective amplification of *tyv (rfbE), prt (rfbS), viaB,* and *fliC* genes by multiplex PCR for

identification of *Salmonella enterica* serovars Typhi and Paratyphi A. *J Clin Microbiol.* 2002;40(2):633-6.

[3]   Grant MA, Hu J, Jinneman KC. Multiplex real-time PCR detection of heat-labile and heat-stable toxin genes in enterotoxigenic *Escherichia coli. J Food Prot.* 2006;69(2):412-6.

[4]   Gordon DM. Geographical structure and host specificity in bacteria and the implications for tracing the source of coliform contamination. *Microbiology.* 2001;147(Pt 5):1079-85.

[5]   Soto SM, Rodriguez I, Rodicio MR, Vila J, Mendoza MC. Detection of virulence determinants in clinical strains of *Salmonella enterica* serovar Enteritidis and mapping on macrorestriction profiles. *J Med Microbiol.* 2006;55(Pt 4):365-73.

[6]   Skyberg JA, Logue CM, Nolan LK. Virulence genotyping of *Salmonella* spp. with multiplex PCR. *Avian Dis.* 2006;50(1):77-81.

[7]   Simmons KW, Wooley RE, Brown J. Comparison of virulence factors and R plasmids of *Salmonella* spp. isolated from healthy and ill swine. *Appl Environ Microbiol* 1988;54(3):760-7.

[8]   Nde CW, Logue CM. Characterization of antimicrobial susceptibility and virulence genes of *Salmonella* serovars collected at a commercial turkey processing plant. *J Appl Microbiol.* 2008;104(1):215-23.

[9]   Nayak R, Stewart T, Wang RF, Lin J, Cerniglia CE, Kenney PB. Genetic diversity and virulence gene determinants of antibiotic-resistant *Salmonella* isolated from preharvest turkey production sources. *Int J Food Microbiol* 2004;91(1):51-62.

[10] Miller MB, Tang YW. Basic concepts of microarrays and potential applications in clinical microbiology. *Clin Microbiol Rev.* 2009;22(4):611-33.

[11] Cheung VG, Morley M, Aguilar F, Massimi A, Kucherlapati R, Childs G. Making and reading microarrays. *Nat Genet.* 1999;21(1 Suppl):15-9.

[12] Fan JB, Gunderson KL, Bibikova M, Yeakley JM, Chen J, Wickham Garcia E, et al. Illumina universal bead arrays. *Methods Enzymol.* 2006;410:57-73.

[13] Cassone M, Giordano A, Pozzi G. Bacterial DNA microarrays for clinical microbiology: the early logarithmic phase. *Front Biosci.* 2007;12:2658-69.

[14] Majtan T, Majtanova L, Timko J, Majtan V. Oligonucleotide microarray for molecular characterization and genotyping of *Salmonella* spp. strains. *J Antimicrob Chemother.* 2007;60(5):937-46.

[15] Bruant G, Maynard C, Bekal S, Gaucher I, Masson L, Brousseau R, et al. Development and validation of an oligonucleotide microarray for detection of multiple virulence and antimicrobial resistance genes in *Escherichia coli. Appl Environ Microbiol* 2006;72(5):3780-4.

[16] Chizhikov V, Rasooly A, Chumakov K, Levy DD. Microarray analysis of microbial virulence factors. *Appl Environ Microbiol.* 2001;67(7):3258-63.

[17] Walsh F, Cooke NM, Smith SG, Moran GP, Cooke FJ, Ivens A, et al. Comparison of two DNA microarrays for detection of plasmid-mediated antimicrobial resistance and virulence factor genes in clinical isolates of Enterobacteriaceae and non-Enterobacteriaceae. *Int J Antimicrob Agents.* 2010;35(6):593-8.

[18] Litrup E, Torpdahl M, Malorny B, Huehn S, Helms M, Christensen H, et al. DNA microarray analysis of *Salmonella* serotype Typhimurium strains causing different symptoms of disease. *BMC Microbiol.* 2010;10:96.

[19] Lindsey RL, Frye JG, Fedorka-Cray PJ, Welch TJ, Meinersmann RJ. An oligonucleotide microarray to characterize multidrug resistant plasmids. *J Microbiol Methods*. 2010;81(2):96-100.

[20] Lynne AM, Rhodes-Clark BS, Bliven K, Zhao S, Foley SL. Antimicrobial resistance genes associated with *Salmonella enterica* serovar newport isolates from food animals. *Antimicrob Agents Chemother*. 2008;52(1):353-6.

[21] Kaldhone P, Nayak R, Lynne AM, David DE, McDermott PF, Logue CM, et al. Characterization of *Salmonella enterica* serovar Heidelberg from Turkey-Associated Sources. *Appl Environ Microbiol*. 2008;74:5038–46.

[22] Lynne AM, Kaldhone P, David DE, White DG, Foley SL. Characterization og antimicrobial resistance in *Salmonella enterica* serotype Heidleberg isolated from food animals. *Foodborne Pathog Dis*. 2008;6:207-15.

[23] Johnson TJ, Giddings CW, Horne SM, Gibbs PS, Wooley RE, Skyberg J, et al. Location of increased serum survival gene and selected virulence traits on a conjugative R plasmid in an avian *Escherichia coli* isolate. *Avian Dis*. 2002;46(2):342-52.

[24] Johnson TJ, Siek KE, Johnson SJ, Nolan LK. DNA sequence of a ColV plasmid and prevalence of selected plasmid-encoded virulence genes among avian *Escherichia coli* strains. *J Bacteriol*. 2006;188(2):745-58.

[25] Johnson TJ, Kariyawasam S, Wannemuehler Y, Mangiamele P, Johnson SJ, Doetkott C, et al. The genome sequence of avian pathogenic *Escherichia coli* strain O1:K1:H7 shares strong similarities with human extraintestinal pathogenic E. coli genomes. *J Bacteriol*. 2007;189(8):3228-36.

[26] Johnson TJ, Johnson SJ, Nolan LK. Complete DNA sequence of a ColBM plasmid from avian pathogenic *Escherichia coli* suggests that it evolved from closely related ColV virulence plasmids. *J Bacteriol*. 2006;188(16):5975-83.

[27] Johnson JR, O'Bryan TT, Delavari P, Kuskowski M, Stapleton A, Carlino U, et al. Clonal relationships and extended virulence genotypes among *Escherichia coli* isolates from women with a first or recurrent episode of cystitis. *J Infect Dis*. 2001;183(10):1508-17.

[28] Mead PS, Slutsker L, Dietz V, McCaig LF, Bresee JS, Shapiro C, et al. Food-related illness and death in the United States. *Emerg Infect Dis*. 1999;5(5):607-25.

[29] Voetsch AC, Van Gilder TJ, Angulo FJ, Farley MM, Shallow S, Marcus R, et al. FoodNet estimate of the burden of illness caused by nontyphoidal *Salmonella* infections in the United States. Clin Infect Dis 2004;38 Suppl 3:S127-34.

[30] Darwin KH, Miller VL. Molecular basis of the interaction of *Salmonella* with the intestinal mucosa. *Clin Microbiol Rev* 1999;12(3):405-28.

[31] Brenner FW, Villar RG, Angulo FJ, Tauxe R, Swaminathan B. *Salmonella* nomenclature. *J Clin Microbiol*. 2000;38(7):2465-7.

[32] Centers for Disease Control and Prevention. Preliminary FoodNet data on the incidence of infection with pathogens transmitted commonly through food--10 states, United States, 2005. *MMWR Morb Mortal Wkly Rep* 2006;55(14):392-5.

[33] Sandvang D, Aarestrup FM, Jensen LB. Characterisation of integrons and antibiotic resistance genes in Danish multiresistant *Salmonella enterica* Typhimurium DT104. *FEMS Microbiol Lett*. 1997;157(1):177-81.

[34] Gebreyes WA, Davies PR, Turkson PK, Morrow WE, Funk JA, Altier C, et al. Characterization of antimicrobial-resistant phenotypes and genotypes among

Salmonella enterica recovered from pigs on farms, from transport trucks, and from pigs after slaughter. *J Food Prot* 2004;67(4):698-705.

[35] Gebreyes WA, Davies PR, Morrow WE, Funk JA, Altier C. Antimicrobial resistance of *Salmonella* isolates from swine. *J Clin Microbiol* 2000;38(12):4633-6.

[36] Gebreyes WA, Thakur S, Davies PR, Funk JA, Altier C. Trends in antimicrobial resistance, phage types and integrons among *Salmonella* serotypes from pigs, 1997-2000. *J Antimicrob Chemother* 2004;53(6):997-1003.

[37] Gebreyes WA, Thakur S, Dorr P, Tadesse DA, Post K, Wolf L. Occurrence of *spvA* virulence gene and clinical significance for multidrug-resistant *Salmonella* strains. *J Clin Microbiol*. 2009;47(3):777-80.

[38] Kaldhone P, Nayak R, Lynne AM, White DG, Logue CM, Foley SL. Characterization of antimicrobial resistance in *Salmonella enterica* serovar Heidelberg from turkey-associated sources. Abstracts of the North Central Branch of the American Society for Microbiology; Marshfield, WI. 2007.

[39] Lynne AM, Dorsey LL, David D, Kaldhone P, Foley SL. Genetic Characterization of antimicrobial resistance in host-adapted *Salmonella enterica*. *Int J Antimicrob Agents*. 2009;34(2):169-72.

[40] Parvathi A, Vijayan J, Murali G, Chandran P. Comparative virulence genotyping and antimicrobial susceptibility profiling of environmental and clinical *Salmonella enterica* from Cochin, India. *Curr Microbiol*. 2010 May 19.

[41] Li Q, Skyberg JA, Fakhr MK, Sherwood JS, Nolan LK, Logue CM. Antimicrobial susceptibility and characterization of *Salmonella* isolates from processed bison carcasses. *Appl Environ Microbiol* 2006;72(4):3046-9.

[42] Smith KP, George J, Cadle KM, Kumar S, Aragon SJ, Hernandez RL, et al. Elucidation of antimicrobial susceptibility profiles and genotyping of *Salmonella enterica* isolates from clinical cases of salmonellosis in New Mexico in 2008. *World J Microbiol Biotechnol*. 2010;26(6):1025-31.

[43] Patchanee P, Zewde BM, Tadesse DA, Hoet A, Gebreyes WA. Characterization of multidrug-resistant *Salmonella enterica* serovar Heidelberg isolated from humans and animals. *Foodborne Pathog Dis*. 2008;5(6):839-51.

[44] Poppe C, Martin L, Muckle A, Archambault M, McEwen S, Weir E. Characterization of antimicrobial resistance of *Salmonella* Newport isolated from animals, the environment, and animal food products in Canada. *Can J Vet Res* 2006;70(2):105-14.

[45] Aarestrup FM, Hasman H, Olsen I, Sorensen G. International spread of bla(CMY-2)-mediated cephalosporin resistance in a multiresistant *Salmonella enterica* serovar Heidelberg isolate stemming from the importation of a boar by Denmark from Canada. *Antimicrob Agents Chemother* 2004;48(5):1916-7.

[46] Randall LP, Cooles SW, Osborn MK, Piddock LJ, Woodward MJ. Antibiotic resistance genes, integrons and multiple antibiotic resistance in thirty-five serotypes of *Salmonella enterica* isolated from humans and animals in the UK. *J Antimicrob Chemother* 2004;53(2):208-16.

[47] del Cerro A, Soto SM, Mendoza MC. Virulence and antimicrobial-resistance gene profiles determined by PCR-based procedures for *Salmonella* isolated from samples of animal origin. *Food Microbiology*. 2003;20:431-8.

[48] Foley SL, Lynne AM. Food animal-associated *Salmonella* challenges: pathogenicity and antimicrobial resistance. *J Anim Sci*. 2008; 86: E173-187E.

[49] Gulig PA, Danbara H, Guiney DG, Lax AJ, Norel F, Rhen M. Molecular analysis of spv virulence genes of the *Salmonella* virulence plasmids. *Mol Microbiol.* 1993;7(6):825-30.

[50] Baumler AJ, Tsolis RM, van der Velden AW, Stojiljkovic I, Anic S, Heffron F. Identification of a new iron regulated locus of *Salmonella typhi*. *Gene.* 1996;183(1-2):207-13.

[51] Prager R, Fruth A, Tschape H. *Salmonella* enterotoxin (*stn*) gene is prevalent among strains of *Salmonella enterica*, but not among *Salmonella* bongori and other Enterobacteriaceae. *FEMS Immunol Med Microbiol.* 1995;12(1):47-50.

[52] Chopra I, Roberts M. Tetracycline antibiotics: mode of action, applications, molecular biology, and epidemiology of bacterial resistance. *Microbiol Mol Biol Rev* 2001;65(2):232-60.

[53] Huovinen P, Sundstrom L, Swedberg G, Skold O. Trimethoprim and sulfonamide resistance. *Antimicrob Agents Chemother* 1995;39(2):279-89.

[54] Shaw KJ, Rather PN, Hare RS, Miller GH. Molecular genetics of aminoglycoside resistance genes and familial relationships of the aminoglycoside-modifying enzymes. *Microbiol Rev* 1993;57(1):138-63.

[55] Livermore DM. beta-Lactamases in laboratory and clinical resistance. *Clin Microbiol Rev* 1995;8(4):557-84.

[56] Chen S, Zhao S, White DG, Schroeder CM, Lu R, Yang H, et al. Characterization of multiple-antimicrobial-resistant *Salmonella* serovars isolated from retail meats. *Appl Environ Microbiol.* 2004;70(1):1-7.

[57] Doublet B, Carattoli A, Whichard JM, White DG, Baucheron S, Chaslus-Dancla E, et al. Plasmid-mediated florfenicol and ceftriaxone resistance encoded by the floR and bla(CMY-2) genes in *Salmonella enterica* serovars Typhimurium and Newport isolated in the United States. *FEMS Microbiol Lett* 2004;233(2):301-5.

[58] White DG, Datta A, McDermott P, Friedman S, Qaiyumi S, Ayers S, et al. Antimicrobial susceptibility and genetic relatedness of *Salmonella* serovars isolated from animal-derived dog treats in the USA. *J Antimicrob Chemother* 2003;52(5):860-3.

[59] White DG, Zhao S, McDermott PF, Ayers S, Friedman S, Sherwood J, et al. Characterization of integron mediated antimicrobial resistance in *Salmonella* isolated from diseased swine. *Can J Vet Res* 2003;67(1):39-47.

[60] Zhao S, McDermott PF, Friedman S, Abbott J, Ayers S, Glenn A, et al. Antimicrobial resistance and genetic relatedness among *Salmonella* from retail foods of animal origin: NARMS retail meat surveillance. *Foodborne Pathog Dis* 2006;3(1):106-17.

[61] Zhao S, White DG, McDermott PF, Friedman S, English L, Ayers S, et al. Identification and expression of cephamycinase *bla*(CMY) genes in *Escherichia coli* and *Salmonella* isolates from food animals and ground meat. *Antimicrob Agents Chemother* 2001;45(12):3647-50.

[62] Olah PA, Sherwood JS, Logue CM. Molecular analysis of *Salmonella* isolates recovered from processed Turkey carcasses. *J Food Prot* 2005;68(4):845-9.

[63] Gebreyes WA, Altier C. Molecular characterization of multidrug-resistant *Salmonella enterica* subsp. enterica serovar Typhimurium isolates from swine. *J Clin Microbiol.* 2002;40(8):2813-22.

[64] Sandvang D, Aarestrup FM, Jensen LB. Characterisation of integrons and antibiotic resistance genes in Danish multiresistant *Salmonella enterica* Typhimurium DT104. *FEMS Microbiol Lett.* 1998;160(1):37-41.

[65] Welch TJ, Fricke WF, McDermott PF, White DG, Rosso ML, Rasko DA, et al. Multiple antimicrobial resistance in plague: an emerging public health risk. *PLoS ONE* 2007;2:e309.

[66] Gazouli M, Sidorenko SV, Tzelepi E, Kozlova NS, Gladin DP, Tzouvelekis LS. A plasmid-mediated beta-lactamase conferring resistance to cefotaxime in a *Salmonella typhimurium* clone found in St Petersburg, Russia. *J Antimicrob Chemother.* 1998;41(1):119-21.

[67] Kesah CN, Coker AO, Alabi SA, Olukoya DK. Prevalence, antimicrobial properties and beta-lactamase production of haemolytic enterobacteria in patients with diarrhoea and urinary tract infections in Legos, Nigeria. *Cent Afr J Med.* 1996;42(5):147-50.

[68] Verdet C, Arlet G, Ben Redjeb S, Ben Hassen A, Lagrange PH, Philippon A. Characterisation of CMY-4, an AmpC-type plasmid-mediated beta-lactamase in a Tunisian clinical isolate of Proteus mirabilis. *FEMS Microbiol Lett.* 1998;169(2):235-40.

[69] Hohmann EL. Nontyphoidal salmonellosis. *Clin Infect Dis.* 2001;32(2):263-9.

[70] Slanec T, Fruth A, Creuzburg K, Schmidt H. Molecular analysis of virulence profiles and Shiga toxin genes in food-borne Shiga toxin-producing *Escherichia coli. Appl Environ Microbiol.* 2009;75(19):6187-97.

[71] Boerlin P. Evolution of virulence factors in Shiga-toxin-producing *Escherichia coli. Cell Mol Life Sci.* 1999;56(9-10):735-41.

[72] Abu-Ali GS, Ouellette LM, Henderson ST, Lacher DW, Riordan JT, Whittam TS, et al. Increased adherence and expression of virulence genes in a lineage of *Escherichia coli* O157:H7 commonly associated with human infections. *PLoS One.* 5(4):e10167.

[73] Murinda SE, Ebner PD, Nguyen LT, Mathew AG, Oliver SP. Antimicrobial resistance and class 1 integrons in pathogenic *Escherichia coli* from dairy farms. *Foodborne Pathog Dis.* 2005;2(4):348-52.

[74] Islam MA, Mondol AS, de Boer E, Beumer RR, Zwietering MH, Talukder KA, et al. Prevalence and genetic characterization of shiga toxin-producing *Escherichia coli* isolates from slaughtered animals in Bangladesh. *Appl Environ Microbiol.* 2008;74(17):5414-21.

[75] Toth I, Schmidt H, Kardos G, Lancz Z, Creuzburg K, Damjanova I, et al. Virulence genes and molecular typing of different groups of *Escherichia coli* O157 strains in cattle. *Appl Environ Microbiol.* 2009;75(19):6282-91.

[76] Zhao S, White DG, Ge B, Ayers S, Friedman S, English L, et al. Identification and characterization of integron-mediated antibiotic resistance among Shiga toxin-producing *Escherichia coli* isolates. *Appl Environ Microbiol* 2001;67(4):1558-64.

[77] Meng J, Zhao S, Doyle MP. Virulence genes of Shiga toxin-producing *Escherichia coli* isolated from food, animals and humans. *Int J Food Microbiol.* 1998;45(3):229-35.

[78] Loukiadis E, Kerouredan M, Beutin L, Oswald E, Brugere H. Characterization of Shiga toxin gene (stx)-positive and intimin gene (eae)-positive *Escherichia coli* isolates from wastewater of slaughterhouses in France. *Appl Environ Microbiol.* 2006;72(5):3245-51.

[79] Rodriguez-Siek KE, Giddings CW, Doetkott C, Johnson TJ, Fakhr MK, Nolan LK. Comparison of *Escherichia coli* isolates implicated in human urinary tract infection and avian colibacillosis. *Microbiology.* 2005;151(Pt 6):2097-110.

[80] Johnson JR, McCabe JS, White DG, Johnston B, Kuskowski MA, McDermott P. Molecular Analysis of *Escherichia coli* from retail meats (2002-2004) from the United States National Antimicrobial Resistance Monitoring System. *Clin Infect Dis.* 2009;49(2):195-201.

[81] Johnson TJ, Wannemuehler Y, Johnson SJ, Stell AL, Doetkott C, Johnson JR, et al. Comparison of extraintestinal pathogenic *Escherichia coli* strains from human and avian sources reveals a mixed subset representing potential zoonotic pathogens. *Appl Environ Microbiol.* 2008;74(22):7043-50.

[82] Johnson JR, Sannes MR, Croy C, Johnston B, Clabots C, Kuskowski MA, et al. Antimicrobial drug-resistant *Escherichia coli* from humans and poultry products, Minnesota and Wisconsin, 2002-2004. *Emerg Infect Dis.* 2007;13(6):838-46.

[83] Moore JE, Corcoran D, Dooley JS, Fanning S, Lucey B, Matsuda M, et al. *Campylobacter. Vet Res.* 2005;36(3):351-82.

[84] Datta S, Niwa H, Itoh K. Age-dependent variation of virulence-associated genes retained in Campylobacter jejuni isolated from chickens in a poultry farm. *J Vet Med Sci.* 2009;71(9):1247-9.

[85] Thakur S, Zhao S, McDermott PF, Harbottle H, Abbott J, English L, et al. Antimicrobial resistance, virulence, and genotypic profile comparison of *Campylobacter jejuni* and *Campylobacter coli* isolated from humans and retail meats. *Foodborne Pathog Dis.* 2010;7(7):835-44.

[86] Gormley FJ, Strachan NJ, Reay K, MacKenzie FM, Ogden ID, Dallas JF, et al. Antimicrobial resistance profiles of *Campylobacter* from humans, retail chicken meat, and cattle feces. *Foodborne Pathog Dis.*;7(9):1129-31.

[87] Galan JE, Curtiss R, 3rd. Cloning and molecular characterization of genes whose products allow *Salmonella* typhimurium to penetrate tissue culture cells. *Proc Natl Acad Sci U S A.* 1989;86(16):6383-7.

[88] Jones BD, Falkow S. Identification and characterization of a *Salmonella typhimurium* oxygen-regulated gene required for bacterial internalization. *Infect Immun.* 1994;62(9):3745-52.

[89] Behlau I, Miller SI. A PhoP-repressed gene promotes *Salmonella typhimurium* invasion of epithelial cells. *J Bacteriol.* 1993;175(14):4475-84.

[90] Chen LM, Kaniga K, Galan JE. *Salmonella* spp. are cytotoxic for cultured macrophages. *Mol Microbiol.* 1996;21(5):1101-15.

[91] Stone BJ, Miller VL. *Salmonella* enteritidis has a homologue of *tolC* that is required for virulence in BALB/c mice. *Mol Microbiol.* 1995;17(4):701-12.

[92] Janakiraman A, Slauch JM. The putative iron transport system SitABCD encoded on SPI1 is required for full virulence of *Salmonella typhimurium. Mol Microbiol.* 2000;35(5):1146-55.

[93] Miller SI, Kukral AM, Mekalanos JJ. A two-component regulatory system (*phoP phoQ*) controls *Salmonella typhimurium* virulence. *Proc Natl Acad Sci U S A.* 1989;86(13):5054-8.

[94]   Gunn JS, Alpuche-Aranda CM, Loomis WP, Belden WJ, Miller SI. Characterization of the *Salmonella typhimurium pagC/pagD* chromosomal region. *J Bacteriol.* 1995;177(17):5040-7.

[95]   Ochman H, Soncini FC, Solomon F, Groisman EA. Identification of a pathogenicity island required for *Salmonella* survival in host cells. *Proc Natl Acad Sci U S A.* 1996;93(15):7800-4.

[96]   Baumler AJ, Norris TL, Lasco T, Voight W, Reissbrodt R, Rabsch W, et al. IroN, a novel outer membrane siderophore receptor characteristic of *Salmonella enterica. J Bacteriol.* 1998;180(6):1446-53.

[97]   Parsot C. *Shigella flexneri*: genetics of entry and intercellular dissemination in epithelial cells. *Curr Top Microbiol Immunol.* 1994;192:217-41.

[98]   Baumler AJ, Tsolis RM, Heffron F. The lpf fimbrial operon mediates adhesion of *Salmonella typhimurium* to murine Peyer's patches. *Proc Natl Acad Sci U S A* 1996;93(1):279-83.

[99]   Haghjoo E, Galan JE. *Salmonella* typhi encodes a functional cytolethal distending toxin that is delivered into host cells by a bacterial-internalization pathway. *Proc Natl Acad Sci U S A.* 2004;101(13):4614-9.

[100] Stein MA, Leung KY, Zwick M, Garcia-del Portillo F, Finlay BB. Identification of a *Salmonella* virulence gene required for formation of filamentous structures containing lysosomal membrane glycoproteins within epithelial cells. *Mol Microbiol.* 1996;20(1):151-64.

[101] van der Velden AW, Baumler AJ, Tsolis RM, Heffron F. Multiple fimbrial adhesins are required for full virulence of *Salmonella typhimurium* in mice. *Infect Immun.* 1998;66(6):2803-8.

[102] Johnson JR, Delavari P, Kuskowski M, Stell AL. Phylogenetic distribution of extraintestinal virulence-associated traits in *Escherichia coli. J Infect Dis.* 2001;183(1):78-88.

In: Molecular Typing Methods for TFM
Editors: S. Foley, R. Nayak, T. Johnson et al.

ISBN: 978-1-62100-643-5
© 2012 Nova Science Publishers, Inc.

Chapter 13

APPLICATION OF DNA MICROARRAY TECHNOLOGY FOR MICROBIAL SOURCE TRACKING

Jonathan G. Frye

Bacterial Epidemiology and Antimicrobial Resistance Research Unit
Agricultural Research Service
US Department of Agriculture
Athens, GA, US

ABSTRACT

Typing of foodborne microorganisms for source tracking was radically improved with the implementation of molecular techniques. These assays were designed to detect genetic differences in lineages of foodborne organisms. Molecular techniques can detect the natural variability in the genome of a microbe and use this information to identify genotypes of the organism that can be traced to a specific food source. DNA microarrays have been employed in this effort and offer several advantages over genomic analyses with other molecular methods. Microarrays usually have DNA probes immobilized on a solid surface, with each probe complementary to a specific sequence in the organism's genome. During hybridization of the microbes' DNA to the microarray, sequences that match probes on the array will hybridize to them and then be detected and scored. The microarray probes are often arrayed at a very high density, enabling a single assay to detect from hundreds to millions of sequences. Because of this, DNA microarrays can determine enough genetic characteristics to be used for typing microbes at sufficient detail to be used for source tracking. However, methods in microarray design, construction, and utilization are complex, resulting in different array platforms developed by investigators or manufactured by commercial companies. Additionally, the data collected by each microarray platform may not yield the same level of discrimination, making it difficult to compare data across microarray platforms. This chapter will explain the basic concepts of DNA microarrays, introduce common platforms, and present examples of microarrays used for typing of foodborne microorganisms.

INTRODUCTION

Background

Detection, typing, and trace-back of microbes remains a major food safety goal [1–3]. Ideally, if a microbial food contaminant or a pathogen isolated from a patient could be detected and identified with enough precision, it would be possible to identify an organism's lineage and use that information to determine sources of foodborne contamination. DNA sequences specific to a microbe have been used extensively to detect and to type them. Detection can be as simple as a Polymerase Chain Reaction (PCR) amplification of a unique sequence. However, typing is usually more complex and depends on the level of discrimination needed to achieve the assay's goal. As data from large sequencing projects ushered in the age of genomics, foodborne microbes were among the first organisms to be completely sequenced [4, 5]. One of the tools developed to capitalize on this information was the DNA microarray. Microarray technology allowed probes to be designed to detect virtually any unique DNA sequence. These probes could be assembled into an array of genetic tests performed in a single assay [6–10]. Analysis can be accomplished by hybridizing labeled DNA to the complementary probes on the microarray and then detecting the hybridizations to specific gene probes. The identification of nucleic acid sequences by hybridization was developed more than 30 years ago, simply described, the DNA microarray is a high density version of the Southern, Northern, or dot blot assays [11]. The advantage of microarrays is they can contain from hundreds to millions of probes and can thus detect large numbers of different nucleic acid sequences [6, 10]. This gives microarrays the potential to determine molecular types of microbes with enough detail for source tracking [1–3].

Microarrays are essentially an array of probes designed to detect specific target sequences [6, 10]. Throughout this chapter, "probe" will refer to the DNA attached to the array used to detect sequences, and "target" to the labeled DNA being analyzed by the microarray. Microarrays were first designed to detect gene expression [6, 10]. This was done by competitive hybridization of differentially labeled complementary DNA (cDNA) synthesized from experimental and control conditions messenger RNA (mRNA). These two targets were hybridized to the microarray, thus allowing differences in a gene's expression to be calculated as the ratio of the hybridization signal from the two samples to each gene's probe. Microarray technology was also developed for many other research goals where a target sample needed to be analyzed for many sequences in a single assay. This included Comparative Genomic Hybridizations (CGH, or Comparative Genomic Indexing, CGI) [7, 12–14], which use whole genome microarrays containing a probe for each gene found in an organism's type strain. In CGH, DNA from an unknown strain is hybridized to a whole genome microarray, and the presence or absence of genes in the unknown strain is determined relative to the sequenced type strain of the organism used to design the microarray [15]. This provides a large amount of genetic information on the unknown strain in a single assay. This data could be used to determine genotypes of unknown strains and could also be used for phylogenetic studies [16–19]. This technique was compared to other molecular typing techniques, such as Pulsed Field Gel Electrophoresis (PFGE), Multilocus Sequence Typing (MLST), etc., and found to be a comparable sub-typing tool [20–23]. Other applications for microarrays included the detection of specific pathogens, virulence genes, antimicrobial resistance genes or other genetic characteristics [19, 24–32]. The arrays could also be used in conjunction with other techniques like PCR, where the amplicons from a PCR or multiplexed assay could be accurately scored on a microarray [31–35]. These assays could be used for detection and/or subtyping of the targeted microbes. The theoretical design, development, and utilization of these microarray techniques have been well described and reviewed in the literature [6–10]. The objective of this chapter is to provide an overview of the technology, its applications and its limitations, and how data derived from various types of microarrays can be used to track foodborne microbes.

Microarray Technology

Microarrays are typically composed of DNA probes that are either PCR products or long, single-stranded oligonucleotides attached to the surface of a solid substrate. Early arrays were usually composed of PCR products of the genes to be detected and were often the entire open reading frame (ORF) [6–10, 36]. This required a DNA template, primers specific for the gene, clean-up following the PCR reaction, and addition of printing buffer before spotting onto the substrate (often referred to as "printing"). As oligonucleotides became less expensive, long oligonucleotides (21–70mer) were designed as probes, synthesized, dissolved in printing buffer, and then spotted onto the substrate, thus alleviating many of the laborious steps required to manufacture PCR probes [37]. In the case of some commercially manufactured microarrays, the oligonucleotides are synthesized in-situ on the substrate surface.

The combination of the specific substrate, type of probes, and detection methods is referred to as the platform. Platforms vary from custom or home-made arrays consisting of probes printed on glass slides to those manufactured by commercial suppliers where probes are synthesized in-situ, printed with inkjet technology, or attached to labeled beads and scored in a solution rather than on a single solid surface [38]. The type of platform chosen for array construction profoundly affects what the microarray can achieve, the type of data the assay will yield, and how it can be interpreted. In most cases, nucleic acid samples, or targets, analyzed by the microarray are labeled in some way so that once hybridized to a probe, they can be detected (Figure 1) [38]. Most often this is with a fluorescent compound that can later be detected by laser excitation and image capture with a photomultiplier tube in a microarray scanner, but labeling can also include chemical and other detection methods. The labeled targets are mixed with hybridization buffer and placed in contact with the probes where they can hybridize to any complementary sequences in the probes. After hybridization, the microarray is washed with buffers to remove any targets that have non-specifically bound to probes or the surface of the array substrate. Next the microarray is scanned to detect hybridization to specific probes. Labeling, hybridization and detection are also dependent on the array platform used [38]. Finally, the images obtained from scanning are analyzed and scored for the detection of sequences in the target sample by the intensity of signal from the hybridization to the probes. While this is an overview of the concept, the technical details mandated by the platform and the assay design differ significantly [38, 39].

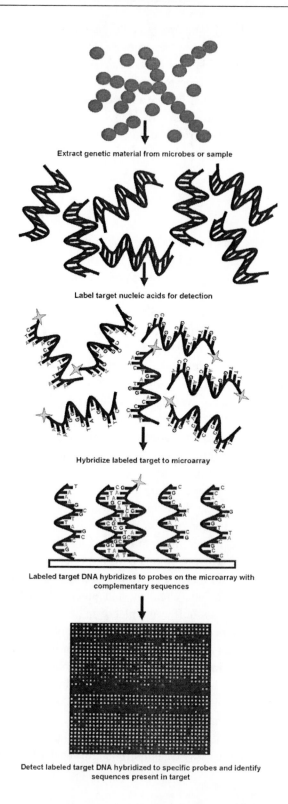

Extract genetic material from microbes or sample

Label target nucleic acids for detection

Hybridize labeled target to microarray

Labeled target DNA hybridizes to probes on the microarray with complementary sequences

Detect labeled target DNA hybridized to specific probes and identify sequences present in target

Figure 1. Analysis of a microbe's genetic material by DNA microarray hybridization.

MICROARRAY ASSAY DESIGN

Microarray Assays for Detection, Identification and Typing

One of the first microarray design decisions that must be made is determining the goal of the assay. Microarrays can be employed many different ways to address food safety issues [1, 3, 39, 40]. Some assays have been designed to detect and identify microbes directly in samples taken from food, animals, patients and the environment. These assays can be highly multiplexed to interrogate the sample for many different organisms or genes in a single assay. As with all DNA sequence detection assay, a major caveat is that presence of a DNA marker does not necessarily indicate a viable or infectious organism was present in the sample. Microarray detection assays can also include an amplification step (e.g., PCR) to increase the sensitivity and enable the detection of small numbers of organisms [34, 35, 41, 42]. These assays can be based on detection of a single DNA sequence for an organism or multiple sequences. As the number of genetic elements detected increases, the assay provides more information about the microbe(s) in the sample. Eventually, enough character states may be determined for the organism to discriminate different subtypes. Assays that can accomplish this can be used for typing and potentially source tracking. In the event that the organism under investigation is in pure culture, and thus detection is not an issue, then a microarray assay can be designed specifically for typing. One of the first types of microarray used for this was the whole genome microarray, designed primarily for gene expression studies, which could be used to perform CGH. Whole genome CGH can be a powerful typing tool, assuming the differences in gene presence and absence of isolates is variable enough to be informative [7, 12–14]. However, before data of gene content differences can be used as a typing method, it must be compared to previous typing methods [16, 21–23, 43]. Other typing arrays have been designed to detect genes that relate specifically to phylogeny or important phenotypes such as virulence and antimicrobial resistance [27, 28, 31, 32, 44–51]. Microarrays have also been designed to directly replace other forms of subtyping. An example of this are microarrays designed to replace serotyping for organisms, such as *Salmonella enterica* and *Escherichia coli* [32, 52, 53]. Some investigators have also invested in microarrays capable of re-sequencing an isolate's whole genome to yield a greater level of genetic discrimination, the single nucleotide polymorphism (SNP) type or sequence type of an organism [54].

Targets for Microarray Detection and Typing Assays

Genes and other sequences to be detected by the microarray need to be carefully chosen during array design (Figure 2). For detection assays, it is imperative to identify genes or sequences that are specific for the organism to be detected, and those sequences that will not cross hybridize with any other sequences in the target sample. This is even more important for typing assays, as it may be desirable to differentiate isolates with very few or small genetic differences. The targets for probe design must vary in their distribution in different types or lineages of a microbe to be informative as to which "type" of the bacteria would have positive or negative hybridizations to each probe. This will require analysis to determine genes that are type specific, such as sequencing or CGH analysis of multiple strains or other genetic information [7, 12–14]. The sequences to be targeted may not necessarily be associated with a lineage's phenotypic characteristics, or the probes may directly target the genes that lead to the phenotype, as in the example of genes that encode antigens responsible for *S. enterica* or *E. coli* serotypes [52, 53]. Whole genome CGH can be used to collect hybridization data on strains found in collections of variants of an organism to help correlate gene presence/absence with the subtypes the assay is designed to differentiate [15, 16, 55]. Eventually, if enough whole genome CGH data is collected, a small number of variably present genes can be identified that are as informative as the whole genome CGH, allowing the use of a smaller set of probes for a microarray or other typing assay, such as multiplex PCR [23, 32, 56–58]. In cases where allele specific information for genes is necessary to successfully determine subtypes, it may be necessary to devise an assay capable of detecting defined SNP types of these genes. In these cases, special platforms, probes and/or labeling techniques may be required to detect SNPs [1, 42, 54, 59–62].

Probe Design

After the genes have been chosen for the assay, probes must be designed to detect them. Almost all DNA sequences can be targeted for detection by microarray, provided they have a unique sequence thermodynamically suitable for probe design [46, 63, 64]. This is most easily accomplished for oligonucleotide probes with freely available computer algorithms that can identify sequences that make good probes and can also compare them to a sequence database to reduce the likelihood of cross reactions with non-target sequences [37, 46, 47, 63–65]. The probe characteristics are dictated mostly by the microarray design and platform used. In the case of commercially manufactured microarrays, probe design is usually included with the service; however, the goals of the assay need to be carefully explained to the company to ensure the desired results are achieved.

DNA MICROARRAY PLATFORMS AND THEIR APPLICATION

Introduction to Popular Microarray Platforms

The choice of platform will affect the assay's design, use, and overall performance. The characteristics of most of the various platforms have been expertly reviewed in several articles [1–3, 38, 39, 66–68]. Therefore, this section will give an overview of platforms that are widely used and responsible for most published applications, discuss their characteristics, and also give some examples of their use, focusing on molecular typing of foodborne organisms. For detailed technical information, please refer to the above referenced articles and the primary literature. In some cases, a few commercial providers have designed microarrays for clinical and/or research purposes. However, most of the microarrays for typing microbes have been custom designed and manufactured by the researchers and clinicians using them. In these cases, the deciding factor for platform choice is usually dictated by the resources available. This includes financial resources and technical skills, as well as access to necessary instrumentation, including, microarray printers, hybridization equipment, scanners and software for analysis. Because of the differences between array platforms, standardization of microarray data across platforms is difficult. Therefore, it is important for anyone using data derived from microarrays to understand clearly how the results should be interpreted. This requires a careful review of the array's design, methods, and validation.

Figure 2. Outline of methods for design, construction and utilization of DNA microarrays.

Commonly used microarrays include custom arrays constructed on a membrane or on glass microscope slides. Membranes were some of the first [69] and consisted of nitrocellulose, positively charged paper or fabric with probes spotted on them either by hand or by using robotics, resulting in a flexible substrate with probes immobilized on its surface. These arrays were processed very similarly to Southern, Northern, or dot blots. However, these had limitations, including the number of probes that could be used and the difficulty and expense of hybridizing and processing the membranes in high volumes of solutions. Glass slides were the next to be widely used, and offered many advantages over membranes, especially the high number of probes that could be placed on the array and the small volume of hybridization solution, which increased the concentration of labeled target and improved sensitivity [8, 9]. Because these have been so widely used, glass slides are the substrate for many of the microarrays used for detection and typing of foodborne microbes. Most other popular platforms are commercially provided. These include in-situ synthesized microarrays by Affymetrix® (Santa Clara, CA, USA), Agilent® (Santa Clara, CA, USA), NimbleGen® (Roche Inc., Madison, WI, USA), and others. Small format microarrays can also be custom designed and ordered from companies, such as the ArrayTube™ (Alere Technologies, formerly Clondiag Chip Technologies, Jena, Germany). Bead-based arrays, such as the Lumenix®(Austin, TX, USA) system provides beads, oligonucleotide design, reagents, and a dedicated instrument (a custom flow cytometer) for scoring hybridizations to the beads. Each of these microarray platforms has their own unique characteristics.

Custom Designed Glass Slide Microarrays

Some of the first microarrays designed and used for nucleic acid analysis were constructed on glass microscope slides [8, 9]. This was enabled by the development of robots capable of printing multiple probes very accurately and in small spots, or "features," allowing thousands of probes to be arrayed on each glass microscope slide. Laser scanners designed to excite fluorescent dye on histological slides and capture highly magnified images with confocal lenses were adapted for scanning microarrays (Figure 2) [8, 9]. This enabled the detection of fluorescently labeled target DNA hybridized to the probes in the minute features on the glass slides. Once this equipment became widely available at research and clinical institutes, it could be used to construct microarrays to investigate almost any sequences. Because these resources are wide-spread, many microarrays described for typing and detection assays are custom glass microscope slide arrays. Additionally, for investigators lacking access to these resources, some commercial companies make custom glass slide microarrays as a fee-for-service arrangement.

These glass microscope slides can be prepared in house, however, best results are usually obtained by purchasing slides commercially manufactured for microarray construction [70]. The slides have specially modified surfaces to enable binding of the probes and to produce low background [70]. The probes designed and printed on the microarrays can be PCR products or oligonucleotides, however, most recently designed arrays use oligonucleotides due to ease of synthesis and no requirement for template DNA, enzymes, and reagents to generate the PCR probes. The length of the probe will dictate what kind of modification of the slide surface is necessary for the probe to bind. For long oligonucleotides (>50mer) and PCR products, the usual choice is amino-silane. This modification allows the DNA to be bound to the surface by ionic bonds between the phosphate backbones of the DNA and the amino groups on the substrate and then attached by cross linking with UV light treatment. For smaller oligonucleotides (<40mer) it is necessary to covalently link them to a substrate coated with epoxy-silane, which requires modification of the probe, usually with an amino group and a six carbon spacer at one end of the oligonucleotide. This can be used to make a covalent linkage to the substrate surface via a reaction between the amino group on the oligonucleotide and the epoxy group on the modified slide surface.

DNA probes for glass microarray construction can be designed by analysis of the target sequences using published free software or software provided by several commercial companies (Figure 2) [37, 46, 47, 63–65]. The user can typically specify the probe length, melting temperature, thermodynamic properties, how many probes per target sequence, location in the sequence, and other parameters to customize the probe sequences designed. Additional steps will have to be taken if the assay is required to differentiate alleles or SNPs through direct hybridization [1, 42, 54, 59–61]. This usually requires very short probes, and a probe for each possible nucleotide at the SNP location. This variable nucleotide is usually positioned in the center of the common probe sequence of each probe. After hybridization, the SNP can be scored based on the relative amount of hybridization to the family of SNP probes, with the perfect match having higher levels of hybridization. However, this is not always possible, and other methods must be employed to detect some SNPs with glass microarrays. Once designed, the probes can be synthesized in-house or ordered from commercial providers. Several commercial companies offer sets of ready-to-print oligonucleiotides designed to construct whole genome microarrays for a number of organisms that can be used for CGH genotyping. These organisms include many of the most important foodborne microbes, such as *Campylobacter jejuni*, STEC *E. coli*, *Listeria* spp., *Salmonella*, etc. Before printing, the probes are dissolved in printing buffer, which is often composed of a salt solution, 50% dimethylsulfoxide (DMSO), or proprietary buffers obtained from the slide manufacturer.

Spotting of the probes onto the glass slide surface is achieved using robotic printers. In the first few years of microarray development, these were hand-made machines, however, most are now 2nd and 3rd generation commercially constructed robots (Figure 2) [8, 9]. Regardless of the type of robot, most glass slide printing is very similar. The printer consists of a deck on which the glass slides are placed with the modified surface facing up. The deck also holds a micro titer plate(s) containing the probe solutions to be printed. A print head holding printing pens that point downward toward the deck is moved over the deck by the robot and lowered (dipped) into the micro titer plate so that the pins can collect a small amount of the probes. The head is then lifted and moved over the slides and lowered to make contact between the pins and the slide surface, depositing a small amount of the probes very accurately onto the substrate. Each pin creates a different spot, or feature, containing many copies of the same sequence probe. Most microarray printing pins are quill type and have a slot reservoir (similar to a fountain pen) in the tip that allows a single dip into the probe solution to print multiple features onto many slides [71]. Between dips into the probe solutions, the pins are lowered into a washing and then a drying station to remove the previous probes from the pins, in order to prevent carryover of previously printed probes into the next set of array features. During printing, the program that controls the robot also records the location of all the probes on the array based on information of the location of probes in the micro titer plate. This information is essential for analysis and will be used later by hybridization analysis software. Once printed, the slides may require post processing before they can be used. This could include UV cross linking of probes to the substrate, denaturing of double stranded DNA PCR probes or blocking the slide surface to reduce non specific target binding (e.g., background hybridization).

Labeling of target DNA for glass slides is also assay specific; however, most applications have some common processes. Labeling of DNA is usually done by direct incorporation of labeled nucleotides during nick-translation or incorporation of a modified nucleotide that can then be chemically linked to a detectable label [8, 9]. During the labeling reaction, a fraction of one of the nucleotides incorporated into the target sequences is modified or includes a dye or tag that can be detected after hybridization. For detection of RNA viruses, reverse transcription may be part of the labeling protocol. Other labeling methods can use direct or indirect chemical labeling. If the assay performs a detection function, or increased sensitivity is required, an amplification step such as PCR may be included during labeling. Special steps during labeling can also be used to detect SNPs in the target sequence and are described below.

After labeling the target DNA, unincorporated dye is usually removed with a clean up step, and the labeled target is mixed with hybridization buffer and denatured by boiling before applied to the surface of the microarray [9]. Hybridization buffer is a salt solution (e.g., sodium chloride and sodium citrate [SSC]) similar to those used in Southern hybridizations, and may contain denaturing chemicals such as DMSO to adjust the stringency of hybridization conditions. The specific buffer composition used is dependent on the array substrate and thermodynamic characteristics of the probes used in the assay. The hybridization solution/target mixture is placed in contact with the microarray surface, and a special cover slip is usually laid over the surface to prevent evaporation during hybridization. Incubation may take a few hours or overnight, and is often done in a sealed hybridization chamber submerged in a water bath to maintain a constant temperature.

After hybridization, the arrays are washed in decreasing concentrations of salt buffers, which slowly increases the stringency of the wash until nonspecific hybridizations are removed [9]. The slide can then be dried and scanned to detect hybridization to each probe. Scanning methods are dependent on the type of microarray and the tag used to label the target DNA. After scanning, the images can be processed with many different software packages, most of which are supplied by the manufacturer of the scanner. This software will allow the data recorded by the printer to identify probes in the microarray images. Further analysis of the image will determine the amount of target DNA hybridization to each probe based on fluorescence (or other signal) at the probe location. The software usually allows for measurement of background hybridization and other parameters to aid in scoring the results. Gene detection array images are generally easier to interpret than gene expression studies using competitive hybridization of control and experimental cDNAs. Usually, positive controls and negative controls are used to determine whether the assay worked within usable parameters and to set cutoff values for positive detection of sequences in the target sample by the probes.

The final step is interpretation of the hybridization results. For glass slide microarrays, the level of detection is usually at the gene or genetic element level and is scored as present or absent (e.g., CGH). If the oligonucleotides are discriminatory enough, alleles of genes or specific SNPs can be detected, which can begin to provide the level of detail given by multi locus sequence typing (MLST) or even whole genome SNP typing, or "re-sequencing."

However, with glass slide microarrays, extra steps and/or multiple probes are usually required to facilitate this level of discrimination. These factors affect how the data can be interpreted. For example, whole genome CGH with long oligonucleotide or PCR product probes will yield gene presence or absence data. However, they cannot usually discriminate specific alleles of genes or determine whether the gene is functional, both of which may result in different types of the organism under investigation. Additionally, if a target strain has genes that were not identified in the type strain(s) used to design the microarray, these genes will be missed and could result in failure to identify certain genotypes of the organism. In the case of detection assays, it is possible that cross hybridization with a similar sequence could give false positive results; likewise, divergence of a gene's sequence in the target strain could result in failure to detect the gene and yield a false negative score. Therefore, validation of a microarray assay with positive and negative controls, followed by blind testing of unknown isolates in comparison to other accepted typing methods, is necessary. Overall, when interpreting data derived from microarray typing or detection assays, it is the responsibility of the person using the data to determine its accuracy. This is not only true for the developers of the assays, but also for anyone considering data collected by these assays. It is crucial to critically assess the validity of the targets, the accuracy of the methods, the results of control assays, and performance of the assays in blind studies. Moreover, as these are relatively new typing methods, the most important consideration will be whether or not the types they yield are truly informative enough for an objective like source tracking.

Custom glass slide microarrays have been successfully designed and used for many detection and a few typing assays, and most of these have been reviewed in the literature [1–3, 38, 39, 67, 68]. CGH using whole genome microarrays has been applied to many foodborne bacterial pathogens [12, 13, 15, 20, 23, 24, 27, 49, 72, 73], some viruses [74], and eukaryotes [61, 75]. One of the first investigated was *Salmonella enterica*, which is one of the most prevalent foodborne bacterial pathogens worldwide. Several groups have used whole or multiple genome *Salmonella* microarrays for genotyping and phylogenetic analysis via CGH [12, 13, 16, 22, 24, 36, 67, 76, 77]. Porwollik *et al.* used CGH data to determine the gene content of representatives of *Salmonella enterica* subspecies I in the *Salmonella* Reference collection B (SARB) as well as the other major subspecies II, IIIa, IIIb, V, VI, VII in *Salmonella* Reference Collection C (SARC) [13, 16]. Among other things, the analysis determined that some *Salmonella* serotypes within the subspecies were polyphyletic based on gene content, indicating that some serotypes are derived from multiple, and in some cases distant, lineages [16]. Based on this the term, "Genovar" was used to describe the different genetic types of *Salmonella* [16]. Several groups used this and other genomic data to devise molecular assays for serotyping, including several small microarrays [30, 32, 58, 78], an assay with a large set of multiplex PCR [79], a rapid multiplex PCR followed by capillary analysis [57], and a Lumenix based method [80]. CGH data for *Salmonella* has been shown to discriminate genetic lineages of *Salmonella* better than serotype and in some cases better than the gold standard, PFGE [16, 81]. However, it has not yet been determined whether CGH could effectively replace PFGE, and it does not seem likely that CGH would be backwards compatible with the extensive data collected for many years by PFGE analyses. Litrup *et al.* compared CGH directly to MLST for certain *Salmonella* serovars and found that cluster analysis of data collected by the two techniques resulted in some of the isolates grouping differently [82]. They suggested that the techniques were somewhat comparable, but because they reported two different measures of genetic variability, they were best used as complementary analyses [82]. Microarrays have been used with some limited success to identify genetic traits associated with foodborne *Salmonella*, including studies of isolates from contaminated almonds [22] and of virulence typing of European isolates [83].

CGH and smaller microarray techniques for typing were developed in a similar manner to *Salmonella* for a number of other foodborne microbes. Some of these are *Campylobacter* [20, 21, 23, 84–86], *Candida* [61], *Cronobacter sakizakii* [87], E. coli [19, 25, 26, 28, 88–90], *Listeria* [43, 91], *Staphylococcus aureus* [92] and others. Most of these have been used for retrospective studies to determine genotypes associated with virulence, antimicrobial resistance, and specific hosts, etc., rather than for tracking foodborne microbes. However, some of the genes and genotypes defined do have an association with human disease and specific animal or environmental sources. Therefore, defining these genotypes may be one of the steps necessary to develop these assays into methods for tracking foodborne microbes. In some cases, simple CGH does not provide enough discrimination to identify types, and other steps were added to the microarray assay to determine type specific alleles via SNP analysis. An example of this type of microarray is one designed to determine MLST types of *Candida* by determining important SNPs that resulted in the different MLST types [61]. This assay employed a probe for each possible SNP, labeled the genes to be tested by PCR, and then determined the allele present based upon the probe with the strongest hybridization signal. Another method developed to type *Noroviruses* combines amplification of specific sequences using RT-PCR targeting the RNA viral genome, followed by hybridization to probes on a glass slide microarray to score the results [74].

Miniaturized Microarrays for Rapid Analyses

Small microarrays capable of rapid analysis can be adapted to very specific typing and detection needs. The ArrayTube (Alere Technologies) is a fairly widely used example of this technology that has produced some microarray assays with potential for clinical applications [33, 93–95]. The ArrayTube consists of 196 oligonucleotide probes immobilized on a membrane in a flow through tube that fits into a standard 1.5 ml microfuge tube. This format allows rapid hybridization, washing and detection of the labeled targets. Additionally, target DNA is labeled with biotin and then detected with horseradish peroxidase-streptavidin conjugate followed by colorimetric development with 3,3',5,5'-tetramethylbenzidine (TMB) and H_2O_2 [52]. This allows labeling and detection without expensive dye linked nucleotides and analysis with a special camera as opposed to a traditional and expensive laser/fluorescent/confocal microarray scanners. The major drawbacks of the ArrayTube are the small number of probes (<196) and the length of the probes requires specially designed assays to detect SNPs. There are several typing assays developed using this technology for foodborne microbes. One, for determination of E. coli serotypes, uses linear amplification of target sequences combined with detection using specific probes on the ArrayTube [52]. Through contracts with the company, investigators can design their own assays for the ArrayTube format. Additionally, Clondiag provides ArrayTube assays designed to genotype E. coli, *Legionella*, *Salmonella*, and *Staphylococcus*, as well as assays to detect antimicrobial resistance genes.

Another unique characteristic of ArrayTubes is their adaptation to universal arrays. Universal arrays have complementary ZIP (cZIP) code sequences attached to the microarray, rather than probes specific for the target genes. This disconnects the sequence detection portion of the assay from the hybridization reaction and enables the same ArrayTube to be adapted for any use by changing the primers in the labeling reaction [96]. This is done by using a primer with a ZIP code sequence on one end and a target-specific probe on the other end. A labeling reaction is performed that will label only those primers that have found a complementary sequence in the target DNA and can then be detected by specific complementary ZIP code (cZIP) hybridization to the ArrayTube. This method has been used for foodborne microbe-typing in an assay designed to detect and type contaminating bacteria in milk samples [97]. The labeling assay can also be used to detect SNPs by way of a Ligation Detection Reaction (LDR) during labeling. This labeling includes detection primers for each SNP, each with a unique ZIP code at the 3' end, and each primer with one of the possible nucleotides for the SNP at the 5' end. A common primer anneals adjacent to the SNP and will only be ligated to the detection primer with the correct base at the SNP, thus attaching the label only to the ZIP code with the correct SNP base, allowing it to be detected by hybridization to the ArrayTube[62].

Commercially Constructed in Situ Synthesized Microarrays

Several companies have developed technologies to manufacture microarrays by synthesis of the oligonucleotide probes directly on the chip substrate. The most widely used of these are Affymetrix (Affymetrix, Inc.), Agilent (Agilent Technologies) and NimbleGen (Roche Inc.), however, several other companies offer similar products. Affymetrix microarrays are constructed by a photolithography process similar to integrated circuit chips. The oligonucleotides are in-situ synthesized by photo-activation of chemical groups at specific locations on the chip using light and a series of masks. After activation of the groups that are to receive the next nucleotide, the nucleotide is washed across the surface of the chip and is added to the growing chains of oligonucleotides only where they were activated. By changing masks and altering nucleotides added, each feature has probes synthesized with a specific sequence, usually 21 to 25mer in length. The high density of these microarrays (up to 2.5 million features), combined with the short oligonucleotide length makes Affymetrix one of the better methods for SNP detection. This is usually achieved through sets of perfect match and mismatch probes with the SNP located in the center of the probes, and scoring achieved by identifying the probe with the most intense hybridization signal. Probe design, labeling, hybridization, washing, and reading of these and other commercial chips are proprietary, but similar in concept to custom glass microarrays.

NimbleGen microarrays are also synthesized in-situ using photo activation, however, a set of computer-controlled mirrors are used to project light and activate residues in specific features rather than masks. This not only allows high density microarray synthesis, but also allows probe lengths of up to 80mer. Agilent uses inkjet technology for in-situ synthesis. For these chips, inkjets accurately deposit specific nucleotides onto growing chains of probes in each feature, resulting in unique 60mer oligonucleotide probes for each feature. This technology also allows printing smaller features at densities up to one million probes per microscope slide. Both of these technologies differ from Affymetrix by being able to make every chip synthesized in a manufacturing run differently, and chips can be altered as needed simply by changing the software that directs the mirrors or the inkjets. For Affymetrix technology, designing a new chip can require making dozens of photolithography masks.

Another feature of commercially manufactured slides is bioinformatic support provided by the company to help design the assay to meet the investigator's goals. These technologies can not only be designed for CGH experiments to detect whole genes, but can also discriminate most SNPs, enabling the identification of allele specific genotypes. In addition, they can be adapted to SNP type, or "re-sequence" a whole genome if there is enough information available on the organism. This approach is very close to whole genome genotyping, which would be the ultimate genetic typing method for foodborne organisms. Re-sequencing chips offer an affordable way to achieve this in the short term, but will likely be replaced by high-throughput sequencing as technological advancements makes that approach much more affordable. Bioinformatic and technical support from commercial providers is also useful in validation and testing of microarray assays. Generally, these types of microarrays are easier to interpret and standardize than homemade custom microarrays. Each of these technologies has been in use for several years, and users are the beneficiaries of this depth of experience. Therefore, results from commercial microarrays are easier to score, however, like all other methods, the typing data they supply is only as good as the targets chosen for the assay and the assay's ability to discriminate subtypes.

Assays developed to use these commercial microarrays are fairly wide-spread, and several have been used for typing foodborne organisms. Affymetrix microarray assays have been designed to detect and type *Noroviruses* in tap and river water with good success [60]. By combining RT-PCR and Affymetrix perfect match/mismatch probes, this assay is sensitive enough to detect viruses in water samples and accurate enough to determine genotypes of *Noroviruses*. A similar assay was also developed using NimbleGen technology to genotype *Noroviruses* as well as other foodborne viruses, including *Coxsackieviruses*, hepatitis viruses, and *Rotaviruses* [98]. The approach with this microarray was to "tile" the whole genome of each virus with a 29mer probe starting ever 5th nucleotide of the genome, thus resulting in overlapping probes covering or "tiling" the whole genomes. Hybridization intensity to each probe is used to determine the different genotypes of the viruses. A similar approach was used to design an assay to determine genomic diversity and evolution of *E. coli* O157 strains, but this NimbleGen tiling array was spaced every 7th base pair (bp) [54]. While this array was used to study evolution of this important foodborne pathogen, it could potentially be used for genotyping and source tracking.

Sphere-Linked Probe Microarrays

While they do not have a conventional solid substrate, assays with sphere- or "bead"-linked probes are very similar to other microarrays. This includes target selection and probe design, since sequences that make good targets and probes on chips perform equally well on spheres in solution. The major difference is that each probe is attached to a sphere rather than a single solid substrate such as a glass microscope slide. The spheres are then hybridized to labeled target and detected by a flow cytometry (FCM). During detection, the sphere-linked probe is also scored for hybridization of the labeled target sequence. Assays using sphere-linked probes can also be designed to detect SNPs using the same approaches as described for chips, such as LDR. One limitation of sphere-based assays is the number of spheres (currently

~100), and thus probes, that can be used in an assay [38]. As the number of different spheres in the assay is increased, sensitivity is reduced. This method has been used to type bacteria, including one assay to determine *Salmonella* serogroups [80]. Assays can be designed by anyone familiar with nucleic acid detection and FCM technology. Commercial companies also offer support in design, specialized bead sets, and dedicated FCM instrumentation, such as Lumenix.

Another technology that includes sphere-linked oligonuclieotide probes detects sequences and scores them by impregnating the oligonucleotide-linked beads into fiber optic bundles [38]. This technique had been developed primarily by Illumina (San Diego, CA, USA) and has some unique characteristics as compared to conventional microarray chip or sphere/FMC based assays. This proprietary technology enables up to one million sequences to be detected in a single assay and can also analyze multiple samples in a 96 well plate format, thus making the method applicable for high-throughput investigations. This method has been applied for detection of a few microbes, such as *Salmonella* and other food and waterborne organisms [41, 99]. Due to the large number of probes that can be used in a single assay and capability for being multiplexed, this technology can be used to develop assays for re-sequencing whole genomes. The major drawback of fiber optic/bead array assays is the technology may be cost prohibitive.

CONCLUSIONS

Microarray technology provides researchers with a powerful tool for high density detection of DNA sequences. This technology has been employed to develop many assays for research and clinical use, some of which have been used to subtype microorganisms with sufficient discrimination to be used for source tracking. However, these assays have also created some new challenges for the investigators that use them. A major issue is that the wide variety of methodologies that can be used to construct microarrays makes data from these assays very difficult to standardize. Additionally, microarray data is often difficult to compare to other typing methods, and may not be backwards compatible with historically accepted typing assays, such as serotype, MLST, PFGE, etc., that have traditionally been used for source tracking. Except for a few commercially designed and validated assays, each assay developed has its own unique methods for interpretation, quality control, and validation. While efforts are being made to standardize some assays across laboratories, a common standard has not been universally accepted [100].

Despite these shortcomings, microarray typing of microorganisms is being used successfully for microbial source tracking, usually in conjunction with other typing methods. Whole genome CGH and SNP assays, which can genotype or re-sequence an entire organism's genome, may offer the possibility of the definitive typing method for source tracking with genetic data. In the next few years, other technologies will likely replace many microarray methods for microbial typing. High-throughput genome sequencing, for example, is being used to define the genome sequence variability found in populations of important microbes. This data is already being used for typing, phylogeny, and evolutionary studies. As new, less expensive methods of whole genome sequencing are developed, it may soon be more economical to sequence an organism genome than to do other assays, such as microarrays. Other methods of typing have also shown promise, such as mass spectrometry, proteomics, and antibody arrays [101]. In the short term, microarrays will be a very useful tool for microbial typing and source tracking, and for certain applications, microarrays will likely continue to be the preferred assay method for some time to come.

ACKNOWLEDGMENTS AND DISCLAIMER

The author would like to acknowledge Charlene R. Jackson and Mark D. Englen for their helpful conversations. The mention of trade names or commercial products in this manuscript is solely for the purpose of providing specific information and does not imply recommendation or endorsement by the U.S. Department of Agriculture.

REFERENCES

[1]   Boxrud D. Advances in subtyping methods of foodborne disease pathogens. *Curr Opin Biotechnol* 2010;21(2):137-41.

[2]   Cebula TA, Jackson SA, Brown EW, Goswami B, LeClerc JE. Chips and SNPs, bugs and thugs: a molecular sleuthing perspective. J *Food Prot* 2005;68(6):1271-84.

[3]   Kostrzynska M, Bachand A. Application of DNA microarray technology for detection, identification, and characterization of food-borne pathogens. *Can J Microbiol* 2006;52(1):1-8.

[4]   Blattner FR, Plunkett G3, Bloch CA, Perna NT, Burland V, Riley M, et al. The complete genome sequence of Escherichia coli K-12. *Science* 1997;277(5331):1453-74.

[5]   McClelland M, Sanderson KE, Spieth J, Clifton SW, Latreille P, Courtney L, et al. Complete genome sequence of Salmonella enterica serovar Typhimurium LT2. *Nature* 2001;413(6858):852-6.

[6]   Eisen MB, Brown PO. DNA arrays for analysis of gene expresssion. *Methods in Enzymology* 1999;303:179-205.

[7]   Forozan F, Karhu R, Kononen J, Kallioniemi A, Kallioniemi OP. Genome screening by comparative genomic hybridization. *Trends Genet* 1997;13(10):405-9.

[8]   Schena M, Shalon D, Davis RW, Brown PO. Quantitative monitoring of gene expression patterns with a complementary DNA microarray. *Science* 1995;270(5235):467-70.

[9]   Shalon D, Smith SJ, Brown PO. A DNA microarray system for analyzing complex DNA samples using two-color fluorescent probe hybridization. *Genome Res* 1996;6(7):639-45.

[10] Watson A, Mazumder A, Stewart M, Balasubramanian S. Technology for microarray analysis of gene expression. *Curr Opin Biotechnol* 1998;9(6):609-14.

[11] Southern EM. Detection of specific sequences among DNA fragments separated by gel electrophoresis. *J Mol Biol* 1975;98(3):503-17.

[12] Garaizar J, Porwollik S, Echeita A, Rementeria A, Herrera S, Wong RM, et al. DNA microarray-based typing of an atypical monophasic Salmonella enterica serovar. *J Clin Microbiol* 2002;40(6):2074-8.

[13] Porwollik S, Wong RM, McClelland M. Evolutionary genomics of Salmonella: gene acquisitions revealed by microarray analysis. *Proc Natl Acad Sci U S A* 2002;99(13):8956-61.

[14] Snijders AM, Pinkel D, Albertson DG. Current status and future prospects of array-based comparative genomic hybridisation. *Brief Funct Genomic Proteo*mic 2003;2(1):37-45.

[15] Porwollik S, McClelland M. Determination of the gene content of Salmonella genomes by microarray analysis. *Methods Mol Biol* 2007;394:89-103.

[16] Porwollik S, Boyd EF, Choy C, Cheng P, Florea L, Proctor E, et al. Characterization of Salmonella enterica subspecies I genovars by use of microarrays. *J Bacteriol* 2004;186(17):5883-98.

[17] Porwollik S, Wong RM, Helm RA, Edwards KK, Calcutt M, Eisenstark A, et al. DNA amplification and rearrangements in archival Salmonella enterica serovar Typhimurium LT2 cultures. *J Bacteriol* 2004;186(6):1678-82.

[18] Porwollik S, Santiviago CA, Cheng P, Florea L, McClelland M. Differences in gene content between Salmonella enterica serovar Enteritidis isolates and comparison to closely related serovars Gallinarum and Dublin. *J Bacteriol* 2005;187(18):6545-55.

[19] Anjum MF, Lucchini S, Thompson A, Hinton JC, Woodward MJ. Comparative genomic indexing reveals the phylogenomics of Escherichia coli pathogens. *Infect Immun* 2003;71(8):4674-83.

[20] Parker CT, Quinones B, Miller WG, Horn ST, Mandrell RE. Comparative genomic analysis of Campylobacter jejuni strains reveals diversity due to genomic elements similar to those present in C. jejuni strain RM1221. *J Clin Microbiol* 2006;44(11):4125-35.

[21] Parker CT, Miller WG, Horn ST, Lastovica AJ. Common genomic features of Campylobacter jejuni subsp. doylei strains distinguish them from C. jejuni subsp. jejuni. *BMC Microbiol* 2007;7:50.

[22] Parker CT, Huynh S, Quinones B, Harris LJ, Mandrell RE. Comparison of genotypes of Salmonella enterica serovar Enteritidis phage type 30 and 9c strains isolated during three outbreaks associated with raw almonds. *Appl Environ Microbiol* 2010;76(11):3723-31.

[23] Pittenger LG, Englen MD, Parker CT, Frye JG, Quinones B, Horn ST, et al. Genotyping Campylobacter jejuni by comparative genome indexing: an evaluation with pulsed-field gel electrophoresis and flaA SVR sequencing. *Foodborne Pathog Dis* 2009;6(3):337-49.

[24] Anjum MF, Marooney C, Fookes M, Baker S, Dougan G, Ivens A, et al. Identification of core and variable components of the Salmonella enterica subspecies I genome by microarray. *Infect Immun* 2005;73(12):7894-905.

[25] Anjum MF, Mafura M, Slickers P, Ballmer K, Kuhnert P, Woodward MJ, et al. Pathotyping Escherichia coli by using miniaturized DNA microarrays. *Appl Environ Microbiol* 2007;73(17):5692-7.

[26] Bonnet C, Diarrassouba F, Brousseau R, Masson L, Topp E, Diarra MS. Pathotype and antibiotic resistance gene distributions of Escherichia coli isolates from broiler chickens raised on antimicrobial-supplemented diets. *Appl Environ Microbiol* 2009;75(22):6955-62.

[27] Chen S, Zhao S, McDermott PF, Schroeder CM, White DG, Meng J. A DNA microarray for identification of virulence and antimicrobial resistance genes in Salmonella serovars and Escherichia coli. *Mol Cell Probes* 2005;19(3):195-201.

[28] Hamelin K, Bruant G, El-Shaarawi A, Hill S, Edge TA, Bekal S, et al. A virulence and antimicrobial resistance DNA microarray detects a high frequency of virulence genes in Escherichia coli isolates from Great Lakes recreational waters. *Appl Environ Microbiol* 2006;72(6):4200-6.

[29] Jaing C, Gardner S, McLoughlin K, Mulakken N, egria-Hartman M, Banda P, et al. A functional gene array for detection of bacterial virulence elements. *PLoS ONE* 2008;3(5):e2163.

[30] Malorny B, Bunge C, Guerra B, Prietz S, Helmuth R. Molecular characterisation of Salmonella strains by an oligonucleotide multiprobe microarray. *Mol Cell Probes* 2007;21(1):56-65.

[31] Peterson G, Bai J, Nagaraja TG, Narayanan S. Diagnostic microarray for human and animal bacterial diseases and their virulence and antimicrobial resistance genes. *J Microbiol Methods* 2010;80(3):223-30.

[32] Peterson G, Gerdes B, Berges J, Nagaraja TG, Frye JG, Boyle DS, et al. Development of microarray and multiplex polymerase chain reaction assays for identification of serovars and virulence genes in Salmonella enterica of human or animal origin. *J Vet Diagn Invest* 2010;22(4):559-69.

[33] Aarts HJ, Vos P, Larsson JT, van Hoek AH, Huehn S, Weijers T, et al. A multiplex ligation detection assay for the characterization of Salmonella enterica strains. *Int J Food Microbiol* 2011;145(Suppl 1):S68-78.

[34] Jarvinen AK, Laakso S, Piiparinen P, Aittakorpi A, Lindfors M, Huopaniemi L, et al. Rapid identification of bacterial pathogens using a PCR- and microarray-based assay. *BMC Microbiol* 2009;9:161.

[35] Palka-Santini M, Cleven BE, Eichinger L, Kronke M, Krut O. Large scale multiplex PCR improves pathogen detection by DNA microarrays. *BMC Microbiol* 2009;9:1.

[36] Porwollik S, Frye J, Florea LD, Blackmer F, McClelland M. A non-redundant microarray of genes for two related bacteria. *Nucleic Acids Res* 2003;31(7):1869-76.

[37] Nielsen HB, Wernersson R, Knudsen S. Design of oligonucleotides for microarrays and perspectives for design of multi-transcriptome arrays. *Nucleic Acids Res* 2003;31(13):3491-6.

[38] Miller MB, Tang YW. Basic concepts of microarrays and potential applications in clinical microbiology. *Clin Microbiol Rev* 2009;22(4):611-33.

[39] Lauri A, Mariani PO. Potentials and limitations of molecular diagnostic methods in food safety. *Genes Nutr* 2009;4(1):1-12.

[40] Rasooly A, Herold KE. Food microbial pathogen detection and analysis using DNA microarray technologies. *Foodborne Pathog Dis* 2008;5(4):531-50.

[41] Ahn S, Walt DR. Detection of Salmonella spp. using microsphere-based, fiber-optic DNA microarrays. *Anal Chem* 2005;77(15):5041-7.

[42] Zhu LX, Zhang ZW, Liang D, Jiang D, Wang C, Du N, et al. Multiplex asymmetric PCR-based oligonucleotide microarray for detection of drug resistance genes containing single mutations in Enterobacteriaceae. *Antimicrob Agents Chemother* 2007;51(10):3707-13.

[43] Borucki MK, Kim SH, Call DR, Smole SC, Pagotto F. Selective discrimination of Listeria monocytogenes epidemic strains by a mixed-genome DNA microarray compared to discrimination by pulsed-field gel electrophoresis, ribotyping, and multilocus sequence typing. *J Clin Microbiol* 2004;42(11):5270-6.

[44] Batchelor M, Hopkins KL, Liebana E, Slickers P, Ehricht R, Mafura M, et al. Development of a miniaturised microarray-based assay for the rapid identification of antimicrobial resistance genes in Gram-negative bacteria. *Int J Antimicrob Agents* 2008;31(5):440-51.

[45] Bruant G, Maynard C, Bekal S, Gaucher I, Masson L, Brousseau R, et al. Development and validation of an oligonucleotide microarray for detection of multiple virulence and antimicrobial resistance genes in Escherichia coli. *Appl Environ Microbiol* 2006;72(5):3780-4.

[46] Frye JG, Jesse T, Long F, Rondeau G, Porwollik S, McClelland M, et al. DNA microarray detection of antimicrobial resistance genes in diverse bacteria. *Int J Antimicrob Agents* 2006;27(2):138-51.

[47] Frye JG, Lindsey RL, Rondeau G, Porwollik S, Long F, McClelland M, et al. Development of a DNA microarray to detect antimicrobial resistance genes Identified in the National Center for Biotechnology Information database. *Microb Drug Resist* 2009;16(1):9-19.

[48] Ma M, Wang H, Yu Y, Zhang D, Liu S. Detection of antimicrobial resistance genes of pathogenic Salmonella from swine with DNA microarray. *J Vet Diagn Invest* 2007;19(2):161-7.

[49] Majtan T, Majtanova L, Timko J, Majtan V. Oligonucleotide microarray for molecular characterization and genotyping of Salmonella spp. strains. *J Antimicrob Chemother* 2007;60(5):937-46.

[50] Perreten V, Vorlet-Fawer L, Slickers P, Ehricht R, Kuhnert P, Frey J. Microarray-based detection of 90 antibiotic resistance genes of gram-positive bacteria. *J Clin Microbiol* 2005;43(5):2291-302.

[51] Vora GJ, Meador CE, Bird MM, Bopp CA, Andreadis JD, Stenger DA. Microarray-based detection of genetic heterogeneity, antimicrobial resistance, and the viable but nonculturable state in human pathogenic Vibrio spp. *Proc Natl Acad Sci U S A* 2005;102(52):19109-14.

[52] Ballmer K, Korczak BM, Kuhnert P, Slickers P, Ehricht R, Hachler H. Fast DNA serotyping of Escherichia coli by use of an oligonucleotide microarray. *J Clin Microbiol* 2007;45(2):370-9.

[53] Yoshida C, Franklin K, Konczy P, McQuiston JR, Fields PI, Nash JH, et al. Methodologies towards the development of an oligonucleotide microarray for determination of Salmonella serotypes. *J Microbiol Methods* 2007;70(2):261-71.

[54] Zhang W, Qi W, Albert TJ, Motiwala AS, Alland D, Hyytia-Trees EK, et al. Probing genomic diversity and evolution of Escherichia coli O157 by single nucleotide polymorphisms. *Genome Res* 2006;16(6):757-67.

[55] Porwollik S, Boyle D, Frye JG, Wilson R, Clifton S, Spieth J, et al. Differences in gene and message content of Salmonella typhimurium detected by an ORF microarray. Monteray CA, USA: American Society for Microbiology, Washington; 2001.

[56] Kim S, Frye JG, Hu J, Fedorka-Cray PJ, Gautom R, Boyle DS. Multiplex PCR-based method for identification of common clinical serotypes of Salmonella enterica subsp. enterica. *J Clin Microbiol* 2006;44(10):3608-15.

[57] Leader BT, Frye JG, Hu J, Fedorka-Cray PJ, Boyle DS. High-throughput molecular determination of Salmonella enterica serovars by use of multiplex PCR and capillary electrophoresis analysis. *J Clin Microbiol* 2009;47(5):1290-9.

[58] Scaria J, Palaniappan RU, Chiu D, Phan JA, Ponnala L, McDonough P, et al. Microarray for molecular typing of Salmonella enterica serovars. *Mol Cell Probes* 2008;22(4):238-43.

[59] Booth SA, Drebot MA, Martin IE, Ng LK. Design of oligonucleotide arrays to detect point mutations: molecular typing of antibiotic resistant strains of Neisseria gonorrhoeae and hantavirus infected deer mice. *Mol Cell Probes* 2003;17(2-3):77-84.

[60] Brinkman NE, Fout GS. Development and evaluation of a generic tag array to detect and genotype noroviruses in water. *J Virol Methods* 2009;156(1-2):8-18.

[61] Lott TJ, Scarborough RT. Development of a MLST-biased SNP microarray for Candida albicans. *Fungal Genet Biol* 2008;45(6):803-11.

[62] Busti E, Bordoni R, Castiglioni B, Monciardini P, Sosio M, Donadio S, et al. Bacterial discrimination by means of a universal array approach mediated by LDR (ligase detection reaction). *BMC Microbiol* 2002;2:27.

[63] Rimour S, Hill D, Militon C, Peyret P. GoArrays: highly dynamic and efficient microarray probe design. *Bioinformatics* 2004.

[64] Wernersson R, Nielsen HB. OligoWiz 2.0--integrating sequence feature annotation into the design of microarray probes. *Nucleic Acids Res* 2005;33:W611-W615.

[65] Kreil DP, Russell RR, Russell S. Microarray oligonucleotide probes. *Methods Enzymol* 2006;410:73-98.

[66] Call DR, Bakko MK, Krug MJ, Roberts MC. Identifying antimicrobial resistance genes with DNA microarrays. *Antimicrob Agents Chemother* 2003;47(10):3290-5.

[67] Garaizar J, Rementeria A, Porwollik S. DNA microarray technology: a new tool for the epidemiological typing of bacterial pathogens? *FEMS Immunol Med Microbiol* 2006;47(2):178-89.

[68] Uttamchandani M, Neo JL, Ong BN, Moochhala S. Applications of microarrays in pathogen detection and biodefence. *Trends Biotechnol* 2009;27(1):53-61.

[69] Wang RF, Kim SJ, Robertson LH, Cerniglia CE. Development of a membrane-array method for the detection of human intestinal bacteria in fecal samples. *Mol Cell Probes* 2002;16(5):341-50.

[70] Todt S, Blohm DH. Immobilization chemistries. *Methods Mol Biol* 2009;529:81-100.

[71] Barbulovic-Nad I, Lucente M, Sun Y, Zhang M, Wheeler AR, Bussmann M. Bio-microarray fabrication techniques--a review. *Crit Rev Biotechnol* 2006;26(4):237-59.

[72] Davis MA, Lim JY, Soyer Y, Harbottle H, Chang YF, New D, et al. Development and validation of a resistance and virulence gene microarray targeting Escherichia coli and Salmonella enterica. *J Microbiol Methods* 2010;82(1):36-41.

[73] Morales CA, Porwollik S, Frye JG, Kinde H, McClelland M, Guard-Bouldin J. Correlation of phenotype with the genotype of egg-contaminating Salmonella enterica serovar Enteritidis. *Appl Environ Microbiol* 2005;71(8):4388-99.

[74] Pagotto F, Corneau N, Mattison K, Bidawid S. Development of a DNA microarray for the simultaneous detection and genotyping of noroviruses. *J Food Prot* 2008;71(7):1434-41.

[75] Leinberger DM, Schumacher U, Autenrieth IB, Bachmann TT. Development of a DNA microarray for detection and identification of fungal pathogens involved in invasive mycoses. *J Clin Microbiol 2005*;43(10):4943-53.

[76] Chan K, Baker S, Kim CC, Detweiler CS, Dougan G, Falkow S. Genomic Comparison of Salmonella enterica serovars and Salmonella bongori by use of an S. enterica serovar Typhimurium DNA microarray. *J Bacteriol* 2003;185(2):553-63.

[77] Porwollik S, McClelland M. Lateral gene transfer in Salmonella. *Microbes Infect* 2003;5(11):977-89.

[78] Huehn S, Malorny B. DNA microarray for molecular epidemiology of Salmonella. *Methods Mol Biol* 2009;551:249-85.

[79] Arrach N, Porwollik S, Cheng P, Cho A, Long F, Choi SH, et al. Salmonella serovar identification using PCR-based detection of gene presence and absence. *J Clin Microbiol* 2008;46(8):2581-9.

[80] Fitzgerald C, Collins M, van DS, Mikoleit M, Brown T, Fields P. Multiplex, bead-based suspension array for molecular determination of common Salmonella serogroups. *J Clin Microbiol* 2007;45(10):3323-34.

[81] Kang MS, Besser TE, Hancock DD, Porwollik S, McClelland M, Call DR. Identification of specific gene sequences conserved in contemporary epidemic strains of Salmonella enterica. *Appl Environ Microbiol* 2006;72(11):6938-47.

[82] Litrup E, Torpdahl M, Malorny B, Huehn S, Christensen H, Nielsen EM. Association between phylogeny, virulence potential and serovars of Salmonella enterica. *Infect Genet Evol* 2010;10(7):1132-9.

[83] Huehn S, La Ragione RM, Anjum M, Saunders M, Woodward MJ, Bunge C, et al. Virulotyping and antimicrobial resistance typing of Salmonella enterica serovars relevant to human health in Europe. *Foodborne Pathog Dis* 2010;7(5):523-35.

[84] Quinones B, Parker CT, Janda JM, Jr., Miller WG, Mandrell RE. Detection and genotyping of Arcobacter and Campylobacter isolates from retail chicken samples by use of DNA oligonucleotide arrays. *Appl Environ Microbiol* 2007;73(11):3645-55.

[85] Quinones B, Guilhabert MR, Miller WG, Mandrell RE, Lastovica AJ, Parker CT. Comparative genomic analysis of clinical strains of Campylobacter jejuni from South Africa. *PLoS ONE* 2008;3(4):e2015.

[86] Taboada EN, Acedillo RR, Carrillo CD, Findlay WA, Medeiros DT, Mykytczuk OL, et al. Large-scale comparative genomics meta-analysis of Campylobacter jejuni isolates reveals low level of genome plasticity. *J Clin Microbiol* 2004;42(10):4566-76.

[87] Healy B, Huynh S, Mullane N, O'Brien S, Iversen C, Lehner A, et al. Microarray-based comparative genomic indexing of the Cronobacter genus (Enterobacter sakazakii). *Int J Food Microbiol* 2009 31;136(2):159-64.

[88] Fukiya S, Mizoguchi H, Tobe T, Mori H. Extensive genomic diversity in pathogenic Escherichia coli and Shigella Strains revealed by comparative genomic hybridization microarray. *J Bacteriol* 2004;186(12):3911-21.

[89] Hamelin K, Bruant G, El-Shaarawi A, Hill S, Edge TA, Fairbrother J, et al. Occurrence of virulence and antimicrobial resistance genes in Escherichia coli isolates from

different aquatic ecosystems within the St. Clair River and Detroit River areas. *Appl Environ Microbiol* 2007;73(2):477-84.

[90] Wu CF, Valdes JJ, Bentley WE, Sekowski JW. DNA microarray for discrimination between pathogenic 0157:H7 EDL933 and non-pathogenic Escherichia coli strains. *Biosens Bioelectron* 2003 30;19(1):1-8.

[91] Borucki MK, Gay CC, Reynolds J, McElwain KL, Kim SH, Call DR, et al. Genetic diversity of Listeria monocytogenes strains from a high-prevalence dairy farm. *Appl Environ Microbiol* 2005;71(10):5893-9.

[92] El GF, Hallin M, De MR, Denis O, Lefort A, Struelens MJ. StaphVar-DNA microarray analysis of accessory genome elements of community-acquired methicillin-resistant Staphylococcus aureus. *J Antimicrob Chemother* 2009;63(5):877-85.

[93] Gall A, Hoffmann B, Harder T, Grund C, Ehricht R, Beer M. Rapid haemagglutinin subtyping and pathotyping of avian influenza viruses by a DNA microarray. *J Virol Methods* 2009;160(1-2):200-5.

[94] Sachse K, Hotzel H, Slickers P, Ellinger T, Ehricht R. DNA microarray-based detection and identification of Chlamydia and Chlamydophila spp. *Mol Cell Probes* 2005;19(1):41-50.

[95] Sachse K, Hotzel H, Slickers P, Ehricht R. The use of DNA microarray technology for detection and genetic characterisation of chlamydiae. *Dev Biol* (Basel) 2006;126:203-10.

[96] Gerry NP, Witowski NE, Day J, Hammer RP, Barany G, Barany F. Universal DNA microarray method for multiplex detection of low abundance point mutations. *J Mol Biol* 1999;292(2):251-62.

[97] Cremonesi P, Pisoni G, Severgnini M, Consolandi C, Moroni P, Raschetti M, et al. Pathogen detection in milk samples by ligation detection reaction-mediated universal array method. *J Dairy Sci* 2009;92(7):3027-39.

[98] Ayodeji M, Kulka M, Jackson SA, Patel I, Mammel M, Cebula TA, et al. A microarray based approach for the identification of common foodborne viruses. *Open Virol J* 2009;3:7-20.

[99] Ahn S, Kulis DM, Erdner DL, Anderson DM, Walt DR. Fiber-optic microarray for simultaneous detection of multiple harmful algal bloom species. *Appl Environ Microbiol* 2006;72(9):5742-9.

[100] Gronlund H, Riber L, Vigre H, Lofstrom C, Folling L, Huehn S, et al. Microarray-based genotyping of Salmonella: Inter-laboratory evaluation of reproducibility and standardization potential. *Int J Food Microbiol* 2011;145(Suppl 1):S79-85.

[101] Murray PR. Matrix-assisted laser desorption ionization time-of-flight mass spectrometry: usefulness for taxonomy and epidemiology. *Clin Microbiol Infect* 2010;16(11):1626-30.

Section III. Analysis and Utility of Molecular Typing Methods

In: Molecular Typing Methods for TFM
Editors: S. Foley, R. Nayak, T. Johnson et al.

ISBN: 978-1-62100-643-5
© 2012 Nova Science Publishers, Inc.

Chapter 14

METHODS FOR THE ANALYSIS OF MOLECULAR TYPING DATA

Steven L. Foley

Division of Microbiology
National Center for Toxicological Research
US Food and Drug Administration
Jefferson, AR, US

ABSTRACT

To best utilize molecular subtyping data to infer relationships between different strains of bacteria, it is important to use the most appropriate methods for data analyses. Several approaches that have been developed that have applications for the analyses of different types of molecular subtyping data. Most molecular subtyping methods rely on restriction enzyme digestion, PCR amplification, DNA hybridization, or DNA sequence differences to distinguish among strains. The data generated from these approaches are quite diverse, including electrophoresis fingerprints, DNA sequences, character or binary data and chromatographic data which influence the choice of analysis methods used. This chapter covers the basics of the different methods to determine the similarity of typing results among strains and examines methods to display the similarity using hierarchical and non-hierarchical approaches for data analysis.

INTRODUCTION

The ability to effectively use the data generated by molecular subtyping methods is essential to infer relationships between different strains of bacteria. A wide range of methods have been developed for different purposes that have application for the analysis of different types of molecular subtyping data. In general, molecular subtyping methods can be broken down into four major types based on the utilization of restriction enzyme digestion, PCR amplification, DNA hybridization, or sequencing to subtype bacterial isolates. These typing methods have various data outputs that include electrophoresis fingerprints, DNA or amino acid sequences, character or binary data or chromatographic data. Each of these types of data creates challenges for their analysis and introducing the analysis methods is the major focus of this chapter.

Molecular typing data can be used for various functions including trying to understand the long-term evolutionary structure of a population of bacteria as well as for shorter term epidemiological studies to determine the relationship of isolates that may be involved in foodborne disease outbreaks. Often the more comprehensive evolutionary studies rely upon cladistic or evolutionary systematic approaches to attempt to determine how organisms are related [1]. In this determination of evolutionary relationships, phylogenetic analyses are often utilized, which typically rely upon DNA or amino acid sequence changes in relatively conserved regions of the bacterial genome to determine how organisms fit into an evolutionary hierarchy. Phylogenetic trees are often generated to show the overall population structure of the organisms being analyzed [2].

Conversely, for epidemiological questions related to the dispersal of bacterial isolates over a shorter period of time, numeric taxonomy or phenetic analysis is usually undertaken. Phenetic methods for classification do not rely on evolutionary relationships when calculating the relatedness of isolates being classified [3]. Many of the most common molecular typing methods, such as pulsed field gel electrophoresis (PFGE), ribotyping and PCR-based approaches, are analyzed using phenetic methods. With these phenetic methods the relatedness among isolates is calculated by their similarity/distance to one another based upon the pattern or profile generated from subtyping, rather than their evolutionary position. Therefore phenetic methods often work best for separating between closely related organisms (such as within a particular serotype of *Salmonella* or *E. coli*) rather than on a larger taxonomic scale [4].

In the analysis of molecular typing data, the individual elements that are used to determine similarity/distance among isolates are referred to as characters [5]. These characters can include bands on a gel, individual nucleotides in a gene sequence, presence of a particular gene, peaks in a chromatograph, etc. For phenetic analyses, each of these characters is converted to a numerical or categorical value (discussed below in more detail) that allows for the calculation of relatedness of isolates based on their particular numerical or categorical pattern characteristics [2, 3]. Another way to define a discreet group of bacterial isolates with a common set of characteristics is the observed taxonomic unit or OTU [5]. For bacteria, the OTU term can be used to define a particular strain or bacterial clone. For cladistic analyses the calculation of evolutionary relatedness is based upon the assumption that the nucleotide/amino acid sequences are inherited from a previous generation and that sequential changes indicate potential evolutionary divergence [1]. There are a number of different algorithms, such as parsimony and likelihood analyses, that have been developed that determine the likely evolutionary relatedness among different bacterial strains; some of which are discussed later in the chapter.

In both phenetic and cladistic analysis it is important to understand how well the analysis of relatedness actually represents the true population structure. With the molecular typing methods, it is important to minimize type I error, which occurs when the analysis determines a relationship between strains that is not truly there; and type II error, when the analysis fails to identify an epidemiological relationship between strains that is actually there [6].

Therefore, a key consideration is how to minimize these errors by choosing the most appropriate typing and analytical methods to determine the relationships of interest (i.e. whether two strains are different vs. how on an evolutionary scale are two strains related).

PREPARING TO CARRY OUT ANALYSIS

In the development of strategies to analyze molecular typing data from multiple bacterial isolates, it is important to consider how to handle the vast amount of typing data and associated demographic information that is collected for each the strains. Typically isolate demographic data are stored in a database, such as those generated by Access (Microsoft, Redmond, WA), Oracle (Redwood Shores, CA), SQL (originally developed by IBM, Armonk, NY) or other programs. These databases are able to efficiently handle and sort different pieces of data and can be integrated with many of the software packages used for the analyses of molecular typing data [7]. The databases provide the ability to link demographic data, such as species, serovar, date and location of isolation, etc., to a particular database entry key. This common entry key also allows for the molecular typing data to be linked to a particular database entry [7]. For specifics on setting up databases, please see the following sources [8, 9].

There are number of different software programs available for the analyses of molecular typing data, including BioNumerics (Applied Maths, Kortrijk, Belgium), GelCompar II (Applied Maths), FPQuest (BioRad, Hercules, CA), and Image (Sanger Institute, UK). Image is a free software program that runs on the Linux platform and can be used for normalizing fingerprinting data from a number of gel images that facilitates comparison of typing results. For details on Image, the reader is referred to the Sanger Institute website for the software (http://www.sanger.ac.uk/resources/software/image/). There are a number of functional similarities among BioNumerics, GelCompar and FPQuest, however BioNumerics is likely the most widely used program for the analysis of a range of molecular typing data. Because of its widespread use, many of the examples provided in this chapter will be described using BioNumerics.

When new isolates are analyzed, new entry keys need to be assigned for each isolate added to the database. Additional information, such as the microbial species, serotype, source, date and geographical location of isolation are often added to the corresponding database fields as well. Depending on how the database is set up, this information can be imported from external sources (Microsoft Excel, Access or other database program) or directly entered into the fields in the analysis program. Next, the molecular subtyping raw data (gel image, sequence, binary data) generated for the set of isolates is imported into the program for analysis. For descriptive purposes, we will describe the analysis of a repetitive element (rep)-PCR gel using the BioNumerics program. To analyze the gel, an "experiment" needs to be established for the particular analysis; in this case it could be named "rep-PCR". The experiment includes information related to the parameters for analysis, such as the sizes of bands in the molecular weight standard (used for in-gel and cross-gel normalization), standard image processing settings (width of gel lanes, brightness, contrast, background subtraction, etc.) and certain comparison settings.

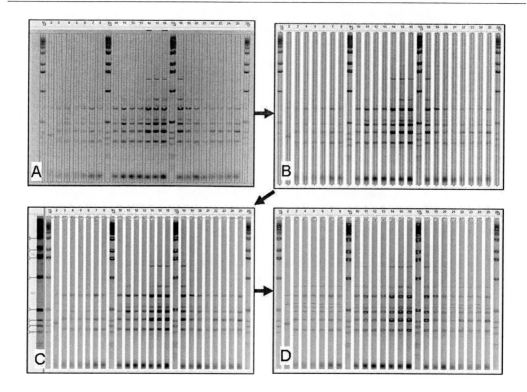

Figure 1. Steps involved in the initial analysis of fingerprint data (rep-PCR gel in this figure). The process is broken down into four basic steps (panels A-D). In panel A the individual lanes of the gel are defined. With a software program like BioNumerics (Applied Maths) this process is automated. The next step (panel B) is image optimization to improve analysis. Techniques such as spectral analysis are run to determine parameters for background subtraction and noise filtering and the image brightness and contrast optimized for the detection of bands. The third step is normalization of the gel image both across the gel and to a reference standard. In panel C, molecular weight standards were run in lanes 1, 9, 17, and 26 of the gel, these standards were normalized to an external reference standard (far left hand portion of panel C). The inclusion of the standards interspersed across the gel allows for normalization of the lanes across the gel and the normalization to the external reference facilitates the comparison of patterns from this gel to others run with the same set of standards. The final step shown in panel D is the identification of individual bands in each of the lanes. This process is automated in some software programs; however the results should likely be double checked to avoid improperly called bands. If needed, bands can be marked or unmarked as needed to ensure proper band calls.

The analysis of the gel image is typically broken down into four steps, defining the lanes on the gel, optimizing the image quality to improve band identification, normalization of the gel to in-run standards and established reference system and lastly identifying the bands present in each lane of the gel (Figure 1). If the gel being analyzed is the first one for a particular experiment type, additional steps need to be taken to define the reference system for the experiment type [7]. This process involves defining the bands in the molecular weight standard that will be used for inter-gel normalization for a specific experiment type. In subsequent gels analyzed using the common standard, in-gel standards will be normalized to the reference system thereby allowing for comparison of fingerprint profiles across multiple gels. Once the gel images have been analyzed and the banding patterns identified for each lane, the individual profiles are linked to a record in the isolate database. This linking allows the results from multiple gels and strains to be compared to one another to determine the relatedness of the different isolates. It should be noted that multiple experiment types can be linked to a single entry key which facilitates a multiple typing method approach to determining population differences. The methods of analyses are covered in more detail below.

TYPES OF DATA

Molecular epidemiologists have a wide range of different phenotying and genotyping methods that can be used for the characterization of bacterial pathogens. These methods are covered extensive in their corresponding chapters in this book; however, when it comes down to the analysis of the results of the methods, they typically can be broken down into four major groups, fingerprint data, sequence data, character or numeric data (including binary data) or chromatographic data. Each of these data types has their own challenges and advantages when it comes to their analysis. Likely the most widely used typing techniques are the fingerprinting methods in which restriction digestion or PCR typing reactions are separated by gel or capillary electrophoresis, and either stained or probed, to reveal a strain associated pattern. Some common fingerprinting methods include PFGE, ribotyping, rep-PCR, randomly amplified polymorphic DNA (RAPD)-PCR, optical mapping and multilocus variable number of tandem repeat analysis (MLVA). The determination of similarity between profiles for the different OTUs relies on the presence (and in some types of analyses, absence) of common bands among the strains analyzed. Additionally, certain types of analyses also take band intensity into account in calculating similarity among strains. To carry out these analyses, the band position and intensity are converted to numerical values (binary for band position and continuous values for intensity) for the calculation of similarities. Some of the most common analysis methods used to calculate similarity include Dice coefficient, Jaccard index and simple matching for position-based analysis and Pearson correlation or cosine coefficient for analyses that incorporate band intensity into the similarity calculations [3]. Typically the similarity is displayed graphically in the form of a dendrogram or tree structure. The most widely used dendrograms are computed using the unweighted pair-group means with arithmetic averages (UPGMA) or neighbor joining methods [3]. These analysis and dendrogram calculation methods are described below in more detail and a description of PFGE data analysis is provided as an example later in this chapter as well.

Historically, DNA and amino acid sequences have been used to try to determine the evolutionary position of isolates through the use of cladistic and phylogenetic analysis of base pair and subsequent amino acid changes in genes of interest [10]. As the access to lower cost sequencing has increased, so have the strategies that use DNA sequencing for molecular subtyping. These methods include multilocus sequence typing (MLST), single nucleotide polymorphism (SNP) analysis and whole genome sequencing (WGS). The analysis strategies for the data can be variable, ranging from a purely phenetic approach to those that utilize more cladistic approaches. For example, in MLST the typical analysis involves the submission of a defined region of sequence for a particular locus to a central MLST database (e.g. www.pubmlst.org) where the sequence is assigned an allele number based on the presence of identical sequences in the database. If the submitted sequence is novel to the database, then it is assigned a new allele number [11]. The output is a numerical profile based on the alleles for each of the loci sequenced. Many of the MLST schemes utilize seven loci, so an example allelic profile could be 12, 13, 1, 45, 1, 2, and 44 for the respective loci; this sequence type profile is then compared to others in the database. Those OTUs that share the most common allele types are determined to be more closely related than those with fewer matches. In this type of analysis, the sequence data are converted into character data and the output is typically a dendrogram or e-Burst diagram displaying the calculated similarity [12]. These analysis methods do not necessarily take into account the underlying genetic similarity within a particular loci sequenced, such that in determining similarity, a locus with five nucleotide differences is given equal weight to one that has only a single base difference. Phylogenetic-based analysis methods, based on multiple alignments, parsimony or likelihood analysis (described below), can provide trees that separate OTUs based on base-pair level similarity among loci and when multiple loci are analyzed, they provide a more comprehensive picture of the underlying relatedness of strains [10]. These approaches are computationally intensive and may not be necessary for basic MLST analysis, but are important for SNP typing. The sequence analysis and tree generation methods are described in more detail below.

Currently (as of 2011), there have not been a large number of studies utilizing WGS specifically for molecular subtyping; however, with the advent and increasing availability of next generation high throughput sequencing, it is likely that that WGS will be more widely used for molecular subtyping in the not too distant future. However, due to the sizes of and the potential variability across bacterial genomes, there will likely be logistical and computational challenges that will need to be evaluated in determining the best analysis methods. Some of the questions that will need to be addressed from a logistical perspective will be whether the whole genomes will need to be subjected to comparative analyses, or could the analyses of defined regions be adequate for subtyping purposes? How will the analysis deal with regions that are not efficiently sequenced in all strains? Also, how would clonality be defined? This may be an issue because there is the potential for spontaneous mutations between generations; thereby bacteria from a common source would likely have slightly varied genomic sequences at the time of sequencing.

In addition to fingerprint and direct sequence data, certain molecular typing data are in the form of numerical values or presence/absence calls. In these cases the determination of relatedness among OTUs is based on the numerical similarity (binary in the case of presence/absence data) across the character set. Some common character and numerical data based typing methods include microarray, antimicrobial susceptibility testing (AST) results, virulence gene profiles, and fatty acid profiles. The analysis of numerical data uses some of the similar methods used in the analysis of fingerprint data because band information is typically converted to numerical values prior to analysis. For binary data, Dice coefficient, Jaccard index or simple matching can be used for analysis, while for non-binary numerical data, Pearson correlation, cosine coefficient, rank correlation, and distance methods can be used [7]. Additionally, certain numerical or character-type data can be converted into categorical data and analyzed; this type of analysis has value in situations where a zero value for each member of a character set is informative in determining relatedness. For many of the aforementioned analyses, a set of all zero values creates computational problems and those strains are not able to be classified (Figure 2). But by converting to categorical data, the zero values are given the same computational consideration as the non-zero values when determining relatedness. This feature can be very important, for example, in analyzing AST profile results were "0" is used to signify susceptibility to a particular antimicrobial, "1" as intermediate susceptibility and "2" as resistant (Figure 2A). Using this numerical classification in most analysis methods, the strain susceptible to all antimicrobials is not able to be analyzed, unless converted to categorical data. In Figure 2B, three isolates that were susceptible to all antimicrobials were determined to have no similarity using Dice coefficient analysis of the numerical values, however when the values were converted to categorical data and analyzed (Figure 2C) they were 100% similar.

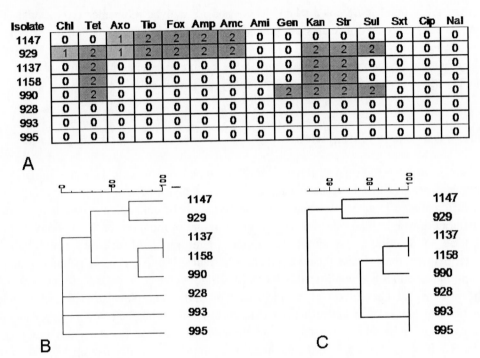

Isolate	Chl	Tet	Axo	Tio	Fox	Amp	Amc	Ami	Gen	Kan	Str	Sul	Sxt	Cip	Nal
1147	0	0	1	2	2	2	2	0	0	0	0	0	0	0	0
929	1	2	1	2	2	2	2	0	0	2	2	2	0	0	0
1137	0	2	0	0	0	0	0	0	0	2	2	0	0	0	0
1158	0	2	0	0	0	0	0	0	0	2	2	0	0	0	0
990	0	2	0	0	0	0	0	0	2	2	2	2	0	0	0
928	0	0	0	0	0	0	0	0	0	0	0	0	0	0	0
993	0	0	0	0	0	0	0	0	0	0	0	0	0	0	0
995	0	0	0	0	0	0	0	0	0	0	0	0	0	0	0

A

B   C

Figure 2. An example of numerical and categorical data generated with antimicrobial susceptibility testing (AST) for eight *Salmonella* isolates. In panel A, "0" is used to signify susceptibility to a particular antimicrobial, "1" as intermediate susceptibility and "2" as resistant to the following antimicrobials chloramphenicol (Chl), tetracycline (Tet), ceftriaxone (Axo), ceftiofur (Tio), cefoxitin (Fox), ampicillin (Amp), amoxicillin/clavulanic acid (Amc), amikacin (Ami), gentamicin (Gen), kanamycin (Kan), streptomycin (Str), sulfisoxazole (Sul), trimethoprim/sulfamethoxazole (Sxt), ciprofloxacin (Cip) and nalidixic acid (Nal). Panel B shows the results of similarity among isolates as calculated using Dice coefficients and the numerical values. Isolates (928, 993 and 995) that were susceptible to all antimicrobials were determined to have 0% similarity (similarity scale on the top of the dendrogram) even though they had identical profiles. When the data are converted into categorical data and the "0" values are given equal computational weight with the other "values" and analyzed (panel C) the three isolates that were fully susceptible were calculated to be 100% similar.

Another potential type of data that is generated in molecular subtyping studies is chromatographic data. While it is currently not as commonly encountered among subtyping data as fingerprint, sequence or categorical data, some of the potential chromatographic data that can be analyzed could include mass spectral profiles, liquid or gas chromatography elution profiles or fragment analysis profiles from automated separation systems. The comparison of chromatographic data typically relies upon both the position and intensity the similarities of chromatographic peaks to distinguish OTUs; thus the data are typically analyzed using methods such as the Pearson correlation, cosine coefficients or other similar methods that are described in the next section.

ANALYTICAL METHODS

There are a number of potential methods used to analyze molecular typing data. The method to choose to use for analysis depends on a number of factors, including the type of data generated, the potential for type I and II errors and the computational resources available to carry out the analyses. In this section of the chapter we examine some of the more commonly used methods for analysis of different types of molecular typing data.

Similarity/Distance Calculation

There have been multiple different algorithms developed to calculate the similarity of patterns and profiles that have been adapted for the analysis of molecular subtyping data. These different algorithms vary in complexity and whether or not certain elements in the data are given more weight than others. The first group includes the more basic methods that are often used to determine the similarity among fingerprint profiles and some types of character/numeric data. These methods include the Jaccard index, Dice coefficients, simple matching index, and Sokal and Sneath's index [3, 7]. For fingerprint data, these methods rely on the presence and absence (for simple matching index and Sokal and Sneath's index calculation) of bands on a gel at a particular position. For character and binary data, the similarity calculations rely on whether or not strains have common factors within the overall data set. To illustrate the basics of the methods, we will use a simplfied example based on the comparison of two strains using PFGE analysis (Figure 3A). In this example the PFGE profile for strain 1 has 13 bands and strain 2 has 12 bands. To carry out the analyses, the gel is separated into subsections along the length of the run; in this example, it is separated into 20 equal subsections and the presence or absence of a band in the corresponding subsections is determined. This allows for the development of a 2 x 2 matrix (Figure 3B) which facilitates the comparison of the presence or absence of bands between the two strains, with block "a" containing the number of instances that a common band was present in both strains, blocks "b" and "c" when a band was present in one strain and not the other, and block "d", the number of location where a band was not present in either. Figure 3C shows the results for the PFGE example. This information is then used in the calculations of similarity. In determining similarity, both the Jaccard index and Dice coefficient rely only on those instances where there is a band (or other character) present in one or both of the strains, while the simple matching index and Sokal and Sneath's index also rely on instances where a band is not present in either strain. In the calculations, both the Jaccard index and simple matching index give equal computational weight to each of the terms in the equation, while the Dice coefficient and Sokal and Sneath's index give more weight to certain values in the equations

[3, 13]. The formulas for each of the similarity equations along with examples based on the example in Figure 3 are given below.

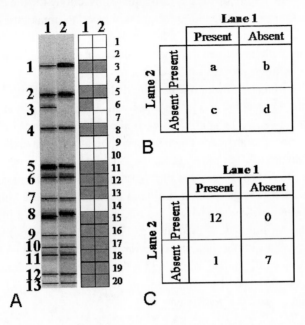

Figure 3. Steps used to calculate the similarity of DNA fingerprint data. In panel A, the PFGE profiles of two isolates are compared and the gel image is separated into 20 equal subsections and the presence (gray box) or absence (white box) of a band in the corresponding subsections is determined. This allows for the development of a 2 x 2 matrix (panel B) where block "a" contains the number of instances a common band was present in both strains, in block "b" and "c" when a band was present in one strain and not the other, and block "d" the number of location where a band was not present in either. The matrix generated from the data in panel A is shown in panel C and is used in the example calculation of similarity in the text.

Jaccard index

$$S_{Jaccard} = \frac{a}{a+b+c} \qquad \frac{12}{12+0+7} = 0.63$$

Dice coefficient

$$S_{Dice} = \frac{2a}{2a+b+c} \qquad \frac{2(12)}{2(12)+0+7} = 0.77$$

Simple matching index

$$S_{Simple} = \frac{a+d}{a+b+c+d} \qquad \frac{12+7}{12+0+1+7} = 0.95$$

Sokal and Sneath's index

$$S_{S\,and\,S} = \frac{2(a+d)}{2(a+d)+b+c} \qquad \frac{2(12+7)}{2(12+7)+0+1} = 0.97$$

Because the Jaccard index and Dice coefficient rely on those instances where there is a band present they are often used for the analysis of fingerprint data because there is no need to arbitrarily split up the length of the gel into equal subsections for the analysis. The number of sub-segments chosen to separate along the gel will have an impact the results of the simple matching index and Sokal and Sneath's index analysis. These methods work well for binary data sets and others with a defined number of discrete segments, because it removes the arbitrary splitting of a fingerprint into subsections.

In other situations more information may be desired for the analysis of fingerprint data, including taking into the account the intensity of bands on a gel, which can be important in some analyses. In these cases, the analysis is carried out such that the position of the band and its intensity are used to generate a densimetric curve; the more intense the band, the larger the peak in the curve (Figure 4A). In other cases, the data analyzed may originate as densimetric curve data from a DNA sequencer, gas chromatograph, liquid chromatography system or mass spectrometer, such that the elution time and peak intensity are valuable to distinguish different OTUs. These position/intensity types of analyses tend to be more computationally challenging than the formulas described above. For example, the formula for the Pearson product-moment correlation coefficient (Pearson correlation) is given below. Figure 4 provides an illustration of the impact of including the band intensity along with band position in calculating the similarity of two ribotype fingerprints from *E. coli* using the Pearson correlation compared to the Dice coefficient.

Pearson correlation (r)

$$r = \frac{\sum_{i=1}^{n} (X_i - \bar{X})(Y_i - \bar{Y})}{\sqrt{\sum_{i=1}^{n} (X_i - \bar{X})^2 \sum_{i=1}^{n} (Y_i - \bar{Y})^2}}$$

$$\bar{X} = \frac{1}{n} \sum_{i=1}^{n} X_i$$

$$\bar{Y} = \frac{1}{n} \sum_{i=1}^{n} Y_i$$

Where X_i is the densimetric values (or numeric coefficients) for the bands in one strain and Y_i the value for the other strain and "n" is the total number of band positions analyzed [7, 14]. Table 1 is provided to illustrate the calculation steps that go into the Pearson correlation to determine the similarity of profiles. The ribotype data from Figure 4 was used to illustrate the calculation of the Pearson correlation methods and will be used as example data for the other curve-based methods for determining similarity examined below.

Some other methods that can be used for the numerical calculation of similarity include Cosine coefficient and Spearman rank-order correlation (rank correlation), which have similarity to the Pearson correlation. With the Spearman rank-order correlation, the different variables (band intensities in our example) are ordered and ranked based on their intensities and the Pearson correlation calculations are carried using the rank numbers [7]. In the ribotyping example above, the band intensity rank in order (from 1.42 kb to 37.12 kb in Figure 4), for 295 are 7, 1, 3, 5, 2, 4, 8, and 6 and for 310 are 8, 1, 5, 7, 2, 3, 6, and 4. When these numbers are used for the Pearson correlation calculations, the rank correlation similarity value is 0.7857 compared to 0.9053, for the unranked calculation. In this example the calculated rank correlation similarity value is lower than the regular Pearson correlation calculations, in large part due to small number of variables (bands) analyzed. The rank correlation has greater utility in larger data sets in which certain raw data values are outliers from the general data that reflects the true representation of the relatedness of two isolates. By using the rank order values to calculate the relatedness the impact of the outliers is minimized [7]. The Cosine coefficient is a somewhat simpler algorithm that utilizes the raw intensity data to determine the relatedness of isolates [7]. The equation for the calculations is given below and for the ribotyping example presented above, the similarity is calculated to be 0.9515.

$$C = \frac{\sum_{i=1}^{n} X_i Y_i}{\sqrt{\sum_{i=1}^{n} X_i^2 \ \sum_{i=1}^{n} Y_i^2}}$$

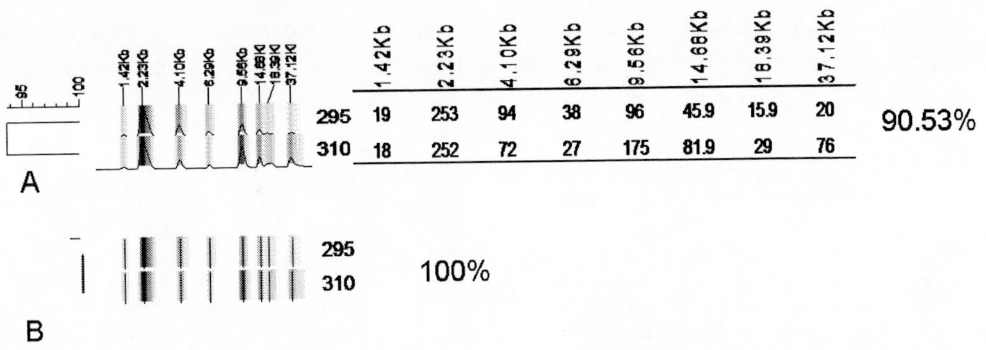

Figure 4. Comparison of Pearson correlation (panel A) and Dice coefficient (panel B) to calculate the similarity of two ribotype fingerprints from *E. coli.* The Pearson correlation calculations rely on both the band position and band intensity to determine the similarity of the OTUs. Panel A provides a curve-based intensity plot along with the corresponding intensity values for each band position. Using the Pearson correlation equation, the strains were found to have 90.53% similar profiles. When only the band positions were used in the Dice coefficient calculations the isolates were found to be 100% similar (panel B).

Some additional methods that can be used to calculate similarity based on band intensity or numerical values include the Canberra metric and Bray-Curtis coefficient [15]. These calculations provide a determination of dissimilarity or difference among strains; thus to determine the similarity among OTUs the value must be subtracted from one.

Canberra Metric

$$CM = \frac{1}{n} \cdot \sum_{i=1}^{n} \frac{|X_i - Y_i|}{(X_i + Y_i)} \quad (\text{Similarity} = 1 - CM)$$

Bray-Curtis

$$BC = \frac{\sum_{i=1}^{n} |X_i - Y_i|}{\sum_{i=1}^{n} (X_i + Y_i)} \quad (\text{Similarity} = 1 - BC)$$

For the ribotyping example the results of the Canberra calculation was 0.2224, thus the similarity was determined to be 0.7776. For the Bray-Curtis coefficient calculation, the result was 0.1669 and therefore the similarity was calculated to be 0.8331.

CLUSTER ANALYSIS

Because most applications of molecular subtyping for foodborne pathogens include more than two isolates, there needs to be efficient ways to visualize the relatedness between the multiple strains that are typically included in a molecular subtyping data set. There are a number of ways to visualize similarity data, and these fall into hierarchical or non-hierarchical categories [7]. With the hierarchical methods, the relatedness is displayed in an ordered arrangement, such as a tree-like structure. Non-hierarchical methods do not use tree-like structures to demonstrate relatedness, but rather the relatedness is shown by a location in a coordinate space. These methods, including principal components analysis (PCA) and multidimensional scaling (MDS), are described later in the chapter. The current section focuses on the hierarchical methods.

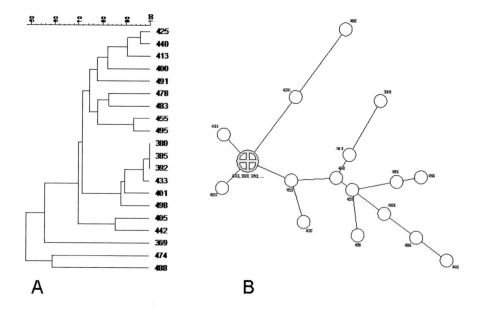

Figure 5. Examples of dendrograms that can be used to display the relationship among the OTUs in a dataset. The dendrogram trees can be either rooted (panel A) or unrooted (panel B) in structure. In the rooted tree, the tree has a node that represents a common ancestral profile for all the OTUs in the dataset. In panel A, this root node is the node with the lowest degree of similarity (left-most node). In unrooted trees the branching occurs without consideration of a potential common ancestor for the OTUs.

One of the most common ways to display data on the relatedness/similarity of bacterial strains is through the use of tree structures termed dendrograms. These dendrograms can be defined as phylogenetic trees for phylogenetic data or phenograms when phenetic data are used to determine similarity [3]. The dendrogram trees can be either rooted or unrooted in structure (Figure 5A and 5B, respectively). The topology or shape of the tree is made up of series of branches and nodes which define how individual strains (OTUs) are related to one another. The exterior branches extend from the strain information at one end to an interior node at the other. The interior branches connect the interior nodes to one another (Figure 6). In rooted trees, the number of exterior branches is equal to the number of samples (*n*) in the analyses, while the number of interior nodes is equal to *n*-1 and the number of interior branches is *n*-2. For unrooted tree the number of exterior branches is also equal to *n*, while the number of interior nodes is equal to *n*-2 and interior branches is *n*-3 [1]. The total number of trees that can be generated for a particular set of strains increases significantly as more strains are included in the analysis, for example if there are 4 strains in the analyses there are potentially 15 different rooted-tree topologies, however if the analyses contain 10 strains the number of potential topologies increases to 34,459,425 [1]. Of these many dendrograms, there is a single tree that best represents the true population structure. Therefore a goal of the analysis methods is to calculate the most representative tree for the population data. There are a number of different algorithms that have been developed to generate the most appropriate phylogenetic tree or phenogram based on molecular typing data.

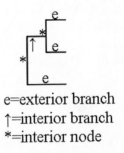

e=exterior branch
↑=interior branch
*=interior node

Figure 6. The topology of a dendrogram (tree) features a series of branches and nodes which define how individual strains (OTUs) are related to one another. The exterior branches "e" extend from the terminal nodes (or leaves, which represent the position of each strain in the tree) at one end to an interior node "*" at the other. The interior branches "↑" connect the interior nodes to one another.

Unweighted Pair-Group Means with Arithmetic Averages (UPGMA) Analysis

Likely the most common method to generate dendrograms (phenograms) based on molecular typing data is the UPGMA analysis [3]. For UPGMA analysis and other hierarchical methods, the procedure begins by computing the similarity of the strains included (based on DNA fingerprint, sequences, etc.) using one of the methods described above (Dice, Jaccard, Pearson, etc.). The calculated similarities of the OTUs are used to generate a similarity matrix, which provide the basis for calculating the optimal phylogenetic tree. From the calculated similarities, the distance (*D*) between the strains/profiles is calculated (*D* = 1-*Similarity*) [2]. Figures 7 and 8 provide an example of the development of a relatively simple UPGMA dendrogram based on six PFGE profiles from *Salmonella*. Based on the PFGE profiles (Figure 7A), the similarity is calculated and used to generate a similarity matrix

(Figure 7B). From the similarity matrix, a distance matrix (Figure 8Aa) is derived and the two strains with the lowest/shortest distance are identified (marked in grey box in the figure). The strains with the lowest distance (5 and 6) are initially clustered together to form a new single OTU (Figure 8B). In this example, the distance is 0.03. When two individual strains/OTUs are clustered together they form a new composite OTU, whose average distance is used to recalculate the distance to the other OTUs, for example the mean distance between OTU 5-6 and strain 1 is calculated as $[(0.36 + 0.38)/2] = 0.37$. The revised distance calculations are repeated for all of the strains and the combination with the shortest distance is identified (Figure 8Ab). The recalculated lowest distance is between OTU 5-6 and strain 4 (0.05) and thus the strains are clustered (OTU 4-5-6) and the distance matrix recalculated again. Isolates 1 and 3 are then joined as an OTU (Figure 8Ac) with a distance of 0.20 and the distances again recalculated until all of the strains and distances have been incorporated to generate a dendrogram. The dendrogram is generated based on the distance calculations for the strains and clusters (Figure 8B). In the dendrogram shown, the internal nodes are marked "a" through "e" in the order that they were added and the distance from the right edge of the tree (end nodes) is proportional to one-half the distances calculated when each strain was added to the analysis (grey boxes in Figure 8A). For example, the branch length between strains 5 and 6 would be calculated to be 0.015. Once the dendrogram is constructed, a scale can be added to show the distance or similarity among the strains. The legend at the top of the dendrogram in Figure 8B is based on the percent similarity which was calculated by the following formula: *Similarity (%) = (1-Distance)*100.* Thus the percent similarity between isolate 5 and 6 would be 97% and between 1 and 6 would be 55% (Figure 8).

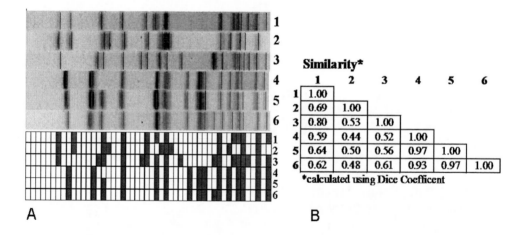

Similarity*

	1	2	3	4	5	6
1	1.00					
2	0.69	1.00				
3	0.80	0.53	1.00			
4	0.59	0.44	0.52	1.00		
5	0.64	0.50	0.56	0.97	1.00	
6	0.62	0.48	0.61	0.93	0.97	1.00

*calculated using Dice Coefficent

A   B

Figure 7. Example PFGE data and similarity matrix used to generate a UPGMA dendrogram. The PFGE profiles of six *Salmonella* are shown in panel A, along with a table illustrating the position of bands along the gel run. These data were used to calculate the similarities among each of the isolates using Dice coefficients and the data was placed in similarity matrix (panel B) which is used in the dendrogram generation.

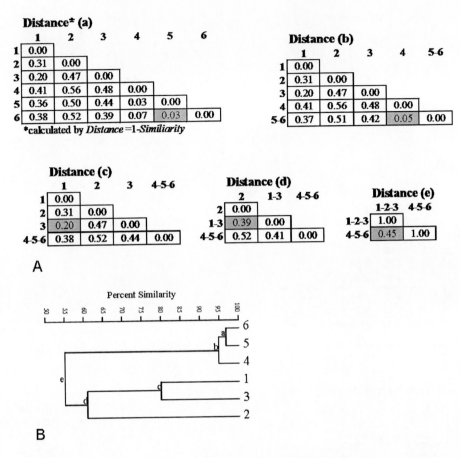

Figure 8. Steps used in the generation of a UPGMA dendrogram. The initial distance matrix in panel A (top left) is calculated by subtracting each of the similarity values (Figure 7B) from 1. From the distance matrix, the isolates with the shortest distance are identified (gray boxes in panel A) and grouped. The steps to determine the distance for the strains outlined in panel A is described in detail in the text. Likewise the process of generating the final dendrogram (panel B) is described in the text as well.

Neighbor Joining

Another method of generating phenograms and phylogenetic trees is the neighbor joining method. Like the UPGMA, neighbor joining trees are based on the distance between OTUs; however, the topology of the tree is different in that the distance from each of the OTU end nodes are not equidistant to root of the tree (Figure 9A). The neighbor joining trees are additive distance trees, such that the sum of the branch links between two OTUs is equal (or approximately equal) to the calculated genetic or phenetic distance between the strains [2]. For example, in the dendrogram in Figure 9A (which is generated from the original data in Figure 7) the distances between strains 2 and 4 were added up to be 0.55 (0.25 + 0.24 + 0.02 + 0.04) compared to 0.56 from the distance calculations in Figures 8Aa and 9B. The discrepancy is most likely due to rounding or minor variations due to topology.

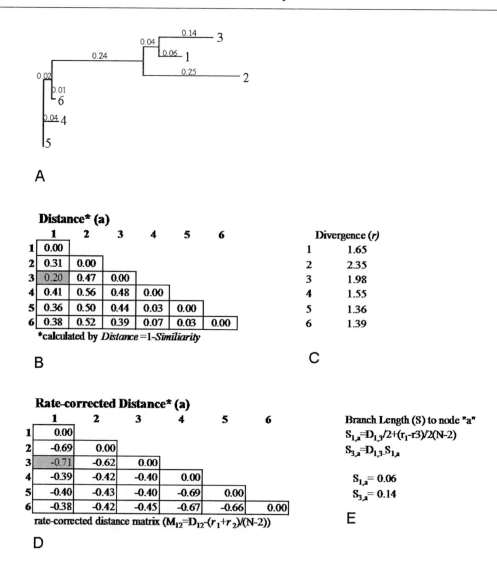

Figure 9. The generation of a neighbor joining tree using the PFGE data from Figure 7. Panel A shows the final neighbor joining tree from the data, while panels B-E demonstrate some of the step used to generate the tree. Panel B displays the initial distance matrix for the data, which is calculated from the similarity matrix in Figure 7. Panel C provides overall divergence (r) of the OTU from the population, which is the sum of the distance of the isolate to all others in the population. The divergence is used to generate a rate-corrected distance matrix using the equation in panel D. The OTU combination with the lowest rate-corrected distance (DRC) are grouped and the branch distances to the internal nodes are calculated using the equations in panel E. The steps in generating the neighbor joining tree are described in greater detail in the text.

The determination of the topology of neighbor joining tree is based on a rate corrected distance between OTUs. In determining which neighbors to join, the distances of the isolates to all others in the population are summed to determine the overall divergence (r) (Figure 9C) of the OTU from the population ($r_1 = \sum D_1$ (e.g. $D_{1,2} + D_{1,3} + D_{1,4}...D_{1,N}$; with the data Figure 9B: $0.38 + 0.20 + 0.41 + 0.36 + 0.38 = 1.65$)). The divergence is used to generate a rate-corrected distance matrix using the formula ($M_{1,2} = D_{1,2} - (r_1 + r_2) / (N - 2)$) (Figure 9D). The combination with the lowest rate-corrected distance (D_{RC}) is determined and these OTUs are grouped to generate the first node in the tree. In the example, this combination is 1 and 3, which has a D_{RC} of -0.71. In order to determine the branch length (S) connecting the terminal node (at OTU 1 in the example) to the new internal node ("a" in the example), the following equation is used $S_{1,a} = D_{1,3}/2 + (r_1 - r_3) / 2(N - 2)$ or 0.06 in Figure 9E. Then to determine the distance from OTU 3 to "a", the following equation is used $S_{3,a} = D_{1,3} - S_{1,a}$ (0.14 in Figure 9E).

Once the distances to the first node are determined, the distance matrix is recalculated to determine the distance from each of the remaining OTUs to node "a". This is a some what different approach than used with the UPGMA, in which the adjusted distances were calculated by averaging the distance from the OTUs joined in a node to the other OTUs. Because the neighbor joining tree is based on additive distance, the actual distances need to be calculated. For example, the distance from OTU 2 to node "a" is calculated by the formula $D_{2,a} = (D_{1,2} + D_{2,3} - D_{1,3})/2$, in this case the distances from 2 to 1 and 2 to 3 are added, which is greater than the distance to "a" by the distance of 1 to 3, thus this distance is subtracted, prior to dividing by 2 to get the distance. In UPGMA, the "$-D_{1,3}$" component is not include in the distance calculation. The process of determining r and the D_{RC} is repeated after recalculating the distance matrix and the next OTUs are combined and the S for each is determined. The process is repeated until all of the OTUs are incorporated and the neighbor joining tree is complete. A description of the process for developing a neighbor joining tree for DNA sequence data is highlighted in Chapter 4 of the book by Salemi and Vandamme [2].

Other Dendrogram Generating Methods

Some additional clustering algorithms include the single linkage (nearest-neighbor) and the complete linkage (furthest-neighbor) methods [3]. The single linkage method utilizes the dissimilarity among strains in its analysis and begins by linking together the two strains which have the least dissimilarity to form a new group, after which the dissimilarity matrix is recalculated and the process repeated until all of the OTUs have been incorporated. In contrast to the UPGMA and the neighbor joining methods, when the dissimilarity matrices are recalculated for the single linkage method, the dissimilarity values are calculated from the member of the newly formed group that has the minimal distance (dissimilarity) to the remaining OTUs yet to be incorporated into the dendrogram. Then the OTU with the shortest distance (nearest neighbor) to any single part of the new group is next incorporated. Because it only takes one link to a member of the existing group, the method is known to have some limitations for certain sets of data due to phenomenon called chaining [16]. For example in the following scenario, where the distance from OTU A to B ($D_{A,B}$) = 2, $D_{A,C}$ = 6, $D_{A,D}$ = 4, $D_{B,C}$ = 3, $D_{B,D}$ = 6, and $D_{C,D}$ = 4, OTU A would be clustered with B, which would then cluster with C, because B and C are closer to one another than A and D. This chaining effect distorts to the overall relatedness such that A and C would be more closely clustered together than A and D, which have a shorter overall distance. There are certain approaches that have been developed to avoid some of these problems with the single linkage (nearest-neighbor) limitations but they are beyond the scope of this chapter, for more information please refer to the book by Webb [16].

With the complete linkage or furthest-neighbor approach, the initial clustering is done as described above for single linkage. The two OTUs with the least dissimilarity are initially clustered together; however the dissimilarity matrices are recalculated using the furthest distance of the newly formed group to the remaining OTUs, rather than the minimum distance of the single linkage. After the recalculation, the two OTUs with the least dissimilarity are grouped and the process repeated until all OTUs are incorporated [16]. The benefit of the complete linkage over the single linkage is that the joining of groups is more closely tied to the overall body of the group rather than to linkages to potential outliers. Thus, the clustering results may be more representative of the overall relatedness of the population of isolates.

Data Resampling

Once the phenograms or phylogenetic trees have been generated, it is important to determine whether or not the tree is representative of the true relatedness among the OTUs analyzed. When the underlying genetic structure of the strains tested is not known, different statistical approaches using resampling of the data are often used for validation of the trees [2]. These techniques are computationally intensive because they carry out multiple rounds of analyses to determine the best representation of the data. With resampling, subsets of the original data from the OTUs are reanalyzed to determine if the resultant trees demonstrate a high degree of similarity to the original tree. If there is a little or no change in the overall tree structure, it can be assumed that the original analysis reliably represented the relationship among the OTUs. Two of the more common resampling methodologies are bootstrapping and jackknifing [3].

Bootstrap Analysis

With the bootstrap analysis, randomly selected data points are chosen to form a pseudosample with the same number of data points as the original data set [17, 18]. This is shown in Figure 10, which utilizes the character data generated from the PFGE analysis in Figure 7. Because in bootstrapping, the resampling is done randomly, it is likely that certain data points will be left out of the pseudosample set, while others will be represented multiple times (for example in Figure 10A, data from positions 4,11,16,19… were removed from the analysis and replaced by data from positions 3,10,15,20…, which are now represented multiple times). The similarities of the isolates in the population are then recalculated using the pseudosample (Figures 10B (original data) and 10C (resampled data)), and the resampling/recalculation process is repeated multiple times (typically 100s to 1000s of times) to determine whether the original dendrogram is likely the best representation of the population of OTUs. In Figure 10C, it is interesting to note the difference in the calculated similarities of OTUs 4, 5 and 6 in the pseudosample compared to the original data set. When bootstrapping analysis was carried out 1000 times with the data using BioNumerics software, it was found that the consensus tree was most similar to the one generated for the pseudosample in Figure 10C rather than the original data in Figure 10B.

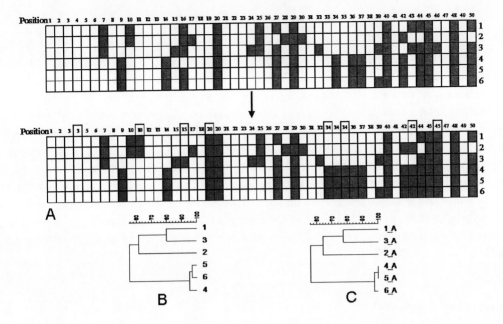

Figure 10. Data resampling of the PFGE data from Figure 7 using bootstrap analysis. In panel A, a psuedosample of the original data are displayed. On the top is the band position data from the PFGE experiments and below the psuedosample in which a fraction of the data points are randomly replaced with other data points from the from the experiments (for example, data from positions 4, 11, 16, 19, 33, 35, 43, and 46 were removed and replaced by data from positions 3, 10, 15, 20, 34, 34, 42, and 45). The dendrogram are then recalculated using the psuedosample and compared to the original tree. Panel B shows the original dendrogram and panel C the dendrogram from the pseudosample. Note the difference in the calculated similarities of OTUs 4, 5 and 6 in the pseudosample compared to the original data.

Jackknife Analysis

Another method used for resampling is termed Jackknife analysis. As with bootstrapping, there are multiple rounds of resampling and calculations carried out to get at the most appropriate representation of similarities among OTUs in a population set [2, 19]. With the Jackknife analysis, a set number of data points (typically a single data point) are dropped from the data set and the similarities are calculated among the strains [7]. This process of removing a data point(s) and recalculating similarities is repeated as done with bootstrap analysis and is used to generate a consensus tree representing the predicted population structure. In microbial source tracking, Jackknifing can also be used to test the robustness of methods to correctly classify isolates of a particular source with its source group. In this type of analysis, individual isolate typing profiles are removed from the phenetic analysis and the similarity matrix and tree are calculated without the isolate [20]. The profile from the removed isolate is compared to the results of the analysis of the different species groups to determine whether the removed isolate was correctly grouped with its original source group or misclassified as coming from a separate source. The removal-recalculation-comparison process is repeated until all of the isolates in the original analysis are tested. The analysis allows for the determination of the percentage of correctly classified isolates and for those that were misclassified, what source they were misclassified as [20].

CLADISTIC APPROACHES TO DATA ANALYSIS

In addition to the phenetic method used to describe the similarity of isolates, there are a number of cladistic methods that have value to infer relationships among strains. These methods can be divided into two major categories that either rely on the distance-based approaches to generate trees, similar to those described above, and those that rely more directly on changes in characters, such as nucleotide or amino acid changes among homologous sequences [21]. In this section we briefly describe the likelihood, parsimony and Bayesian analysis methods. These methods are widely used for phylogenetic analysis to determine the underlying evolutionary divergence of strains in a population. However, they are currently less widely used in epidemiological and source tracking applications so they are not covered in as much detail as some of the other analysis methods above. For more in-depth coverage of the methods, the reader is recommended to view one of the many good references on the subjects [1, 21-24].

Parsimony Analyses

Parsimony analysis methods are used to determine phylogenies based on the minimum number of character changes in data set that define the different OTUs in phylogenetic tree or phenogram [25]. In the case of phylogenetic analysis, the goal of parsimony analysis is to identify the tree(s) that arise from the character sets with the minimum evolutionary changes possible that explains the data analyzed [26]. With the maximum parsimony analysis approach, the ideal tree generated is the one with the shortest total branch lengths or overall tree length [26]. There are a number of different methods that can be used to generate the different trees that are compared to one another to determine which has the shortest tree length. The different methods handle the changes in the character data sets in different means. For example, when analyzing nucleotide sequence data, it is known that different types of substitutions happen at different rates, transitions (purine to purine or pyrimidine to pyrimidine substitutions) occur more frequently than transversions (purine to pyrimidine or pyrimidine to purine substitutions), therefore some methods give more weight to transversions in calculating phylogenetic differences, while others do not weigh substitutions differently [25]. Additionally, there are different approaches to handling reversibility, or when a character state change (nucleotide transition, for example) reverts back to its original state during the evolutionary process. Some methods, such as the Camin-Sokal parsimony, do not allow for reversions; while others, such as the Wagner parsimony and Dollo parsimony, allow for reversions in the parsimony calculations [26].

Likelihood Analyses

The parsimony analyses have a number of potential limitations in making the most representative phylogenetic inferences among certain OTUs, in large part due to their attempts to identify the simplest trees to explain the observed data. With the analysis of more divergent character sets (DNA sequences for example), it is less likely that the simplest tree generated with parsimony analysis is the one that truly represents the evolutionary dynamics. Thus additional methods, such as the likelihood analyses, have been developed to address these challenges [22, 27]. The maximum likelihood method provides means to correct for the changes that are observed in divergent DNA sequence that occur over long periods of time versus those in rapidly evolving sequences, this allows for the development of a more representative phylogenetic tree. In contrast to identifying the simplest tree, the maximum likelihood methods aim to identify the tree structure that has the highest probability of predicting the observed sequence data [23]. In order to determine the probabilities, some underlying information on the rates of sequence evolution needs to be evaluated, such as the chances of transition vs. transversion events, reversion events or a string substitutions at a particular locus (A $\rightarrow$ C $\rightarrow$ T) occurring within the data set analyzed. These model parameters are incorporated into the likelihood methods for identifying the most representative tree for the population. The maximum likelihood methods are statistically based and allow for the testing of different phylogenetic hypotheses to determine the different analysis models (such as transition and transversion rates) that are most appropriate for a particular data set.

One of the main limitations of the likelihood methods is that they can be very computationally intensive, due to the calculations of a large number of phylogenetic trees for each data set in order to identify which tree is the best for the dataset. There are certain approaches that can be used to streamline the number of trees evaluated, but these run the risk of missing the best fit tree [22]. One way to assess the confidence in the generated trees is to carryout bootstrap analysis on the data to see if the chosen maximum likelihood tree is likely the best representation [23]. As with the original maximum likelihood itself, a drawback of bootstrapping is the computational resources needed to carryout the analysis.

Bayesian Analyses

An extension of the maximum likelihood methods are Bayesian analyses, in which prior or posterior probabilities outside the likelihood analysis are incorporated to predict the trees that most truly represent the data set [28]. Prior probabilities are information that the analyst believe may contribute to phylogenetic relationships that are incorporated into the Bayesian model prior to the analysis of the genetic data [23]. In epidemiological studies this information could include the belief that bacterial strains that come from common sources, or are temporally related, would more likely be related to one another, than those from diverse sources or distinct time periods. These prior probabilities are incorporated with the maximum likelihood methods to help identify the most representative tree. Because prior probabilities can rely on potentially subjective information, caution is needed in choosing the parameters to avoid potential bias. Computationally, Bayesian analyses uses methods such as the Markov chain Monte Carlo algorithms to reduce the computational requirements to carry out the analyses, which is potentially beneficial compared to maximum likelihood analyses [23]. The details of the computational processes are beyond the scope of this chapter; however the reader is referred to some informative reviews Bayesian analysis methodologies and approaches for phylogenetics and epidemiological investigations [23, 28-30].

NON-HIERARCHICAL ANALYSES

Non-hierarchical analysis methods are becoming more widely used for the analysis of large data sets that are generated by a number of typing schemes [3]. For example, microarrays are increasingly being used for genotyping and expression studies. With these studies, large data sets, typically 1000s of data points, can make identifying key pieces of information difficult without improved data handling [31]. The goal of the non-hierarchical clustering is to separate OTUs into distinct groups with high levels of similarity among the members of the groups. There are a number of approaches to non-hierarchical clustering; we will look at a few of them here including principal components analysis and multidimensional scaling.

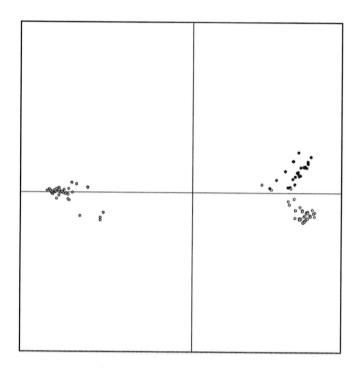

Figure 11. Two-dimension principal components analysis (PCA) plot of virulence factor presence/absence in *E. coli* isolates. Isolates from different sources form three major clusters based on the virulence factors present in the isolates. The isolates in the different clusters are predominantly from different sources, thus the PCA analysis identified portions of the data that best distinguished isolates from different sources.

Principal Component Analysis (PCA)

Principal component analysis (PCA) is likely the most widely used of the non-hierarchical analysis methods [32]. PCA is often carried out on data sets with a large numbers of data points (such as in microarray experiments), thus one of the goals of PCA is to identify a limited set of variables within the larger data set that best describes the data [16]. PCA methods can be used to analyze both continuous and binary data sets that are often encountered with certain molecular subtyping methods. To analyze gel image files, the data needs to be converted to numerical data (see Figure 7, where the PFGE data are converted to binary data). The data are used to generate a character table in which the character values for each OTU are entered. If there are two variables entered for each character, the values are plotted in a 2D scatter plot, while if more than two values for each OTU are analyzed the results can be plotted in a 3D scatter plot. Once the scatter plots are completed, a regression line is generated from the data points that identify the maximum variance in the data set. This vector is used to define the first principal component. Next, the second principal component is identified as the vector perpendicular to the first principal component line that has the next highest variance. If 3D scatter plots are generated, the third principal component is then identified as the orthogonal line with the first and second components that has the remaining highest variance [16]. The process of defining principal components is continued until most of the total variance in the data set is identified [33]. These principal components lines are used to generate a new scatter plot (first and second components for 2D plot, and first, second and third for 3D plots) in which the data are transformed such that the principal component line serves as the axis for the scatter plot of data points. PCA is an unsupervised analysis and thus prior grouping knowledge is not taken into the determination of relationships [16]. In the PCA graphical plots, those OTUs that are highly related to one another remain grouped together, while those with differences are separated from the group (Figure 11).

Multidimensional Scaling (MDS)

Multidimensional Scaling (MDS) in another non-hierarchical analysis method that relies on calculated similarities among OTUs (see Figure 7). In conducting MDS analysis, a dissimilarity matrix is generated and distances between the OTUs are calculated and plotted in the coordinate space [34]. The output of analysis is a multidimensional (e.g. 3D) representation of the relatedness of the OTUs, with the positioning of OTUs in coordinate space optimized such that there is the minimum sum of squared error in the distance between OTUs (Figure 12). Thus this added dimensionality allows an increased ability to display the relatedness among OTUs, because the analysis is not as confined by some of the structural issues that are often associated with the hierarchical dendrogram structures [16]. One of the drawbacks of the MDS analysis is that the output is more complex with the added dimensions, which can make it more difficult to analyze the output in two dimensional displays. Therefore computer programs are necessary to freely rotate the output in 3D space allows for a better appreciation of the overall calculated population structure. There are different algorithms that can be used to carry out MDS analyses and the choice of the appropriate model for the particular data set will likely have an impact on the results. The different models/algorithms are reviewed by Van Deun and Delbeke (http://www.mathpsyc.uni-bonn.de/doc/delbeke/delbeke.htm), and more comprehensive information on MDS can be obtained from the books by Cox and Cox [35] and Borg and Groenen [36]. It is likely that in the future there will be a wider application of non-hierarchical methods in the analysis of molecular typing data for use in microbial source tracking applications.

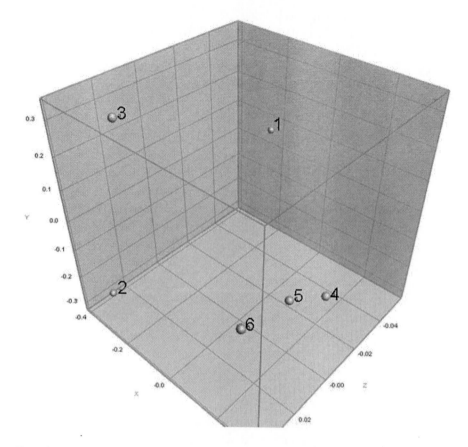

Figure 12. A three-dimensional multidimensional scaling representation of the relatedness of the PFGE profiles from Figure 7. The positioning of strains in the coordinate space is optimized to minimize the sum of squared error in the distance between the strains.

CONCLUSIONS

The goal of this chapter was to provide an overview of some of the most common techniques that are used for the analysis of molecular typing data, and provide relevant references for those interested in gaining a more in-depth understanding of the methods. Indeed, there is a wealth of information on the various methods, often with multiple books directed at a single set of analysis techniques. The ability to appropriately choose and implement the analysis methods for the particular type of data or epidemiological question asked is essential to ensure that users are drawing the correct conclusions from their data. The ability to draw correct conclusions is extremely important when using the data in microbial source tracking schemes, because the molecular typing results are often used to link a foodborne pathogen that made a person ill to a particular source in the food production system.

DISCLAIMER

The use of trade names is for identification purposes only, and does not imply endorsement by the U.S. Food and Drug Administration or the U.S. Department of Health and Human Services. The views presented in this manuscript do not necessarily reflect those of the FDA.

REFERENCES

[1]   Nei M, Kumar S. Molecular Evolution and Phylogenetics. New York: Oxford University Press; 2000.

[2]   Van de Peer Y. Phylogeny inference based on distance methods. In: Salemi M, Vandamme A, editors. The Pylogenetic Handbook: A Practical Approach to DNA and Protein Phylogeny. New York: Cambridge University Press; 2003. p. 101-19.

[3]   Riley L. Molecular Epidemiology of Infectious Diseases-Principles and Practices. Washington, DC: ASM Press; 2004.

[4]   Foley SL, Lynne AM, Nayak R. Molecular typing methodologies for microbial source tracking and epidemiological investigations of Gram-negative bacterial foodborne pathogens. *Infect Genet Evol.* 2009;9(4):430-40.

[5]   DeSalle R. What's in a character? *J Biomed Inform.* 2006;39(1):6-17.

[6]   Dawson B, Trapp R. Basic & Clinical Biostatistics. 4 ed. New York: McGraw-Hill Companies; 2004.

[7]   Applied Maths. BioNumerics Manual 6.0 ed. Sint-Martens-Latem, Belgium: Applied Maths; 2009.

[8]   Simsion G, Witt G. Data Modeling Essentials. 3 ed. San Francisco: Morgan Kaufmann; 2005.

[9]   Revesz P. Introduction to Databases: From Biological to Spatio-Temporal. London: Springer-Verlag; 2010.

[10]   San Mauro D, Agorreta A. Molecular systematics: A synthesis of the common methods and the state of knowledge. *Cell Mol Biol Lett.* 2010;15(2):311-41.

[11]   Feil EJ, Enright MC. Analyses of clonality and the evolution of bacterial pathogens. *Curr Opin Microbiol.* 2004;7(3):308-13.

[12]   Spratt BG, Hanage WP, Li B, Aanensen DM, Feil EJ. Displaying the relatedness among isolates of bacterial species -- the eBURST approach. *FEMS Microbiol Lett.* 2004;241(2):129-34.

[13]   Bonin A, Ehrich D, Manel S. Statistical analysis of amplified fragment length polymorphism data: a toolbox for molecular ecologists and evolutionists. *Mol Ecol.* 2007;16(18):3737-58.

[14]   Kirk R. Statistics an Introduction. Orlando, FL: Holt, Rinehart and Winston, Inc.; 1989.

[15]   Wolda H. Similarity indices, sample size and diversity. *Oecologia* (Berl). 1981;50:296-302.

[16]   Webb A. Statistical Pattern Recognition. 2 ed. Hoboken, NJ: John Wiley and Sons; 2002.

[17] Pitt DG, Kreutzweiser DP. Applications of computer-intensive statistical methods to environmental research. *Ecotoxicol Environ Saf.* 1998;39(2):78-97.

[18] Henderson AR. The bootstrap: a technique for data-driven statistics. Using computer-intensive analyses to explore experimental data. *Clin Chim Acta.* 2005;359(1-2):1-26.

[19] Efron B. Bootstrap methods: another look at the jackknife. *Ann Stat.* 1979;7(1):1-26.

[20] David DE, Lynne AM, Han J, Foley SL. Evaluation of virulence factor profiling in the characterization of veterinary *Escherichia coli* isolates. *Appl Environ Microbiol.* 2010;76(22):7509-13.

[21] Horner DS, Pesole G. Phylogenetic analyses: a brief introduction to methods and their application. *Expert Rev Mol Diagn.* 2004;4(3):339-50.

[22] Whelan S, Lio P, Goldman N. Molecular phylogenetics: state-of-the-art methods for looking into the past. *Trends Genet.* 2001;17(5):262-72.

[23] Holder M, Lewis PO. Phylogeny estimation: traditional and Bayesian approaches. *Nat Rev Genet.* 2003;4(4):275-84.

[24] Salemi M, Vandamme A. The Pylogenetic Handbook: A Practical Approach to DNA and Protein Phylogeny. New York: Cambridge University Press; 2003.

[25] Swofford D, Sullivan J. Phylogeny inference based on parsimony and other methods. In: Salemi M, Vandamme A, editors. The Pylogenetic Handbook: A Practical Approach to DNA and Protein Phylogeny. New York: Cambridge University Press; 2003. p. 160-81.

[26] Felsenstein J. Parsimony in systematics: biological and statistical issues. *Ann Rev Ecol Syst.* 1983;14:313-33.

[27] von Haeseler A, Strimmer K. Phylogeny inference based on maximum-likelihood methods. In: Salemi M, Vandamme A, editors. The Pylogenetic Handbook: A Practical Approach to DNA and Protein Phylogeny. New York: Cambridge University Press; 2003. p. 137-52.

[28] Huelsenbeck JP, Ronquist F, Nielsen R, Bollback JP. Bayesian inference of phylogeny and its impact on evolutionary biology. *Science.* 2001;294(5550):2310-4.

[29] Greenland S. Bayesian perspectives for epidemiological research: I. Foundations and basic methods. *Int J Epidemiol.* 2006;35(3):765-75.

[30] Greenland S. Bayesian perspectives for epidemiological research. II. Regression analysis. *Int J Epidemiol.* 2007;36(1):195-202.

[31] Fang H, Xu J, Ding D, Jackson SA, Patel IR, Frye JG, et al. An FDA bioinformatics tool for microbial genomics research on molecular characterization of bacterial foodborne pathogens using microarrays. *BMC Bioinformatics.* 2010;11 Suppl 6:S4.

[32] Abdi H, Williams L. Principal Component Analysis. Wiley Interdisciplinary Review: *Computational Statistics.* 2010;2:In press.

[33] Chan YH. Biostatistics 302. Principal component and factor analysis. *Singapore Med J.* 2004;45(12):558-65, quiz 66.

[34] Kachigan SK. Multivariate Statistical Analysis: A Conceptual Introduction. Second ed. New York: Radius; 1991.

[35] Cox T, Cox M. Multidimensional Scaling. 2 ed. Boca Raton, FL: Chapman and Hall/CRC; 2001.

[36] Borg I, Groenen P. Modern Multidimensional Scaling: Theory and Applications. New York: Springer-Vorlag; 1997.

In: Molecular Typing Methods for TFM
Editors: S. Foley, R. Nayak, T. Johnson et al.

ISBN: 978-1-62100-643-5
© 2012 Nova Science Publishers, Inc.

Chapter 15

USE OF MOLECULAR TYPING IN
EPIDEMIOLOGICAL INVESTIGATIONS

Walid Q. Alali
Center for Food Safety
University of Georgia
Griffin, GA, US

ABSTRACT

Epidemiological investigations of foodborne disease are conducted to determine the cause of the illnesses and to develop future control measures to prevent more cases from occurring. Molecular typing methods have revolutionized the way outbreak investigations are conducted. These typing methods provide information about the relatedness of isolates from human clinical cases to those from food sources implicated in an outbreak. During an investigation, epidemiologists need to interpret the molecular typing data within the framework of the epidemiological information collected for maximum effectiveness. This chapter examines the steps in the epidemiological investigation of foodborne diseases and explores the vital roles of molecular typing to the successful investigation.

INTRODUCTION

Foodborne outbreaks in the United States have changed in the past decades from localized sporadic "church supper" like outbreaks to large multistate events. This shift is primarily due to changes in food production, distribution patterns, food consumption, and food safety practices. In the U.S., it is estimated that foodborne diseases cause 47.8 million illnesses, 127,839 hospitalizations, and 3,037 deaths each year [1]. The change in foodborne disease nature has accompanied with new means for outbreak detection. Existing and improved surveillance systems (e.g., FoodNet and PulseNet of the CDC [Centers for Disease

Control and Prevention]) in the U.S. with new microbiological and molecular techniques have greatly enhanced the ability to investigation foodborne outbreaks [2, 3]. The challenge of diffuse multistate outbreaks is the ability to correlate molecular typing data to epidemiological information to come up, in a timely manner, with information that correctly investigate and identify the source of the foodborne outbreak.

The use of molecular typing methods has revolutionized the way an outbreak investigation is conducted. These methods provide valuable data on the relatedness of isolates from human clinical cases of foodborne disease as well as isolates from the food source implicated in the outbreak. Epidemiologists rely on molecular typing of isolates, but should consider the typing data within the framework of the epidemiological information collected during outbreak investigation. The PulseNet of CDC (an electronic database of pulsed field gel electrophoresis [PFGE] fingerprints from specific foodborne pathogens submitted by several laboratories in several U.S. states) is an example of an active collection of PFGE patterns/data that is used to initiate possible (case clusters) outbreak investigation and source identification.

Introduction to Epidemiological Investigation

The main goals of epidemiological investigation are to identify a problem, collect data, formulate and test hypotheses, and develop conclusions and recommendation for prevention and control. In foodborne illness outbreaks, epidemiological investigations are conducted to determine the cause of the outbreak and to recommend control measures to prevent more cases of illness from happening.

Epidemiology is the study of the distribution and determinants of health-related states or events frequency in specific populations (human or animal), and the application of this study to control health problems. First reported epidemiological investigation was conducted by John Snow in 1850s in London. He investigated the cause of cholera outbreak, determined the number of cases and their spatial distribution, and concluded that a water pump was the source of infection. Snow had the handle of the pump removed to prevent more cases of cholera.

The nature and magnitude of foodborne outbreaks has changed over the years; from small-scale potluck like outbreaks to multi-state with sporadic number of cases outbreaks. Methodology of investigating an outbreak has also evolved to cope with the current nature of outbreaks.

Steps to Epidemiological Investigation of Foodborne Outbreak

The steps for conducting a foodborne outbreak epidemiologic investigation do not necessarily proceed in a specific sequence. In reality, several steps in the investigation may happen at the same time.

1. Verify the Existence of a Possible Outbreak

An outbreak is suspected when the reported number of cases exceeds the expected baseline rate of disease. Although CDC defines an outbreak of foodborne illness as two or more persons experiencing a similar illness after ingestion of a common food or different food in a common place, the baseline rate should be examined on per disease basis. For instance, a single case of foodborne botulism in the U.S. can be serious to initiate an investigation, while it may require several cases of norovirus infections to initiate an investigation. Therefore, a comparison of the current number of cases (incidence) with the baseline rate (past levels) of the same disease is required to determine whether we may have an outbreak.

In the U.S., State public health agencies receive reports on foodborne illnesses from local health providers and microbiologists. Public health laboratories screen patient stool samples (from patients with foodborne illness symptoms) for specific bacterial pathogens (e.g., *Salmonella* and *E. coli* O157:H7) and further analyze these isolates for genetic relatedness using molecular typing 'DNA fingerprinting' techniques. Results of molecular typing are reported to the CDC PulseNet database. State public health and CDC workers look for groups of isolates with similar DNA fingerprints "clusters" that help in determining the existence of an outbreak.

2. Defining and Finding Cases

It is important to create a case definition that helps deciding which individuals can be classified as cases. Case definition may include information on time and place of exposure, laboratory findings, and clinical symptoms. Since laboratory confirmed diagnosis is not always feasible, reports on both probable and laboratory confirm cases can be used during the outbreak investigation. More cases might become available as: a) investigators search their databases, b) survey groups that may have been exposed, and c) results of laboratory testing become available.

3. Describe the Data Using an Epidemic Curve

To search for common association among cases based on time, place, and person variables, data collected can be plotted on a graph (epidemic curve). This curve describes the association of the time of illness and all the cases associated with the outbreak. The shape of the epidemic curve can suggest the type of outbreak. Common or point source outbreak may suggest one source of infection within short period of time as in potluck dinner foodborne outbreak. On the other hand, propagated-source or person-to-person outbreak may suggest disease transmission from one person to another as in a community-wide outbreak of shigellosis. Continual source outbreak is an extended outbreak of foodborne illness where the source of infection continues to be contaminated as the case of food handler related outbreak.

4. Generating and Testing Hypotheses

An 'educated guess' can be made about the cause of the outbreaks through conducting interviews with cases and others whom considered at risk population (e.g., members of household where a case was identified; i.e., controls). Investigators ask about foods that the ill people actually ate before they got sick, and then further narrow it to the specific foods that many of the ill people remember eating. To test the hypothesis, statistical methods are applied to see whether cases were more likely than controls (people did not sick) have eaten a certain type of food (case-control study). It is not unusual that investigators find no association between the cases and a particular food item. It may be that more information needs to be collected or the outbreak has ended without knowing the source.

5. Conduct an Environmental Assessment

Environmental investigation is conducted to figure out how the food was contaminated. This investigation may includes inspecting a food facility, review records and practices at an operation, assess their HACCP (Hazard Analysis Critical control Points) plan, and trace back of the origin of the contaminated food from the restaurant, to retail store, to food processer, and can go up to the farm. A facility inspection may require environmental sample collection (e.g., microbial swabs), collecting food items, and visual assessment of the operation. It is unusual that food involved in the outbreak is composed of multiple ingredients that were produced at several food facilities. Investigator would source tracebacks the suspected food ingredients to multiple food facilities that could potentially be linked to the causative agent.

6. Implement Control and Prevention Measures

Steps should be taken to contain the outbreak as soon as the preliminary data indicate a food vehicle (i.e., hypothesis is generated). Additional recommendations for control and prevention can be released as the investigation progresses. Outbreak control measure may include: destroying contaminated foods, sterilizing contaminated water, requiring an infectious food handler to stay away from work until he or she is well, closing facilities associated with producing contaminated food, and communicate with consumers to get rid of suspected food at their home.

Investigators should take notice that an outbreak ends when the number of new cases drop back to the baseline level before the outbreak. The epidemic curve would illustrate the changes in the number of cases over time and whether cases are dropping. Outbreak investigation can provide new information on new food vehicle, possible route of contamination, and gaps in the food production systems. It also provide new venue for research to better understand how contamination occur and how to prevent it from happening again.

INTRODUCTION TO MOLECULAR TYPING

Molecular typing is a method to identify and compare relatedness of DNA fragments within a particular species. Prior to molecular typing development, phenotypic characterization of bacteria were determined by traditional culture methods, by serology, by biochemical testing, and/or by antibiograms [4]. Molecular typing generates isolate-specific genotypic characters that can be used to identify the sources and routes of spread of pathogens through food production systems [5, 6]. Furthermore, typing is used in epidemiologic investigation of outbreaks to determine the genetic similarity among pathogens isolated from ill persons as well as contaminated food, and to identify clusters of cases (epidemiologically related strains) to assess that a possible outbreak is happening.

The choice of which typing method to use in a given situation depends on a number of criteria [7-9]. These are: the stability of the markers assessed by the typing method over the study period, the typeability of the isolates, discriminatory power, reproducibility of the typing results if testing is performed at a different time and/or place, bacterial species, time required to conduct the typing and produce the results, accessibility to reagents and equipment as well as the personnel skill to conduct the test, ease of use and the cost associated with typing and data analysis [10].

MOLECULAR TYPING METHODS USED IN EPIDEMIOLOGICAL INVESTIGATIONS

The most common typing method used in epidemiological investigations is PFGE due to its high discriminatory power between related and non-related isolates and the high reproducibility (low laboratory-to-laboratory variability) [11]. Additionally, standardized PFGE laboratory protocols have made it easier to compare the results (typing patterns) between different state laboratories and even worldwide [12]. The CDC Molecular typing network for foodborne bacterial disease surveillance (PulseNet) is an electronic database of PFGE fingerprints from specific foodborne pathogens (*Salmonella*, *E. coli* O157:H7, *Shigella*, *Listeria*, and *Campylobacter*) submitted by several state public health laboratories, USDA-FSIS, and FDA laboratories [13-15]. PFGE, however, is considered a costly technique, labor intensive, and require highly trained personnel to perform the work. Furthermore, the analysis of PFGE patterns/images is usually done via specific software that can be cost-prohibited and requires special training.

Another typing method is multilocus sequence typing (MLST). It has been used in epidemiological investigation due to its discriminatory power, ease in creating electronic databases, and less labor intensive compared to PFGE [16]. The MLST method is based on sequencing multiple housekeeping genes (usually 400 – 450 bp in length each) in bacterial isolates to determine their genetic relatedness [17-19]. These housekeeping genes may have sufficient variability to produce distinct sequences to determine relatedness among isolates. A series of MLST network databases (www.mlst.net) that is similar to PulseNet PFGE was developed to share MLST results [20]. However, MLST methods provide only limited genetic information, as they analyze only the sequence of highly conserved genes, therefore, restricting its discriminatory power between related strains.

Multiple locus variant-repeat analysis (MLVA) is another technology that has been used in epidemiological investigations such as outbreaks caused by *Salmonella* spp. [21-24], and *E. coli* O157:H7 [25, 26]. Because of the high discriminatory power and the relative simplicity of MLVA, PulseNet is considering MLVA as an alternative or confirmatory method to PFGE in outbreak investigations [27]. This method is based on differences in the variable number of tandem repeats (VNTR) on multiple loci on the chromosome of bacteria. The MLVA method detects variations in short sequence repeat motifs of the bacterial genomes of interest, and has been particularly effective for bacterial species that are highly monomorphic [28, 29].

Several other methods have demonstrated some potential to be used in epidemiological investigations such as plasmid analysis [30-34], restriction fragment length polymorphism

(RFLP) [35, 36], ribotyping [37, 38], amplified fragment length polymorphisms (AFLP) [39, 40], random amplified polymorphic DNA PCR (RAPD-PCR) [36, 41], and repetitive element PCR (Rep-PCR) [42, 43].

Molecular typing can be conducted at different levels; at local city and county laboratories, at the state public health department, at a reference laboratory (e.g., FDA and USDA), and at different research institutions nationally and internationally. The typing method of choice will be dependent on the outbreak level and size of the epidemiological investigation. City and county laboratories might not have the resources to conduct molecular typing using PFGE for PulseNet. Other typing methods can be used; however, data compatibility would be an issue. Therefore, isolates can be sent out to state public health laboratories for typing.

MAKING SENSE OF MOLECULAR TYPING DATA IN EPIDEMIOLOGICAL INVESTIGATIONS

Molecular typing data are often transformed into another form of data to ease the analysis and visualization of the data. Transformation to binary data is a common practice. The raw outcomes of molecular typing methods for bacterial isolates are basically: 1) a gel band patterns (i.e., fingerprints), 2) DNA sequences, and 3) presence or absence of one or multiple genes (i.e., binary or frequency data) [11]. The first two forms of outcomes are often analyzed using commercial software to determine the similarities (or dissimilarities) among the patterns or sequences of the isolates. Based on certain cut-off values, patterns or sequences are then interpreted into either: related (i.e., indistinguishable, clonal, or genetically linked) or un-related isolates. The association between epidemiologically linked isolates and molecular typing related isolates can be assessed using chi-square test with 95% confidence intervals [44]. Descriptive statistical methods are used to better visualize patterns especially for large typing datasets. Methods such as cluster analysis [45] and principal component analysis [46, 47] are commonly used for data visualization. Moreover, statistical models can be employed to examine associations between typing data and the risk factors in a study. Logistic regression models are classic example for dealing with binary data and risk factors [48]. When typing data are on the form of multiple outcomes (e.g., AFLP multiple binary outcomes), more complex statistical models (e.g., multivariate generalized linear model) are ought to be used to determine the association with the risk factors. Furthermore, advances in statistical modeling allow adjusting for the correlation (i.e., dependences) that may exist among the multiple outcomes [49].

Although several molecular typing methods are known to have high discriminatory power, they might not always distinguish between epidemiologically related and unrelated isolates. There are two criteria need to be considered when typing isolates; especially when large number of isolates are tested as the case in multi-state foodborne outbreak investigation. First is the discriminatory power of the typing methods. That is, the ability of different methods to discriminate a set of isolates (related vs. unrelated). Second is the genotypic diversity of the isolates. A group of isolates that are epidemiologically unrelated can be clonal due to the lack of genotypic diversity in the isolates [50]. For instance, *S.* Typhimurium isolates from human clinical cases in different geographical regions, but with indistinguishable PFGE patterns might not suggest an outbreak of a common food source. If epidemiological data indicate that human cases salmonellosis is linked to foods from different (not a common source) animal origins (e.g., chicken, pork, seafood), then it is probably baseline infections with high prevalent clone *S.* Typhimurium, rather than an outbreak. Another example is *Legionella pneumophila* (a waterborne pathogen) clinical isolates with similar PFGE patterns was recovered from many patients in different districts of Paris, France water system with no common source and no geographical (time and location) clustering [51].

Molecular typing data should be evaluated within the context of time and location of cases where isolates came from, and other current epidemiological data such as types of food consumed and exposure to animals. Time frame is important as variability in typing results increases between related isolates when epidemiological investigation takes longer time period [10, 52]. Clustering in space (i.e., geographical clustering) is also important to determine the source of infection. Related isolates obtain from sporadic locations are often harder to epidemiologically link than clusters. Other molecular analysis data (identification of biological markers) obtained on related isolates such as antimicrobial resistance profiles, virulence genes, and serotypes may further distinguish (confirm) which isolates are truly related from those that are not related. Furthermore, using more than molecular typing methods in series could confirm presumptive related isolates (e.g., using PFGE followed by MLVA).

Molecular typing data networks and libraries serve as a reference storage database that are used to compare current isolate subtype to previously typed isolates. PulseNet (www.cdc.gov/pulsenet) is a library for PFGE fingerprints of specific foodborne pathogens where typing data are continuously monitored and analyzed for related isolates [13, 53]. Furthermore, PulseNet is used to compare trends in foodborne pathogen types over periods of time. Another molecular typing library is MLST (www.mlst.com) where patterns are uploaded to the site from all over the world. This network can be used to monitor international multi-country outbreaks with clonal strains. These typing libraries are often used by multiple state and public laboratories and by researchers and epidemiologists over time to study distribution and frequencies of certain clones as well as assessment of clusters of related isolates (potential existence of an outbreak). Therefore, it is critical that standardized protocols for molecular typing of isolates are developed and implemented at various laboratories to reduce the inter-laboratory variability and increase typing reproducibility to enhance the ability of typing data comparisons [10].

CONCLUSIONS AND FUTURE DIRECTIONS

Current outbreak investigations rely heavily on data from molecular typing method of bacterial isolates. However, epidemiologists need to consider the molecular typing data in the context of the investigation (time and space). There are several molecular typing methods and the choice depends on the cost of equipment, reagents and materials, time needed to conduct the analysis, typeability of the isolates, labor associated with the analysis, and the level of skills and training of the person carrying out the analysis. The PulseNet program should consider integrating results of DNA typing from other molecular typing methodologies. This will allow laboratories with limited resources to conduct their own less expensive molecular typing testing and to compare to the larger database.

There is no doubt that use of molecular typing methods has enhanced outbreak detection and investigation. Data outcome of these methods can be complex to visualize and simplify to a form that epidemiologists can use in outbreak investigation. There is a need to build more mathematical and statistical models to better describe molecular typing data and assess the variability associated with these data.

The global trade and U.S. food exports/ imports have changed dramatically over the past decade. It is important that international networks of molecular typing and data sharing expand to include all countries. Multistate outbreaks will soon changes to multi-country type of events. Standardized protocols for molecular typing and data analysis are needed across the globe. Training scientists on using of molecular typing methods in outbreak investigation, especially in developing countries, will improve their public health and enhance the safety of U.S. imported foods.

REFERENCES

[1] Scallan E, Hoekstra RM, Angulo FJ, Tauxe RV, Widdowson MA, Roy SL, et al. Foodborne illness acquired in the United States-major pathogens. *Emerg Infect Dis.* 2011;17(1):7-15

[2] Hedberg CW, MacDonald KL, Osterholm MT. Changing epidemiology of food-borne disease: a Minnesota perspective. *Clin Infect Dis.* 1994;18(5):671-80; quiz 81-2.

[3] Tauxe RV. New approaches to surveillance and control of emerging foodborne infectious diseases. *Emerg Infect Dis.* 1998;4(3):455-6.

[4] Farber JM. An introduction to the hows and whys of molecular typing. *J Food Protect.* 1996;59(10):1091-101.

[5] Miller JM. Molecular technology for hospital epidemiology. *Diagn Microbiol Infect Dis.* 1993;16(2):153-7.

[6] Jang TN, Fung CP, Yang TL, Shen SH, Huang CS, Lee SH. Use of pulsed-field gel electrophoresis to investigate an outbreak of *Serratia marcescens* infection in a neonatal intensive care unit. *J Hosp Infect.* 2001;48(1):13-9.

[7] Laber TL, Iverson JT, Liberty JA, Giese SA. The Evaluation and Implementation of Match Criteria for Forensic Analysis of DNA. *J Forensic Sci.* 1995;40(6):1058-64.

[8] Marples RR, Rosdahl VT, Pessat OAN, Vickery A, Godard C, Mamizuka EM, et al. International quality control of phage typing of Staphylococcus aureus. *J Med Microbiol.* 1997;46(6):511-6.

[9] Olive DM, Bean P. Principles and applications of methods for DNA-beased typing of microbial organisms. *J Clin Microbiol.* 1999;37(6):1661-9.

[10] van Belkum A, Tassios PT, Dijkshoorn L, Haeggman S, Cookson B, Fry NK, et al. Guidelines for the validation and application of typing methods for use in bacterial epidemiology. *Clin Microbiol Infect.* 2007;13(Suppl 3):1-46.

[11] Foley SL, Lynne AM, Nayak R. Molecular typing methodologies for microbial source tracking and epidemiological investigations of Gram-negative bacterial foodborne pathogens. *Infect Genet Evol.* 2009;9(4):430-40.

[12] Murchan S, Kaufmann ME, Deplano A, de Ryck R, Struelens M, Zinn CE, et al. Harmonization of pulsed-field gel electrophoresis protocols for epidemiological typing of strains of methicillin-resistant *Staphylococcus aureus*: a single approach developed by consensus in 10 European laboratories and its application for tracing the spread of related strains. *J Clin Microbiol.* 2003;41(4):1574-85.

[13] Swaminathan B, Barrett TJ, Hunter SB, Tauxe RV. PulseNet: the molecular subtyping network for foodborne bacterial disease surveillance, United States. *Emerg Infect Dis.* 2001;7(3):382-9.

[14] Ribot EM, Fair MA, Gautom R, Cameron DN, Hunter SB, Swaminathan B, et al. Standardization of pulsed-field gel electrophoresis protocols for the subtyping of *Escherichia coli* O157:H7, *Salmonella*, and *Shigella* for PulseNet. *Foodborne Pathog Dis.* 2006;3(1):59-67.

[15] Swaminathan B, Barrett TJ, Fields P. Surveillance for human *Salmonella* infections in the United States. *J AOAC Int.* 2006;89(2):553-9.

[16] Sails AD, Swaminathan B, Fields PI. Utility of multilocus sequence typing as an epidemiological tool for investigation of outbreaks of gastroenteritis caused by *Campylobacter jejuni. J Clin Microbiology.* 2003;41(10):4733-9.

[17] Maiden MC, Bygraves JA, Feil E, Morelli G, Russell JE, Urwin R, et al. Multilocus sequence typing: a portable approach to the identification of clones within populations of pathogenic microorganisms. Proc Natl Acad Sci U S A. 1998;95(6):3140-5.

[18] Maiden MC. Multilocus sequence typing of bacteria. *Annu Rev Microbiol.* 2006;60:561-88.

[19] Spratt BG. Multilocus sequence typing: molecular typing of bacterial pathogens in an era of rapid DNA sequencing and the internet. *Curr Opin Microbiol.* 1999;2(3):312-6.

[20] Enright MC, Spratt BG. Multilocus sequence typing. *Trends Microbiol.* 1999;7(12):482-7.

[21] Heck M. Multilocus variable number of tandem repeats analysis (MLVA) - a reliable tool for rapid investigation of *Salmonella* Typhimurium outbreaks. *Euro Surveill.* 2009;14(15):2-.

[22] Larsson JT, Torpdahl M, Petersen RF, Sorensen G, Lindstedt BA, Nielsen EM. Development of a new nomenclature for *Salmonella* Typhimurium multilocus variable number of tandem repeats analysis (MLVA). *Euro Surveill.* 2009;14(15).

[23] Nygard K, Lindstedt BA, Wahl W, Jensvoll L, Kjelso C, Molbak K, et al. Outbreak of *Salmonella* Typhimurium infection traced to imported cured sausage using MLVA-subtyping. *Euro Surveill.* 2007;12(3):E070315 5.

[24] Best EL, Hampton MD, Ethelberg S, Liebana E, Clifton-Hadley FA, Threlfall EJ. Drug-resistant *Salmonella* Typhimurium DT 120: use of PFGE and MLVA in a putative international outbreak investigation. *Microb Drug Resist.* 2009;15(2):133-8.

[25] Keys C, Kemper S, Keim P. Highly diverse variable number tandem repeat loci in the *E. coli* O157:H7 and O55:H7 genomes for high-resolution molecular typing. *J Appl Microbiol.* 2005;98(4):928-40.

[26] Noller AC, McEllistrem MC, Pacheco AG, Boxrud DJ, Harrison LH. Multilocus variable-number tandem repeat analysis distinguishes outbreak and sporadic *Escherichia coli* O157:H7 isolates. *J Clin Microbiol.* 2003;41(12):5389-97.

[27] Gerner-Smidt P, Hise K, Kincaid J, Hunter S, Rolando S, Hyytia-Trees E, et al. PulseNet USA: a five-year update. *Foodborne Pathog Dis.* 2006;3(1):9-19.

[28] Lindstedt BA. Multiple-locus variable number tandem repeats analysis for genet fingerprinting of pathogenic bacteria. *Electrophoresis*. 2005;26(13):2567-82.

[29] Benson G. Tandem repeats finder: a program to analyze DNA sequences. *Nucleic Acids Res*. 1999;27(2):573-80.

[30] Domingue G, Willshaw GA, Smith HR, Perry N, Radford D, Cheasty T. DNA-based subtyping of verocytotoxin-producing *Escherichia coli* (VTEC) O128ab:H2 strains from human and raw meat sources. *Lett Appl Microbiol*. 2003;37(6):433-7.

[31] Mayer LW. Use of plasmid profiles in epidemiologic surveillance of disease outbreaks and in tracing the transmission of antibiotic resistance. *Clin Microbiol Rev*. 1988;1(2):228-43.

[32] Schaberg DR, Tompkins LS, Falkow S. Use of agarose gel electrophoresis of plasmid deoxyribonucleic acid to fingerprint gram-negative bacilli. *J Clin Microbiol*. 1981;13(6):1105-8.

[33] Liu PY, Lau YJ, Hu BS, Shyr JM, Shi ZY, Tsai WS, et al. Analysis of clonal relationships among isolates of *Shigella sonnei* by different molecular typing methods. *J Clin Microbiol*. 1995;33(7):1779-83.

[34] Nayak R, Stewart T, Wang RF, Lin J, Cerniglia CE, Kenney PB. Genetic diversity and virulence gene determinants of antibiotic-resistant *Salmonella* isolated from preharvest turkey production sources. *Int J Food Microbiol*. 2004;91(1):51-62.

[35] Olsen JE, Brown DJ, Skov MN, Christensen JP. Bacterial typing methods suitable for epidemiological analysis. Applications in investigations of salmonellosis among livestock. *Vet Q*. 1993;15(4):125-35.

[36] Nielsen EM, Engberg J, Fussing V, Petersen L, Brogren CH, On SL. Evaluation of phenotypic and genotypic methods for subtyping *Campylobacter jejuni* isolates from humans, poultry, and cattle. *J Clin Microbiol*. 2000;38(10):3800-10.

[37] Bailey JS, Fedorka-Cray PJ, Stern NJ, Craven SE, Cox NA, Cosby DE. Serotyping and ribotyping of *Salmonella* using restriction enzyme *Pvu*II. *J Food Prot*. 2002;65(6):1005-7.

[38] Landeras E, Mendoza MC. Evaluation of PCR-based methods and ribotyping performed with a mixture of *Pst*I and *Sph*I to differentiate strains of *Salmonella* serotype Enteritidis. *J Med Microbiol*. 1998;47(5):427-34.

[39] Lindstedt BA, Heir E, Vardund T, Kapperud G. Fluorescent amplified-fragment length polymorphism genotyping of *Salmonella enterica* subsp. *enterica* serovars and comparison with pulsed-field gel electrophoresis typing. *J Clin Microbiol*. 2000;38(4):1623-7.

[40] de Boer P, Duim B, Rigter A, van Der Plas J, Jacobs-Reitsma WF, Wagenaar JA. Computer-assisted analysis and epidemiological value of genotyping methods for *Campylobacter jejuni* and *Campylobacter coli*. J Clin Microbiol. 2000;38(5):1940-6.

[41] Mare L, Dick LM, van der Walt ML. Characterization of South African isolates of *Salmonella enteritidis* by phage typing, numerical analysis of RAPD-PCR banding patterns and plasmid profiles. *Int J Food Microbiol*. 2001;64(3):237-45.

[42] Dombek PE, Johnson LK, Zimmerley ST, Sadowsky MJ. Use of repetitive DNA sequences and the PCR to differentiate *Escherichia coli* isolates from human and animal sources. *Appl Environ Microbiol*. 2000;66(6):2572-7.

[43] Mohapatra BR, Broersma K, Nordin R, Mazumder A. Evaluation of repetitive extragenic palindromic-PCR for discrimination of fecal *Escherichia coli* from humans, and different domestic- and wild-animals. *Microbiol Immunol.* 2007;51(8):733-40.

[44] Mantel N. Chi-Square Tests with 1 Degree of Freedom - Extensions of Mantel-Haenszel Procedure. *J Am Stat Assoc.* 1963;58(303):690-7.

[45] Yoshida J, Umeda A, Ishimaru T, Akao M. Cluster analysis on multiple drugs susceptibility supplements genotyping of methicillin-resistant *Staphylococcus aureus*. *Int J Infect Dis.* 2001;5(4):205-8.

[46] Laster L. Statistical background of methods of principal component analysis. *J Periodontol.* 1967;38(6):Suppl:649-66.

[47] Wilkes JG, Rushing L, Nayak R, Buzatu DA, Sutherland JB. Rapid phenotypic characterization of *Salmonella enterica* strains by pyrolysis metastable atom bombardment mass spectrometry with multivariate statistical and artificial neural network pattern recognition. *J Microbiol Methods.* 2005;61(3):321-34.

[48] Bonin A, Ehrich D, Manel S. Statistical analysis of amplified fragment length polymorphism data: a toolbox for molecular ecologists and evolutionists. *Mol Ecol.* 2007;16(18):3737-58.

[49] Alali WQ, Scott HM, Norby B. Assessing the similarity of antimicrobial resistance phenotypes among fecal *Escherichia coli* isolates from two aggregated occupational cohorts of humans versus swine using cluster analysis and multivariate statistics. *Prev Vet Med.* 2010;94(1-2):77-83.

[50] Blanc DS. The use of molecular typing for epidemiological surveillance and investigation of endemic nosocomial infections. Infect Genet Evol. 2004;4(3):193-7.

[51] Lawrence C, Reyrolle M, Dubrou S, Forey F, Decludt B, Goulvestre C, et al. Single clonal origin of a high proportion of *Legionella pneumophila* serogroup 1 isolates from patients and the environment in the area of Paris, France, over a 10-year period. *Journal of Clinical Microbiology.* 1999;37(8):2652-5.

[52] van Belkum A. High-throughput epidemiologic typing in clinical microbiology. *Clin Microbiol Infect.* 2003;9(2):86-100.

[53] Swaminathan B, Gerner-Smidt P, Ng LK, Lukinmaa S, Kam KM, Rolando S, et al. Building PulseNet International: an interconnected system of laboratory networks to facilitate timely public health recognition and response to foodborne disease outbreaks and emerging foodborne diseases. *Foodborne Pathog Dis.* 2006;3(1):36-50.

In: Molecular Typing Methods for TFM
Editors: S. Foley, R. Nayak, T. Johnson et al.

ISBN: 978-1-62100-643-5
© 2012 Nova Science Publishers, Inc.

Chapter 16

CURRENT ISSUES, CHALLENGES AND FUTURE DIRECTIONS FOR SUBTYPING OF BACTERIAL FOODBORNE PATHOGENS

Steven L. Foley[1], *Rajesh Nayak*[1], *Sanjay K. Shukla*[2] *and Timothy J. Johnson*[3]

[1] Division of Microbiology
National Center for Toxicological Research
US Food and Drug Administration
Jefferson, AR, US
[2] Center for Human Genetics
Marshfield Clinic Research Foundation
Marshfield, WI, US
[3] Department of Veterinary and Biomedical Sciences
College of Veterinary Medicine
University of Minnesota
St. Paul, MN, US

ABSTRACT

Several different molecular subtyping methods can be used for the differentiation of bacterial foodborne pathogens to aid in the delineation of potential sources of contamination. Molecular typing methodologies can be evaluated based on a number of criteria, including performance factors such as typeability, reproducibility and discriminatory ability, and convenience factors, such as cost, ease of use and equipment requirements. At present, no typing method is ideal based on these criteria. Many of the most discriminatory methods take a longer time to perform and are more costly. Future approaches to subtyping will likely focus on improving the performance of current methods and also developing novel technologies. One likely approach is the application of next generation sequencing technologies for whole-genome typing of bacterial pathogens. Future subtyping methods should provide improved tools to rapidly identify the source of bacterial contamination and provide a holistic understanding of factors that facilitate the distribution of pathogens along the food production, processing and consumption continuum.

INTRODUCTION

The chapters of this book have examined many of the most widely used methods for molecular subtyping of bacterial foodborne pathogens, which remain an important cause of morbidity and mortality throughout the world. Recent estimates in the United States indicate that bacterial illnesses known to originate from food contribute to approximately 3.6 million infections, 36,000 hospitalizations and 861 deaths each year [1]. On a global scale, the numbers are much larger and are a major concern for public health. Because of their impact on public health, it is important to be able to understand the sources of contamination to develop comprehensive strategies to limit foodborne illnesses.

The first section of this book (Chapters 1 to 5) provided an overview of foodborne pathogens and highlighted their molecular characteristics that impact their ability to colonize, contaminate and disseminate in the farm-to-the-fork continuum. The second section of the book (Chapters 6 to 13) focuses on the molecular subtyping methods, which play a crucial role in understanding the dissemination of pathogens through the food chain. Molecular typing techniques rely on differential amplification of specific sequences within the bacterial genome using PCR, the differential restriction of the bacterial genome using restriction enzymes, or the direct detection of differences in the genetic sequences using DNA sequencing methods. The subsequent chapters of the book describe the analyses and application of subtyping methods for bacterial foodborne pathogens. This concluding chapter explores some of the overall characteristics and challenges of the current molecular subtyping methods and tries to explore some of the future directions where molecular subtyping methods may be heading.

CURRENT ISSUES AND CHALLENGES
WITH SUBTYPING TECHNOLOGIES

With the current typing technologies, no single universal technique can be applied to all scenarios, as each of the methods has their own set of strengths and weaknesses to consider when evaluating the techniques. According to van Belkum and colleagues, characteristics to evaluate molecular subtyping methods can be broken down into performance criteria and convenience criteria [2]. The performance criteria relate directly to the performance of the method, such as typeability, discriminatory power, reproducibility, the stability of the targets, and epidemiological concordance. The convenience criteria relate to characteristics outside of the direct performance, such as cost, time to results (rapidity), ease of use, accessibility of equipment and reagents, flexibility of the method to type multiple pathogens and data analysis methods [2]. This section of the chapter looks at a number of these characteristics with an emphasis on the more commonly used methods and how they will affect the development of an ideal future method.

Characteristics of the Current Molecular Subtyping Methods

Typeability

A key feature of typing methods is the ability to effectively type different organisms. Because some typing methods, such as some PCR methods, rely on the presence of an adequate number of primer binding sites in close enough proximity to one another to amplify the fragments, strains lacking the target sequences cannot be typed. This lack of typeability can be observed in some *Salmonella* serovars when RFLP-PCR of the *fliC* gene is carried out. The gene is present in serotype Gallinarum isolates but not in a number of other serovars [3, 4]; thus, many *Salmonella* isolates are "untypeable" using RFLP-PCR of the *fliC* gene. Similarly, with ribotyping, there needs to be an adequate number of rRNA genes present for the probes to bind. *Campylobacter* has only three ribosomal operons, thus ribotyping is likely not the ideal choice for typing *Campylobacter* [5]. Also, if strains are difficult to lyse or if they produce DNAses or other inhibitory products, it may make it impossible to adequately resolve a profile for use in subtyping. This lack of resolution has been reported for PFGE with certain foodborne pathogens [6, 7]. Additionally, mutations in PCR primer binding sites may lead to problems with PCR-based methods and MLST, which rely on PCR products for characterizing isolates.

Discriminatory Ability

The ability to discriminate between isolates that are not closely related (clonal) is a desirable characteristic for subtyping methods. Different methods have different abilities to distinguish among unique strains. This discriminatory ability is often based on the genetic target of the typing method and the ability to resolve and detect the resultant profiles. For example, with MLST using housekeeping genes for sequencing, there may not be enough diversity to distinguish among strains in short term epidemiological studies. However, the methods work well for longer term evolutionary studies. The discriminatory ability can be increased by sequencing targets that are known to be more polymorphic, such as virulence genes [8, 9]. Additionally, PFGE has been considered to be fairly discriminatory using a single restriction enzyme digestion; however, in certain instances greater discrimination is needed, thus groups like PulseNet and others often use a second (or more) enzyme to improve the discriminatory ability of PFGE [10, 11]

Stability

Typing methods use different targets to separate bacterial strains. The bacterial genome is dynamic; mutations during DNA replication and horizontal gene transfer events lead to genomic diversity. For the effective application of molecular subtyping for epidemiological investigations, the targets of the subtyping should be diverse enough that they are able to adequately separate distinct strains, yet not so unstable that they change significantly during the course of a disease outbreak or as the contaminated product moves along the farm-to-fork continuum. One of the potential drawbacks of traditional MLST using housekeeping genes is that the loci may be too stable to distinguish among closely related strains and would be best suited for longer-term evolutionary studies [10]. Because of this drawback, some molecular epidemiologists have incorporated virulence genes into MLST protocols, which will likely enable the detection of more diversity among isolates [6, 9, 12]. Additionally, because of potential issues of stability, the "Tenover" criteria for PFGE analysis [23] allowed some variation in the restriction patterns among "closely related" isolates that potentially originated from a common source, because an isolate may have a single genetic event (insertion, deletion or point mutation) during the investigation period that could lead to a change in the profile [13]. More recent interpretive criteria from the U.S. Centers for Disease Control and Prevention takes into account the underlying genetic stability of a particular species/serovar and epidemiological variables when evaluating whether pattern differences are significant [14].

Reproducibility

Reproducibility is important in molecular epidemiology and subsequent source tracking applications because it is essential for a method to produce the same result each time clones are subtyped. If reproducibility is a problem, then linkages between an ill person and a source of contamination could be missed since the subtyping would return separate results for the strains from a common source. Because of the importance of reproducibility in molecular epidemiological applications, procedures are typically highly standardized. A prime example of this is with the PulseNet program and PFGE [15]. The standardized PulseNet methods allow PFGE results from one laboratory to be compared to others across the country (and in some cases worldwide), which has allowed the detection of diffuse outbreaks that could have been missed in the pre-PulseNet era [16]. A potential tradeoff for this standardization is that the procedure may take more time (due to added washes, longer incubation times and electrophoresis conditions) than the bare minimum, which could lead to less reproducibility. Some PCR-based methods have more issues with reproducibility due to differences in polymerase enzyme lots, efficiency of thermal cyclers, low stringency reaction conditions and electrophoresis differences [17]. The tradeoff for potentially less reproducible typing results is speed in the time to results, ease of performance, relatively low costs and high throughput.

Time to Result

Another important factor, especially when trying to determine the source of a pathogen during an outbreak, is the turn around time from when a sample is collected until it is subtyped and compared to other isolates associated with the infection. Unfortunately, this time is often fairly long (up to 14 days), so that isolation and species identification can take several days even before subtyping begins. The time to type a pure culture varies, from a few hours to several days. In general, the PCR-based methods are relatively quick. DNA can be isolated from a culture in less than an hour, the PCR reactions set and run in two to three hours and separated and stained within a few more hours. The rep-PCR based DiversiLab system (bioMérieux Clinical Diagnostics) states that typing results can be obtained in about four hours with their system. On the other end of the spectrum, PFGE analysis generally takes at least two days to complete, due to the times for cell lysis, restriction digestion and running of the pulsed field gel [18]. As discussed above, there are trade-offs with the time to results; PCR methods tend to be less reproducible and in many cases demonstrate lower levels of discrimination than lengthier methods, such as PFGE.

Ease of Use

Each of the molecular typing methods requires some manipulation by an analyst. Even the highly automated RiboPrinter (DuPont Qualicon, Wilmington, DE) requires the user to prepare the front end steps (culturing and DNA isolation) before the automated system takes over. Others, such as PFGE, AFLP and MLST, require significantly more technical expertise, both in the laboratory and in data analysis. PCR-based methods are typically straightforward on the laboratory side, in that they require the DNA isolation, setting up the PCR master mixes and reactions and carrying out electrophoresis to separate the fragments. Often the challenge for the PCR methods is in the analysis and identification of bands on a gel. Samples can have similar patterns, with the exception of faint bands that are present in one sample and absent in another. The dilemma that arises for the analyst is whether the faint bands are present due to variation in the PCR reaction (slight differences in template concentration or PCR efficiency) or whether they are true differences. Thus, experience is required for the analysis of subtyping data to improve their utility in a source tracking scheme.

Resources Needed/Costs

In addition to the scientific merits, another practical issue in comparing molecular subtyping methods is cost, both in terms of per sample analysis and the cost of the equipment needed. Some molecular typing methods, while discriminatory, are more expensive than their counterparts. For example, MLST, MLVA and AFLP typically use an automated DNA sequencer, which can be expensive to purchase, maintain and operate. Additionally, PFGE requires specialized electrophoresis equipment. Conversely, PCR-based methods require limited specialized equipment or reagents to complete. These methods typically require a standard thermal cycler, gel documentation system and basic PCR reagents (primers, dNTPs, Taq polymerase, etc.). The trade off is that many of the PCR techniques are often less reproducible and discriminatory than the methods requiring specialized equipment. However, PCR methods may be appropriate if a large number of samples need to be screened in a short amount of time, as they generally require less time per sample and cost less than many other methods. These characteristics may be why PCR-based methods are widely used in environmental and water microbiology, where typically a large number of samples are screened and subtyped [19, 20].

Applying Molecular Subtyping to Source Tracking Schemes

Molecular typing cannot stand alone in a source tracking scheme. A major component of the scheme is the epidemiological investigation, which is covered in Chapters 1 and 15. The interpretation of typing results needs to be done in context. For example, with certain *Salmonella* serotypes, such as Enteritidis, the PFGE patterns are often homogeneous [11], thus sporadic identification of common profiles from different sources may not necessarily indicate the presence of a common source outbreak. However, a significant increase in the pattern over a baseline level may indicate an outbreak. Where there is a high degree of homogeneity of genotypic profiles with a particular typing method, the use of additional methods to distinguish among strains is important. In the case of *Salmonella* serovars Enteritidis and Typhimurium and *E. coli* O157:H7, PulseNet has begun using MLVA in some instances to further discriminate among isolates with common PFGE profiles to determine whether they display clonality or whether they are distinct [21]. Multiple genotypic differentiations of bacterial isolates are important in a source tracking application because it will narrow the search for the source by eliminating non-clonal strains from the investigation. A combination of typing methods is often required to effectively differentiate between certain isolates. In using multiple methods, the order in which the methods are used can be important in improving the efficiency of the source tracking protocol. For example, in the case of *S.* Enteritidis, if an uncommon PFGE pattern is detected among case patients, then MLVA may not need to be used. If a PFGE pattern is rare, its detection in the food supply chain would be significant and help focus the epidemiological investigation more strategically.

FUTURE DIRECTIONS

An Ideal Method

An ideal typing method would be highly discriminatory, produce reproducible results in a short time, inexpensive, and easy to perform and analyze. Advances have been made to address the short-comings of the current methods through automation, which can reduce time and improve reproducibility. However, limitations still remain and often these advancements come at a higher price tag that may limit their widespread use. There will continue to be advances to the currently used methods, similar to what has been done with rep-PCR (DiversiLab system), ribotyping (RiboPrinter) and AFLP (Applied Biosystems), where most steps are automated. Some of the current methods utilizing Sanger sequencing will be adapted for the Next Generation Sequencing (NGS) platforms, which could facilitate the analyses of a greater number of loci in MLST or SNP analysis. The use of whole genome sequencing for molecular subtyping will be used widely in the future as the technologies improve and the cost of sequencing each bacterial genome is reduced.

Backwards Compatibility

One of the important considerations in using molecular typing methods for use in outbreak and source tracking investigations is backwards compatibility. This means that the results of the new method can be compared or aligned with the results of methods, such as PFGE, for which a great number of foodborne pathogens have been analyzed and database platforms, such as PulseNet, have been built upon. The typing information in these databases has laid the foundation for understanding the epidemiology of foodborne illnesses. Thus, using technologies that are compatible with relatively long history and large datasets of PFGE information would be extremely important to avoid losing years of collective understanding of the molecular epidemiology of foodborne pathogens.

The Current Pipeline

One of the current bottlenecks in the process of rapid molecular typing is the time that it takes to detect and isolate the pathogen of interest. Advances in basic and applied research, including improved selective and differential media, flow cytometry, mass spectrometry, biosensors and real time-PCR based methods, have aided in the rapid detection of foodborne pathogens from various food and environmental matrices [22, 23]. In general, as these isolation and detection methods advance, they should be rapid, accurate, sensitive, simple to perform and cost effective. More importantly, they should be able to detect low CFU counts in the sample, preferably with little enrichment, and capable of delivering results in real time. Furthermore, they need to be compatible with isolation of a pure culture of the foodborne pathogen for molecular subtyping. Ideally, the time to results, from sample collection to subtyping a bacterial strain will be reduced to hours or a few days instead of days or weeks, as is the status quo.

Next Generation Sequencing

One of the newer technologies that have been developed over the last decade is the NGS platforms. These platforms have a great deal of potential for the characterization and subtyping of foodborne pathogens that are involved in outbreaks [24]. At present, genomes of bacterial foodborne pathogens have been sequenced using the NGS, and the number will continue to grow rapidly. Whole genome sequence comparisons, either as a subtyping method or as a tool to identify valuable SNPs and potential targets for MLST, MLVA or PCR-based methods, will become more widespread in the near future.

Chapter 2 covers microbial genomics using NGS and previews several developing technologies, such as the Pacific Biosciences platform based on single-molecule real-time sequencing, the Ion Torrent system (Life Technologies) using semiconductor technology to detect nucleotides based on the detection of protons released during the DNA synthesis step, and nanopore sequencing, which identifies nucleotides [25].

Another trend in NGS is that the instruments will move out of large core sequencing centers to individual research and public health laboratories (see Chapter 2). Several factors will contribute to this decentralization; these include the increasing infrastructure and personnel costs of operating core centers, the marketing of less expensive and more user friendly sequencers, and tools for sequence analysis, assembly, annotation and comparative genomics. For example, the 454 GS Junior system from Roche is a relatively low cost sequencer that provides lower throughput than the standard Roche 454 instruments (35-40 Mb versus 400-600 Mb/run). However, the Junior 454 GS sequence throughput is manageable for an individual laboratory or group of laboratories to carry out the wet laboratory portions of the procedure and handle the analyses without taking the system off-line because too large of volumes of sequence data are generated to be efficiently analyzed in a timely fashion. Such "bench top" sequencers can add value to the molecular subtyping laboratory, as they would generate whole genome sequence data and have the capability for sample "barcoding" for multiplexing foodborne pathogens. This approach could allow for the simultaneous targeting of multiple loci from a large number of samples in a SNP or MLST-type application.

Advances in Bioinformatics

In addition to advances in the typing methods, there will be a number of advances in the area of bioinformatics to support the different typing methods. With PFGE, for example, as more samples are analyzed and placed into databases such as PulseNet, new tools will be needed to sort through the multitude of patterns when comparing isolates from various sources during surveillance and outbreaks to those already present in the database [10]. Additionally, if NGS is routinely used for molecular subtyping, there will be need for bioinformatics tools to aid in the assembly of sequence contigs, to compare sequences, and to aid in the determination of whether or not any differences are epidemiologically relevant.

Genomes of foodborne pathogens range from ~1.7 to ~5 million base pairs of DNA [26, 27]. Therefore, there are a large number of data points to compare between individual strains. If a large number of strains are analyzed as part of the source tracking approach, refined tools will be necessary to allow efficient comparison of sequences among bacterial isolates. Robust databases will need to created that can be searched routinely, similar to current searching tools available for PFGE databases, to determine whether a particular isolate is of concern. Additionally, data storage may be a concern as more and more genomes are sequenced and large volumes of raw and analyzed data are compiled.

Epidemiological relevance is important because bacterial genomes are dynamic, as they are constantly evolving under different selective pressures and high mutation rates. Thus, it is possible that a pathogen isolated from a human patient may have some sequence differences from the original bacteria, isolated from the contaminated source. Because of the potential for divergence in genome sequences from isolates collected at different points along the food production-to-processing-to- consumption continuum, there will be a need to establish epidemiologically-relevant cutoffs for a common strain originating from a common source.

One of the potential beneficial features of using genome sequencing as a subtyping tool is that there are a number of valuable pieces of information that can be deciphered about the isolates that may play a role in the clinical approach to the disease. For example, filters can be developed to screen for the presence of known antimicrobial resistance genes or those genes associated with the development of more severe infections. Such information could help guide whether a patient is administered antimicrobial therapy or treated with another appropriate drug.

Going Forward

At present, we have several methods to differentiate bacterial foodborne pathogens. Each method has strengths and weaknesses. Some of the newer methods that may replace current methods are still under development, and these methods have their own technical and practical hurdles that need to be overcome before they are widely used for subtyping bacterial pathogens. Nonetheless, the future of molecular subtyping is promising; with the newer technologies on the horizon we should be able to multitask, gaining information about the relatedness of foodborne pathogens as well as information that will guide the subsequent response to these detected pathogens. These newer source tracking/typing methods will provide an improved understanding of factors that facilitate the distribution of pathogens along the food production, processing and consumption continuum. Through a better understanding how pathogens colonize and survive in the food supply, we will be able to develop novel approaches to limit the impact of foodborne pathogens on human health.

DISCLAIMER

The use of trade names is for identification purposes only, and does not imply endorsement by the U.S. Food and Drug Administration or the U.S. Department of Health and Human Services. The views presented in this manuscript do not necessarily reflect those of the FDA.

REFERENCES

[1]   Scallan E, Hoekstra RM, Angulo FJ, Tauxe RV, Widdowson MA, Roy SL, *et al.* Foodborne illness acquired in the United States--major pathogens. *Emerg Infect Dis.* 2011;17(1):7-15.

[2]   van Belkum A, Tassios PT, Dijkshoorn L, Haeggman S, Cookson B, Fry NK, *et al.* Guidelines for the validation and application of typing methods for use in bacterial epidemiology. *Clin Microbiol Infect.* 2007;13 Suppl 3:1-46.

[3]   Kwon HJ, Park KY, Yoo HS, Park JY, Park YH, Kim SJ. Differentiation of *Salmonella enterica* serotype gallinarum biotype pullorum from biotype gallinarum by analysis of phase 1 flagellin C gene (*fliC*). *J Microbiol Methods.* 2000;40(1):33-8.

[4]   Dauga C, Zabrovskaia A, Grimont PA. Restriction fragment length polymorphism analysis of some flagellin genes of *Salmonella enterica.* *J Clin Microbiol.* 1998;36(10):2835-43.

[5]   Bouchet V, Huot H, Goldstein R. Molecular genetic basis of ribotyping. *Clin Microbiol Rev.* 2008;21(2):262-73.

[6]   Foley SL, Simjee S, Meng J, White DG, McDermott PF, Zhao S. Evaluation of molecular typing methods for *Escherichia coli* O157:H7 isolates from cattle, food, and humans. *J Food Prot.* 2004;67(4):651-7.

[7]   Corkill JE, Graham R, Hart CA, Stubbs S. Pulsed-field gel electrophoresis of degradation-sensitive DNAs from *Clostridium difficile* PCR ribotype 1 strains. *J Clin Microbiol.* 2000;38(7):2791-2.

[8]   Zhang W, Jayarao BM, Knabel SJ. Multi-virulence-locus sequence typing of *Listeria monocytogenes.* *Appl Environ Microbiol.* 2004;70(2):913-20.

[9]   Chen Y, Zhang W, Knabel SJ. Multi-virulence-locus sequence typing identifies single nucleotide polymorphisms which differentiate epidemic clones and outbreak strains of *Listeria monocytogenes.* J Clin Microbiol. 2007;45(3):845-56.

[10]   Hyytia-Trees EK, Cooper K, Ribot EM, Gerner-Smidt P. Recent developments and future prospects in subtyping of foodborne bacterial pathogens. *Future Microbiol.* 2007;2:175-85.

[11]   Zheng J, Keys CE, Zhao S, Meng J, Brown EW. Enhanced subtyping scheme for *Salmonella enteritidis.* *Emerg Infect Dis.* 2007;13(12):1932-5.

[12] Foley SL, White DG, McDermott PF, Walker RD, Rhodes B, Fedorka-Cray PJ, *et al.* Comparison of subtyping methods for differentiating *Salmonella enterica* serovar Typhimurium isolates obtained from food animal sources. *J Clin Microbiol.* 2006;44(10):3569-77.

[13] Tenover FC, Arbeit RD, Goering RV, Mickelsen PA, Murray BE, Persing DH, *et al.* Interpreting chromosomal DNA restriction patterns produced by pulsed-field gel electrophoresis: criteria for bacterial strain typing. *J Clin Microbiol.* 1995;33(9):2233-9.

[14] Barrett TJ, Gerner-Smidt P, Swaminathan B. Interpretation of pulsed-field gel electrophoresis patterns in foodborne disease investigations and surveillance. *Foodborne Pathog Dis.* 2006;3(1):20-31.

[15] Ribot EM, Fair MA, Gautom R, Cameron DN, Hunter SB, Swaminathan B, *et al.* Standardization of pulsed-field gel electrophoresis protocols for the subtyping of *Escherichia coli* O157:H7, *Salmonella*, and *Shigella* for PulseNet. *Foodborne Pathog Dis.* 2006;3(1):59-67.

[16] Gerner-Smidt P, Hise K, Kincaid J, Hunter S, Rolando S, Hyytia-Trees E, *et al.* PulseNet USA: a five-year update. *Foodborne Pathog Dis.* 2006;3(1):9-19.

[17] Swaminathan B, Barrett TJ. Amplification methods for epidemiologic investigations of infectious diesease. *J. Microbiolog. Methods* 1995;2:129-39.

[18] Foley SL, Zhao S, Walker RD. Comparison of molecular typing methods for the differentiation of *Salmonella* foodborne pathogens. *Foodborne Pathog Dis.* 2007;4(3):253-76.

[19] Dombek PE, Johnson LK, Zimmerley ST, Sadowsky MJ. Use of repetitive DNA sequences and the PCR To differentiate *Escherichia coli* isolates from human and animal sources. *Appl Environ Microbiol.* 2000;66(6):2572-7.

[20] Simpson JM, Santo Domingo JW, Reasoner DJ. Microbial source tracking: state of the science. *Environ Sci Technol.* 2002;36(24):5279-88.

[21] Hyytia-Trees E, Smole SC, Fields PA, Swaminathan B, Ribot EM. Second generation subtyping: a proposed PulseNet protocol for multiple-locus variable-number tandem repeat analysis of Shiga toxin-producing *Escherichia coli* O157 (STEC O157). *Foodborne Pathog Dis.* 2006;3(1):118-31.

[22] Velusamy V, Arshak K, Korostynska O, Oliwa K, Adley C. An overview of foodborne pathogen detection: in the perspective of biosensors. *Biotechnol Adv.* 2010;28(2):232-54.

[23] Bhunia AK. Biosensors and bio-based methods for the separation and detection of foodborne pathogens. *Adv Food Nutr Res.* 2008;54:1-44.

[24] Lienau EK, Strain E, Wang C, Zheng J, Ottesen AR, Keys CE, *et al.* Identification of a salmonellosis outbreak by means of molecular sequencing. *N Engl J Med.* 2011;364(10):981-2.

[25] Lund J, Parviz BA. Scanning probe and nanopore DNA sequencing: core techniques and possibilities. *Methods Mol Biol.* 2009;578:113-22.

[26] Nuijten PJ, Bartels C, Bleumink-Pluym NM, Gaastra W, van der Zeijst BA. Size and physical map of the *Campylobacter jejuni* chromosome. *Nucleic Acids Res.* 1990;18(21):6211-4.

[27] McClelland M, Sanderson KE, Spieth J, Clifton SW, Latreille P, Courtney L, *et al.* Complete genome sequence of *Salmonella enterica* serovar Typhimurium LT2. *Nature.* 2001;413(6858):852-6

INDEX

D

E

F

G

H

I

N

Q

R

T

U

V

W

Y

Z